ANNUAL REVIEW OF
PLANT PHYSIOLOGY

ANNUAL REVIEW OF PLANT PHYSIOLOGY

WINSLOW R. BRIGGS, *Editor*
Carnegie Institution of Washington, Stanford, California

PAUL B. GREEN, *Associate Editor*
Stanford University

RUSSELL L. JONES, *Associate Editor*
University of California, Berkeley

VOLUME 27

1976

ANNUAL REVIEWS INC.   4139 EL CAMINO WAY   PALO ALTO, CALIFORNIA 94306

ANNUAL REVIEWS INC.
Palo Alto, California, USA

International Standard Book Number: 0–8243–0627–9
Library of Congress Catalog Card Number: A51–1660

Annual Reviews Inc. and the Editors of its publications assume no
responsibility for the statements expressed by the contributors to this Review.

REPRINTS

The conspicuous number aligned in the margin with the title of each article in this
volume is a key for use in ordering reprints. Available reprints are priced at the
uniform rate of $1 each postpaid. The minimum acceptable reprint order is 10
reprints and/or $10.00, prepaid. A quantity discount is available.

PRINTED AND BOUND IN THE UNITED STATES OF AMERICA

Leonard Machlis
1915–1976

The Editorial Committee dedicates this volume to
the memory of Professor Leonard Machlis in honor
of his valued association with the *Annual Review of
Plant Physiology* for more than 21 years. Professor
Machlis was instrumental in establishing this series,
serving as Associate Editor from 1950 through 1958
and as Editor from 1959 to 1972.

CONTENTS

ANNUAL REVIEWS INC. is a nonprofit corporation established to promote the advancement of the sciences. Beginning in 1932 with the *Annual Review of Biochemistry,* the Company has pursued as its principal function the publication of high quality, reasonably priced Annual Review volumes. The volumes are organized by Editors and Editorial Committees who invite qualified authors to contribute critical articles reviewing significant developments within each major discipline.

Annual Reviews Inc. is administered by a Board of Directors whose members serve without compensation.

Annual Reviews are published in the following sciences: Anthropology, Astronomy and Astrophysics, Biochemistry, Biophysics and Bioengineering, Earth and Planetary Sciences, Ecology and Systematics, Energy, Entomology, Fluid Mechanics, Genetics, Materials Science, Medicine, Microbiology, Nuclear Science, Pharmacology and Toxicology, Physical Chemistry, Physiology, Phytopathology, Plant Physiology, Psychology, and Sociology. In addition, two special volumes have been published by Annual Reviews Inc.: *History of Entomology* (1973) and *The Excitement and Fascination of Science* (1965).

Photo by Frank Salisbury

Ann. Rev. Plant Physiol. 1976. 27:1–17

PLANT PHYSIOLOGY AND THE HUMAN ECOSYSTEM

♦7599

Johannes van Overbeek

Department of Biology, Texas A&M University, College Station, Texas 77843

CONTENTS

INTRODUCTION

Plant physiology shows how plants work. The gain in knowledge in this discipline has been truly enormous. This is well documented in the Fiftieth Anniversary Issue 1924–1974 of *Plant Physiology* (10). Another journal that has contributed greatly to the dissemination of the progress in plant physiological knowledge is the *Annual Review of Plant Physiology*. It was therefore a high honor to be asked by its editor, Dr. Winslow Briggs, to contribute a prefatory chapter to this journal's twenty-seventh annual volume.

The world food supply is the topic I have chosen for discussion. I have selected it for two principal reasons: first, growing the plants to feed the rising tide of population has become the world's most pressing agricultural, social, political, and moral problem. Second, a breakthrough is needed in the creation of new food plants capable of producing more and higher quality food with less supplementary energy input. Research opportunities exist in this field because plant physiology is a basic science that underlies agricultural production, and it would not be unreasonable to expect that such a breakthrough could have its inception in a plant physiological laboratory.

In order to understand world food supply it is necessary to interrelate it with the available supply of energy and population distribution. This can be done by adopting the concept of the human ecosystem. Here humans are part of a life-support system in which the whole planet is involved. The system obtains all its energy necessary to operate from the radiant energy of the sun. The primary producers are the green photosynthesizing cells of plants and blue-green algae. The primary consumers are the animals and humans who eat plants. The secondary consumers are animals and humans that eat animals. Other components of the human ecosystem are the decomposers, microorganisms, worms, fungi, and beetles which make recycling possible. Physical entities such as the air, the rocks, the soil, the waters, and even the fossil fuel deposits are all part of the human ecosystem. Today the major primary producers in the system are our farm crops.

HUMAN POPULATION (9)

History

A plausible view proposed by Edward Deevey (8) holds that human populations grew in three consecutive surges (Figure 1). Each surge resulted from a human invention. The population on earth at a given time is plotted on the ordinate. Beginning about a million years ago in the lower Paleolithic, small organized bands of hunters equipped with stone tools and weapons lived on whatever the natural ecology of the land provided. Paleolithic hunters also roamed the North American continent and probably were largely responsible for the extermination of most of the large mammals in this hemisphere. The Stone Age lasted 990,000 years, until about 10,000 years ago, and during that time the population increased from half a million to five million. Deevey estimated that the total number of Stone Age hunters and gatherers that lived during this long period could have been 36 billion.

The second population surge was due to the invention of agriculture. At this point the natural ecology of the land could no longer support the population of five million. Man had learned to make the land more productive, and as a consequence during some 9700 years the world population rose to a maximum of half a billion.

A new epoch began 300 years ago, the scientific and industrial revolution. The characteristic that enabled human numbers to increase further was the use of supplementary energy. More recently, agricultural production was increased through the use of fossil energy, primarily petroleum. Today there are nearly four billion people living on earth, and although the rate of population increase has materially diminished in most industrial nations, it has not yet declined in the poorer nations where more than half of the world's population is living under crowded and nutritionally marginal conditions.

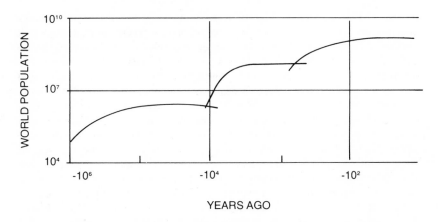

Figure 1   Growth of the human population plotted on a log-log scale. The population grew in three surges, each brought about by a human invention: first step: Stone Age hunters; second step: agriculture; third step: industrial agriculture. Now with a world population of 4×10^9, the human ecosystem is left without grain reserves and in parts of South East Asia hunger is an endless nightmare. (After E. S. Deevey, "The Human Population." Copyright 1960 by Scientific American, Inc. All rights reserved.)

Distribution

The world today can be divided into three groups according to the rate of population growth (3). A growth rate of less than 1.5 percent (doubling time more than 47 years) is found in North America, Western Europe, and the USSR; this group contains 25.6% of the world population. A second group, comprising 27.6% of the world population, has a growth rate of more than 1.5 percent, but less than 2.5 (doubling time 28 years); China, Japan, and South Africa belong to it. The third group, which contains 46.8% of the world population, has a growth rate of over 2.5 percent; India, Pakistan, Bangladesh, Indonesia, the Philippines, most of Africa, South and Central America belong to this group of most rapidly reproducing nations. In absolute numbers, the yearly increase in population during 1972 was 71 million for the world as a whole, 13.3 million for China, 12.8 million for India, 3.4 million for Indonesia, 2.2 million for the USSR, 1.3 million for the USA, and 1.3 million for the Philippines. On the whole, one might state that of every 100 babies that are born, 85 are born in countries already overburdened with people, where there is the greatest likelihood for famine to strike when population growth outpaces local food production. Bangladesh and India are prime examples.

Control

It is well recognized that the increase in population we are observing today is due to a decrease in the death rate (deaths per 1000 population) and not to an increase in the birth rate (babies born per 1000 people). India, the world's largest democracy, inhabited by nearly 600 million people, provides a clear example of this unbalance between birth and death rates. In 1901 her birth rate was 46 with a death rate of 44. The population growth was 46–44 = 2 or 0.2 percent. There was no demographic problem, although many suffered from widespread diseases such as malaria. Infant and child mortality was high. In 1931 when general hygiene became more widespread the death rate dropped to 36, but the birth rate remained at 46. During 1931 then, as a consequence of a reduced death rate, the population growth rose to 10 per 1000 or 1.0 percent. By 1961 when DDT controlled malaria and allowed many more children to live, the death rate dropped still further, but the birth rate now also began to drop. The balance was 40–21 = 19 or 1.9 percent. In 1973 the death rate had dropped still more than the birth rate, which was also dropping, and the balance now was 37–14 = 23 or 2.3 percent. It is a fact that India has the largest officially sponsored family planning program of any nation. This program began in 1952 when the population was growing at the rate of 6 million per year. Yet in spite of all efforts to control it, the yearly population increase today is 12 million. Family planning did not halt the population explosion in India.

By contrast, in the industrialized societies birth rates are nearly as low as the death rates. Women reduced their fertility voluntarily for economic and social reasons. Educated women enjoy being part of the work force, and they do not want to reduce their standard of living by having more mouths to feed and bodies to clothe. Even during the recession of the 1930s women reduced their fertility. This is the more remarkable because at that time contraceptive materials and methods were primitive and unreliable in comparison to what is available today. We can conclude that it is the will of women themselves to reduce their fertility, and not so much the easy availability of pills and other methods of birth control. These only facilitate their determination not to become pregnant.

Why is birth control so difficult in poor countries? There are many cultural, religious, and biological reasons why it is so hard to control births in poor countries and even in segments of the population in developed countries. Biologically, humans come equipped with a genetic potential for a strong sex drive. It is inherent in the species, and in the evolution of man it must have been a major reason why the species survived and became established. Animals have an estrous period. In chimps this occurs infrequently, less than once per year. In the human female, by contrast, there is no such distinct estrous period, so she is sexually continually available. The sex drive is highest in teenagers (13), in whom there is also a tendency for the non-use of contraceptives for hedonistic and other reasons (14). Female fertility is usually highest during the early and middle twenties (20). Sexual intercourse is a natural biological phenomenon, and whenever healthy young people are brought together —and especially when social and moral pressures are removed—"it" will happen. It must be clear that antinatalistic legislation and reinstitution of social and moral restraints are ways to control births. These measures seem to be working in Mainland China, but they require a governmental control of cultural education beginning practically at birth. Such steps are not likely to be taken by a nation except following a disaster such as famine or a devastating war. In 1948 both China and India emerged from such disasters. Today, a quarter of a century later, it would appear that the people of China may have a better future ahead of them than those of India.

Political Decision Making

People, in small groups or in nations, have very strong feelings about all kinds of moral positions in which science has no bearing. This is especially true in the area of population and food. The purpose of politics is to reconcile such large-scale differences of opinion so that the government can function. In science logic is based on objectivity, and our decisions are based on this objectivity ethic as long as we are acting as scientists. Governmental decisions are often based not on physical objectivity, but on rationalities which are metaphysical such as religious or political principles. Economic and legal rationalities are also often dominant in political decision making.

It is no wonder then that during the 1974 World Population Conference, sponsored by the United Nations at Bucharest, so little agreement was obtained, and that some would not even agree that there was such a thing as overpopulation in the world. Proposals for even the most elementary standards of family size were not adopted for lack of general approval, although there was agreement on the liberation and education of women. Before the problems of energy, food, and population can be resolved on a global basis there must be global goals on family limitation, and these can only be worked out through political bargaining.

ENERGY (1)

The rise of the industrial nations to prosperity and affluence was brought about largely by the availability of low cost energy. The amount of industrial energy used per capita is in fact a standard measure of prosperity of a nation. Energy today takes the place of slave labor in the past. As long as 25 years ago, Harrison Brown, in his lectures at CalTech, used to point out that when world fossil energy consumption is plotted on a geological scale the graph looks like a spike (Figure 2). The human use of energy is just a flash in terms of geological time. Consumption of fossil fuel has been grossly wasteful, as in wars and in massive use of "gas guzzling" automobiles. When in 1973 the Arabian oil producing countries banded together and placed an embargo on oil exports to the United States and the Netherlands, people in industrial nations began to realize what it would be like to be without the energy that most of us had been taking for granted. One reason political leaders did not

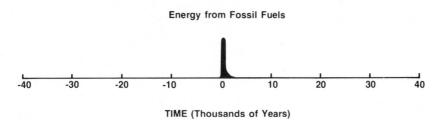

Figure 2 Consumption of fossil fuels appears like a flash when plotted on a time scale of 1000-year units. (After M. K. Hubert, *Science*, Vol. 109, pp. 103–9, Fig. 8, 4 Feb. 1949.)

worry about energy was that the original projections for the total world consumption of fossil fuel called for a peak about the year 2200, with all of the known reserves used up by the year 2800 (4). This world supply of fossil fuels includes coal as well as oil and gas. Petroleum products are in high demand and their use doubles every few years; in 1973 gas and oil were in sufficiently low supply that the Arabian nations could effectively use the petroleum supply as a political weapon. The result was tripling of fuel prices for Middle Eastern supplies and a dislocation of established commercial patterns. Among the casualties was the increasing food production in the poor countries.

Industrialized Agriculture

Western style mechanized agriculture uses more petroleum than any single industry. A group of Cornell researchers analyzed in detail the energy inputs needed to produce a crop of corn (maize) on one acre (17). They found that the corn yield had increased from 34 bushels in 1945 to 81 in 1970, a 2.4-fold increase. In order to achieve this gain in yield they found that the supplementary energy input had to be increased from 0.9×10^6 kcal in 1945 to 2.9×10^6 kcal in 1970, a 3.2-fold increase. The 1970 corn yield represents 8.2×10^6 kcal, composed of 2.9×10^6 kcal supplementary energy and 5.3×10^6 kcal photosynthetic input. We are beginning to realize that it is petroleum energy that is increasing the carrying capacity of the land, which in turn makes the present large human populations possible.

Another interesting study, by John and Carol Steinhart (19) deals with the energy use of the whole US food system. Here we find (Figure 3) that the farm input of supplementary energy for farm machinery, fertilizers, irrigation, etc is about twice as large as the actual food calories consumed by our population. If we add to that the energy used by the food processing industries, we find that by the time the food is canned or packaged it represents an energy input six times greater than the caloric food value of its contents. By the time the food is refrigerated, commercially and at home, and finally cooked and served it has taken a caloric input ten times larger than its food value. However, this enables a working couple to have a tasty dinner on the table 30 minutes after they come home.

The Green Revolution

The Green Revolution was a term coined by a Washington correspondent to describe the successful introduction of high-yielding rice varieties by the International Rice Research Institute (IRRI) in the Philippines. The term has caught on and is now broadly used for successful application of scientific agriculture to tropical food crops. It has its advocates and its dissenters, but the truth is somewhere in the middle as the following discussion will illustrate.

In the early 1940s the Rockefeller Foundation was interested in giving medical aid to underdeveloped countries. The Foundation studies indicated that the basic difficulty was the people's inadequate diet, so the decision was made to help them grow better crops in the hope that a better agriculture would solve many of the medical problems. This led to the establishment of the wheat and maize research center (CIMMYT) in Mexico in 1943, which a few decades later became famous

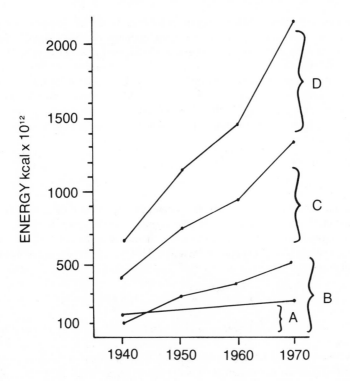

Figure 3   Energy use in the United States' food system compared to the caloric content of the food consumed. A. Food calories consumed. B. Energy used on the farm. C. Energy used by processing industries. D. Energy used for refrigeration and cooking, commercial and domestic. (Data from J. and C. Steinhart, *Energy: Sources, Use, and Role in Human Affairs.* North Scituate, Mass.: Duxbury Press, 1974).

for its high-yielding semidwarf wheats developed by Norman Borlaug. In 1962 the Rockefeller Foundation was joined by the Ford Foundation in establishing the IRRI, which in only a few years developed a successful line of high-yielding semi-dwarf rice varieties. The success of these two stations led to the establishment of a whole international network of agricultural research centers, all devoted to the quick improvement of all the major crops in the poor countries (25). This was a major humanitarian act which should provide temporary relief to the poor suffering masses. Maybe it will provide the atmosphere in which strong leadership can bring human fertility under control.

An admirable aspect of each research institute such as the IRRI is its organiza-tion, which allows adequate financing with freedom to make local decisions. The key to quick success is undoubtedly the existence of a narrowly defined goal. The IRRI scientists, no matter what their discipline, have to keep in mind that all research should contribute toward increased grain yield and quality (6).

During 1943 when CIMMYT began its work and even in 1962 when IRRI set its goal, few seriously entertained the thought that the world's supply of cheap energy would become so limited within our lifetime that it would seriously hamper availability of fertilizer, irrigation water, and farm mechanization. Selection of rice and wheat varieties was based on their capacity to respond to fertilizer. Quickly maturing varieties were selected so that with the aid of irrigation three crops a year could be produced. Unfortunately, the manufacturing of fertilizer requires natural gas both for energy and for a source of hydrogen to reduce the atmospheric nitrogen to ammonia:

$$7CH_4 + 10H_2O + 4N_4O \xrightarrow[\text{pressure}]{\text{temp}} 16NH_3 + 7CO_2$$

It is the largest item on the supplementary energy budget (17). Fertilizer is expensive in terms of money too. It is an item poor farmers cannot afford. However, within the organization of the research institutes it should be easy to modify the goals so that economy of crop production is included. This would encourage optimal use of biological nitrogen fixation:

$$N_2 + 3(H_2) + 12\ ATP \xrightarrow{\text{nitrogenase}} 2\ NH_3 + 12\ ADP + 12\ P_i$$

It would also encourage research in crop rotation and use of animal and human manures.

It is by no means a foregone conclusion that the price of nitrogen fertilizer will remain as high as it is at present. As I understand it, Arabian oil producers still burn their natural gas. If they begin using it for ammonia manufacture, nitrogen fertilizer might easily be overproduced with a concommitant reduction in price. This would not be the first time that this has happened in the fertilizer industry. However, farmers, in particular the small producers, should have an alternate to commercial fertilizer to which they can turn when production costs go too high.

What are the other negative aspects of the Green Revolution way of growing crops? The following have been mentioned: New rice varieties were unfamiliar in taste and texture. This has been overcome by selection of mutants with the desired qualities within the original IR8 line. Similarly, resistance to insects and diseases can be bred into the IR8 line. There has also been criticism that the statistics showing increased yields under actual farming conditions were more due to return of favorable weather than to new varieties. Then there is criticism that the new varieties are not enough to cope with the yearly increases in population. An additional 3 million tons of grain are needed in India each year just to keep up with the increase in population. Failure of the birth control program cannot possibly be blamed on the green revolution. Human behavior is difficult to predict, as the following story will illustrate.

In 1968, at the Second International Conference on the War on Hunger, the Philippine success with the Green Revolution was a major topic. The Philippine Undersecretary for Agriculture, Dr. Dioscoro Lopez Umali, came to Washington and brought with him a Philippine farmer who had markedly increased his production through the use of the new miracle rice. Before a distinguished audience, Dr. Lopez translated the farmer's story as he spoke. The farmer had 10 children and said that because of the new high yielding variety, he and his neighbors would now have enough food for all, and all could enjoy seeing their women in the condition in which they were most beautiful—pregnant! This sudden switch from concern about food shortages to praise for pregnancy was a frightening idea to some of the audience. It seems that whenever the carrying capacity of the land is increased in the human ecosystem, the species immediately takes advantage of it and loses no time in striving for the maximum. Even in the developed industrial nations, which at present experience a very low fertility rate, no demographer would dare to predict that it would remain that low in the years ahead. A wave of prosperity, a rash of advertising featuring happy large families with washing machines or station wagons, and a change in social values may well trigger a swing back to high female fertility.

WORLD FOOD SUPPLY (2)

Public opinion to the contrary, crop yields in the poorer countries have increased since the early 1960s. Scientific agriculture and the Green Revolution, aided by favorable weather and relatively cheap energy and fertilizers, have increased yields substantially. There were even periods when the per capita yield increased in poorer nations so that diets improved. However, in most instances the increases in food production were gobbled up by a free-wheeling population growth. This brings disaster whenever something goes wrong such as unfavorable weather. This happened about 1966 in the Indian provinces of Bihar and Uttar Pradesh, which are located in the "rain shadow" of the Himalayas. For several years there had been favorable rainfall and because of a great population pressure, families settled in the area hoping the favorable conditions would continue. But they did not and a prolonged drought withered the crops and the people suffered. Even though there was ample water 40 feet below the soil level, there was neither energy nor pumps available. Many US church people later provided the wells, and I am confident that some of the US "surplus" grain brought some relief.

Elected political leaders do not wish to be identified with birth control programs even in the most overcrowded countries. There often is no effective family planning program. However, food production is encouraged in the mistaken belief that it is an alternative option to birth control. What people in these areas do not want to understand is that in order to create a better way of life for themselves it is necessary to do several things at the same time. Birth control must go hand in hand with increased crop production, and at the same time the country's economy must be developed so as to put more money in the hands of the people. Biologists realize this, and as some of you may recall, at the 1969 International Botanical Congress in Seattle a resolution was passed which stated in part that "there is no solution to the final problem (feeding the world) unless population control is achieved." At that time the objective of the food scientists was to step up food production to keep up with population growth until such time that the human fertility had been reduced to the point that it equalled the death rate. This was achieved in the industrialized nations, but nowhere in the poorer nations.

Protein Problems

A most common form of malnutrition is a deficiency of one or more essential amino acids in the human diet. It is common among the poor of the world, including many in the USA. The deficiency is most widespread and does most harm in growing children. In its extreme form it is called Kwashiorkor, a West African term. The amino acid deficiency prevents normal protein synthesis in the growing child so that brain tissue and muscle tissue become underdeveloped. In the brain, damage is permanent, so that even if a child survives it will be mentally deficient.

The key to the problem lies in the ammonia that plants use to synthesize amino acids. The ammonia can come either from nitrogen fertilizer or from biological nitrogen fixation as in legumes. Many poor people are also uneducated in knowledge about nutrition. If they knew—as the Javanese do—that the young leaves of spinach and many other plants have much high grade protein in them, they could save the health of their young children. Also, mixing protein sources such as blending corn meal and soybean meal prevents amino acid deficiency. Corn is low in tryptophan (55 egg protein units) while soy meal is high in this amino acid (127 units). Similarly, lysine is low (38 units) in corn meal but this is compensated for by the high (111 units) content of soy meal. Quality of all grains, including corn, is constantly being improved through plant breeding. Wheat is now so nutritious that a man can live on bread alone, but not women and children.

Deficient protein nutrition in the poor is one aspect of the protein problem. Another aspect is that affluent people prefer to obtain their amino acids from animal protein rather than from beans (5). Steak, chicken, pork, turkey, milk, and eggs simply taste better than the equally nutritious plant products. During the past two decades most of the industrial nations have prospered, and in terms of real dollars the purchasing power of the workers has doubled, so a high demand has been created for animal protein. Grains—food grains as well as feed grains—are fed to the animals, which adds an extra consumer to the food chain.

However, animals were not fed plant proteins exclusively; some received fishmeal. The greatest fishmeal producer of all was Peru, which contributed over 10 million metric tons of fishmeal to the animal industry. In May and June of 1972 the Peruvian fishing boats, accustomed to netting a total of a million tons of anchoveta a month, were forced to return empty. The fabulous Peruvian fish catch had suddenly failed. The fishmeal export dried up and the affluent industrial nations, e.g. Japan and West Europe, shifted to a protein substitute to feed their animals: American soybean meal. The USA is the world's largest soybean producer and exporter. The Peruvian fish failure created a temporary vacuum in the protein food market and prices doubled and tripled. This precipitated the high cost of protein food we are experiencing. However, this was not the only cause for high food prices as we will see later.

Because we are looking at the world food problem from the standpoint of the human ecosystem, a word should be said about the causes of the sudden failure of the Peruvian fish. Even though Peru lies close to the equator, the coast, especially from May to October, is remarkably cool. This is caused by a great upwelling of antarctic water all along the coast of Peru and northern Chile. This upwelling brings minerals, particularly phosphates and nitrates, to the surface. There, with the benefit of light, a tremendous photosynthesis takes place in phytoplankton. Photosynthetic carbon fixation of 200 milligrams per cubic meter of water per day has been observed at the surface of the upwelling, while in the waters immediately adjacent to it the photosynthetic carbon fixation was only 15 mg. The phytoplankton is eaten by herbivorous zooplankton, and this in turn constitutes the food for billions of small anchovy, called anchoveta (*Engraulis ringens*). On the rocks of the coast millions of guano birds live on the anchoveta.

What happened to the fish that early part of 1972? The weather changed and the winds which usually blow from the east now blew from the west. This happens periodically and it is said to come and go in 7-year cycles. The wind is called El Niño, the Christmas Child, because it starts blowing in December, piling warm water on the coast and thereby preventing the antarctic current from rising to the surface. Without sufficient minerals the phytoplankton cannot grow and the basis of the food chain is removed; no more fish. Biologists suspect that overfishing was an additional cause for the failure of the anchoveta, and in 1974 fishing was resumed with an allowed limit of 4 million metric tons per year. With such precautions, one hopes the abundance will return.

Grain Crisis

During 1972, the year that on the Peruvian coast an ill wind blew 10 million metric tons (mmt) of fishmeal away, adverse weather conditions in Russia caused a shortage of some 13 mmt of grain. The Russians then purchased quietly 12 mmt of wheat in the United States. This amounted to one-fourth of the entire US wheat production. Its major effect was that it virtually eliminated the reserves ("surpluses") which the US had maintained for decades and which had served well in maintaining stable and low food prices. After the Russian grain purchase the price of wheat, which had held steady at about $70 per metric ton for a decade, suddenly rose to $140 and in early 1974 peaked at $220. Poor weather conditions around the world caused other crop failures. India, for example, was forced to buy 7 mmt at the high export prices, using millions of rupees that had been budgeted for family planning. In 1974 the US corn crop was the worst in a quarter century. The obvious lesson, and it is an ancient one, is that in order to maintain economic stability it is essential to maintain substantial grain reserves. The principal outcome of the World Food Conference held in Rome in 1974 was a resolution to establish world food reserves.

The actual dimensions of the world's grain production are as follows:

soybeans..............53 mmt; US production is 75% of world production
feed crops...........510 mmt   35%
wheat ....300 mmt   15%
rice ....400 mmt   1%
world total.........1263 mmt

These are harvest figures attained before the multiple crises made the cost of energy and the price of food soar (21).

Optimum Population

The size of the population in the human ecosystem will be determined by the food production of the world's agriculture and fisheries. Fishing is still a form of hunting, and with the use of modern boats and gear there is a constant threat of overfishing. The latest statistics show a world fish catch of 66 mmt, of which the US share was 4 percent. These 66 mmt of fish may be considered equivalent to soybeans, and may be added to the world agriculture figure of 1263, making a total of 1329 mmt of "grain" produced annually. It would seem unlikely that this figure will increase substantially during the remainder of this decade.

The affluence of a nation is reflected in its grain consumption. The annual consumption by a mainland Chinese is one-fourth of a ton, while the average North American consumes a whole ton because he uses much more animal protein than the average Chinese (5). Today the world is estimated to have a human population of nearly 4 billion. If the world's grain were equally shared between all its inhabitants (China may already have achieved such an egalitarian condition) one-third of a ton per person would be available. This is nearer to the standard of living of the Chinese than that of the North Americans. The data may also be presented according to the following balance sheet:

World Grain Production.................................1.329 billion tons
World Population......................................4 billion people
If we all ate like North Americans
   (one ton per person per year)
   the world could support ....1.329 billion people
If we all ate like Chinese
   (4 persons live on one ton per year)
   the world could support..........................5.3 billion people

If we consider the living standard of North Americans an optimum which everyone on this earth should achieve, it is clear that it is too late for that. We passed that point at about the time when Thomas Malthus first sounded the alarm. Even if we consider the living standard of mainland Chinese optimum, we are too late because the young people are already here who will make the population exceed 5.3 billion before the end of this century. But could we not continue to extrapolate the growth of agricultural production through the last quarter of this century? I doubt it, because in agricultural production we have reached the point of diminishing returns (18:Figure 4). To produce more one needs more energy that is no longer abundantly available. The best of the agricultural land has been used, often foolishly for new housing developments, cities, airports, super highways. Land is still being lost through erosion and salination because of poor farming practices. The more yields are pushed upward the more agricultural technologists are required. These are not available in the poorer countries. On the positive side, new land is still available in South America and Australia.

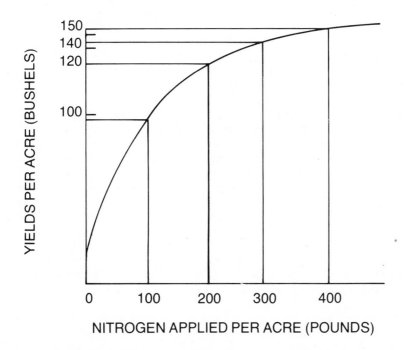

Figure 4   The law of diminishing returns demonstrated on fertilizer application to irrigated corn. Crop yields diminish with increasing applications of nutrients. (After C. J. Pratt, Chemical Fertilizers." Copyright 1965 by Scientific American, Inc. All rights reserved.)

PLANT PHYSIOLOGY

Understanding Crop Plants

Plant physiology is to agronomy what human physiology is to medicine. The fullest possible understanding of crop plants is essential. Work on crop plants, particularly tropical species, is rewarding both in terms of physiology and of agronomy. An example is the discovery of a new more efficient mechanism for the uptake of carbon dioxide (PEP carboxylase) by physiologists of the Hawaiian Sugar Planters Association (12). Another is the discovery by workers in Japan and the Philippines that silicon is a nutrient element for the normal growth of rice plants. Even little discoveries, e.g. that flowering in pineapples can be induced geotropically by laying the plant on its side, are exciting as they help one understand plants better (23).

Periodic meetings between field agronomists and plant physiologists are often fruitful as they improve mutual understanding and lead to solutions of problems. During a winter day, a group of agronomists of a large California farming company met with plant physiologists in the Shell Development Company laboratory for a session on agricultural problems. Clogged irrigation canals (hundreds of miles of them) was one of the problems. They caused levee breaks, flooding, and lawsuits. By the next spring we had a workable solution: acrolein, a volatile, water soluble, nonresidual chemical (22, 24). It has also proved effective in tropical countries against the water snails that carry blood flukes causing schistosomiasis. Meetings between plant breeders and plant physiologists are often profitable in the analysis of growth processes. Thus Phinney (16) demonstrated that some of the dwarfing of corn strains is due to deficiency of gibberellic acid. The simple application of a few drops of GA during the seedling stage can make the genetic dwarfs turn into normal phenotypes. By working with geneticists a physiologist learns that there is no such thing as corn or wheat or cotton, but that each species consists of an endless number of varieties mostly differing only by one gene. Plant breeders, of course, have made use of this variation by creating the high yielding, disease and insect-resistant strains of corn, wheat, and rice, but physiologists could make more use of single gene differences by using them in their search to understand how crop plants function.

Creating Economy Models

At this particular time, fertilizers happen to be expensive and practically unavailable to farmers in the poorer countries, with the result that it is difficult for farmers to grow the high-yielding semidwarf varieties that depend for their ammonia on synthetic fertilizer. Physiologists and their biochemist associates have gone far in understanding the process of biological nitrogen fixation, and excellent summaries have been published by Burris (10) and Hardy (2). Interdisciplinary effort is now called for to make wheat and rice plants produce their crops with the aid of ammonia from biological nitrogen fixation rather than from synthetic fertilizer. Perhaps a combination can be found in which a suitable rice or wheat variety harbors in its rhizosphere a compatable variety of microbial nitrogen fixer. Eventually such a combination may be found in which the bacteria fix their nitrogen inside modified roots. One hopes such a combination might function as rhizobia do in soybeans. Other approaches could be the deliberate culture of blue-green algae in rice fields. Such conditions have existed in nature for hundreds of years and made it possible for tropical farmers to grow rice crops without the benefit of synthetic fertilizer. All sorts of methods have been used in the human ecology of the tropics: blue-green algae and milk fish in the rice fields, introduction of human and animal manure, crop rotation, etc. Finally, in the modern laboratory it may be possible to transfer the nitrogenase operon, perhaps riding on a virus, into the crop plant or into the microorganisms of the soil in which the crop plant is rooted. It is time to set goals now and start cooperative projects. The objective is to grow nutritious crops without the high cost in energy now required to manufacture and transport fertilizers.

Recently plant physiologists have learned how to culture isolated plant protoplasts by digesting the cell wall away with appropriate enzymes (7, 15). This makes it possible for researchers to manipulate the chromosomes as is now being done with animal cells which do not have a wall. The isolated protoplast regenerates a cell wall and such cells have the capacity to develop into an entire plant. This new extension of tissue-growing technique will make it possible not only to grow new varieties, but even may lead to the creation of entirely new species. The following new development will show how this might be accomplished.

During the mid 1930s there were some geneticists who expressed the opinion that the evolution of major new forms could not take place from small stepwise mutations, but by some sort of quantum jump. Richard Goldschmidt was one of these. This idea was recently revived by Mary-Claire King and Alan C. Wilson (11). They had made an exhaustive comparison of the genes of man and chimpanzee by biochemical methods. They confirmed earlier findings that there is only a one percent difference in nucleotide differences in DNA of the two species. When they compared amino acid sequences of common proteins they confirmed that the average human protein is 99 percent identical to the chimpanzees. Human and chimpanzee genes, it can be concluded, are remarkably similar.

Yet in spite of the very close resemblance in molecular makeup between humans and apes, an ape is still an ape and not a man. In the embryology of apes, however, there is a stage in which an adult man resembles a fetal ape. The human species never grew up, it appears, and retained the small jaws and naked skin of the ape embryo. King & Wilson propose that the order of genes on the chromosomes may change owing to inversion, translocation, duplication of genes, or fusion or deletion of chromosomes. Humans have 46 and chimpanzees have 48 chromosomes. Microscopic studies of *Drosophila* salivary chromosomes had shown that no two species have the same gene order. Gene rearrangements may therefore be an important source for evolutionary changes. Microscopic studies of human and chimpanzee chromosomes indicate that at least ten large inversions and translocations and one chromosomal fusion have occurred since the two lineages diverged.

If we once more turn our thoughts to the protoplast cultures of plants, we can imagine that ways will be found to bring about in their chromosomes inversions, translocations, duplications, and fusions. After the cell wall has reformed and the modified cell develops into a plant, we may find that we have created an entirely new plant. We would have learned to speed up evolution in the hope of finding plants which require less energy input to grow a crop than we have today.

Learning from Photosynthesis

During my lifetime biologists have learned to understand two of the most fundamental biological processes: (*a*) the flow of genetic information, also known as the dogma of the new biology; and (*b*) photosynthesis. I doubt that any other generation of biologists has been so fortunate.

Photosynthesis, starting with blue-green algae some 3 billion years ago, splits water molecules with quanta of visible light. This is quite a feat as in the upper atmosphere ultraviolet quanta split water but not visible radiation. Because of the organization of the thylakoid, the photosynthetic membrane, blue-green algae managed to split water with safe visible radiation. This process is still retained in modern blue-green algae as well as in our higher plants.

The hydrogen released from the split water reduces carbon dioxide and other materials which become sugars, starch, amino acids, etc, i. e. the plant body. The oxygen released as a waste product over the billions of years changed an originally reducing environment into the oxydizing medium which surrounds us today. As a consequence of this, availability of free oxygen respiration became possible and glucose could now be converted into the biological energy of ATP with efficiency 20 times greater than was heretofore possible in the reducing environment. This in turn made possible the evolution of the large, eukaryotic multicellular animals from which humans ultimately arose. The ever-increasing oxygen content of the atmosphere gave rise to the ozone layer in the upper atmosphere which began to shield the earth from the sun's ultraviolet radiation. And so life on land became possible. On the land plants evolved and giant forests arose, which of course grew by photosynthesis. They absorbed much of the earth's carbon dioxide and exuded more oxygen into the atmosphere. Over millions of years forests died and accumulated carboniferous debris in thick layers which became our coal beds, and other biological material became our oil and gas pools. All the fossil fuel upon which our industrial civilization depends was made by photosynthesis from carbon dioxide and water with the energy of the sun's visible radiation. When we burn it we release the energy as heat and return the carbon dioxide and water to the environment from which it was originally taken.

It would seem that once we have exhausted the earth's fossil fuel we cannot count on the steady flow of energy we have grown accustomed to unless we can learn to imitate photosynthesis in a large way. This means the splitting of water with the visible rays of the sun's energy. Humanity, of course, could survive using the process of photosynthesis directly, e.g. production of fuel alcohol or hydrogen, but that would not support the numbers of humanity that exist today. No one can predict the future, but if one looks at the spike of Figure 2, one realizes that modern technological humanity has been riding the wave of fossil energy like a surfboard rider. Our human ecosystem is sustained by supplementary fossil energy, and when that is gone survival will not be so easy. . . . unless we learn to imitate photosynthesis by splitting the water molecule in a massive way with the sun's energy. There will be additional sources of energy such as atomic energy, but here radioactive contaminants and wastes pose serious difficulties; recycling water appears infinitely more healthful.

In conclusion, it is clear that plant physiology has a fundamental role in the struggle for world food supply. It provides the basic knowledge of how crop plants grow and produce. In the area of biological nitrogen fixation many important agricultural applications have already been made. Knowledge of the process has grown so profound that it is reasonable to expect that in the coming decade nitrogen fixation capacity will be introduced in cereal grains, either in their roots or in their rhizosphere. If successful this would do away with the need these grain crops now have for chemical fertilizer. Another promising area, but with applications farther in the future, is protoplast cultures. It could enable man to modify plant chromosomes, inducing inversions, translocations, fusions, etc which would lead to the creation of new plant species. Some of these might be better adapted to our rapidly changing environment. They could be more resistant to droughts and pests than our present crop plants and thus would require a lower supplemental energy input.

Literature Cited

1. Abelson, P. H., ed. 1974. *Science* 184 (No. 4134):245–386. Twenty-six articles dealing with energy
2. Abelson, P. H., ed. 1975. *Science* 188 (No. 4188):501–650. Twenty-five articles dealing with food supply
3. Biró, A., ed. 1973. *Ceres* No. 36 population special. Official United Nations FAO journal dealing with world food supply
4. Brown, H. 1954. *The Challenge of Man's Future.* Viking
5. Brown, L. R. 1974. *In the Human Interest.* Norton. Deals with world food supply
6. Chandler, R. F. 1969. *11th Int. Bot. Congr.,* Symp. World Food supply, Seattle (Allis-Chalmers)
7. Carlson, P. S., Polacco, J. C. 1975. *Science* 188:622–25
8. Deevey, E. S. 1971. In *Man and the Ecosphere,* ed. P. R. Ehrlich. Freeman
9. Flanagan, D., ed. 1974. *Sci. Am.* Sept. issue contains 11 articles on human population.
10. Gibbs, M., ed. 1974. *Plant Physiology* 50th Anniv. Issue 54 (No. 4)
11. King, M. C., Wilson, A. C. 1975. *Science* 188:107–16; also by same authors, *New Scientist* 3 Jul. 1975

12. Kortschak, H. P., Hartt, C. E., Burr, G. O. 1965. *Plant Physiol.* 40:209
13. Lincoln, R., ed. 1974. *Family Planning Perspectives* 6 (3). Planned Parenthood Federation, NY
14. Ibid 1975. 7 (1)
15. Murashige, T. 1974. *Ann. Rev. Plant Physiol.* 25:135–66
16. Phinney, B. O. 1957. *Proc. Natl. Acad. Sci. USA* 43:398–404
17. Pimentel, D. et al 1973. *Science* 2 Nov.: 443–49
18. Pratt, C. J. 1970. In *Plant Agriculture,* ed. J. Janick. Freeman
19. Steinhart, J. S. and C. E. 1974. *Science* 184:307–16
20. United States Bureau of the Census July 1974. *World Fertility Patterns,* a chart
21. Van Doren, C., ed. 1975. *Britannica* Book of the Year. Contains recent agricultural production statistics
22. van Overbeek, J. 1960. *U.S. Patent No. 2,959,476:* Method of Controlling Aquatic Plants
23. van Overbeek, J., Cruzado, H. J. 1948. *Am. J. Bot.* 35:410–12
24. van Overbeek, J., Hughes, W. J., Blondeau, R. 1959. *Science* 129:335–36
25. Wade, N. 1975. *Science* 188:585–89

Ann. Rev. Plant Physiol. 1976. 27:19–38

BIOSYNTHESIS, INTRACELLULAR TRANSPORT, AND SECRETION OF EXTRACELLULAR MACROMOLECULES[1]

❖7600

Maarten J. Chrispeels[2]

Department of Biology, University of California, San Diego, La Jolla, California 92093

CONTENTS

[1]The preparation of this review was supported in part by a contract from ERDA [E(04-3)-34/159] and a grant from the NSF (GB 30235).
[2]It is a pleasure to thank Drs. J. E. Varner and K. D. Johnson for their critical reviews of the completed manuscript.

A variety of macromolecules synthesized within the cytoplasm of the plant cell need to be transported across the plasma membrane to arrive at the site of their function. Examples of such substances include structural and enzymatic components of the cell wall, mucilages, and hydrolytic enzymes. The biosynthesis of these extracellular macromolecules occurs in special cell organelles resulting in the segregation of these substances within the cytoplasm. This segregation is the first step in their subsequent intracellular transport and transfer to the cell's exterior. It is therefore impossible to discuss the process of secretion—the transport of macromolecules out of the cell—without discussing at the same time the site of synthesis of these molecules. There is no recent comprehensive review covering both the biochemical and the cytological aspects of the biosynthesis, the intracellular transport and the secretion of macromolecules in plant cells. However, several excellent reviews dealing with particular aspects of this complex problem have been published in recent years (8, 31, 84, 85, 91, 94, 111, 118, 120, 137). Several of these reviews have stressed the role of the Golgi apparatus in the synthesis and transport of cell wall precursors (39, 80, 88, 89, 94).

In this review I focus primarily on the biochemical data which have been obtained in the last few years and attempt to integrate the information obtained with different secretory systems. Improved methods for fractionating cellular organelles, the availability of new marker enzymes for the different organelles, several new metabolic poisons, and the characterization of the glycosyltransferases involved in glyco-protein and polysaccharide synthesis have all contributed to recent advances in our understanding of the processes involved in the transport and secretion of mac-romolecules.

Initially much of the information about intracellular transport and secretion was obtained with cytochemical and autoradiographic methods, first with the light microscope and later with the electron microscope. It has been pointed out many times, recently in a critical review by O'Brien (94), that these are not the proper methods to study a dynamic process such as secretion. That may well be true, but recent biochemical observations all support the hypotheses formulated by the earlier cytologists who claimed that various cytoplasmic organelles, especially the ergasto-plasm and the Golgi apparatus, were involved in the elaboration, transport, and secretion of extracellular molecules.

The cells of higher and lower plants secrete a large variety of macromolecules, and there are a number of cell types in which the biochemical parameters of secretion can be studied profitably. All plant cells produce a cell wall or an extracel-lular matrix consisting of different macromolecules, most of which are synthesized in the cytoplasm. Thus a normal plant cell devotes a fair proportion of its metabolic activity to the synthesis of extracellular macromolecules without being specialized for this particular function in the same way that certain gland cells are. Attempts to measure the biochemical parameters of secretion must take into account the fact that the measurements will be performed against the background of all the other metabolic activities of the cell. For example, the incorporation of radioactive amino acids into proteins will be primarily into cytoplasmic proteins and to a lesser degree into the proteins which are transported out of the cell.

Many plants contain glands and some of the gland cells are highly specialized for the secretion of slimes or digestive enzymes. However, it is usually quite difficult to obtain these cells in sufficient quantity for biochemical work. Some plant cells occupy an intermediate position between these two extremes: they are highly specialized for the biosynthesis of extracellular substances and they can be obtained in sufficient quantities for biochemical studies. The aleurone cells of cereal grains and the cells of the root cap fall in this category.

Extracellular substances sometimes contain unique constituents (e.g. fucose in root cap slime or hydroxyproline in extensin) which facilitate the study of their synthesis and transport in the cytoplasm. The judicious choice of an experimental system is therefore of great importance in the study of secretion, and a number of macromolecules and secretory systems that have been studied successfully are discussed below.

CHARACTERISTICS OF EXTRACELLULAR MACROMOLECULES

Matrix Polysaccharides in the Walls of Higher Plants

The cell walls of higher plants consist of a network of cellulose microfibrils embedded in a complex matrix of pectins, hemicellulose, and glycoproteins (4, 90). Pectic substances are a complex mixture of polysaccharides which can be extracted from the wall with aqueous solutions of chelating agents. Various acidic polysaccharides rich in galacturonic acid (e.g. rhamnogalacturonan) and neutral polysaccharides (e.g. arabinogalactan) can be separated from this mixture. The hemicellulose fraction of the wall consists of the alkali-soluble polymers and contains xyloglucans, glucomanans, and other heteropolymers. Labeling studies with certain radioactive sugars (arabinose, xylose, rhamnose, galactose) should provide a convenient way to study the biosynthesis and the secretion of these polysaccharides.

Root Cap Slime

Root cap slime is a mixture of highly hydrated polysaccharides which are secreted by the outer cells of the root cap. Slime from corn roots is rich in uronic acids, galactose, xylose, arabinose, and fucose (51) and can be separated electrophoretically into at least three components (140). Fucose was not found in the root tips of species other than *Zea mays* (140) but its presence in corn slime suggests that radioactively labeled fucose should be the precursor of choice to study the biosynthesis and secretion of root cap slime.

Hydroxyproline-Rich Cell Wall Glycoprotein (Extensin)

The primary cell walls of higher plants contain a hydroxyproline-rich cell wall glycoprotein called extensin (72). Analysis of peptides obtained from cell wall digests indicates that extensin is a glycoprotein with at least two types of glycopeptide linkages: one between arabinose and hydroxyproline (71) and one between galactose and serine (21, 74). Since only small amounts of protein-bound hydroxyproline are present in the cytoplasmic proteins of most tissues it is possible to trace the biosynthesis and the secretion of extensin by following the formation of protein-bound radioactive hydroxyproline.

Sulfated Polysaccharides

Many species of algae produce sulfated polysaccharides. Cytochemical techniques at the light and the electron microscope level have been used to demonstrate that these substances are located primarily in the cell walls and the intercellular mucilage, or occur as a covering layer on the surface of the organisms (for a review of these substances, see reference 76). Radioactive sulfate can be used to study the site of sulfation and the transport of the sulfated polysaccharides from the cytoplasm to the exterior of the cells.

Hydrolytic Enzymes Secreted by Aleurone Cells of Cereal Grains

The aleurone cells of cereal grains synthesize and release into the starchy endosperm a number of hydrolytic enzymes in response to the hormone gibberellic acid (GA_3). The hormone greatly enhances both the synthesis and the release of some of these enzymes such as α-amylase (43) and protease (59), while it primarily affects the release, but not the synthesis of several others, such as ribonuclease (26), β-glucanase (66), and phosphatase (6). The release of the enzymes from the tissue is preceded and accompanied by marked structural changes (64, 65, 133): the proliferation of rough endoplasmic reticulum (rough ER), the swelling of the aleurone grains, and the breakdown of the cell walls. Since isolated aleurone layers can be obtained easily in large quantity they provide a convenient system to study enzyme secretion and the hormonal control of this process.

Cell Wall Enzymes

The wall is a metabolically active compartment of the cell containing numerous enzymes (72), which can be studied by examining the enzymatic complement of purified cell walls. Another way to study cell wall enzymes is to examine the enzymatic activities present in the culture medium of suspension-cultured cells. Cells grown in liquid suspensions synthesize and release into the culture medium many macromolecules which are normal cell wall constituents when cells are not grown in liquid cultures. Using both methods, it has been found that various oxidases, glycosidases, and endopolysaccharidases are normal wall constituents. Enzyme secretion can be studied in any tissue where an enzyme or a particular isozyme is found associated with the cell wall or with the culture medium.

THE ROLE OF CYTOPLASMIC ORGANELLES IN BIOSYNTHESIS AND TRANSPORT

More than 15 years ago Whaley and his collaborators first drew attention to the presence of hypertrophied dictyosomes in the root cap cells of corn (138) and postulated that these organelles were involved in the secretion of root cap slime (82) and the formation of the cell plate (136). Autoradiographic investigations of root cap slime synthesis by Northcote and Pickett-Heaps (92, 102) were consistent with this interpretation: when wheat roots were pulsed with ^{3}H-glucose the radioactivity first appeared in the dictyosomes; when the 10 min pulse was followed by a chase of cold glucose the radioactivity disappeared from the dictyosomes and appeared in the extruded slime. Similar investigations by Neutra & Leblond (86, 87) on the metabolic fate of ^{3}H-glucose fed to intestinal goblet cells led to the conclusion that the Golgi apparatus is the site where sugars become incorporated into the mucopolysaccharides secreted by these cells. About the same time Palade and collaborators (18, 60–62, 124) reported in a series of elegant experiments that the rough ER in exocrine pancreas cells functions in the biosynthesis of extracellular proteins, and that these proteins are processed by the Golgi apparatus and accumulate in secretory granules which are released when the cells are appropriately stimulated.

These observations, all made a decade or more ago, together with many other observations made more recently on a variety of plant and animal cell types, have given rise to the concept that the rough endoplasmic reticulum and the Golgi apparatus form a functionally integrated membrane system involved in the biosynthesis and the secretion of proteins, glycoproteins, and polysaccharides. According to this concept the polypeptides of secretory proteins are synthesized on the polysomes associated with the rough ER, and then released directly into the lumina of the rough ER. This vectorial discharge of completed polypeptides distinguishes proteins which are to be secreted from those which will remain in the cytosol of the cell. The proteins are then transported via smooth transition elements to the Golgi apparatus and post-translational modifications can occur anywhere along this transport route. The proteins accumulate in secretory vesicles which pinch off the maturing face of the dictyosome. These vesicles move to the plasma membrane where their content is discharged by a process of reverse pinocytosis. The transport and secretion of polysaccharides is thought to occur in a similar way except that the process begins with the biosynthesis of the polysaccharides in the Golgi apparatus.

Although this interpretation of the role of the ER and the Golgi apparatus in the formation and the secretion of extracellular macromolecules is widely accepted, the biochemical evidence which supports it is still quite meager, at least for plant cells. As recently as 1972, O'Brien (94) argued after a critical review of all the evidence, that the cellular sites of synthesis and/or transport of cell wall precursors "are not evident as recognizable differentiations in the cells of higher plants." Others disagreed with his interpretation of the evidence (31, 88, 89, 118), and the additional evidence which has accumulated in the intervening 4 years strongly supports the idea that the ER and the Golgi apparatus play important roles in the biosynthesis and the secretion of extracellular macromolecules.

Involvement of the Endoplasmic Reticulum in Protein Secretion

Studies on the ultrastructure of plant and animal cells indicate a correlation between the presence of extensive stacks of rough ER and the synthesis of proteins which are transported. For example, gland cells of certain insectivorous plants secrete digestive enzymes when insects have been trapped or the glands have been artificially fed. The secretion of the enzymes is accompanied by ultrastructural changes including the formation of rough ER (117). Aleurone cells synthesize and secrete hydrolytic enzymes in response to GA_3. These events are preceded by the hormone-induced formation of an extensive rough ER (64). Stressing the tissue with osmoticum inhibits the synthesis of extracellular enzymes and causes the disappearance of the rough ER (5). Extensive stacks of rough ER cisternae are also found in the cotyledons of developing legume seeds, whose cells synthesize large amounts of storage proteins (7). These proteins are not secreted, but they are transported to the protein bodies, a process involving intracellular transport that has many analogies to secretion.

Involvement of the rough ER in protein synthesis has been demonstrated by autoradiography for three different cell types (aleurone cells, gland cells, and a single-cell alga) known to be involved in the synthesis of extracellular proteins. Pulse-chase experiments with radioactive amino acids showed that radioactivity became associated with the rough ER when short pulses or radioactive amino acid were used, and that the radioactivity associated with the rough ER decreased during the chase (17, 20, 41). However, no attempts were made in these studies to show that the radioactivity was present in the proteins which are normally secreted by these cells. The only plant proteins which have been shown by autoradiography to be synthesized on rough ER are the storage proteins of *Vicia faba* cotyledons (7).

The involvement of the endoplasmic reticulum in either the synthesis, the storage, or the transport of hydrolytic enzymes in aleurone cells is suggested by several lines of experimentation. In GA-treated wheat aleurone layers more than half of the cytoplasmic α-amylase is present in membrane-bound vesicles which band at the same density as the ER on isopycnic sucrose gradients (48, 49). [The failure of Jones (67) to find organelle-associated α-amylase in GA_3-treated aleurone layers of barley is discussed later.] Using fluorescent antibodies, Jones & Chen (67a) recently have shown that the α-amylase in GA_3-treated aleurone cells of barley is located nearly exclusively around the nucleus; this localization corresponds to the stacks of rough ER cisternae found in these cells. It is unfortunate that both sets of experiments lack a dynamic dimension (e.g. pulse-chase), and it is therefore not possible to determine whether the α-amylase in the ER is present in a metabolic or a static pool.

Secreted proteins are often glycoproteins which undergo post-translational modifications after the polypeptide moiety has been synthesized (40). Both modifications of amino acid residues (e.g. prolyl hydroxylation) and attachment of sugar residues are known to occur. In plant cells, as in animal cells, the biosynthesis of protein-bound hydroxyproline involves a post-translational modification of the prolyl residues. Proline is first incorporated into protein and then hydroxylated by peptidylproline hydroxylase (23, 115, 116). Initially the peptidylproline hydroxylase involved in collagen biosynthesis was thought to be localized in the cytosol (113), but recent experiments utilizing ferritin-labeled antibodies against the enzyme have shown it to be located in the cisternae of the rough ER (95). This localization has been confirmed by cell fractionation experiments (53). Cell fractionation experiments with carrot phloem parenchyma tissue showed the same enzyme to be present in the cytosol (115), but little care was taken to insure the integrity of the cytoplasmic organelles during tissue homogenization. The true intracellular localization of this enzyme probably remains to be discovered.

The attachment of sugar residues to the polypeptide moiety is carried out by glycosyltransferases and has only been studied in the biosynthesis of extensin (24, 69) and peroxidase (Shannon, personal communication). In extensin hydroxyproline residues are glycosylated with arabinose (71) and serine residues with galactose (21, 72). A glycosylated serine residue is normally followed by four glycosylated hydroxyproline residues (73), and the sequence ser-hyp-hyp-hyp-hyp could well be the recognition signal for both glycosyltransferases.

In many animal glycoproteins a carbohydrate side chain containing N-acetyl glucosamine and mannose residues is covalently linked to an asparagine residue (126). The proteins possessing this linkage in the sequence Asn-X-(Ser, Thr), with X being any amino acid, could be the recognition signal for the glycosyltransferase attaching the carbohydrate to the protein. This same sequence has been found recently in the plant proteins peroxidase (134) and mung bean vicilin (37).

Involvement of the Endoplasmic Reticulum in Polysaccharide Secretion

Ultrastructural studies of several cell types known to be involved in the biosynthesis of cell wall macromolecules have shown characteristic organization and distribution patterns of ER cisternae near the site of cell wall deposition, suggesting that the ER may play a role in cell wall formation. For example, the formation of the cell plate at the time of cytokinesis (56), the deposition of callose during sieve plate formation (93), and the formation of thickenings on the walls of primary tracheary elements (27, 102) are all accompanied by definite distribution patterns of the ER. Many cisternae of the ER were observed near the plasma membrane during the regeneration of a new cell wall by naked tobacco protoplasts (16).

Autoradiographic experiments using short pulses of ^{3}H-glucose showing radioactivity associated with endoplasmic reticulum and dictyosomes suggest that both organelles may function in polysaccharide synthesis (99, 100). Bowles & Northcote (10, 11) have recently claimed that the ER plays a major role in the biosynthesis of the noncellulosic cell wall polysaccharides. They examined the metabolic fate of ^{14}C-glucose in corn root tips and determined its conversion to other sugars as well as the presence of radioactivity in various subcellular fractions. They found that a "microsomal" fraction contained 90% of the total membrane-lipids and 90% of the organelle-associated radioactivity derived from ^{14}C-glucose, while a dictyosome-rich fraction contained less than 10% of the membrane-lipids or the organelle-associated radioactivity. The distribution of the radioactivity in the various sugars resembled the distribution in the pectin-hemicellulose fraction of the wall, and from these data they concluded that the ER plays a major role in pectin-hemicellulose biosynthesis and transport. However, a number of important controls still need to be done to justify this conclusion. Marker enzymes should be used to determine the purity of the organelle fractions; attempts must be made to determine whether the radioactivity was present in polysaccharides or in other molecules (e.g. glycolipids); pulse-chase experiments should be carried out to determine whether the radioactive molecules were present in a metabolically active pool.

Several cytochemical stains are available to localize carbohydrate residues at the electron microscope level. Dictyosome cisternae and secretory vesicles normally stain positively for carbohydrate when the thin sections are examined with either the silver-hexamine or the silver-proteinate stain (127), but ER cisternae do not give a positive reaction (47, 101, 112, 114). Either the ER contains little carbohydrate or it is masked in some way. Ray et al (108) have used isopycnic gradients and enzyme markers to separate and identify the subcellular organelles involved in the biosynthesis and transport of cell wall glucans in pea epicotyls. They concluded that the ER plays at best a minor role in these processes because ER-rich fractions do not contain a metabolically active pool of wall precursors, and do not contain the UDP-glucose:β-1,4 glucan-glucosyltransferase found in the dictyosome fraction. This does not exclude the possibility that the ER contributes to cell wall formation in a different way. For example, the ER may play a role in furnishing precursors and enzymes to the plasma-membrane which is now generally thought to be the site of cellulose biosynthesis (see below). Such a role would be consistent with the ultrastructural observations showing that ER profiles subtend the plasma-membrane in cells which are depositing a secondary wall.

Involvement of the Golgi Apparatus in Glycoprotein and Polysaccharide Synthesis and Secretion

Since the original proposal by Mollenhauer et al (82) that the hypertrophied dictyosomes of corn root cap cells are engaged in the accumulation and secretion of slime, many morphological observations have been made correlating apparent dictyosome activity (e.g. the presence of large or numerous dictyosomes or secretory vesicles) with cell wall formation and polysaccharide formation. All these observations will not be reviewed or even cataloged here since they add little to our understanding of the secretory process. Perhaps the most elegant morphological demonstration of this function of the Golgi apparatus comes from the work of Manton (77, 78) and of Brown and his collaborators (13–15, 55) on the production of scales by certain unicellular green algae such as *Pleurochrysis scherffelii.* The cell-covering of this alga consists of many small scales, the formation of which can be followed in the cell's single dictyosome. Each scale has a noncellulosic and a cellulosic microfibrillar component, as well as an amorphous matrix of sulfated polysaccharides, and these three subcomponents are assembled in different parts of the Golgi apparatus. Scales in different stages of assembly can be seen in the various cisternae and a completed scale is present in the cisterna closest to the cell membrane.

Morphologically distinct components of the cell wall are not usually visible in the dictyosomes of higher plants, but cytochemical evidence shows that the cisternae and the secretory vesicles are rich in carbohydrate (47, 101, 112, 114). The intensity of the carbohydrate-specific staining reaction increases from the forming face of the dictyosomes, where new cisternae are formed out of ER material, to the maturing face where secretory vesicles are budded off (85, 101, 112). This suggests that carbohydrates are continually synthesized and accumulate in the cisternae as they mature.

Many attempts have been made to demonstrate the role of the Golgi apparatus in polysaccharide synthesis and secretion by means of autoradiography, but the interpretation of the results has sometimes been difficult (for a review see 94). In many cases pulse-chase experiments did not unequivocally demonstrate that silver grains first appeared over the dictyosomes and then disappeared during the chase-period. Many of the difficulties of interpretation may be due to nonspecific labeling (e.g. glucose is rapidly metabolized and its products incorporated into many macromolecules) and to the rapid turnover of the radioactivity in the Golgi apparatus. Radioactive polysaccharides in the Golgi apparatus turn over very rapidly while radioactivity continues to accumulate in other cell structures. Some of these problems can be avoided by a judicious choice of radioactive precursor and cell type.

Some recent examples of the successful use of autoradiography to elucidate the role of the Golgi apparatus in polysaccharide synthesis are described below. In corn root tips galactose is not extensively metabolized and in cells entering division it was found to be incorporated into the Golgi apparatus within 10 min and then transferred from that organelle to the forming cell plate (29). Similarly, Paull & Jones (97, 98) observed that fucose became incorporated into the Golgi bodies of corn root cap cells and was then transferred to the root cap slime in the periplasmic space. Autoradiographs of subcellular organelles isolated from corn root tips incubated with ^{3}H-fucose showed that all the silver grains were associated with Golgi bodies and not with other membranous organelles present in these fractions (Paull & Jones, private communication). Autoradiography has also been used to demonstrate that the Golgi apparatus is the site of polysaccharide sulfation in algae with secrete sulfated polysaccharides, although it is not clear whether sulfation occurs before or after the sugars are polymerized (38, 105).

Some attempts have been made to analyze the carbohydrate content of isolated dictyosomes or secretory vesicles. Van der Woude et al (131) isolated secretory vesicles from pollen tubes and showed that the polysaccharides they contained were similar in composition to some of the polysaccharides found in the cell walls. Northcote and co-workers (10, 11, 52), examining the metabolic fate of ^{14}C-glucose in root tips, found that it was metabolized extensively to galactose, arabinose, and xylose and that molecules containing these radioactive sugars were present in dictyosome and ER-rich fractions isolated from this tissue. The distribution of radioactive label in these organelle fractions resembled the distribution of the label in pectin and hemicellulose, suggesting that these macromolecules may be synthesized in the Golgi bodies and/or the ER.

Additional evidence establishing the Golgi apparatus as the site of biosynthesis and intracellular transport of polysaccharides and glycoproteins comes from studies on isolated Golgi-rich fractions. Ray et al (108), utilizing the observation that inosinediphosphatase is a marker enzyme for dictyosomes (30), observed that UDP-glucose: β-1,4 glucan glucoslytransferase is associated with a dictyosome-rich fraction isolated from etiolated pea epicotyls. When the intact tissue was pulsed with ^{14}C-glucose and the membranous organelles fractionated on sucrose gradients, radioactivity first appeared in a fraction rich in dictyosomes and later in a fraction containing small (secretory?) vesicles. During a chase with cold glucose, radioactivity first disappeared from the cisternae-rich fraction and later from the vesicles (35). These observations suggest that the Golgi apparatus functions in the synthesis and the transport of β-1,4 glucans. More recently Powell & Brew (103) found that

UDP-galactose:N-acetyl glucosamine β-1,4 galactosyltransferase, a marker enzyme for Golgi bodies from animal tissues, is associated with dictyosome-rich fractions isolated from onion stems. Another glycosyltransferase, UDP-arabinose arabinosyltransferase, has been found in dictyosome-rich fractions of carrot root phloem parenchyma by Gardiner & Chrispeels (46). This enzyme is involved in the synthesis of polysaccharides and glycoproteins (69). When carrot tissue was pulsed with ^{14}C-proline, radioactivity in protein-bound ^{14}C-hydroxyproline first appeared in a dictyosome-rich fraction, and it disappeared from that fraction during a chase with cold proline. The authors concluded that the Golgi apparatus plays a role in the biosynthesis and the secretion of the hydroxyproline-rich glycoprotein extensin, confirming an earlier observation by Dashek (28) that subcellular fractions rich in dictyosomes and smooth membranes are involved in the transport of this protein. Involvement of the Golgi apparatus in glycoprotein secretion in algae is demonstrated by the autoradiographic observations of Callow & Evans (17) and the work of Herth et al (55) showing that the scales of *Pleurochrysis scherffelii*, which are made in the Golgi apparatus, contain a glycoprotein.

Involvement of the Plasma Membrane in Cellulose Synthesis

Not all extracellular macromolecules are synthesized intracellularly and transported to the exterior of the cell, and several lines of evidence indicate that in higher plants cellulose is synthesized on the plasma membrane and not in any of the cytoplasmic organelles involved in the synthesis of other cell wall components. Initially, the most convincing evidence favoring the extracellular biosynthesis of cellulose was provided by the autoradiographic experiments of Wooding (139). He showed that radioactive glucose fed to cells of the vascular cambium of sycamore seedlings was incorporated into the secondary walls before it appeared in any cytoplasmic organelles. More recently Northcote and collaborators (10, 11, 52) determined the metabolic fate of ^{14}C-glucose fed to corn root tips. They concluded that cellulose was not synthesized and transported by cytoplasmic organelles, and that glucose was present in the cell wall as a result of its direct incorporation at the plasma membrane. Two hours after the start of the incubation nearly two-thirds of the radioactivity in the cell wall was in glucose while the rest was in other sugars. However, in the cytoplasmic organelles believed to be involved in polysaccharide synthesis and transport more than three-fourths of the radioactivity was in xylose, arabinose, and galactose and less than 5% in glucose.

Only a few direct attempts have been made in recent years to demonstrate the subcellular location of cellulose synthetase (or, more precisely, β-1,4 glucan synthetase) by means of cell fractionation experiments. Ray et al (108) found that an organelle fraction rich in dictyosomes contained most of the UDP-glucose:β-1,4 glucan glucosyltransferase activity present in pea stem homogenates. The enzymatic reaction yielded an alkali-insoluble product, digestible by cellulase consisting of β-1,4 linked glucose residues. Van Der Woude et al (130) subsequently showed that the same enzymatic activity could be found either in the dictyosome fraction or in the plasma membrane fraction of onion stem homogenates, depending on the concentration of UDP-glucose used for the in vitro enzyme assay. More recently Shore

& Maclachlan (122) confirmed the work of Ray et al (108) and found that in IAA-treated decapitated pea seedlings the enzyme is also found in the endoplasmic reticulum.

The presence of β-1,4 glucan synthetase in either the Golgi apparatus or the ER does not necessarily imply that this is the normal site of cellulose synthesis. Indeed, the Golgi apparatus is probably engaged in the synthesis of hemicellulosic glucans (e.g. xyloglucans). The organelle may also function in the transport of cellulose synthetase and other cell surface enzymes from their site of synthesis—the polysomes—to their site of action—the plasma membrane or the periplasmic space (31, 137). Thus it is possible that dictyosome cisternae and secretory vesicles contain the capacity for cellulose synthesis, but that in higher plants this capability is not normally expressed until the vesicles have fused with the plasma membrane. Engels (36) has recently claimed that this capacity may already be expressed in the secretory vesicles of petunia pollen tubes. X-ray analysis of isolated secretory vesicles led him to conclude that they contain cellulose.

There is little doubt that the capacity for cellulose synthesis is expressed in the Golgi apparatus of some lower plants such as the unicellular green alga *Pleurochrysis scherffelii.* The wall of this organism consists of a number of small scales which have a typical morphology and consist of both cellulosic and noncellulosic components. These different components are synthesized and assembled in differentiated regions of the cell's single Golgi apparatus (14). These findings suggest that the Golgi apparatus contains not only the enzymes necessary to synthesize both components but also the matrix which determines scale morphology. An ultrastructural investigation of cell wall formation in *Micrasterias denticulata,* another alga with a highly patterned wall, led Kiermayer & Dobberstein (70) to postulate that the Golgi apparatus functions in the biosynthesis and the transport of the noncellulosic components of the wall as well as in the transport of cellulose synthetase and a matrix for microfibril assembly to the plasma membrane. They suggested that in *Micrasterias* cellulose synthesis is delayed until the enzyme and the matrix have become incorporated in the cell membrane, a condition similar to higher plants, while in *Pleurochrysis* there is no time-lag between the formation of the template in the Golgi apparatus and the start of cellulose synthesis. Whether or not such a time-lag exists in plant cells may well depend on the nature of the wall which must be synthesized.

Few attempts have been reported to directly test the hypothesis, formulated more than 10 years ago on the basis of morphological evidence (104), that cellulose synthesis occurs extracellularly. Cotton fibers deposit large amounts of cellulose, first in their primary walls and later in their secondary walls. Franz & Meier (45) observed that intact[3] fibers can catalyze the transfer of glucose from UDP-glu `ose to an alkali-insoluble product. Delmer et al (32) later showed that this product was probably a glycolipid, but that the fibers also catalyzed the transfer of glucose from GDP-glucose to an alkali-insoluble and β-1,3 glucanase resistant product. How-

---

[3]The fibers are broken in the process of removing them from the boll, but it is assumed that a new plasma membrane seals off the cytoplasm at the broken end.

ever, recent evidence (D. Delmer, personal communication) indicates that this product is not cellulose but a callose-like β-1,3 glucan. Shore et al (123) examined the transfer of glucose from UDP-glucose to a cellulose-like product in pea stem slices. They observed that the initial rate of glucosyl transfer approached the rate of in vivo cellulose synthesis, and that changes in the rate of cellulose deposition were paralleled by changes in the rate of UDP-glucose glucosyl transfer. Normal tissue homogenization procedures destroyed the enzymatic activity, and this was taken as evidence that the enzyme was located at the cell surface. More controls are needed to confirm that the transfer of glucosyl units occurred extracellularly, and that cellulose rather than callose was the product of this reaction. These experiments suggest the feasibility of directly testing the hypothesis that cellulose is made extracellularly in higher plants.

A Soluble Mode of Secretion?

The secretion of a variety of macromolecules has been shown to be mediated by cytoplasmic organelles, but this does not rule out the possibility that other macromolecules pass through the plasma membrane without being packaged in secretory vesicles. Jones (67) recently has claimed that such a soluble mode of secretion operates in the secretion of α-amylase by barley aleurone cells. Two lines of evidence have been presented to substantiate this claim. First, when GA$_3$-treated aleurone layers were carefully homogenized—carefully enough to prevent the disruption of the glyoxysomes—about 95% of the α-amylase was not associated with membranous organelles but was present in the supernatant (67). However, Varner & Mense (132) observed that most of the α-amylase associated with GA$_3$-treated barley aleurone layers could be inactivated by a 15 min treatment with 1 mM HCl, a treatment which did not damage the cells. They concluded that the inactivated enzyme was not truly intracellular, and was either in the periplasmic space or bound to the wall. The same conclusion was reached by Jacobsen & Knox (58), who used cytochemical methods to localize α-amylase in the aleurone tissue. Thus most of the α-amylase associated with GA$_3$-treated aleurone layers has already been secreted but not yet released from the tissue. This conclusion was also reached by Firn (42), who showed that more than half of the α-amylase in GA$_3$-treated aleurone layers was associated with membrane-bounded vesicles if the α-amylase associated with the cell walls was first inactivated by treating the tissue with dilute HCl. This confirmed an earlier observation by Gibson & Paleg (48) that in wheat aleurone layers nearly half of the α-amylase is present in membrane-bounded vesicles. These vesicles band at the same density as the endoplasmic reticulum in isopycnic sucrose gradients (49).

The second line of evidence, recently presented by Chen & Jones (19, 20) to document the soluble mode of enzyme secretion, is based on autoradiography of aleurone cells pulsed or pulsed-chased with radioactive leucine. After a short pulse silver grains were found primarily over the rough ER, but if the pulse was followed by a 60 min chase, the silver grains were equally distributed over the cytoplasm. The authors interpreted this to mean that the proteins were made on the rough ER and then released in the cytosol before being secreted. However, the duration of the chase-period was too long considering that, according to the data presented in these papers, there is but a very short lag between the synthesis of the enzymes and their release into the medium. Rather, these data, together with those discussed above, suggest that the ER may be involved in the biosynthesis and the intracellular transport of these enzymes. Such a conclusion is supported by the ultrastructural investigations of Vigil & Ruddat (133), showing an asymmetric distribution of the ER in the aleurone cells and an accumulation of smooth ER near the base of the cells where enzyme secretion is thought to be most intense (65, 133).

CELLULAR METABOLISM AND THE CONTROL OF SECRETION

In most plant cells, unlike in many animal cells, synthesis and secretion of extracellular macromolecules appear to be one continuous process, and there are but a few examples of the temporal dissociation of these processes. The rate of synthesis and secretion of macromolecules can be modulated in many plant cells, and examples of temporal and hormonal control of the biosynthesis and the secretion of macromolecules have been described. Such modulation involves not only a change in the rate of synthesis of the secretory product, but also a change in the entire cellular machinery involved in the biosynthesis and the transport of the secretory product.

One way to gain some insight into the process of secretion is to consider the membranous organelles involved in secretion not as distinct structures but as part of an endomembrane system which has functional if not always structural continuity. Secretion can then be thought of as the physical transfer of membranous elements with their contents from one part of this system to another. This interpretation of secretion, known as the membrane flow hypothesis, has been advanced by several investigators in recent years (31, 84, 137). This hypothesis provides a useful framework to formulate questions and may eventually help us understand how the entire secretory process is controlled. At the moment we know very little about the control of secretion and the relationship between cellular metabolism and secretion. One way to explore this relationship is by the use of metabolic poisons. When carrying out such experiments it is important to distinguish effects of these chemicals on the secretory process itself from the effects on the synthesis of secretory product, on the formation of secretory organelles, and on the release of secreted molecules through a second barrier such as the cell wall.

Is Metabolic Energy Required to Secrete Macromolecules Already Present in the Cytoplasm?

The secretion of the hydroxyproline-rich cell wall glycoprotein precursors has a Q_{10} between 2 and 3 in a physiological temperature range and is inhibited by various inhibitors of metabolic energy generation (34). Inhibitors of energy metabolism also prevent the secretion of α-amylase by barley aleurone cells, but have no effect on the release of the enzyme through the cell wall (132). It is not clear, however, that such experiments provide an answer to the question at the head of this paragraph. It is impossible to determine whether the energy is needed for the completion of biosynthetic events—which may go on in the Golgi cisternae as well as in the secretory vesicles on their way to the wall—or for such events as membrane transformation, vesicle transport, and vesicle fusion.

Is Protein Synthesis Required for Secretion?

Is concomitant protein synthesis needed to allow the secretion of proteins and polysaccharides which have already been synthesized? Is protein synthesis required for the continued production of extracellular substances and the maintenance of the secretory apparatus? The answer to the first question appears to be negative. The secretion of molecules already present in the cytoplasm occurs normally in the presence of cycloheximide (34, 54, 119, 132). The answer to the second question is positive, but it is not clear which proteins are necessary for the continued activity of the secretory pathway. Long-term treatment of *Drosophyllum* glands with cycloheximide greatly depressed the production of the polysaccharide "fangschleim." Morré et al (83) found no effect of puromycin on the production of slime by corn root tips, but they did not present any evidence that the drug was actually inhibiting protein synthesis at the low concentrations used. Ultrastructural evidence also indicates that treatment with cycloheximide inhibits Golgi activity and the apparent discharge of Golgi vesicles into the cell wall. It is tempting to speculate that this inhibition is the result of the turnover of certain essential membrane proteins and/or glycosyltransferases. However, cycloheximide inhibits several other cell functions (79), and this may also account for the decrease in Golgi activity.

Time-lag between the Biosynthesis and the Secretion of Macromolecules

Autoradiographic investigations of the synthesis and secretion of extracellular macromolecules have shown that a relatively short period (10 to 30 min) of chasing the radioactive label is usually sufficient to cause a decrease of the silver grains over the organelles involved in the biosynthesis and the intracellular transport (92). A detailed kinetic analysis of the synthesis and the secretion of cell wall glycoproteins by Chrispeels (22, 24) showed that about 15 min elapsed between the biosynthesis of the protein and its arrival in the cell wall. Incorporation of ^{14}C-proline, was followed within a few minutes by hydroxylation of peptidylproline, which in turn was followed within a few minutes by the glycosylation of the peptidylhydroxyproline. The completed glycoprotein was then secreted a few minutes later. Pulse-chase experiments showed that the half life of the completed glycoprotein in the cytoplasm was approximately 8 min (Chrispeels, unpublished results). A kinetic analysis of polysaccharide secretion in pea stems by Eisinger & Ray (35) also showed that there is approximately a 10 min time-lag between the synthesis of a polysaccharide and its arrival in the wall. These results suggest that the processing of glycoproteins and polysaccharides through the Golgi apparatus—from its forming face to its maturing face—and through the other elements of the secretory system proceeds quite rapidly. Assuming that a dictyosome contains 4 to 5 cisternae, one can calculate that a cisterna has to mature every 1 to 2 min. Time-lapse photography and morphometric analysis of scale production in *Pleurochrysis scherffelii* shows that this is indeed the case and that a new Golgi cisterna is formed every 2 min (13). Bowles &

Northcote (11) have suggested that turnover may be even more rapid, and they calculated turnover times for the entire dictyosome of 0.3 min for root cap slime secretion and 2.5 min for hemicellulose plus pectin secretion. These calculations were based on the assumption that the Golgi-rich fraction they isolated from corn root tips contained all the dictyosomes.

Guide Elements in Secretion?

One of the least understood steps in the secretory process involves the migration of secretory vesicles to the plasma membrane and the subsequent fusion of the membrane surrounding the secretory vesicle with the plasma membrane. It has been suggested (44) that the cytoplasm may contain guide elements which guide the secretory vesicles to the site of fusion. Two cytoplasmic structures which could serve this function are the microfilaments and the microtubules. Microfilaments have been shown to play a role in cytoplasmic streaming (135), a process which may be necessary for secretion, while microfibrils have been implicated in the accumulation of secretory vesicles at the cell plate (56) and appear to "guide" the secretory vesicles to their destination. The notion that guide elements may exist in the cytoplasm is strengthened by the observation that the discharge of secreted material through the cell wall occurs in a polar fashion in several cell types. For example, in root cap cells of corn, slime either accumulates between the outer tangential wall and the cell membrane or is discharged through this wall (68). In aleurone cells, the GA_3-induced and enzyme-mediated dissolution of the wall occurs primarily along the inner tangetial wall (65), indicating that enzyme secretion itself may be polar, as suggested by the polar distribution of endoplasmic reticulum in these cells (133). Cell wall thickening does not occur uniformly in xylem tracheary elements and other cell types but is localized in certain areas, and numerous workers have noticed the presence of bands of microtubules in the cytoplasm adjacent to the localized thickenings (57). It is clear from autoradiographic experiments that cell wall materials accumulate in the thickenings (99), but little is known about the actual site of secretion of the cell wall precursors. Goosen-de Roo (50) has suggested that secretion occurs at the plasma membrane between the microtubule bands—and thus between the thickenings—rather than at the site of the thickenings.

Some investigators have used drugs which disrupt the structure and the function of microtubules and microfilaments to determine whether these cytoplasmic structures must be intact for secretion to occur. Cytochalasin B, a microfilament disrupting drug, and colchicine, an agent which causes microtubule disaggregation, have been applied to aleurone tissue (25), carrot phloem parenchyma cells (25), and pollen tubes (44) to study their effect on the secretion of various macromolecules. Although these same drugs inhibit secretion in animal cells (33, 121), they were found to be without effect on the secretory process of these plant cells, suggesting that structural integrity of the microfilaments or the microtubules is not a prerequisite for secretion. Two recent reports disagree with this interpretation. In *Micrasterias* cytochalasin B blocks cell wall formation and causes the accumulation of apparent secretory vesicles in the cytoplasm (128), while colchicine blocks the secretion of scales in *Pleurochrysis* (14).

Hormonal Control of Enzyme Secretion

The best studied example of hormonal control of enzyme secretion involves the response of cereal grain aleurone tissue to gibberellic acid. The hormone greatly enhances the synthesis and the secretion of certain hydrolytic enzymes (43, 59), while it primarily affects the release but not the synthesis of other enzymes (6, 9, 26, 66). Jones has speculated (66) that GA_3 may mediate the secretory process itself, at least in the case of β-glucanase. The limiting step in the release of these enzymes from the tissue could be either their secretion through the plasma membrane or their release through the wall. Varner & Mense (132) were able to distinguish between these two alternatives and concluded that GA_3 does not directly affect the secretion of α-amylase across the plasma membrane. In a recently published study on the effect of GA_3 on the release of acid phosphatase from barley aleurone cells, Ashford & Jacobsen (6) presented conclusive evidence that GA_3 exerts its effect on the cell wall rather than on the plasma membrane. They found that secretion of acid phosphatase into the periplasmic space occurred both in the presence and the absence of GA_3, but release of the enzyme from the periplasmic space into the incubation medium was dependent on GA_3. Gibberellic acid has been shown to enhance the activity of cell wall degrading enzymes (12) and to cause the dissolution of the aleurone cell wall (65). It seems likely that the GA_3-mediated release of various hydrolytic enzymes from the periplasmic space into the medium surrounding the cells depends on the prior synthesis and secretion of cell wall degrading enzymes. This may well account for the observation by Jones (66) that the "secretion" (i.e. the release from the tissue) of β-glucanase is dependent on GA_3.

Another well-studied system of hormonal control of an extracellular enzyme involves the enhancement of de novo cellulase synthesis in abscission zones accompanying ethylene-induced leaf and fruit abscission (2, 75). It has been claimed that ethylene specifically affects the secretion of cellulase because it increases the proportion of the enzyme associated with the cell wall relative to that in the cytoplasm (3). More recent evidence indicates that there are two molecular forms of cellulase, a cytoplasmic and a cell wall-associated form, and that ethylene specifically enhances the activity and probably the synthesis of the cell wall-associated form (109). The data suggest that ethylene enhances the synthesis and the secretion of the extracellular form of the enzyme, but do not provide evidence for a specific role for this hormone in the secretion of the enzyme. In animal cells there are many well-documented cases of a hormone-triggered release of accumulated secretory products, but in plant cells there is as yet no evidence favoring the existence of such a process.

Hormonal Control of Cell Wall Formation

Several plant hormones affect the rate of cell enlargement in a variety of tissues, and these hormonal effects are accompanied by changes in the rates at which wall precursor macromolecules are synthesized and deposited in the cell walls. For example, ethylene treatment of etiolated peas causes the cessation of stem elongation and an acceleration of the deposition of hydroxyproline-rich proteins in the cell walls (110, 116). Indoleacetic acid treatment of pea segments causes a two and a half-fold rise in their ability to incorporate ^{14}C-glucose into cell wall polymers; the increase can be measured 15 min after hormone treatment and reflects an enhancement of cell wall polysaccharide synthesis (1). Treatment of excised lettuce hypocotyls with gibberellic acid causes them to elongate five to six times faster than the controls, and this enhancement of elongation is accompanied by an acceleration of wall synthesis. The acceleration is most pronounced 8 hours after hormone treatment (125). Incubation of aleurone tissue with GA_3 causes a marked reduction in the synthesis of pentose-containing cell wall macromolecules (63).

In only a few of these studies has the effect of the hormone on the glycosyltransferases involved in polysaccharide or glycoprotein synthesis been investigated. Treatment of onion stems with 2,4-D (129) or of pea stems (106, 107) with IAA causes an increase in the particulate UDP-glucose:β–(1,4) glucan–glucosyltransferase activity of these tissues. The hormone brings about a three to fourfold increase in the enzyme activity (106) if the tissue has been pre-aged to allow the endogenous enzyme level to fall to less than 20% of its initial value. Johnson & Chrispeels (63) observed that the UDP-arabinose arabinosyltransferase present in extracts of barley aleurone tissue declined when the tissue was incubated with buffer and that the presence of GA_3 in the incubation medium greatly accelerated this decline. These data suggest that hormonal control of cell wall synthesis is mediated via hormonally induced changes in the levels and/or activities of the membrane-bound glycosyltransferases involved in polysaccharide synthesis.

The available evidence suggests that plant hormones do not affect the secretory process directly, but that they modulate the biosynthesis and the subsequent secretion of a variety of extracellular macromolecules, including enzymes, cell wall glycoproteins, and cell wall polysaccharides. These biochemical events are accompanied by the formation of those components of the endomembrane system necessary for the biosynthesis, the intracellular transport, and the secretion of these macromolecules. GA_3-treatment of aleurone tissue (64, 133) and ethylene treatment of pea stems (96) causes a proliferation of the rough ER, while GA_3-treatment of lettuce hypocotyls causes the appearance of numerous Golgi bodies in these cells (125). Little is known about the manner in which rough ER and dictyosomes are formed in plant cells or about the influence of hormones on these processes. The membrane flow hypothesis mentioned earlier provides at least a conceptual framework to investigate this problem. Mollenhauer & Morré (81) recently observed that polysomes are always present in the narrow space between the forming face of a dictyosome and the cisterna of the rough ER which runs parallel to this forming face. These polysomes may be engaged in the synthesis of membrane components, some of which play a role in the biosynthesis of secretory products (e.g. glycosyltransferases). To understand how hormones enhance the rates of biosynthesis and secretion of extracellular macromolecules, it will be necessary to study their effect on the biogenesis of the membranous organelles involved in these processes.

Literature Cited

1. Abdul-Baki, A. A., Ray, P. M. 1971. *Plant Physiol.* 47:537–44
2. Abeles, F. B. 1969. *Plant Physiol.* 44:447–52
3. Abeles, F. B., Leather, G. R. 1971. *Planta* 97:87–91
4. Albersheim, P., Bauer, W. D., Keegstra, K., Talmadge, K. W. 1973. In *Biogenesis of Plant Cell Wall Polysaccharides,* ed. F. Loewus, 117–48. New York: Academic
5. Armstrong, J. E., Jones, R. L. 1973. *J. Cell Biol.* 59:444–55
6. Ashford, A. E., Jacobsen, J. V. 1974. *Planta* 120:81–105
7. Bailey, C. J., Cobb, A., Boulter, D. 1970. *Planta* 95:103–18
8. Beams, H. W., Kessel, R. G. 1968. *Int. Rev. Cytol.* 23:209–76
9. Bennett, P., Chrispeels, M. J. 1972. *Plant Physiol.* 49:445–47
10. Bowles, D. J., Northcote, D. H. 1972. *Biochem. J.* 130:1133–45
11. Ibid 1974. 142:139–44
12. Briggs, D. E. 1973. In *Biosynthesis and its Control in Plants,* ed. B. V. Milborrow, 219–77. New York: Academic
13. Brown, R. M. Jr. 1969. *J. Cell Biol.* 41:109–23
14. Brown, R. M. Jr. 1975. In *International Symposium of Plant Cell Differentiation,* ed. M. S. Pais. In press
15. Brown, R. M. Jr., Franke, W. W., Kleinig, H., Falk, H., Sitte, P. 1970. *J. Cell Biol.* 45:246–71
16. Burgess, J., Fleming, E. N. 1974. *J. Cell Sci.* 14:439–49
17. Callow, M. E., Evans, L. V. 1974. *Protoplasma* 80:15–27
18. Caro, L. G., Palade, G. E. 1964. *J. Cell Biol.* 20:473–95
19. Chen, R., Jones, R. L. 1974. *Planta* 119:193–206
20. Ibid, 207–20
21. Cho, Y., Chrispeels, M. J. 1975. *Phytochemistry.* In press
22. Chrispeels, M. J. 1969. *Plant Physiol.* 44:1187–93
23. Ibid 1970. 45:223–27
24. Chrispeels, M. J. 1970. *Biochem. Biophys. Res. Commun.* 39:732–37
25. Chrispeels, M. J. 1972. *Planta* 108:283–87
26. Chrispeels, M. J., Varner, J. E. 1967. *Plant Physiol.* 42:398–406
27. Cronshaw, J. 1965. *Can. J. Bot.* 43:1401–7
28. Dashek, W. V. 1970. *Plant Physiol.* 46:831–38

29. Dauwalder, M., Whaley, W. G. 1974. *J. Cell Sci.* 14:11–27
30. Dauwalder, M., Whaley, W. G., Kephart, J. E. 1969. *J. Cell Sci.* 4:455–97
31. Dauwalder, M., Whaley, W. G., Kephart, J. E. 1972. *Sub-Cell. Biochem.* 1:255–59
32. Delmer, D. P., Beasly, C. A., Ordin, L. 1974. *Plant Physiol.* 53:149–53
33. Diegelmann, R. F., Peterkofsky, B. 1972. *Proc. Natl. Acad. Sci. USA* 69:892–96
34. Doerschug, M. R., Chrispeels, M. J. 1970. *Plant Physiol.* 46:363–66
35. Eisinger, W., Ray, P. M. 1972. *Plant Physiol.* 49:2 (Suppl.)
36. Engels, F. M. 1973. *Acta Bot. Neerl.* 23:209–15
37. Ericson, M. C., Chrispeels, M. J. 1974. *Plant Physiol.* 53:52 (Suppl.)
38. Evans, L. V., Callow, M. E. 1974. *Planta* 117:93–95
39. Evans, L. V., Callow, M. E. 1975. In *Perspectives in Experimental Biology,* ed. P. S. Davies, N. Sunderland. Oxford: Pergamon
40. Eylar, E. G. 1965. *J. Theor. Biol.* 10:89–113
41. Figier, J. 1969. *Planta* 87:275–89
42. Firn, R. D. 1975. *Planta* 125:227–33
43. Filner, P., Varner, J. E. 1967. *Proc. Natl. Acad. Sci. USA* 58:1520–26
44. Franke, W. W., Herth, W., Van Der Woude, W. J., Morré, D. J. 1972. *Planta* 105:317–41
45. Franz, G., Meier, H. 1969. *Phytochemistry* 8:579–83
46. Gardiner, M., Chrispeels, M. J. 1975. *Plant Physiol.* 55:536–41
47. Genevès, L. 1974. *J. Microsc.* 19:65–88
48. Gibson, R. A., Paleg, L. G. 1972. *Biochem. J.* 128:367–75
49. Gibson, R. A. 1974. PhD thesis. Univ. Adelaide, Australia
50. Goosen-De Roo, L. 1973. *Acta Bot. Neerl.* 22:279–300
51. Harris, P. J., Northcote, D. H. 1970. *Biochem. J.* 120:479–91
52. Harris, P. J., Northcote, D. H. 1971. *Biochim. Biophys. Acta* 237:56–64
53. Harwood, R., Grant, M. E., Jackson, D. S. 1974. *Biochem. J.* 144:123–30
54. Hemmes, D. E., Hohl, R. E. 1971. *J. Cell Sci.* 9:175–91
55. Herth, W., Franke, W. W., Stadler, J., Bittiger, H., Keilich, G. 1972. *Planta* 105:79–92

56. Hepler, P. K., Newcomb, E. H. 1967. *J. Ultrastruct. Res.* 19:498–513
57. Hepler, P. K., Palevitz, B. A. 1974. *Ann. Rev. Plant Physiol.* 25:309–62
58. Jacobsen, J. V., Knox, R. B. 1973. *Planta* 112:213–24
59. Jacobsen, J. V., Varner, J. E. 1967. *Plant Physiol.* 42:1596–1600
60. Jamieson, J. D., Palade, G. E. 1966. *Proc. Natl. Acad. Sci. USA* 55:424–31
61. Jamieson, J. D., Palade, G. E. 1967. *J. Cell Biol.* 34:577–96
62. Ibid, 597–615
63. Johnson, K. D., Chrispeels, M. J. 1973. *Planta* 111:353–64
64. Jones, R. L. 1969. *Planta* 87:119–33
65. Ibid. 88:73–86
66. Jones, R. L. 1971. *Plant Physiol.* 47:412–16
67. Jones, R. L. 1972. *Planta* 103:95–109
67a. Jones, R. L., Chen, R. F. 1976. *J. Cell. Sci.* In press
68. Juniper, B. E., Pask, G. 1973. *Planta* 109:225–31
69. Karr, A. L. 1972. *Plant Physiol.* 50:275–82
70. Kiermayer, O., Dobberstein, D. 1973. *Protoplasma* 77:437–51
71. Lamport, D. T. A. 1969. *Biochemistry* 8:1155–63
72. Lamport, D. T. A. 1970. *Ann. Rev. Plant Physiol.* 21:235–70
73. Lamport, D. T. A. 1973. See Ref. 4, 149–64
74. Lamport, D. T. A., Roerig, S., Katona, L. 1973. *Biochem. J.* 133:125–32
75. Lewis, L. N., Varner, J. E. 1970. *Plant Physiol.* 46:194–99
76. Mackie, W., Preston, R. D. 1974. In *Algal Physiology and Biochemistry,* ed. W. P. D. Stewart, 40–85. Oxford: Blackwell
77. Manton, I. 1966. *J. Cell Sci.* 1:375–80
78. Ibid 1967. 2:411–18
79. McMahon, D. 1975. *Plant Physiol.* 55:815–21
80. Mollenhauer, H. H., Morré, D. J. 1966. *Ann. Rev. Plant Physiol.* 17:27–46
81. Mollenhauer, H. H., Morré, D. J. 1974. *Protoplasma* 79:333–36
82. Mollenhauer, H. H., Whaley, W. G., Leech, J. H. 1961. *J. Ultrastruct. Res.* 5:193–200
83. Morré, D. J., Jones, D. D., Mollenhauer, H. H. 1967. *Planta* 74:286–301
84. Morré, D. J., Mollenhauer, H. H. 1974. In *Dynamic Aspects of Plant Ultrastructure,* ed. A. W. Robards, 84–137. New York: McGraw-Hill
85. Morré, D. J., Mollenhauer, H. H., Bracker, C. E. 1973. In *Origin and Continuity of Cell Organelles,* ed. J. Reinert, H. Ursprung, 82–126. Berlin: Springer
86. Neutra, M., Leblond, C. P. 1966. *J. Cell Biol.* 30:119–36
87. Ibid, 137–50
88. Northcote, D. H. 1971. *Endeavour* 30:26–33
89. Northcote, D. H. 1971. *Symp. Soc. Exp. Biol.* 25:51–69
90. Northcote, D. H. 1972. *Ann. Rev. Plant Physiol.* 23:113–32
91. Northcote, D. H. 1974. In *Plant Carbohydrate Biochemistry,* ed. J. B. Pridham. Proc. Phytochem. Soc. No. 10. New York: Academic
92. Northcote, D. H., Pickett-Heaps, J. D. 1966. *Biochem. J.* 98:159–67
93. Northcote, D. H., Wooding, F. B. P. 1966. *Proc. R. Soc. B* 163:524–37
94. O'Brien, T. P. 1972. *Bot. Rev.* 38:88–117
95. Olsen, B. R., Berg, R. A., Kishida, Y., Prockop, D. J. 1973. *Science* 182:825–28
96. Osborne, D. J., Ridge, I., Sargent, J. A. 1970. In *Plant Growth Substances,* ed. D. J. Carr, 534–42. New York: Springer
97. Paull, R. E., Jones, R. L. 1975. *Planta* In press
98. Paull, R. E., Jones, R. L. 1976. *Plant Physiol.* In press
99. Pickett-Heaps, J. D. 1966. *Planta* 71:1–14
100. Pickett-Heaps, J. D. 1967. *J. Ultrastruct. Res.* 18:287–303
101. Pickett-Heaps, J. D. 1968. *J. Cell Sci.* 3:55–64
102. Pickett-Heaps, J. D., Northcote, D. H. 1966. *J. Exp. Bot.* 17:20–26
103. Powell, J. T., Brew, K. 1974. *Biochem. J.* 142:203–9
104. Preston, R. D. 1964. In *The Formation of Wood in Forest Trees,* ed. M. H. Zimmerman, 169–88. New York: Academic
105. Ramus, J. 1973. See Ref. 4, 33–59
106. Ray, P. M. 1973. *Plant Physiol.* 51:601–8
107. Ibid, 609–14
108. Ray, P. M., Shininger, T. L., Ray, M. M. 1969. *Proc. Natl. Acad. Sci. USA* 64:605–12
109. Reid, P. D., Strong, H. S., Lew, F., Lewis, L. N. 1974. *Plant Physiol.* 53:732–37
110. Ridge, I., Osborne, D. J. 1970. *J. Exp. Bot.* 21:843–56
111. Roland, J. C. 1972. *Int. Rev. Cytol.* 36:45–91
112. Roland, J. C., Sandoz, D. 1969. *J. Microsc.* 8:263–68

113. Rosenbloom, J., Prockop, D. J. 1968. In *Repair and Regeneration: Scientific Basis for Medical Practice*, ed. J. E. Dunphy, H. W. Van Winkle, 117–35. New York: McGraw-Hill
114. Rougier, M. 1971. *J. Microsc.* 10:67–82
115. Sadava, D., Chrispeels, M. J. 1971. *Biochim. Biophys. Acta.* 227:278–87
116. Sadava, D., Chrispeels, M. J. 1973. *Dev. Biol.* 30:49–55
117. Schnepf, E. 1963. *Planta* 59:351–79
118. Schnepf, E. 1969. *Protoplasmatologia* VIII/8:2–181
119. Schnepf, E. 1972. *Planta* 103:334–39
120. Schnepf, E. 1973. In *Grundlagen der Cytologie*, ed. G. C. Hirsch, H. Ruska, 461–77
121. Schofield, J. G. 1971. *Nature, New Biol.* 234:215–16
122. Shore, G., Maclachlan, G. A. 1975. *J. Cell Biol.* 64:557–71
123. Shore, G., Raymond, Y., Maclachlan, G. A. 1975. *Plant Physiol.* 56:34–38
124. Siekevitz, P., Palade, G. E. 1966. *J. Cell Biol.* 30:519–30
125. Srivastava, L. M., Sawhney, V. K., Taylor, I. E. P. 1975. *Proc. Natl. Acad. Sci. USA* 72:1107–11
126. Spiro, R. G. 1970. *Ann. Rev. Biochem.* 39:599–38
127. Thiéry, J. P. 1967. *J. Microsc.* 6:987–1018
128. Tippit, D. H., Pickett-Heaps, J. D. 1974. *Protoplasma* 81:271–96
129. Van Der Woude, W. J., Lembi, C. A., Morré, D. J. 1972. *Biochem. Biophys. Res. Commun.* 46:245–53
130. Van Der Woude, W. J., Lembi, C. A., Morré, D. J. 1974. *Plant Physiol.* 54:333–40
131. Van Der Woude, W. J., Morré, D. J., Bracker, C. E. 1971. *J. Cell Sci.* 8:331–51
132. Varner, J. E., Mense, R. 1972. *Plant Physiol.* 49:187–89
133. Vigil, E. L., Ruddat, M. 1973. *Plant Physiol.* 51:549–58
134. Welinder, K. G., Smillie, L. B. 1972. *Can. J. Biochem.* 50:63–90
135. Wessels, N. K. et al 1971. *Science* 171:135–43
136. Whaley, W. G., Dauwalder, M., Kephart, J. E. 1966. *J. Ultrastruct. Res.* 15:169–80
137. Whaley, W. G., Dauwalder, M., Kephart, J. E. 1972. *Science* 175:596–99
138. Whaley, W. G., Kephart, J. E., Mollenhauer, H. H. 1959. *Am. J. Bot.* 46:743–51
139. Wooding, F. B. P. 1968. *J. Cell Sci.* 3:71–80
140. Wright, K., Northcote, D. H. 1974. *Biochem. J.* 139:525–34

Ann. Rev. Plant Physiol. 1976. 27:39–69

NUCLEAR ORGANIZATION[1] ❖7601

Walter Nagl[2]

Department of Biology, University of Kaiserslautern, German Federal Republic, and
Institute of Botany, University of Vienna, Austria

CONTENTS

I. INTRODUCTION

During the last 3 or 4 years more progress has been achieved in thè elucidation of chromosomal and nuclear structure of higher organisms than during the previous 50 years. The main reason for this is the combination of the classical cytological techniques with biochemical ones, and the increasing attention paid to eukaryotic chromosome organization by molecular biologists who had hitherto been more interested in the simpler chromosomes of prokaryotes. The object of this essay, which is the first under this title in the *Annual Review of Plant Physiology,* is to summarize the advances made in our understanding of the nucleus in terms of its structure and function.

Structure and function are two aspects of living matter. Many functions can be better—or perhaps solely—analyzed if their structural basis is known, and con-

[1]Abbreviations used: C (DNA amount of the haploid chromosome set); cot (the product of DNA concentration given in moles per liter and the time of reassociation given in seconds); f1 (the very lysine-rich fraction of histones); kb (kilobases, i.e. 1000 bases [base pairs] in RNA[DNA]); G_1 (the interphase period between mitosis and DNA synthesis); G_2 (the interphase period between DNA synthesis and mitosis); hnRNA (heterogeneous nuclear RNA); mRNA (messenger RNA); rDNA (ribosomal DNA, i.e. the DNA sequences coding for rRNA); rRNA (ribosomal RNA); S (period of DNA replication); tRNA (transfer RNA).

[2]I am very grateful to Dr. Peter Barlow, University of Cambridge, for his critical reading of the manuscript, and to Mrs. Silvia Kühner for help in collecting the literature.

39

versely, many structures can be understood only if their functional significance is elucidated. Since this essay is addressed primarily to plant physiologists, the structure of the cell nucleus will be described on the basis of its functional organization. One of the central questions of eukaryotic biology—how organisms differentiate—will lead from the basic organization of nuclei to its modification during development.

Most biologists have some idea of what the cell nucleus is, but the concept of organization, although central in biology and widely used, is far from clearly understood. Atlan (11) gave a mathematical definition of organization. He stated that the word "organization" is used to mean either a state or a process, or both. Generally what we think of as organization has both a structural and a functional aspect. If we consider the definitions of organization given in the literature, we find two major trends that contradict each other. Organization is either meant as (a) a constraint between parts, or regularity and order, where order is viewed essentially as repetitive order; or (b) as a nonrepetitive order which is measured by an information content, i.e. a degree of unexpectedness directly related to variety and heterogeneity. The definition and model of Atlan (11) involves a kind of optimization process so that any optimum organization could correspond to a compromise between maximum information content (i.e. variety) and maximum redundancy. This interpretation fits the organization of the cell nucleus surprisingly well. Its structure and function are based on both variety (unique units of genetic information) and repetitiveness (reiterated units that are noninformative in a genetic sense).

II. ORGANIZATION OF NUCLEAR DNA

The DNA of eukaryotic chromosomes differs from the DNA in prokaryotes by its greater amount, greater information content, increased degree of redundancy, association with basic proteins, and compartmentation from the cytoplasm by being enclosed within the nuclear membranes.

In the evolution of multicellular organisms, the range of DNA content per haploid genome extends over two orders of magnitude. The minimum DNA content of the genome possessed by each class of eukaryotes increases in a manner that relates to evolutionary complexity (371). This is precisely what we would expect if the greater complexity of organization is based on a larger store of genetic information. However, the mean DNA content of some of the relatively primitive forms is often higher than that of the more advanced. Further, there is often an inordinately wide spread of DNA values within certain phyla, and even among species within a single genus, species therefore that are closely related and consequently of comparable complexity (330, 370). The range of variation in DNA is especially large in amphibians and angiosperms, and much of it is not attributable to polyploidy. So, although there has been an increase in minimum amount of nuclear DNA during evolution, the DNA per haploid chromosome set—known as the C value—does not display much correlation with evolutionary complexity. While mammals usually have 2–3 pg (10^{-12}g) DNA per haploid genome, amphibians and angiosperms show DNA contents between 1 and 100 pg (25, 289, 330). Taking 10^6 daltons as the approximate size of a gene (corresponding to a length of some 1500 base-pairs, which would code for a protein of 500 amino acids or about 50,000 daltons) the relatively small human genome could specify almost two million genes. The number of genes consistent with mutation rates is, however, much less than this coding potential (232), the amount of DNA appears to be greater by two orders of magnitude or so than would be expected (296). Thus there is a C value paradox, whereby the nuclear DNA content apparently neither relates to differences in the number of unique, protein-coding genes nor to evolutionary complexity.

These findings raise two questions: (a) What is the structural basis of such variation in nuclear DNA contents? (b) What is the functional significance of the excess DNA? Let us first discuss the structural basis, which reflects on something unique in eukaryotic chromosome organization.

(a) Variation in chromosome strandedness (polynemy) was earlier considered to play an important role in evolution. Although light and electron microscopic evidence and data on half chromatid exchange support the idea that the chromatid is at least composed of subchromatids (81, 158) or a polyneme core (383), most biochemical and genetic experiments favor the hypothesis that all chromatids are unineme (63, 206, 318, 330, 394). The problem, however, has not yet been resolved conclusively (81, 385).

(b) Variation in the DNA content is surely caused by tandem duplications and deletions of DNA sequences in several instances (73, 211, 298, 329).

(c) Sparrow & Nauman (370) found a series of genome doublings in grasses and other groups and interpreted them in terms of cryptoendopolyploidy, i.e. end-to-end doublings in length. Also, the geometric increase in DNA amounts of gymnosperms (323) and Ranunculaceae (149) was interpreted in this way. To avoid one-sided information, the reader also remember that variation of DNA content is only the one side of the DNA story. There are also mechanisms to stabilize the amount of DNA in spite of variation in chromosome number, etc (219).

(d) Characterization of the eukaryotic genome by biochemical techniques has brought some new aspects into discussion. Since a relationship exists between the melting point of DNA and its base composition (344) and between its buoyant density in a CsCl gradient and its base composition (249), DNA fractions differing in their base composition can be separated. In several instances, a fraction of the DNA exhibits a base composition sufficiently different from the bulk of the nuclear DNA so that one or more satellite bands form on either the heavy or light side of the main band when the DNA is centrifuged to equilibrium in a CsCl gradient. Such DNA is referred to as GC- and AT-rich satellite DNA, respectively. Satellite DNA is composed of very simple but highly reiterated sequences, yet few highly repetitive DNAs appear as satellites (83). [For the detection of hidden satellites see (162, 368).] Satellite DNA is mainly located in the heterochromatin (429) and may contribute to the variation in nuclear DNA content. Ingle et al (193) listed the buoyant densities and amounts of nuclear satellite DNAs in relation to total nuclear DNA content for numerous dicots [for a monocot see (70); for variation in heterochromatin see (291)].

(e) The key to understanding the widespread variation in nuclear DNA content and the organization of eukaryotic chromosomes was the detection of repetitive DNA sequences as a general feature of eukaryotic DNAs (52, 213, 356). DNA, denatured by heat or high pH, is capable of undergoing strand reassociation under appropriate conditions of temperature, salt concentration, and time. Renaturation kinetics, and the cot-curves derived from them, allow an estimate to be made of the percentage of DNA corresponding to various degrees of base-sequence complexity and repetitiveness.

In general, eukaryotic DNA appears to fall into three classes of sequences: (a) unique sequences, where there is only one copy of each sequence in the haploid genome, and which may represent most of the protein coding genes; (b) intermediate repetitive DNA, a fraction that comprises a spectrum of varying degrees of repetition and whose function will be discussed later; and (c) the smallest size class, the highly reiterated sequences, which occur up to an excess of 10^6 copies per genome and which are located in the constitutive heterochromatin (this highly repetitive fraction can sometimes be separated as satellite DNA). Table 1 shows the variable contribution of repetitive DNA to the nuclear DNA content in plants.

Now the question to be answered is how the unique and the intermediate repetitive sequences are organized in the chromosome. Studies of dipteran polytene chromosomes and of the giant chromosomes in macronucleus anlagen of ciliates have led to the conclusion that repetitive and unique sequences occur in an almost regular alternating pattern (39, 50, 321). The basic type of experiment on which the conclusion of general occurrence of such an interspersion rests is the reassociation of trace quantities of long, radioactively labeled DNA fragments with short, unlabeled fragments present in excess. The mixture is incubated to low cot, so that only repetitive stretches can undergo reassociation, and is then passed over a hydroxyapatite column which binds only double-stranded DNA at 0.12 M phosphate buffer. By this technique long, radioactive fragments were found to be retained by the hydroxyapatite because they contained repetitive sequence elements that had paired with the short, unlabeled DNA fragments. The interspersion pattern was thus established for various animals (50, 53, 102, 103, 250, 313) and wheat (133, 357) and cotton (418). By using fragments of measured length, it was possible to arrive at quantitative estimates of the average spacing distances (102, 155).

To avoid a wrong impression, it should be noted that not all repetitive sequences are noninformative, but also involve some important genes. An estimation of the number of repetitive genes per nucleus is obtained by hybridization of the labeled gene product (RNA) with the denatured DNA on filters (147). The rate of reassociation is a function of the number of copies of nucleotide pairs in the DNA which are complementary to the RNA. The location of the genes in the chromosomes is performed by hybridization of the labeled RNA to the denatured DNA in microscopic preparations (308).

The most ubiquitous examples of reiterated genes are those that code for the stable RNAs: the ribosomal 16–18S RNA, 26–28S RNA, and 5S RNA, as well as the various tRNAs [see Table 2 for rRNA genes; for tRNA genes see (77, 346); for the organization of rDNA in plants refer also to (93, 133, 150, 192, 262, 352, 396, 430)]. Much work has been devoted to the organization of the ribosomal genes. The single genes are all separated by spacer segments; but while the spacer between the genes for the 18S and 28S RNA is transcribed, that *between* these "transcription units"

Table 1 Approximate proportions of repeated-sequence DNAs in the nuclear DNA of some plants, as determined by reassociation experiments

Taxum	Species	2C DNA Content[a]	Repetitive DNA (%)	Reference
Yeasts	*Torulopsis candida*	1.16×10^{10}d	5.3	74
	Candida macedoniensis	8.31×10^9d	7.1	74
	Hansenula holstii	6.52×10^9d	8.4	74
	Saccharomyces exiguus	1.13×10^{10}d	10.8	74
	Debaryomyces hansenii	6.05×10^9d	13.8	74
Fungi	*Neurospora crassa*	3.2×10^7d	13.5	114
	Coprinus lagopus	3.6×10^7d	15.0	114
	Mucor azygospora	3.4×10^7d	16.5	114
	Phycomyces blakesleeanus	1.9×10^{10}d	30.0	113
Dicots	*Raphanus sativus*	3.1 pg	18	221
	Capsella bursa-pastoris (4 ×)	1.7 pg	46	132
	Anemone coronaria	19.9 pg	53	94
	Anemone blanda	32.0 pg	57	94
	Linum usitatissimum	1.5 pg	59	91
	Lamium purpureum	2.7 pg	60	132
	Anemone pavoniana	29.3 pg	62	94
	Beta vulgaris	2.7 pg	63	132
	Veronica persica (4 ×)	1.9 pg	63	132
	Anemone cylindrica	21.9 pg	65	94
	Anemone riparia	21.0 pg	67	94
	Stellaria media (7 ×)	2.5 pg	69	132
	Senecio vulgaris (8 ×)	3.5 pg	74	132
	Pisum sativum	9.9 pg	75	132
	Tropaeolum majus	7.3 pg	82	132
	Vicia faba	29.3 pg	85	132
Monocots	*Hyacinthus orientalis* (4 ×-1)	98.1 pg	75	132
	Zea mays	11.0 pg	78	132
	Poa trivialis	6.9 pg	82	132[b]
	Avena sativa (6 ×)	43.0 pg	83	132
	Triticum aestivum (6 ×)	36.2 pg	83	132
	Secale cereale	18.9 pg	92	132
	Allium cepa	35.5 pg	95	132

[a] Although there is not a simple positive correlation between nuclear DNA content and the percentage of repetitive DNA, it can be seen clearly that there is an increase in both mean DNA content and mean percentage of repetitive DNA from yeasts to monocots. Most of the repetitive sequences represent noncoding material.

[b] See also (328). The data obtained by various research groups may differ because of reassociation conditions and criteria for their interpretation.

Table 2 Approximate number of repetitive genes for rRNA in diploid G_1 nuclei (2C DNA content) in some plants and, for comparison, in a bacterium, two animals, and man. Determination made by DNA/RNA hybridization on filters

Taxum	Species	Frequency	Reference
Bacteria	Bacillus subtilis	5	299
Insecta	Drosophila hydei ♀	240	175
	Drosophila hydei ♂	200	175
Amphibia	Xenopus laevis, soma	1,150	35
	Xenopus laevis, oocytes[a]	2,000,000	247
Mammalia	Homo sapiens	440	54
Fungi	Saccharomyces cerevisiae	140	347
	Saccharomyces carlsbergensis	140	332
Algae	Chlamydomonas reinhardii	200	186
	Chlamydomonas reinhardii[b]	400	186
	Acetabularia mediterranea[a]	13,000	400
	Acetabularia mediterranea[a]	23,000	380
Gymnosperms[c]	Taxus baccata	2,500	193
	Juniperus chinensis	4,100	193
	Pinus sylvestris	10,700	193
	Picea abies	19,300	193
	Larix decidua	26,000	193
Dicots	Nicotiana tabaccum	2,200	193
	Beta vulgaris	2,300	192
	Linum usitatissimum[d]	3,473	92
	Phaseolus coccineus	4,000	193
	Aquilegia alpina	4,600	193
	Helianthus annuus	6,700	192
	Brassica rapa	8,600	193
	Vicia faba	9,500	248
Monocots	Secale cereale	5,700	193
	Zea mays	6,200	192
	Tradescantia virginiana	8,600	193
	Triticum vulgare (6×)	12,700	192
	Allium cepa	13,900	193
	Hyacinthus orientalis (4×)[e]	32,000	396

[a] Amplification of ribosomal genes.

[b] Only the genes for 18S RNA; the two values are due to cell-cycle-specific amplification of the genes.

[c] Frequencies for ribosomal genes between 75,000 and 330,000 have been given for a number of gymnosperms by Hotta & Miksche (184).

[d] var. Stormont Cirrus, L-genotroph.

[e] i.e. 8743 per nucleolus organizer.

is only partly transcribed. This was demonstrated by electron microscopy of active ribosomal cistrons in animals (258, 259) and *Acetabularia* (380, 400), and is also true of the 5S RNA genes (55). The function of these spacers is not known, but evidently they are not subject to the same rigid evolutionary restriction against sequence divergence as are the gene regions (55, 56). Models for the organization of the complete gene and spacer regions and for the "processing" of rRNA have been given by several authors (33, 56, 168, 372).

Most of the protein-coding genes are found among the unique DNA sequences. The best founded exceptions are the genes for the histone mRNAs. These genes have a frequency of some hundreds per genome, probably a necessity for the rapid synthesis of histones during DNA replication (34, 209, 422).

The presence of noninformative repetitive DNAs in eukaryotes and their characteristic pattern of interspersion imply that this kind of organization has functional significance. It has been suggested that both the chromomeric structure of the chromosomes and the problem of "too much" DNA could be interpreted in terms of chromomeres that were made up of families of identical tandem-repeats, as originally proposed in the master-slave model by Callan (62), and for some time also proposed on the basis of circularization experiments on eukaryotic DNAs by Thomas (394). If sheared DNA is treated with exonuclease III to make single-stranded ends and then annealed at 60–65°C, it forms some 15–20% stable circles (for details see 30, 326, 395). However, renaturation kinetics of the DNA from several eukaryotes must be interpreted by postulating the occurrence of a larger unique fraction (52, 222). It was therefore emphasized that DNA rings can be generated, not only by blocks of reiterated genes, but also by moderately repetitive DNA interspersed between unique genes. Actually, this distribution could lead to the same relationship between ring frequency and fragment length. It is now widely accepted that most repetitive sequences do not represent slave genes, but rather are noninformative DNA which may have some regulatory function affecting patterns of gene activity, the processing and stability of the transcribed RNA, its translation, and cellular and higher levels of differentiation (see section IV).

An interesting idea has been put forward by Bennett (25, 26), who suggested that the noninformative DNA may affect developmental rates because of its physical properties which he referred to as the "nucleotype." A positive correlation between nuclear DNA content and the duration of the mitotic cycle has now been well established (125, 126, 415), but a relationship also exists between DNA content and the duration of meiosis, cell size, organ size, and minimum generation time (25, 27, 324). From an evolutionary point of view, it seems that nuclear DNA contents decreased in many taxa of plants and animals during their specification and adaptation (14, 15, 120, 290, 322, 330, 381). In other taxa, however, an increase in DNA has been assumed to occur during evolution (73, 115, 330, 370), as in geographic genotypes of *Pinus sitchensis* (257) and in gymnosperms in general; this probably has something to do with the selection for larger cell size, particularly of tracheids (323).

However, the problem is more complicated than suggested above. Because the duration of the mitotic cycle is proportional to the DNA content in diploid plants, the loss of noninformative DNA would permit shorter cycles. This could have selective advantage to organisms undergoing selection for rapid development, e.g. annuals (370). Indeed, the mean nuclear DNA content of annual species is significantly lower than that of perennial species, and that of ephemeral species is still lower; in contrast, obligate perennials have a higher mean unclear DNA content than facultative perennials (25, 26; see also 324). It is interesting to note that polyploid species display, in spite of their increased DNA values, the same or even a shorter mitotic and meiotic cycle, perhaps because two or more genomes can reduplicate and synthesize faster than one (27, 205, 414).

Another puzzling aspect is the fact that although the main strategy in the evolution of the Anthemideae appears to be a reduction of chromosome size and DNA content (290), a number of annuals have been found which exhibit higher DNA contents than their perennial relatives (291). The annuals, despite their higher DNA amounts, show shorter mitotic cell cycles than the perennials (283). One point that could explain this paradox was the finding in all those annuals of a disproportionately increased percentage of heterochromatin, and with it of highly repetitive, fast replicating DNA [(283, 284); see also the similar findings by Evans & Rees (125)].

III. ORGANIZATION OF CHROMATIN

The DNA of eukaryotic chromosomes is not found as a naked molecule in the cell, nor even in the nucleus, but is always associated with basic proteins, the histones, thus forming a nucleoprotein complex, the nucleohistone (e.g. 195, 212; for review see 130). The histones are thought to stabilize the DNA duplex, to induce a tertiary structure, and to block the accessibility of the DNA for enzymes. Through these effects histones represent general repressors of gene activity and may be a prerequisite for the evolution of multicellular organisms. The tissue-specific activation of certain genes during development is assumed to occur as a result of local loosening of the DNA-histone association by other acidic proteins of the nucleus (for reviews see 130, 201). Therefore, in actual fact the genetically active material in the nucleus is chromatin, and not DNA per se.

The importance of the histones is demonstrated by their evolutionary stability. In all animals and plants, five major fractions are found by separation on polyacrylamide gel electrophoresis, and even the amino acid sequence of calf and pea histone, for instance, is very similar, only the very lysine-rich fraction f1 showing some variability (38, 105, 310, 351, 389).

The DNA-histone complex can be completely cleaved by 2.6 M NaCl, and it can be reconstituted through removing the salt by gradient dialysis (212). This is because the main forces holding the complex together are ionic bindings between the negatively charged phosphate groups of the DNA chains and the NH_2 groups of the histones that act like polycations. The binding of the histones is not gene-specific. There are, however, differences in the strength of the binding of various fractions to DNA. Lysine residuals (as well as synthetic polylysines) prefer AT pairs (297, 379), while arginine residuals prefer GC pairs (75; see also 359, 360). This preference, however, has been questioned recently (432). Bram (44) suggested that AT-rich binding sites are in general necessary for protein-induced superstructures. The formation of such a tertiary structure of the DNA (superhelix) is one of the most important effects of the histones and is well documented by X-ray diffraction analyses (305, 306, 311) and circular dichroism spectroscopy (409). The radius of the superhelix is 50 Å, with a pitch of 120 Å. Recently Bram et al (45, 46) detected by neutron scattering experiments that the superhelix is itself coiled. Thus the various types of chromatin fibers seen in the electron microscope can be explained this way: free DNA appears as a fibril some 25 Å in diameter, the supercoil as a fiber of 100 Å, and the coiled-supercoil as a fiber of 200 Å diameter (Figure 1).

How the histones promote the superhelix has not yet been resolved. Several models have been put forward on the basis of biophysical, biochemical, and electron microscopic studies (22, 119, 229, 354, 359, 360). The question of which fraction of the histones is the most important one in inducing the tertiary structure has been repeatedly investigated. The very lysine-rich f1 is apparently ineffective in supercoiling, but it is responsible for the quaternary coiling of the DNA and for cross-linking of nucleohistone fibers [(see 138, 171, 180, 200, 240, 304, 359, 360) for the role of individual histone fractions].

The clue to a new understanding of chromatin structure has been made by the discovery that histones occur in clusters separated from each other (60, 76, 312, 331). Kornberg & Thomas (215) report that histones are found in the following conformation: f1 forms monomers, $(f2a1)_2(f3)_2$ appear as tetramers, and (f2a2, f2b) occur as oligomers. Kornberg (214) then suggested that the structure of chromatin is based on repeating unit of two of each of the histone molecules (with the exception of f1, which occurs only once per subunit) and about 200 nucleotide pairs of the DNA. A chromatin fiber could be composed of many such subunits forming a flexibly jointed chain (Figure 1). The subunit model of chromatin was also suggested by other authors working with various techniques such as nuclease digestion and electrophoresis of the fragments produced, neutron scattering studies, and electron microscopy of spread chromatin (18, 179, 239, 301–303, 350, 376). Therefore, it is now generally accepted that the native configuration of chromatin of plants and animals is that of particles on a string, along which nuclease-resistant, histone-complexed, and tightly supercoiled regions of the DNA alternate with extended, histone-free spacer regions (46, 242, 255, 304, 410, 411). Oudet et al (304) suggested the term "nucleosomes" for the repeating units.

Histone-maintained supercoiling of DNA has been envisaged as a general mechanism of repression of transcription (4, 37, 200, 254, 311). Chromatin is known to be much less effective as a template for DNA-dependent RNA polymerase than extracted DNA. In addition to the tertiary and quaternary structure, inactivation on a large scale can be performed by cross-linking of the chromatin fibers which then result in chromatin condensation. While f1 does not have much effect on DNA supercoiling, it plays the dominant role in chromatin condensation (31). F1 histone is thought to function in gene inactivation (238, 261, 353), and, significantly, it also shows the highest species- and tissue-specific variation (319, 351, 392, 399). It must be emphasized that this transitorily condensed chromatin, which is known mainly from mammals, must not be equated with heterochromatin. While constitutive

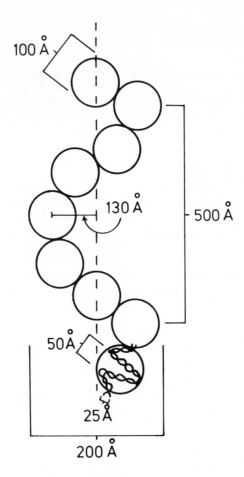

Figure 1   Relationships between DNA structure, histone oligomers, and chromatin fibrils of various sizes according to the model of Bram et al (45, 46). The DNA duplex of an approximate diameter of 25 Å is supercoiled within the chromatin subunits (nucleosomes, ν-bodies) with a pitch of 50 Å to give rise to the 100 Å fiber as seen in the electron microscope. The whole nucleohistone complex is coiled again with a pitch of 500 Å and a radius of 130 Å to give rise to the 200 Å fiber as seen in the electron microscope. The stretches of free DNA between the nucleosomes normally are longer than shown in this scheme.

heterochromatin is characterized by its high content of repetitive DNAs, condensed chromatin is primarily characterized by changes in the nucleohistone complex (3, 12).

In the activation of previously repressed regions of the genome, the associated histones must be effectively removed from the appropriate region of DNA (238). This can be done by histone modification, binding of acidic chromosomal proteins to the histones, or derepressor (chromosomal) RNA.

Modification of histones by phosphorylation, acetylation, and methylation is generally accepted as a mechanism to bring about changes in the strength of DNA-histone bonds and of template activity (107, 243, 386, 435, 436). Circular dichroism studies have shown that chromatin with phosphorylated f1 displays a spectrum similar to free DNA (2), and in active nuclei a higher degree of f2a1 acetylation has been observed than in inactive nuclei (154, 420). To avoid confusion it must be realized that phosphorylation of f1 at a different site leads to mitotic chromosome *condensation* (42, 164).

A major role in chromatin decondensation and gene activation is proposed for the nuclear acidic (or nonhistone) proteins [R. D. Cole in (117) suggested the term "hertones"]. They mainly form H-bridges to the histones (194) and act as polyanions (5, 7, 28, 374) competing with the negative charges of the DNA phosphates. Thus the acidic proteins loosen the DNA-histone interactions, the result of which is chromatin decondensation and increased RNA synthesis (183, 348, 421, 433). The hertones show much more chemical diversity and tissue specificity than the histones (88, 104, 157, 204, 375, 390, 426), and therefore it was thought that hertones reverse the histone-induced inhibition of RNA synthesis in a gene-specific manner. Various ingenious experiments support the hypothesis of hertone-stimulated activity of tissue-specific genes (118, 148, 216, 217, 391, 419). The hertones are now envisaged as the most important factor in the control of differential gene activity (21; for reviews see 67, 130, 382).

Without going into details, attention will also be drawn to the role of hormones in the regulation of gene activity via chromatin decondensation. Libby (235) suggested that the first effect of animal hormones is the modification of histones, resulting in an enhancement of RNA synthesis. But phytohormones also have been found to affect the DNA-histone bindings and template activity (17, 129, 159, 428; review in 130).

Chromosomal or derepressor RNA have been thought to control derepression of eukaryotic DNA (37, 138). In spite of recent criticism of this concept (8), the role of chromosomal RNA in the regulation of differential gene activity was confirmed recently (182, 252, 253).

IV. ORGANIZATION OF CHROMOMERES

In this section I will discuss the functional organization of the interphase and working nucleus, bearing in mind the fact that the chromatin is not a homogeneous mass filling the nuclear cavity, but represents a number of individual structural and functional entities, the chromosomes with their subunits the chromomeres.

Over 98% of the chromosomal DNA (see 24) is located in bead-like structures called chromomeres, which are most clearly visible in lampbrush chromosomes and in polytene chromosomes where the sister chromomeres join to form bands. In pachytene chromosomes, the number of chromomeres is reduced due to the less stretched state of the bivalents and the resulting fusion of neighboring chromomeres. The organization of the highly condensed DNA into chromomeres is somewhat unclear. Sonnenbichler (362, 363) suggested that histones, particularly f1, cause cross-linking of nucleohistone fibers. Sorsa & Sorsa (364) developed a model of the chromomere wherein the DNA is condensed through several orders of coiling. It has also been suggested that the chromosomes are composed of axial or core fibers and epichromatin or chromomere fibers (365, 383), but actually both types may be different parts of the same DNA molecule, differently folded due to a particular distribution of repetitive sequences (366).

The chromomere is generally considered to be the functional subunit of the chromosome with respect to transcription and possibly also to replication (24, 97, 314, 317). Functionally, chromomeres correspond to single genes. The key observation is that a deficiency or deletion of a band in *Drosophila* polytene chromosomes produces exactly the same phenotype as a revertible point mutation located in the same band. These findings, and the observation that a single gene product is synthesized by a puff (160), have led to the "one chromomere = one gene" hypothesis [(202, 230, 394; for recent criticism of this concept see (417)]. Although a chromomere may contain many copies of one and the same gene, organized in a kind of master-slave condition (discussed in 62, 394, and in section II of this chapter), or may represent a polycistronic operon (300), it is more likely that the bulk of the DNA sequences represent noninformational repetitive sequences involved in the control of gene activity (39, 51, 101, 116, 144, 145, 202, 367). Wu et al (427) and Bonner & Wu (39) found that in *Drosophila* there are about as many families of intermediate-repetitive DNAs as there are chromomeres (ca 4500), all sequences of each individual chromomere being of the same family and separating stretches of single-copy DNA from each other.

Chromomeres apparently are transcribed in toto. But whereas in a few cases the total length of the transcript is transported into the cytoplasm (97, 98, 223), most of the heterogeneous nuclear RNA (hnRNA) does not leave the nucleus (47). The rest of the high molecular weight nuclear RNA, composed of unique and repetitive sequences (181, 264, 358), is processed and polyadenylated before being transported into the cytoplasm and becoming the polysomal mRNA (49, 90, 109, 198, 199, 241, 263, 343, 344). Entirely repetitive transcripts often missing the poly(A) segment at the 3' end evidently include those of the repetitive histone genes (1). The function of both the repetitive and the poly(A) segment in the transcribed RNA of eukaryotes is not well understood. It was suggested that they may play some role in the processing of the molecules by providing sites at which it is cleaved, in controlling the stablity of mRNA or the formation of ribonucleoprotein complexes (informofers and informosomes; see 244, 265, 340, 378 for description), or act as recognition elements in translation (discussed in 90, 99, 100, 109, 145, 199, 233, 234, 262).

Considering the organization of DNA, chromatin, and the RNA transcribed from it, operative models for the function of eukaryote chromosomes have been developed. Expanding the operon model for bacteria, Georgiev (144, 145) developed the "transcripton" model for eukaryotes. According to this model, the transcription unit (corresponding to a chromomer) can be divided into two portions: one large, partly repetitive, noninformative acceptor zone, and another rather small, informative, structural zone. The acceptor zone contains—besides the promoter that binds RNA polymerase—several acceptor loci for regulatory proteins; the informative zones are equivalent to structural genes each with a terminator sequence at the 3' end. The whole transcription unit is transcribed into the giant hnRNA (or pre-mRNA) molecule.

Britten & Davidson (51, 101) proposed a concept of differential gene activation accounting for turning on a large set of genes through a single stimulus, e.g. a hormone, at a particular stage of development. This model for differential gene regulation also attributes regulatory functions to the repetitive sequences, but in a more differentiated manner. However, this cannot be discussed here.

Crick (89) stimulated the study of eukaryotic chromosomes by suggesting a model in which the interchromomere region contains the gene while the chromomere is identified as the control element. The central idea is that the recognition sites, needed for control purposes, are mainly unpaired stretches of double-stranded DNA, i.e. they are single-stranded (the "unpairing postulate"). It is likely that these sites would be palindromic sequences (361).

This model, however, has been criticized for a variety of reasons. For instance, searches for single-stranded DNA in eukaryotes did not reveal the amount necessary to support the model (231). Moreover, Paul (311) improved the model by proposing that it is the hertones which are involved in making the recognition sites accessible. These destabilizing molecules bind to AT-rich regions causing a localized reduction in supercoiling. This now permits the approach of an RNA polymerase to the promoter. The accumulation of nascent RNA, also a polyanion, can cause further unwinding of the adjacent regions (e.g. loop or puff formation).

Speiser (373) developed the idea that both the interchromomeres and the chromomeres contain different types of genes. It is assumed that the interchromomeres are miniature puffs, formed at sites of genes coding for the basic cellular activities. The chromomeres, on the other hand, developed during evolution by saltatory replications from the basic genome, code for specialized proteins and there are the loci of stage- and tissue-specific gene activities (puffing patterns!).

An interesting approach toward the understanding of the role of heterochromatic repetitive DNA in chromosomal function has been taken by Guillé & Quetier (163). They propose that the intermediate-repetitive sequences located in intercalary heterochromatin play a major role in the quantitative control of gene activity. Each chromomere contains zones of certain DNA sequences and histones called a "quantitative command unit." The molecular structure is composed of AT-repeats, lysine-rich histones, and GC-repeats associated with arginine-rich histones. Attached to this unit is a "qualitative command unit" that contains a sequence to which chromosomal RNA or acidic nuclear proteins might be bound. The number of former units could determine the maximum number of times the latter could be transcribed, although they themselves are not transcribed. The number of the second type of units, which are transcribed, would then determine the maximum number of times the adjacent mRNA molecule can be read by the ribosomal machinery, although the command units themselves would not be translated. The model is not only consistent with the present knowledge on the structure of chromosomes and their transcripts, but also provides a particularly understandable basis for the occurrence of DNA amplification in obviously noncoding heterochromatin (e.g. 276; D. Schweizer and W. Nagl, unpublished) and metabolic DNAs (287, 316).

316). Such events so far have not been studied satisfactorily, partly because there was no plausible explanation for their existence.

Light microscopic studies support the hypothesis that the chromomere is also the unit of replication, the "replicon" of eukaryotes (24, 317). Eukaryotic DNA is a multi-replicon structure with replicons of variable length (63, 189, 388). Each replicon has its own starting point at which DNA synthesis is initiated at different times during the S period. DNA synthesis first produces smaller fragments of daughter DNA [also called "intermediate fragments" to distinguish them from the much shorter Okazaki-type pieces in the replication of the 5'—3'—strand (388)]. Then replication moves ahead with two replication forks in opposite directions to create a serial array of "eye forms" or "bubbles," as shown by the autoradiography of isolated DNA. Finally the intermediate pieces in adjacent replicons fuse until the total DNA molecule of a chromosome is replicated. The movement of the replication forks apparently occurs at a constant rate of 2,6 kb/min/fork (36). In spite of this constant rate, S phase duration within the same organism may vary enormously in cells at different developmental stages (19, 65). This variation is accomodated, not by gross diversity in replication rate, but rather by striking differences in the number of initiation sites operative for replication at any time in the S phase. Occlusion of initiation sites presumably depends on the packaging of DNA into chromatin (reviews: 19, 36, 64, 65, 106, 325, 338, 387). Recently, Seale (349) found that the nucleosomes segregate with the daughter chromosomes, and that replication-sized DNA fragments are associated with the histone oligomers. He therefore suggested that the chromatin subunits represent the eukaryotic replicon [for the problems of histone association with replicating DNA see also (423)]. The suggestion of Seale (349) is consistent with the findings that the chromomere may contain several initiation sites which can be activated independently (36; see also 6).

The long duration of chromatin replication in species with high DNA content suggests that the DNA increase is achieved by tandem increase of the DNA within the chromomere and not by multinemy or increase in the number of chromomeres, i.e. activatable initiation sites [but see also the opposite results in Amphibia (424)]. The varying size of chromomeres may be also the key for the characteristic pattern of early replicating euchromatin and late replicating heterochromatin in most eukaryotic chromosomes (236). However, changes in the rate of replication may also occur (e.g. 185).

V. ORGANIZATION OF CHROMOSOMES IN NUCLEI

Let us now take a look at the nucleohistone fibers as they constitute the chromosome as a whole, particularly as seen clearly in chromatin spread on a water surface and dried by the critical point technique. The DNA is very tightly packed into those chromatin fibrils, so that length ratios (length of DNA: length of chromatin fiber, the so-called "packaging ratio") of 25:1 to 150:1 can be found (16, 80, 82, 110, 153, 224; for review see 232). The variability in the ratio depends on whether the fibril was prepared as the supercoil with 100 Å diameter or as the coiled supercoil of 200 Å diameter (45, 46, 110, 225, 228, 306, 320). The diameter of the fibrils observed and their degree of coiling also depend on factors such as transcriptional activity, fixation, and divalent cations present in the nucleoplasm or in the isolation medium (40, 112, 178, 188, 335). It has already been shown that there is a general rule that chromatin active in RNA synthesis appears to be decondensed, while chromatin inactive in RNA synthesis is in a condensed state (at least in mammals). During mitosis all the chromosomes condense very tightly and become inactive in RNA synthesis (e.g. 280). Whether the cross-linking of the chromatin fibers during condensation is achieved by folding (110, 187) or by further coiling (146, 364) has not yet been discerned. It was suggested that peptides containing aromatic amino acids interact selectively with DNA helices to form a "sticky complex" (140), or that the interspersed repetitive sequences in the DNA have some affinity to each other and thus bring about the closer packaging of the fibrils (384). There is also a suggestion that allosteric proteins synthesized at a particular stage of the cell cycle cause mitotic chromosome condensation (87); attachment of these proteins to nucleohistone may lead to conformational changes which allow dimerization or polymerization. Recently the involvement of histone phosphorylation, particularly of f1, was emphasized as the control step in mitotic chromosome condensation (42, 164; see also section III).

In ultrathin sections of plant nuclei, variable degrees of chromatin condensation can be observed during the working state (interphase). For instance, "micropuffs" and clusters of ribonucleoprotein granules have been found in nuclei of plants with the "reticulate" type of structure (79, 124, 220, 221). On the other hand, inactivated nuclei display extremely condensed chromatin [e.g. nuclei in maturing sieve elements (59), in spermatids of the liverwort *Sphaerocarpos* (431), and in animal sperm cells (208)].

Some more words on the various types of condensed chromatin may help to avoid misuse of terms and misunderstanding of findings frequently found in the literature. Condensed chromatin generally falls into three classes:

(*a*) The constitutive or karyotypical heterochromatin (57, 251) is characterized by its presence in both homologs of the diploid karyotype (except in cases of structural heterozygosity) and in all cells of an organism, with a few exceptions (e.g. egg cells). Constitutive heterochromatin probably represents the only type of herochromatin occurring in plants. It is rich in highly repetitive DNA and satellite DNA (see section II), mitotically condensed throughout interphase, and detectable as "C-bands" in mitotic chromosomes after differential Giemsa staining (e.g. 341). Further, it is late replicating in most or all organisms and genetically is fairly inert (131, 307, 327, 429).

(*b*) Facultative heterochromatin (57) occurs in just one of the two homologs and is best illustrated by the sex chromatin of female mammals, which is the result of chromosome inactivation and gene dosage compensation (245, 246). It has, of course, the same DNA sequences as the homologous chromosome, e.g. the active X chromosome, but shows the same functional behavior as the constitutive heterochromatin. Therefore it is similar to the third category.

(*c*) Functionally condensed euchromatin is found in spermiogenetic, haemopoietic, and other tissues of mammals. This condensed chromatin is often falsely equated with heterochromatin, and thus the results seem to contradict each other. Condensed chromatin is not a different type of chromatin, but only a reversibly altered state (e.g. 334).

Mitotically condensed chromosomes belong to the functionally condensed chromatin, but it is very likely that a different mechanism of condensation is involved in interphasic and mitotic condensation.

A point which complicates the interpretation of the relationship between the degree of chromatin condensation and template activity is the fact that nuclei also display species-specific diameters of chromatin fibrils (434) and species-specific nuclear structures (for classification see 289, 403). The reasons for the different basic structures of nuclei are not well understood. Lafontaine (221) suggests that the gross organization of interphase nuclei is a function of the genome size, and in particular of the DNA per chromosome. High DNA amounts are associated with much intermediate-repetitive DNA [as in many monocots (132)], which may indeed facilitate or predispose the nucleus toward the development of a "reticulate" or "chromonematic" organization where the electron density is obviously the same in the euchromatic threads as in the heterochromatic chromocenters. The converse conclusion that a low DNA content leads to the concentration of chromatin in chromocenters (221) is, however, unlikely. Although it was found that the higher the DNA content the less the chance of finding satellite DNA in plant species (193), the occurrence of chromocenters (containing mainly the satellite DNA) is not restricted to species with low nuclear DNA content.

Chromosomes of functionally active nuclei, although decondensed and individually not discernible [except in species with the structural type of "prochromosome" nuclei, e.g. in Cucurbitaceae, or "chromosome" nuclei, e.g. in Heteroptera and Orthoptera (403)], have an ordered arrangement within the interphase nucleus (29, 139). Therefore, it has been suggested that the chromosomes are held in particular positions through the attachment of their centromeres, telomeres, or other heterochromatic sites to the nuclear envelope (48, 84, 85, 136, 172, 227, 333, 383). The nuclear membranes have also been thought to control chromosome replication, pairing, and recombination (170, 191, 207, 225, 282). Models have been developed in which the inner halves of the nuclear pore complexes are the regulating units permanently associated with the chromosomes [the so-called "cyclomeres" (122)]. However, neither DNA replication nor its initiation are restricted to the nuclear envelope (86, 108, 190), and the attachment of telomeres during the formation of the synaptonemal complex at the onset of meiosis is the only proven fact.

Another idea on nuclear organization was put forward by DuPraw (110). He suggested that all chromosomes of a haploid set are connected to each other by interchromosomal fibrils to form a unique circular genome which is folded into chromosomes in certain regions. This idea, based on observing whole-mount preparations of mitotic chromosomes spread by the Kleinschmidt technique and dried by the critical point method, has been accepted by several authors (72, 121). The interchromosomal fibrils are 1–20 μm long and connect mainly telomeres and centromeres (226); they synthesize RNA (345), and may contain ribosomal cistrons as shown by in situ hybridization (173). They are also thought to be the material basis for chromosome stickiness in abnormal condensation caused by physiological disturbances or "chromosome poisoning," which results in the entanglement of chromatin fibers between unrelated chromosomes (256). Although in recently published papers the existence of interchromosomal fibrils has become firmly established (151, 152, 197), I think it is more likely that they are preparation artifacts (see also 41, 425). Biochemical evidence is against DNA fibers longer than the chromosome, and the arrangement of mitotic chromosomes is either random (294) or influenced by the nucleolus (174) [see also the opposite findings (203)]. Moreover, the number and sites of attachment of interchromosomal fibrils on two identical sister chromatids is highly variable. If the connecting DNA is linearly continuous with the DNA of the chromosome arms—as suggested by the "one chromosome set = one circular DNA" hypothesis—it is predictable that these connectives should be symmetrical for two identical sister chromatids. Further analysis focused attention on the possible occurrence of phosphotriester linkages within the DNA of eukaryotes to give rise to asymmetrical branch-points along double-stranded molecules (111). In my opinion, however, the interchromosomal fibrils are a phenomenon related to that of subchromatids. Their existence in microscopic preparations cannot be ignored, but they should not be interpreted as a fact of chromosome structure.

Cavalier-Smith (71) suggested that the telomeric region of eukaryote chromosomes contain palindromic DNA sequences. These are necessary to allow termination of DNA replication at the 5' ends of linear DNA molecules where no 3'OH end is available for DNA polymerase after degradation of the primer RNA. If all chromosomes have identical palindromes—which is likely for several reasons—which are sometimes single-stranded, one might expect nonhomologous chromosomes on occasion to join together by base pairing between these cohesive ends. Thus in principle the chromosomes could associate reversibly into a single super-chromosome; end-to-end associations have been seen repeatedly, and in plant cells as well (9, 10, 266, 277). An interesting feature of this model is that it can also be interpreted in the opposite direction; that is, it might serve as a basis for explaining the evolution of eukaryotic chromosome complements from a ring-shaped prokaryotic chromosome. In this connection the findings of Haapala & Soyer (167) should be noticed. These authors reported that the chromosomes of the eukaryote *Euglena gracilis* are circular and membrane-attached. But while these chromosomes are composed of DNA and histones, the circular, membrane-attached chromosomes of the Dinophyceae are not complexed with histones, and might display an earlier ("mesokaryotic") evolutionary stage of chromosome development.

Unfortunately space does not allow discussion of the unique situation found in the organization of mesokaryotic nuclei; recent progress is reported elsewhere (287; for original papers refer to 156, 165, 166, 336, 337, 369, 408). Neither is there space to discuss the organization of the nuclear envelope, the nuclear pores, the nucleolus, nuclear crystals, and the nucleo-cytoplasmic interactions. The interested reader is asked to turn to other reviews recently published on those topics (32, 35, 128, 135, 137, 342, 355, 393, 416).

VI. CHANGES IN NUCLEAR ORGANIZATION
DURING DIFFERENTIATION

For a long time it has been thought that the genetic information stored in the nucleus is identical in all cells of an individual, and that during development the expression of specific genes is brought about by the evocation of certain gene activities from this constant source by cytoplasmic and environmental stimuli (see 397 for a discussion).

I wish to demonstrate in this section that the nucleus shows a dynamic organization rather than a constant one and that changes in nuclear organization accompany many developmental steps.

Cells of embryonic or meristematic tissues pass through mitotic cycles. When a cell starts to differentiate, it usually leaves the cycle and become arrested either in G_1 or, more rarely in G_2 (e.g. 68, 127). In some lower plants (169, 293) and in most angiosperms, however, differentiating cells that have left the mitotic cycle continue to synthesize DNA and to double their chromosomes in endo cycles [endomitosis and endoreduplication; for reviews see (20, 96, 143, 289, 398, 405)]. Endo cycles result in endopolyploid nuclei. Endopolyploidy is not the exception, but the rule for differentiated plant cells. Butterfass (61) estimated that about 80% of the somatic cells of a plant, e.g. sugar beet, are endopolyploid.

The difference between the endomitotic and the endoreduplication cycle is of a morphological nature. The endomitotic cycle is characterized by some structural changes resembling mitotic transformation of the chromosomes (142). In angiosperms, mitosis is "curtailed" to endomitosis at very early prophase, the so-called dispersion stage or Z (*Zerstäubung*) phase, during which the heterochromatin is temporarily decondensed (20, 61, 143, 268, 272, 278, 288, 401, 402, 405). In the endoreduplication cycle any mitosis-like stage is omitted, and endo-G and endo-S periods follow each other. It must be emphasized first that somatic polyploidy may also be regularly reached via blocking of mitosis; such restitution cycles are very frequent in mammalian tissues, but they also occur in the anther tapetum, the endosperm, and the suspensor of several angiosperms (123, 267). Secondly, the occurrence of a mitosis with diplochromosomes is not a proof for the previous passage of the cell through an endoreduplication cycle, as uncritically stated in many papers (see discussion in 20, 283). The restitution cycle is apparently not under the same rigorous control as the endo cycles, and also has the disadvantage of possible irregularities that would accompany a disturbed mitosis.

Most plant tissues show a characteristic pattern of various degrees of endopolyploidy in their cells. The highest levels are found in cells of the ovule and of galls (Table 3). Since the examples of high endopolyploidy in animals are also known from tissues that nourish the embryo, e.g. trophoblast (279), and in glands (23, 141), some functional significance of endopolyploidy has been envisaged. DNA synthesis after the cessation of mitotic activity may be necessary for cell enlargement (69, 413) and for the higher rate of synthetic activity required by those specialized cells of glands, suspensors, endosperms, etc (26, 78, 280, 281), but this interpretation might not fit all cases (260). Another advantage of endomitosis may be that RNA synthesis

Table 3 Examples for high degrees of endopolyploidy in cells of the ovule and of galls in angiosperms

Species	Tissue	Degree (n)[a]	Reference
Quercus robur	Nutritive tissue of gall[b]	1,024	176
Tropaeolum majus	Integument	1,024	267
Tropaeolum majus	Embyro suspensor	1,024	267
Melampyrum pratense	Endosperm haustorium.	1,536	123
Plantago atrata	Endosperm haustorium	1,536	95
Echinocystis lobata	Endosperm	3,072	407
Phaseolus vulgaris	Embryo suspensor	4,096	269
Poa nemoralis	Nutritive tissue of gall[c]	4,096	177
Scilla bifolia	Fruit elaiosome	4,096	377
Phaseolus coccineus	Embryo suspensor	8,192	43
Arum maculatum	Endosperm haustorium	24,576	123

[a] (n) indicates the number of chromosome sets per nucleus, as estimated by DNA measurements or volumetry.
[b] Induced by the gall-wasp *Andricus marginalis*.
[c] Induced by the gall-mite *Mayetiola poae*.

is not discontinued by the onset of any chromosome coiling as in mitosis (134, 280), and so it allows an uninterrupted course of differentiation. In general, an incompatibility between proliferation and differentiation has been found for several tissues (66). Therefore, endopolyploidization is a way to liberate a cell from autosynthetic activities for the development of heterosynthetic (cell-specific) functions. Finally, there is some evidence that growth through endopolyploidization is more economical than growth by mitotic proliferation of cells (less cell wall synthesis, no spindle formation, no chromosome condensation and decondensation, no breakdown and reconstruction of nuclear envelope, etc), and there is evidently more immunity from disturbances that would upset mitotic activity (274, 405). Probably polyploidy also has some advantage for photosynthesis (61, 161).

Endomitotic nuclei have a tendency to develop chromatin structures different from those in the diploid ancestor nuclei (143, 288, 403). The most striking structures occur when the sister chromosomes, produced by a succession of endo cycles, do not separate from each other, but stay together to form giant (or polytene) chromosomes (for plants see 20, 43, 196, 269, 285, 288, 289, 404, 405). Details cannot be given here, but, in general, the scheme of nuclear organization described in the preceding paragraphs is also valid for endopolyploid and polytene nuclei. But the latter display structures and functions much clearer due to their enormous size and activity (196, 270, 271, 273, 285, 406; Figure 2). As the various size of functional structures shows, differential usage of the multiple templates is a common way of regulating the relative quantities of gene products in endopolyploid nuclei.

In addition to endo cycles with complete DNA replication, nuclei may also undergo partial DNA synthesis. Recently there has been a spate of publications on differential DNA replication, probably because the "dogma of DNA constancy" hindered their publication in earlier years. Nuclear cycles with differential DNA replication can be understood as progressive reductions of endo cycles. If all but a small portion of the genome (normally heterochromatin or satellite DNA is stricken) is replicated in an endo-S period, this is referred to as underreplication. If, on the other hand, only a short DNA sequence (e.g. the ribosomal genes) is replicated, this is termed extra-replication or DNA amplification (Figure 3). A

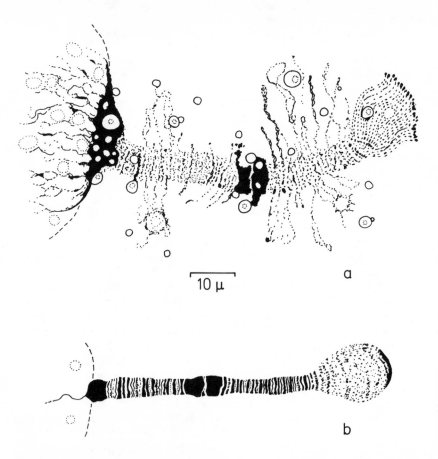

Figure 2 Camera lucida drawing of a nucleolus organizing polytene chromosome of the *Phaseolus* suspensor, illustrating the relationships between gene activity, functional chromatin condensation, and heterochromatin: (*a*) active polytene chromosome (high rate of RNA synthesis); (*b*) inactive chromosome (very low rate of RNA synthesis). In both states the heterochromatin is condensed, except the nucleolus organizing region, which is decondensed in *a*; the euchromatin is decondensed in *a*, displaying separated chromomeres and loops which represent revealed chromomeres, but the euchromatin is functionally condensed in *b*, forming bands by the fusion of neighboring chromomeres. Note presence in *a* and absence in *b* of functional structures and micronucleoli. For details see (285).

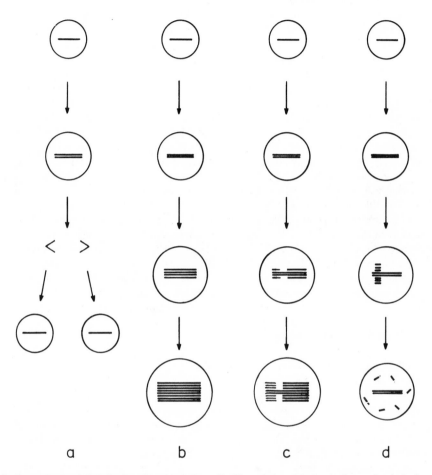

Figure 3 Possible behavior of nuclei during cell differentiation. The bar indicates the *diploid* chromosome complement. (*a*) The result of the mitotic cycle are two nuclei with identical genomes. Differentiation is brought about by specific activation of the one or the other gene. (*b*) If a nucleus undergoes a series of endocyles during differentiation of the cell, an endopolyploid nucleus arises with multiple chromosome sets, and therefore with DNA templates that can be used differentially (polyteny is just a special morphological expression of endopolyploidy). (*c*) A nucleus which underwent underreplication cycles arrives at a state characterized by changes in the relative amounts of various templates. (*d*) DNA amplification (here shown to take place at the tetraploid level after one endocycle) leads to the reversible increase of a certain template. When this template is no longer needed it is degraded like "metabolic DNA." [According to Nagl (286).]

further difference between under- and extra-replication is the irreversibility of the former and the transitory character of the latter (58, 287).

In plants, underreplication of repetitive DNA was shown to take place in elongating cells of pea epicotyls (412), during fruit maturation in Cucurbitaceae (315), and polytenization of the suspensor cell nuclei in *Phaseolus* (237). Amplification is best known from animal oocytes and sciarid salivary glands, but recent cytological and biochemical studies revealed that it also occurs in plants, more frequently than thought earlier (examples listed in 58 and 287). The most striking examples have been found in the suspensor polytene chromosomes of *Phaseolus* (13, 237), in tissue cultures of *Nicotiana* (295, 309) and *Crepis* (339), and in aseptic protocorm cultures of the orchid *Cymbidium* (276, 292). Underreplication and amplification apparently are a further adaptation for the economy of DNA synthesis required for differentiation (see discussion in 20, 286). Thus nuclear organization may change dramatically during cell differentiation, leading to new balances of genes in various cells of a multicellular individual.

The reader's attention will also be drawn to the apparent involvement of hormones in the control of nuclear organization. Several experiments have shown that endopolyploidization and amplification are regulated by the hormonal balance available to a cell (210, 218, 275, 277, 286, 292). On the other hand, a cell with an endopolyploid or differentially replicated nucleus displays a changed pattern of gene expression compared with a diploid cell. Thus hormone-directed differentiation may well be mediated in part via changes of nuclear organization (see also 210).

VII. CONCLUDING REMARKS

In these concluding remarks, I will point out those aspects of the complex organization of the cell nucleus which are the most important for the evolution and differentiation of higher organisms, according to my mind. In the foregoing paragraphs I have tried to discuss several levels of nuclear organization from different points of view, and the reader has certainly realized that many findings still can be interpreted controversially. Since not all the arguments could be given in detail, sufficient references have been included to cover any further information.

The organization of the cell nucleus is based on two parameters, variety and redundancy. The development of a high number of repetitive, noninformative DNA sequences mainly located adjacent to each unique, protein-coding gene, evidently is a prerequisite for the complex control of differential gene activity. The DNA is not, however, the sole vehicle of the genetic apparatus in eukaryotes, but rather it is the chromatin. The association of oligomers of histones with the DNA results in a tertiary structure or superhelix in discrete regions of the DNA, appearing, after appropriate preparation, as chromatin subunits (nucleosomes) like beads on a string. In toto, the superhelix corresponds to the 100 Å fiber in electron microphotos, while the 200 Å fiber is the expression of a quaternary structure, the coiled supercoil, which is induced by the very lysine-rich histone fraction f1.

The result of histone association and supercoiling is not only a tight packaging of long DNA molecules into relatively short chromatin fibers and chromosomes, but also a general and unspecific repression of the genome—another prerequisite for the differentiation of tissues and organs, in which only a few genes are allowed to be transcribed. The selective activation of genes is under control of acidic chromosomal proteins (hertones) which act as polyanions, thus removing the histones from appropriate stretches of the DNA.

The interspersion of repetitive and unique sequences in the DNA is expressed at the chromosomal level by the formation of chromomeres, which are the units of transcription and replication. Chromomeres are transcribed in toto, but the repetitive, noncoding part is degraded during the procession and polyadenylation of the hnRNA to the polysomal mRNA, and might confer some regulatory function for the stability or translation of the mRNA. The size of the chromomeres depends on the amount of repetitive DNA belonging to them, and this determines the duration of DNA replication and the mitotic cell cycle and the minimum generation time of the species. The functions of the repetitive DNAs, satellite DNAs, and heterochromatin-DNAs, therefore, can also be understood on the basis of their "nucleotypic" effects.

The largest subunits of the nucleus are the chromosomes. In the process of differentiation, large portions of the chromosomes apparently must be inactivated more efficiently than can be done by supercoiling. This is achieved by a cross-linking of the chromatin fibrils. As in the case of mitotic chromosome condensation, enzymatic modification of the histones, particularly of f1, may play a key role in condensation-decondensation and inactivation-activation processes.

In addition, differentiation is accompanied by changes in nuclear organization. The most common change is endopolyploidization instead of mitotic proliferation. Endopolyploidization is less sensitive to disturbances, allows a more economical growth, and is a differential usage of multiple DNA templates. Thus endopolyploidy and its special case polyteny provide the basis for high synthetic capacity and fine modulation of gene activity.

Probably much more frequently than is known today, differences in the capacity and modulation of gene activity are already realized at the level of the DNA template through differential DNA replication (under- and extra-replication). Thus maturing and mature cells can possess nuclei with nonidentical amounts and combinations of genetic information and control sequences.

Finally, I wish to mention some unsolved problems. It is, for instance, not yet known what the function of the bulk DNA really is; there are many suggestions and models available, but only a few facts. Further, the interactions between histones, hertones, hormones, and enzymes modifying the chromosomal proteins are only poorly understood, particularly in plants. Actually, nobody knows whether, for example, repetitive DNAs and histone modifications have completely the same functions in all animal phyla and lower and higher plants. The question of how nucleohistone fibrils are organized in condensed interphase and mitotic chromosomes is not yet answered. It is also not certain whether endopolyploidy is the result of differentiation, stabilized because of its high selective advantage, or a prerequisite of the mode of differentiation found in angiosperms, insects, and other groups. The control and the particular role of polyteny, underreplication, and amplication is still open to speculation. Therefore, in spite of the recent progress in karyology, this is still a large field for continuing research.

Literature Cited

1. Adesnik, M., Salditt, M., Thomas, W., Darnell, J. E. 1972. *J. Mol. Biol.* 71:21–30
2. Adler, A. J., Langan, T. A., Fasman, G. D. 1972. *Arch. Biochem. Biophys.* 153:769–77
3. Allfrey, V. G., Inoue, A., Karn, J., Johnson, E. M., Vidali, G. 1974. *Cold Spring Harbor Symp. Quant. Biol.* 38:785–801
4. Allfrey, V. G., Littau, V. C., Mirsky, A. E. 1963. *Proc. Natl. Acad. Sci. USA* 49:414–21
5. Ansevin, A. T., MacDonald, K. K., Smith, C. E., Hnilica, L. S. 1975. *J. Biol. Chem.* 250:281–89
6. Arcos-Terán, L. 1972. *Chromosoma* 37:233–96
7. Arnold, E. A., Yawn, D. H., Brown, D. G., Wyllie, R. C., Coffey, D. S. 1972. *J. Cell Biol.* 53:737–57
8. Artman, M., Roth, J. S. 1971. *J. Mol. Biol.* 60:291–301
9. Ashley, T., Wagenaar, E. B. 1972. *Can. J. Genet. Cytol.* 14:716–17
10. Ibid 1974. 16:61–76
11. Atlan, H. 1974. *J. Theor. Biol.* 45:295–304
12. Auer, G., Zetterberg, A. 1972. *Exp. Cell Res.* 75:245–53
13. Avanzi, S., Durante, M., Cionini, P. G., D'Amato, F. 1972. *Chromosoma* 39:191–203
14. Bachmann, K., Harrington, B. A., Craig, J. P. 1972. *Chromosoma* 37:405–16
15. Bachmann, K., Rheinsmith, E. L. 1973. *Chromosoma* 43:225–36
16. Bahr, G. F., Golomb, H. M. 1974. *Chromosoma* 46:247–54
17. Bajaj, S., Fellenberg, G. 1972. *Z. Pflanzenphysiol.* 68:178–80
18. Baldwin, J. P., Boseley, P. G., Bradbury, E. M., Ibel, K. 1975. *Nature* 253:245–49
19. Barlow, P. W. 1972. *Cytobios* 6:55–79
20. Barlow, P., Nagl, W. 1976. *Endopolyploidy and Polyteny in Differentiation.* Berlin, Heidelberg, New York: Springer. In press
21. Barrett, T., Maryanka, D., Hamlyn, P. H., Gould, H. J. 1974. *Proc. Natl. Acad. Sci. USA* 71:5057–61
22. Bartley, J., Chalkley, R. 1973. *Biochemistry* 12:468–74
23. Beermann, W. 1962. *Protoplasmatologia* VI/D. Vienna: Springer
24. Beermann, W., Ed. 1972. *Developmental Studies on Giant Chromosomes,*

1–33. Berlin, Heidelberg, New York: Springer. 227 pp.
25. Bennett, M. D. 1972. *Proc. R. Soc. London B* 181:109–35
26. Bennett, M. D. 1973. *Brookhaven Symp. Biol.* 25:344–66
27. Bennett, M. D., Finch, R. A., Smith, J. B., Rao, M. K. 1973. *Proc. R. Soc. London B* 183:301–19
28. Berlowitz, L., Kitchin, R., Pallotta, D. 1972. *Biochim. Biophys. Acta* 262:160–68
29. Bianchi, N. O. 1973. *Experientia* 29:1301
30. Bick, M. D., Huang, H. L., Thomas, C. A. Jr. 1973. *J. Mol. Biol.* 77:75–84
31. Billett, M. A., Barry, J. M. 1974. *Eur. J. Biochem.* 49:477–84
32. Birnstiel, M. 1967. *Ann. Rev. Plant Physiol.* 18:25–58
33. Birnstiel, M., Chipchase, M., Speirs, J. 1971. *Prog. Nucleic Acid Res. Mol. Biol.* 11:351–89
34. Birnstiel, M., Telford, J., Weinberg, E., Stafford, D. 1974. *Proc. Natl. Acad. Sci. USA* 71:2900–4
35. Birnstiel, M., Wallace, H., Sirlin, J. L., Fischberg, M. 1966. *Natl. Cancer Inst. Monogr.* 23:431–76
36. Blumenthal, A. B., Kriegstein, H. J., Hogness, D. S. 1974. *Cold Spring Harbor Symp. Quant. Biol.* 38:205–23
37. Bonner, J., Dahmus, M. E., Fambrough, D., Huang, R. C., Marushige, K., Tuan, Y. H. 1968. *Science* 159:47–56
38. Bonner, J., Garrard, W. T. 1974. *Life Sci.* 14:209–21
39. Bonner, J., Wu, J. R. 1973. *Proc. Natl. Acad. Sci. USA* 70:535–37
40. Bornkamm, G. W., Sonnenbichler, J. 1973. *Chromosoma* 43:261–68
41. Boss, J. 1972. *Experientia* 28:483–84
42. Bradbury, E. M., Inglis, R. J., Matthews, H. R. 1974. *Nature* 247:257–61
43. Brady, T. 1973. *Cell Differ.* 2:65–75
44. Bram, S. 1974. *Cold Spring Harbor Symp. Quant. Biol.* 38:83–86
45. Bram, S., Baudy, P., Butler-Browne, G., Ibel, K. 1974. *Biochimie* 56:1339–41
46. Bram, S., Butler-Browne, G., Baudy, P., Ibel, K. 1975. *Proc. Natl. Acad. Sci. USA* 71:1043–45
47. Brandhorst, B. P., McConkey, E. H. 1974. *J. Mol. Biol.* 85:451–63
48. Brasch, K., Setterfield, G. 1974. *Exp. Cell Res.* 83:175–85

49. Britten, R. J. 1969. *Problems in Biology: RNA in Development,* ed. E. W. Hanley, 187–212. Salt Lake City: Univ. Utah Press
50. Britten, R. J. 1972. *Brookhaven Symp. Biol.* 23:80–94
51. Britten, R. J., Davidson, E. H. 1969. *Science* 165:349–57
52. Britten, R. J., Kohne, D. E. 1968. *Science* 161:529–40
53. Britten, R. J., Smith, J. 1970. *Carnegie Inst. Washington Yearb.* 68:376–86
54. Bross, K., Krone, W. 1972. *Humangenetik* 14:137–41
55. Brown, D. D., Sugimoto, K. 1973. *J. Mol. Biol.* 78:397–415
56. Brown, D. D., Sugimoto, K. 1974. *Cold Spring Harbor Symp. Quant. Biol.* 38:501–5
57. Brown, S. W. 1966. *Science* 151:417–25
58. Buiatti, M. 1976. *Applied and Fundamental Aspects of Plant Cell and Tissue Culture,* ed. J. Reinert, S. Bajaj. Berlin, New York: Springer. In press
59. Burr, F. A., Evert, R. F. 1973. *Protoplasma* 78:81–97
60. Bustin, M. 1973. *Nature New Biol.* 245:207–9
61. Butterfass, T. 1966. *Mitt. Max-Planck Ges.* 1:47–58
62. Callan, H. G. 1967. *J. Cell Sci.* 2:1–7
63. Callan, H. G. 1972. *Proc. R. Soc. London B* 181:19–41
64. Callan, H. G. 1974. *Cold Spring Harbor Symp. Quant. Biol.* 38:195–203
65. Callan, H. G., Taylor, J. H. 1968. *J. Cell Sci.* 3:615–25
66. Cameron, I. L., Jeter, J. R. Jr. 1971. See Ref. 68, 191–222
67. Cameron, I. L., Jeter, J. R. Jr. 1975. *Acidic Proteins of the Nucleus.* New York: Academic. 343 pp.
68. Cameron, I. L., Padilla, G. M., Zimmermann, A. M., Eds. 1971. *Developmental Aspects of the Cell Cycle.* New York, London: Academic
69. Capesius, I., Stöhr, M. 1974. *Protoplasma* 82:147–53
70. Capesius, I., Bierweiler, B., Bachmann, K., Rücker, W., Nagl, W. 1975. *Biochim. Biophys. Acta* 395:67–73
71. Cavalier-Smith, T. 1974. *Nature* 250:467–70
72. Chiarelli, B. 1974. *Boll. Zool. Ital.* 41:123–25
73. Chooi, W. Y. 1971. *Genetics* 68:195–211
74. Christiansen, C., Bak, A. L., Stenderup, A., Christiansen, G. 1971. *Nature New Biol.* 231:176–77

75. Clark, R. J., Felsenfeld, G. 1972. *Nature New Biol.* 240:226–29
76. Clark, V. M., Lilley, D. M. J., Howarth, W. O., Richards, B. M., Pardon, J. F. 1974. *Nucleic Acids Res.* 1:865–80
77. Clarkson, S. G., Birnstiel, M. L., Serra, V. 1973. *J. Mol. Biol.* 79:391–410
78. Clutter, M., Brady, T., Walbot, V., Sussex, I. 1974. *J. Cell Biol.* 63:1097–1102
79. Colman, O. D., Stockert, J. C. 1970. *Cienc. Invest. Argent.* 26:509–11
80. Comings, D. E. 1972. *Adv. Hum. Genet.* 3:237–431
81. Comings, D. E. 1974. *Chromosomes and Cancer,* ed. J. German, 95–133. New York: Wiley
82. Comings, D. E. 1974. *The Cell Nucleus,* ed. H. Busch, 1:537–63. New York, London: Academic. 667 pp.
83. Comings, D. E., Mattoccia, E. 1972. *Exp. Cell Res.* 71:113–31
84. Comings, D. E., Okada, T. A. 1970. *Exp. Cell Res.* 62:293–302
85. Ibid. 63:62–68
86. Comings, D. E., Okada, T. A. 1973. *J. Mol. Biol.* 75:609–18
87. Comings, D. E., Riggs, A. D. 1971. *Nature* 233:48–50
88. Cowden, R. R., Curtis, S. K. 1975. *J. Morphol.* 145:1–12
89. Crick, F. 1971. *Nature* 234:25–27
90. Crippa, M., Meza, I., Dina, D. 1974. *Cold Spring Harbor Symp. Quant. Biol.* 38:933–42
91. Cullis, C. A. 1973. *Nature* 243:315–16
92. Cullis, C. A. 1975. *Modification of the Information Content of Plant Cells,* ed. R. Markham, D. R. Davies, D. A. Hopwood, R. W. Horne, 27–36. Amsterdam, New York: North Holland, American Elsevier. 350 pp.
93. Cullis, C. A., Davies, D. R. 1974. *Chromosoma* 46:23–28
94. Cullis, C. A., Schweizer, D. 1974. *Chromosoma* 44:417–21
95. Czapska-Dziekanowska, D. 1965. *Acta Biol. Cracov. Ser. Bot.* 8:101–12
96. D'Amato, F. 1964. *Caryologia* 17:41–52
97. Daneholt, B. 1972. *Nature New Biol.* 240:229–32
98. Daneholt, B. 1975. *Cell* 4:1–9
99. Darnell, J. E., Jelinek, W. R., Molloy, G. R. 1973. *Science* 181:1215–21
100. Darnell, J. E., Philipson, L., Wall, R., Adesnik, M. 1971. *Science* 174:507–10
101. Davidson, E. H., Britten, R. J. 1973. *Q. Rev. Biol.* 48:565–613
102. Davidson, E. H., Hough, B. R., Amenson, C. S., Britten, R. J. 1973. *J. Mol. Biol.* 77:1–23

64   NAGL

103. Davidson, E. H., Hough, B. R., Klein, W. H., Britten, R. J. 1975. *Cell* 4:217–38
104. Davis, R. H., Wilson, R. B., Ebaldi, M. S. 1975. *Can. J. Biochem.* 53:101–5
105. De Lange, R. J., Fambrough, D. M., Smith, E. L., Bonner, J. 1969. *J. Biol. Chem.* 244:5669–79
106. Denhardt, D. T. 1972. *J. Theor. Biol.* 34:487–508
107. Desai, L. S., De Bault, L. E., Morrissey, G., Foley, G. E. 1972. *Chromosoma* 38:329–40
108. Deumling, B., Franke, W. W. 1972. *Hoppe-Seyler's Z. Physiol. Chem.* 353:287–97
109. Dina, D., Meza, I., Crippa, M. 1974. *Nature* 248:486–90
110. Du Praw, E. J. 1970. *DNA and Chromosomes.* New York: Holt, Rinehart & Winston
111. Du Praw, E. J. 1972. *Adv. Cell Mol. Biol.* 2:13–18
112. Du Praw, E. J., Bahr, G. F. 1969. *Acta Cytol.* 13:188–205
113. Dusenberg, R. L. 1975. *Biochim. Biophys. Acta* 378:363–77
114. Dutta, S. K. 1974. *Nucleic Acids Res.* 1:1411–20
115. Edwards, G. A., Endrizzi, J. E., Stein, R. 1974. *Chromosoma* 47:309–26
116. Elder, D. 1973. *J. Theor. Biol.* 39:673–75
117. Elgin, S. C. R., Bonner, J. 1973. *The Biochemistry of Gene Expression in Higher Organisms,* ed. J. K. Pollak, J. W. Lee, 141–63. Sidney: Aust. & N. Z. Book Co.
118. Elgin, S. C. R., Boyd, J. B., Hood, L. E., Wray, W., Wu, F. C. 1974. *Cold Spring Harbor Symp. Quant. Biol.* 38:821–33
119. Elgin, S. C. R., Froehner, S. C., Smart, J. E., Bonner, J. 1971. *Adv. Cell Mol. Biol.* 1:1–57
120. El-Lakany, M. H., Dugle, J. R. 1972. *Evolution* 26:427–34
121. Emmerich, G., Scharrer, Z. S. von, Stengel-Rukowski, S., Zang, K. D. 1973. *Humangenetik* 19:227–34
122. Engelhardt, P., Pusa, K. 1972. *Nature New Biol.* 240:163–66
123. Erbrich, P. 1965. *Cesterr. Bot. Z.* 112:197–262
124. Esponda, P., Giménez-Martín, G. 1971. *Experientia* 27:855–56
125. Evans, G. M., Rees, H. 1971. *Nature* 233:350–51
126. Evans, G. M., Rees, H., Snell, C. L., Sun, S. 1972. *Chromosomes Today* 3:24–31

127. Evans, L. S., Van't Hof, J. 1974. *Exp. Cell Res.* 87:259–64
128. Fabergé, A. C. 1974. *Cell Tissue Res.* 151:403–15
129. Fellenberg, G. 1971. *Planta* 100:347–56
130. Fellenberg, G. 1974. *Chromosomale Proteine.* Stuttgart: Ulmer
131. Flamm, W. G. 1972. *Int. Rev. Cytol.* 32:1–51
132. Flavell, R. B., Bennett, M. D., Smith, J. B., Smith, D. B. 1974. *Biochem. Genet.* 12:257–79
133. Flavell, R. B., Smith, D. B. 1976. *Cell.* In press
134. Flickinger, R. A., Daniel, J. C., Greene, R. F. 1970. *Nature* 228:557–59
135. Franke, W. W. 1974. *Philos. Trans. R. Soc. London, Ser. B* 268:67–93
136. Franke, W. W., Krien, S. 1972. *Naturwissenschaften* 59:37
137. Franke, W. W., Scheer, U. 1974. See Ref. 82, 219–347
138. Frenster, J. H. 1969. *Handbook of Molecular Cytology,* ed. A. Lima-de-Faria, 251–76. Amsterdam, London: North Holland
139. Fussell, C. P. 1975. *Chromosoma* 50:201–10
140. Gabbay, E. J., Sanford, K., Baxter, C. S., Kapicak, L. 1973. *Biochemistry* 12:4021–29
141. Gage, L. P. 1974. *J. Mol. Biol.* 86:97–108
142. Geitler, L. 1939. *Chromosoma* 1:1–22
143. Geitler, L. 1953. *Protoplasmatologia* VI /C. Wien: Springer
144. Georgiev, G. P. 1969. *J. Theor. Biol.* 25:473–90
145. Georgiev, G. P., Varshavsky, A. J., Ryskov, A. P., Church, R. B. 1974. *Cold Spring Harbor Symp. Quant. Biol.* 38:869–84
146. Gersh, E. S., Gersh, I. 1973. *Can. J. Genet. Cytol.* 15:509–22
147. Gillespie, D., Spiegelman S. 1965. *J. Mol. Biol.* 12:829–42
148. Gilmour, R. S., Paul, J. 1970. *FEBS Lett.* 9:242–44
149. Goepfert, D. 1975. *Chromosoma* 49:383–90
150. Goldberg, R. B., Bemis, W. P., Siegel, A. 1972. *Genetics* 72:253–66
151. Golomb, H. M., Bahr, G. F. 1973. *Lancet* 1973/I: 260
152. Golomb, H. M., Bahr, G. F. 1974. *Exp. Cell Res.* 84:79–87
153. Golomb, H. M., Bahr, G. F. 1974. *Chromosoma* 46:233–45
154. Gorovsky, M. A. 1970. *J. Cell Biol.* 47:631–36

155. Graham, D. E., Neufeld, B. R., Davidson, E. H., Britten, R. J. 1974. *Cell* 1:127–37
156. Grassé, P. P., Hollande, A., Cachon, J., Cachon-Enjument, M. 1965. *C. R. Acad. Sci. Paris D* 260:1743–47
157. Gregor, D., Reinert, J., Matsumoto, H. 1974. *Plant Cell Physiol.* 15:875–81
158. Greilhuber, J. 1973. *Oesterr. Bot. Z.* 121:1–11
159. Grieshaber-Scheubel, D., Fellenberg, G. 1972. *Z. Pflanzenphysiol.* 66:106–12
160. Grossbach, U. 1969. *Chromosoma* 28: 136–87
161. Guern, M., Bourdu, R., Roux, M. 1975. *Photosynthetica* 9:40–51
162. Guillé, E., Grisvard, J. 1971. *Biochem. Biophys. Res. Comm.* 44:1402–9
163. Guillé, E., Quetier, F. 1973. *Prog. Biophys. Mol. Biol.* 27:123–42
164. Gurley, L. R., Walters, R. A., Tobey, R. A. 1974. *J. Cell Biol.* 60:356–64
165. Haapala, O. K., Soyer, M.-O. 1973. *Nature New Biol.* 244:195–97
166. Haapala, O. K., Soyer, M.-O. 1974. *Hereditas* 78:146–50
167. Haapala, O. K., Soyer, M.-O. 1975. *Hereditas* 80:185–94
168. Hackett, P. B., Sauerbier, W. 1975. *J. Mol. Biol.* 91:235–56
169. Hallet, J.-N. 1970. *C. R. Acad. Sci. Paris D* 271:2110–13
170. Hanania, N., Harel, J. 1973. *Biochimie* 55:357–59
171. Hanlon, S., Johnson, R. S., Chan, A. 1974. *Biochemistry* 13:3963–71
172. Harrisson, C. M. H. 1971. *Tissue & Cell* 3:523–50
173. Henderson, A. S., Warburton, D., Atwood, K. C. 1973. *Nature* 245:95–97
174. Heneen, W. K., Nichols, W. W. 1972. *Cytogenetics* 11:153–64
175. Hennig, W. 1968. *J. Mol. Biol.* 38:227–39
176. Hesse, M. 1968. *Oesterr. Bot. Z.* 115:34–83
177. Ibid 1969. 117:411–25
178. Heumann, H.-G. 1974. *Chromosoma* 47:133–46
179. Hewish, D. R., Burgoyne, L. A. 1973. *Biochem. Biophys. Res. Commun.* 52:504–10
180. Hjelm, R. P. Jr., Huang, R. C. C. 1974. *Biochemistry* 13:5275–83
181. Holmes, D. S., Bonner, J. 1974. *Proc. Natl. Acad. Sci. USA* 71:1108–12
182. Holmes, D. S., Mayfield, J. E., Sander, G., Bonner, J. 1972. *Science* 177:72–74
183. Holt, T. K. 1971. *Chromosoma* 32: 428–35
184. Hotta, Y., Miksche, J. P. 1974. *Cell Differ.* 2:299–305
185. Housman, D., Huberman, J. A. 1975. *J. Mol. Biol.* 94:173–81
186. Howell, S. H. 1972. *Nature New Biol.* 240:264–67
187. Hsu, T. C. 1973. *Ann. Rev. Genet.* 7:153–76
188. Huberman, J. A. 1973. *Ann. Rev. Biochem.* 42:355–78
189. Huberman, J. A., Riggs, A. 1968. *J. Mol. Biol.* 32:327–41
190. Huberman, J. A., Tsai, A., Deich, R. A. 1973. *Nature* 241:32–36
191. Infante, A. A., Nauta, R., Gilbert, S., Hobart, P., Firshein, W. 1973. *Nature New Biol.* 242:5–8
192. Ingle, J., Sinclair, J. 1972. *Nature* 235:30–32
193. Ingle, J., Timmis, J. N., Sinclair, J. 1975. *Plant Physiol.* 55:496–501
194. Itzhaki, R. F. 1971. *Biochem. J.* 125:221–24
195. Itzhaki, R. F. 1974. *Eur. J. Biochem.* 47:27–33
196. Ivanovskaya, H. V. 1973. *Tsitologiya* 15:1445–52
197. Jaffray, J. Y., Geneix, A. 1974. *Humangenetik* 25:119–26
198. Jelinek, W., Adesnik, M., Salditt, M., Sheiness, D., Wall, R., Molloy, G., Philipson, L., Darnell, J. E. 1973. *J. Mol. Biol.* 75:515–32
199. Jelinek, W., Molloy, G., Salditt, M., Wall, R., Sheiness, D., Darnell, J. E. 1974. *Cold Spring Harbor Symp. Quant. Biol.* 38:891–98
200. Johns, E. W. 1972. *Nature New Biol.* 237:87–88
201. Johnson, J. D., Douvas, A. S., Bonner, J. 1974. *Int. Rev. Cytol. Suppl.* 4:273–362
202. Judd, B. H., Young, M. W. 1974. *Cold Spring Harbor Symp. Quant. Biol.* 38:573–79
203. Juricek, D. K. 1975. *Chromosoma* 50:313–26
204. Kadohama, N., Turkington, R. W. 1973. *Can. J. Biochem.* 51:1167–76
205. Kaltsikes, P. J. 1971. *Can. J. Genet. Cytol.* 13:656–62
206. Kavenoff, R., Zimm, B. H. 1973. *Chromosoma* 41:1–27
207. Kay, R. R., Haines, M. E., Johnston, I. R. 1971. *FEBS Lett.* 16:233–36
208. Kaye, J. S. 1969. See Ref. 138, 361–80
209. Kedes, L. H., Birnstiel, M. L. 1971. *Nature New Biol.* 230:165–69
210. Kessler, B. 1973. See Ref. 117, 333–56
211. Keyl, H. G. 1965. *Chromosoma* 17: 139–80

212. Kleiman, L., Huang, R. C. C. 1972. *J. Mol. Biol.* 64:1–8
213. Kolata, G. B. 1973. *Science* 182:1009–11
214. Kornberg, R. D. 1974. *Science* 184:868–71
215. Kornberg, R. D., Thomas, O. J. 1974. *Science* 184:865–68
216. Kostraba, N. C., Montagna, R. A., Wang, T. Y. 1975. *J. Biol. Chem.* 250:1548–55
217. Kostraba, N. C., Wang, T. Y. 1972. *Biochim. Biophys. Acta* 262:169–80
218. Kovoor, A., Melet, D. 1972. *Nucleic Acids and Proteins in Higher Plants,* ed. G. L. Farkas, 29–32. Budapest: Académiai Kiadó
219. Kraemer, P. M., Deaven, L. L., Crissman, H. A., Van Dilla, M. A. 1972. *Adv. Cell Mol. Biol.* 2:47–108
220. Lafontaine, J. G. 1968. *Ultrastructure in Biological Systems. III. The Nucleus,* ed. A. J. Dalton, F. Haguenau, 151–96. New York: Academic
221. Lafontaine, J. G. 1974. See Ref. 82, 149–85
222. Laird, C. D. 1971. *Chromosoma* 32:378–406
223. Lambert, B. 1973. *Nature* 242:51–53
224. Lampert, F. 1969. *Naturwissenschaften* 56:629–33
225. Lampert, F. 1971. *Humangenetik* 13:285–95
226. Lampert, F. 1971. *Nature New Biol.* 234:187–88
227. Lampert, F. 1971. *Humangenetik* 13:285–95
228. Lampert, F., Lampert, P. 1970. *Humangenetik* 11:9–17
229. Lang, D. 1973. *J. Mol. Biol.* 78:247–54
230. LeFevre, G., Jr. 1974. *Cold Spring Harbor Symp. Quant. Biol.* 38:591–99
231. Levy, S., Simpson, R. T. 1973. *Nature* 241:139–41
232. Lewin, B. 1974. *Gene Expression-2. Eukaryotic Chromosomes.* London: Wiley. 467 pp.
233. Lewin, B. 1975. *Cell* 4:11–20
234. Ibid, 77–93
235. Libby, P. R. 1972. *Biochem. J.* 130:663–69
236. Lima-de-Faria, A., Jaworska, H. 1972. *Hereditas* 70:39–58
237. Lima-de-Faria, A., Pero, R., Avanzi, S., Durante, M., Stahle, U., D'Amato, F., Granström, H. 1975. *Hereditas* 79:5–20
238. Lindigkeit, R., Bellmann, K., Fenske, H., Böttger, M., Holtzhauer, M., Eichhorn, I. 1974. *FEBS Lett.* 44:146–52
239. Lishanskaya, A. I., Mosevitskii, M. I. 1975. *Biochem. Biophys. Res. Commun.* 62:822–29
240. Littau, V. C., Burdick, C. J., Allfrey, V. G., Mirsky, A. E. 1965. *Proc. Natl. Acad. Sci. USA* 54:1204–12
241. Lodish, H. F., Jacobson, A., Firtel, R., Alton, T., Tuchman, J. 1974. *Proc. Natl. Acad. Sci. USA* 71:5103–8
242. Lohr, D., Van Holde, K. E. 1975. *Science* 188:165–66
243. Louie, A. J., Candido, E. P. M., Dixon, G. H. 1974. *Cold Spring Harbor Symp. Quant. Biol.* 38:803–19
244. Lukanidin, E. M., Zalmanzon, E. S., Komaromi, L., Samarina, O. P., Georgiev, G. P. 1972. *Nature New Biol.* 238:193–97
245. Lyon, M. F. 1968. *Ann. Rev. Genet.* 2:31–52
246. Lyon, M. F. 1972. *Biol. Rev.* 47:1–35
247. Macgregor, H. C. 1968. *J. Cell Sci.* 3:437–44
248. Maher, B. P., Fox, D. P. 1973. *Nature New Biol.* 245:170–72
249. Mandel, M., Marmur, J. 1968. *Methods Enzymol.* 12 B:195–206
250. Manning, J. E., Schmid, C. W., Davidson, N. 1975. *Cell* 4:141–55
251. Marquardt, H. 1971. *Handbuch Allgem. Pathol.* 2/II/1, ed. H. W. Altmann, 1–163. Berlin, Heidelberg, New York: Springer. 765 pp.
252. Mayfield, J. E., Bonner, J. 1971. *Proc. Natl. Acad. Sci. USA* 68:2652–55
253. Ibid 1972. 69:7–10
254. McCarthy, B. J., Nishiura, J. T., Doeneche, D., Nasser, D. S., Johnson, C. B. 1974. *Cold Spring Harbor Symp. Quant. Biol.* 38:763–71
255. McGhee, J. D., Engel, J. D. 1975. *Nature* 254:449–50
256. McGill, M., Pathak, S., Hsu, T. C. 1974. *Chromosoma* 47:157–67
257. Miksche, J. P. 1971. *Chromosoma* 32:343–52
258. Miller, O. L. Jr., Beatty, B. R. 1969. *J. Cell. Physiol.* 74, Suppl. 1:225–32
259. Miller, O. L. Jr., Beatty, B. R., Hamkalo, B. A., Thomas, C. A. Jr. 1970. *Cold Spring Harbor Symp. Quant. Biol.* 35:505–12
260. Millerd, A., Spencer, D. 1974. *Aust. J. Plant Physiol.* 1:331–41
261. Mirsky, A. E., Silverman, B. 1972. *Proc. Natl. Acad. Sci. USA* 69:2115–19
262. Mohan, J., Flavell, R. B. 1974. *Genetics* 76:33–44
263. Molloy, G. R., Darnell, J. E. 1973. *Biochemistry* 12:2324–30
264. Molloy, G. R., Jelinek, W., Salditt, M., Darnell, J. E. 1974. *Cell* 1:43–53

265. Molnár, J., Juhász, P. 1972. *Acta Biochim. Biophys. Acad. Sci. Hung.* 7:195–206
266. Moutschen, J., Degraeve, N., Monfort, B. 1972. *Cytologia* 37:119–30
267. Nagl, W. 1962. *Oesterr. Bot. Z.* 109:431–94
268. Ibid 1968. 115:322–53
269. Nagl, W. 1969. *Nature* 221:70–71
270. Nagl, W. 1969. *Naturwissenschaften* 56:221–22
271. Nagl, W. 1969. *Chromosoma* 28:85–91
272. Nagl, W. 1970. *Caryologia* 23:71–78
273. Nagl, W. 1970. *J. Cell Sci.* 6:87–107
274. Nagl, W. 1970. *Z. Pflanzenphysiol.* 63:316–26
275. Nagl, W. 1971. *Z. Naturforsch.* 26b:1390–91
276. Nagl, W. 1972. *Cytobios* 5:145–54
277. Nagl, W. 1972. *Am. J. Bot.* 59:346–51
278. Nagl, W. 1972. *Chromosomes Today* 3:17–23
279. Nagl, W. 1972. *Experientia* 28:217–18
280. Nagl, W. 1973. *Chromosoma* 44:203–12
281. Nagl, W. 1973. *Bull. Soc. Bot. Fr.* 1973:289–302
282. Nagl, W. 1973. *Cytobiologie* 8:140–45
283. Nagl, W. 1974. *Dev. Biol.* 39:342–46
284. Nagl, W. 1974. *Nature* 249:53–54
285. Nagl, W. 1974. *Z. Pflanzenphysiol.* 73:1–44
286. Nagl, W. 1974. *Tissue Culture and Plant Science 1974*, ed. H. E. Street, 19–42. London, New York: Academic. 502 pp.
287. Nagl, W. 1975. *Prog. Bot.* 37:186–210
288. Nagl, W. 1976. *Mechanisms and Control of Cell Division*, ed. T. L. Rost, E. M. Gifford Jr. Stroudsburg, Pa: Dowden, Hutchison & Ross. In press
289. Nagl, W. 1976. *Zellkern und Zellzyklen.* Stuttgart: Ulmer. In press
290. Nagl, W., Ehrendorfer, F. 1973. *Oesterr. Bot. Z.* 121:165–69
291. Nagl, W., Ehrendorfer, F. 1974. *Plant Syst. Evol.* 123:35–54
292. Nagl, W., Hendon, J., Rücker, W. 1972. *Cell Differ.* 1:229–37
293. Nagl, W., Ullmann, H. 1973. *Oesterr. Bot. Z.* 121:99–105
294. Nur, U. 1973. *Chromosoma* 40:263–67
295. Nuti Ronchi, V., Martini, G., Parenti, R., Geri, C., Giorgi, L., Grisvard, J. 1974. *Third Int. Congr. Plant Tissue Cell Cult., Leicester.* Abstr. No. 136
296. O'Brien, S. J. 1973. *Nature New Biol.* 242:52–54
297. Ohba, Y. 1966. *Biochim. Biophys. Acta* 123:84–90
298. Ohno, S. 1970. *Evolution by Gene Duplication.* New York: Springer
299. Oishi, M., Sueoka, N. 1965. *Proc. Natl. Acad. Sci. USA* 54:483–91
300. Olenov, Yu. M. 1974. *Tsitologiya* 16:403–19
301. Olins, A. L., Carlson, R. D., Olins, D. E. 1975. *J. Cell Biol.* 64:528–37
302. Olins, A. L., Olins, D. E. 1974. *Science* 183:330–32
303. Oosterhof, D. K., Hozier, J. C., Rill, R. L. 1975. *Proc. Natl. Acad. Sci. USA* 72:633–37
304. Oudet, P., Gross-Bellard, M., Chambon, P. 1975. *Cell* 4:281–300
305. Pardon, J. F., Richards, B. M., Cotter, R. I. 1974. *Cold Spring Harbor Symp. Quant. Biol.* 38:75–81
306. Pardon, J. F., Wilkins, M. H. F. 1972. *J. Mol. Biol.* 68:115–24
307. Pardue, M. L., Gall, J. G. 1970. *Science* 168:1356–8
308. Pardue, M. L., Gall, J. G. 1972. *Chromosomes Today* 3:47–52
309. Parenti, R., Guillé, E., Grisvard, J., Durante, M., Giorgi, L., Buiatti, M. 1973. *Nature New Biol.* 246:237–39
310. Patthy, L., Smith, E. L., Johnson, J. 1973. *J. Biol. Chem.* 248:6834–40
311. Paul, J. 1972. *Nature* 238:444–46
312. Paul, J., More, I. A. R. 1973. *Exp. Cell Res.* 82:399–410
313. Pays, E., Ronsse, A. 1975. *Biochem. Biophys. Res. Commun.* 62:862–67
314. Peacock, W. J. 1973. See Ref. 117, 3–20
315. Pearson, G. G., Timmis, J. N., Ingle, J. 1974. *Chromosoma* 45:281–94
316. Pelc, S. R. 1972. *Int. Rev. Cytol.* 32:327–55
317. Pelling, C. 1966. *Proc. R. Soc. London B* 164:279–89
318. Petes, Th. D., Newlon, C. S., Byers, B., Fangman, W. L. 1974. *Cold Spring Harbor Symp. Quant. Biol.* 38:9–16
319. Pipkin, J. L., Larson, D. A. 1973. *Exp. Cell Res.* 79:28–42
320. Pooley, A. S., Pardon, J. F., Richards, B. M. 1974. *J. Mol. Biol.* 85:533–49
321. Prescott, D. M., Murti, K. G., Bostock, C. J. 1973. *Nature* 242:576–600
322. Price, H. J., Bachmann, K. 1975. *Am. J. Bot.* 62:262–67
323. Price, H. J., Sparrow, A. H., Nauman, A. F. 1973. *Brookhaven Symp. Biol.* 25:390–421
324. Price, H. J., Sparrow, A. H., Nauman, A. F. 1973. *Experientia* 29:1028–29
325. Prokofieva-Beligovskaya, A. A. 1971. *Tsitologiya* 13:679–92
326. Pyeritz, R. E., Thomas, C. A. Jr. 1973. *J. Mol. Biol.* 77:57–73
327. Rae, P. M. M. 1972. *Adv. Cell Mol. Biol.* 2:109–49

328. Ranjekar, P. K., Lafontaine, J. G., Pallotta, D. 1974. *Chromosoma* 48:427–40
329. Rees, H., Jones, G. H. 1967. *Heredity* 22:1–18
330. Rees, H., Jones, R. N. 1972. *Int. Rev. Cytol.* 32:53–92
331. Renz, M. 1975. *Proc. Natl. Acad. Sci. USA* 72:733–36
332. Retèl, J., Planta, R. J. 1968. *Biochim. Biophys. Acta* 169:416–29
333. Rimpau, J., Lelley, T. 1972. *Z. Pflanzenzuecht.* 67:197–201
334. Ringertz, N. R. 1969. See Ref. 138, 656–84
335. Ris, H., Kubai, D. F. 1970. *Ann. Rev. Genet.* 4:263–94
336. Rizzo, P. J., Noodén, L. D. 1974. *Biochim. Biophys. Acta* 349:402–14
337. Roberts, B., Whitten, J. M., Gilbert, L. I. 1974. *Chromosoma* 47:193–201
338. Rudkin, G. T. 1972. See Ref. 24, 58–85
339. Sacristán, M. D., Dobrigkeit, I. 1973. *Z. Naturforsch.* 28c:564–67
340. Samarina, O. P., Lukanidin, E. M., Georgiev, G. P. 1973. *Karolinska Symp. Res. Methods Reprod. Endocrinol.* 6: 130–60
341. Sarma, N. P., Tandon, S. L. 1974. *Current Sci.* 43:635–37
342. Scheer, U. 1973. *Dev. Biol.* 30:13–28
343. Scherrer, K. 1973. See Ref. 340, 95–125
344. Schildkraut, C. L., Marmur, J., Doty, P. 1962. *J. Mol. Biol.* 4:430–43
345. Schneider, L. K. 1973. *J. Cell Biol.* 56:608–11
346. Schweizer, E., MacKechnie, C., Halvorson, H. O. 1969. *J. Mol. Biol.* 40:261–77
347. Scott, N. S., Ingle, J. 1973. *Plant. Physiol.* 51:677–84
348. Scott, S. E. M., Sommerville, J. 1974. *Nature* 250:680–82
349. Seale, R.L. 1975. *Nature* 255:247–49
350. Shaw, B. R., Cordon, J. L., Sahasrabuddhe, C. G., Van Holde, K. E. 1974. *Biochem. Biophys. Res. Commun.* 61:1193–98
351. Sherod, D., Johnson, G., Chalkley, R. 1974. *J. Biol. Chem.* 249:3923-31
352. Siegel, A., Lightfoot, D., Ward, O., Keener, S. 1973. *Science* 179:682–83
353. Silverman, B., Mirsky, A. E. 1973. *Proc. Natl. Acad. Sci. USA* 70: 2637–41
354. Simpson, R. T. 1972. *Biochemistry* 11:2003–8
355. Smetana, K., Busch, H. 1974. See Ref. 82:73–147
356. Smith, D. B., Flavell, R. B. 1974. *Biochem. Genet.* 12:243–56
357. Smith, D. B., Flavell, R. B. 1975. *Chromosoma* 50:223–42
358. Smith, M. J., Hough, B. R., Chamberlin, M. E., Davidson, E. H. 1974. *J. Mol. Biol.* 85:103–26
359. Smythies, J. R., Benington, F., Bradley, R. J., Morin, R. D., Romine, W. O. Jr. 1974. *J. Theor. Biol.* 47:309–15
360. Ibid, 383–95
361. Sobell, H. M. 1973. *Adv. Genet.* 17:411–90
362. Sonnenbichler, J. 1969. *Nature* 223: 205–6
363. Sonnenbichler, J. 1974. *Hoppe-Seyler's Z. Physiol. Chem.* 355:1477–78
364. Sorsa, M., Sorsa, V. 1968. *Ann. Acad. Sci. Fenn. Ser. A4* 127:1–10
365. Sorsa, V. 1974. *Cold Spring Harbor Symp. Quant. Biol.* 38:601–8
366. Sorsa, V. 1975. *Hereditas* 79:109–16
367. Sorsa, V., Green, M. M., Beermann, W. 1973. *Nature New Biol.* 245:34–37
368. Southern, E. 1970. *Nature* 227:794–98
369. Soyer, M. -O., Haapala, O. K. 1974. *Histochemistry* 42:239–46
370. Sparrow, A. H., Nauman, A. F. 1973. *Brookhaven Symp. Biol.* 25:367–89
371. Sparrow, A. H., Price, H. J., Underbrink, A. G. 1972. *Brookhaven Symp. Biol.* 23:451–94
372. Speirs, J., Birnstiel, M. 1974. *J. Mol. Biol.* 87:237–56
373. Speiser, Ch. 1974. *Theor. Appl. Genet.* 44:97–99
374. Spelsberg, T. C., Hnilica, L. S. 1969. *Biochim. Biophys. Acta* 195:63–75
375. Spelsberg, T. C., Sarkissian, I. V. 1970. *Phytochemistry* 9:1385–91
376. Sperling, R., Bustin, M. 1974. *Proc. Natl. Acad. Sci. USA* 71:4625–29
377. Speta, F. 1972. *Naturkundl. Jahrb. Linz* 1972: 9–65
378. Spirin, M. 1969. *Eur. J. Biochem.* 10:20–35
379. Sponar, J., Sormavá, Z. 1972. *Eur. J. Biochem.* 29:99–103
380. Spring, H., Trendelenburg, M. F., Scheer, U., Franke, W. W., Herth, W. 1974. *Cytobiologie* 10:1–65
381. Stebbins, G. L. 1966. *Science* 152:1463–69
382. Stein, G. S., Spelsberg, T. C., Kleinsmith, L. J. 1974. *Science* 183:817–24
383. Stubblefield, E., Wray, W. 1970. *Chromosoma* 32:262–94
384. Sutton, W. D. 1972. *Nature New Biol.* 237:70–71
385. Swift, H. 1974. *Cold Spring Harbor Symp. Quant. Biol.* 38:963–79
386. Szopa, J. 1974. *Acta Biochim. Pol.* 21:1–7
387. Taylor, J. H. 1974. *Int. Rev. Cytol.* 37:1–20

388. Taylor, J. H., Wu, M., Erickson, L. C. 1974. *Cold Spring Harbor Symp. Quant. Biol.* 38:225–31
389. Temussi, P. A. 1975. *J. Theor. Biol.* 50:25–33
390. Teng, C. S. 1974. *Biochim. Biophys. Acta* 366:385–95
391. Teng, C. S., Teng, C. T., Allfrey, V. G. 1971. *J. Biol. Chem.* 246:3597–3609
392. Teraoka, H. 1973. *Plant Cell Physiol.* 14:1053–61
393. Thaler, I. 1966. *Protoplasmatologia* II/B/2b/8
394. Thomas, C. A. Jr. 1971. *Ann. Rev. Genet.* 5:237–56
395. Thomas, C. A. Jr., Zimm, B. H., Dancis, B. M. 1973. *J. Mol. Biol.* 77:85–99
396. Timmis, J. N., Sinclair, J., Ingle, J. 1972. *Cell Differ.* 1:335–39
397. Tobler, H. 1972. *Nucleic Acid Hybridization,* ed. H. Ursprung, 1–9. Berlin, Heidelberg, New York: Springer. 76 pp.
398. Torrey, J. G. 1965. *Encycl. Plant Physiol.* 15/1:1256–1327
399. Towill, L. E., Noodén, L. D. 1973. *Plant Cell Physiol.* 14:851–63
400. Trendelenburg, M. F., Spring, H., Scheer, U., Franke, W. W. 1974. *Proc. Natl. Acad. Sci. USA* 71:3626–30
401. Tschermak-Woess, E. 1954. *Planta* 44:509–31
402. Tschermak-Woess, E. 1959. *Chromosoma* 10:497–503
403. Tschermak-Woess, E. 1963. *Protoplasmatologia* VI/1
404. Tschermak-Woess, E. 1967. *Caryologia* 20:135–52
405. Tschermak-Woess, E. 1971. See Ref. 251, 569–625
406. Tschermak-Woess, E., Enzenberg-Kunz, U. 1965. *Planta* 64:149–69
407. Turala, K. 1966. *Oesterr. Bot. Z.* 113:235–44
408. Tuttle, R. C., Loeblich, A. R. III 1974. *Science* 185:1061–62
409. Vandegrift, V., Serra, M., Moore, D. S., Wagner, T. E. 1974. *Biochemistry* 13:5087–92
410. van Holde, K. E., Sahasrabuddhe, C. G., Shaw, B. R. 1974. *Nucleic Acids Res.* 1:1579–86
411. van Holde, K. E., Sahasrabuddhe, C. G. 1974. *Biochem. Biophys. Res. Commun.* 60:1365–70
412. van Oostveldt, P., van Parijs, R. 1972. *Arch. Int. Physiol. Biochim.* 80:416–8
413. van Parijs, R., Vandendriessche, L. 1966. *Arch. Int. Physiol. Biochim.* 74:579–86
414. Van't Hof, J. 1966. *Exp. Cell Res.* 53:145–54
415. Van't Hof, J., Sparrow, A. H. 1963. *Proc. Natl. Acad. Sci. USA* 49:897–902
416. Vasiliev, A. E., Gamaley, Y. V. 1975. *Tsitologiya* 17:371–89
417. Vlad, M., Macgregor, H. C. 1975. *Chromosoma* 50:327–47
418. Walbot, V. 1975. *Plant Physiol. Suppl.* 56:25
419. Wang, T. Y. 1970. *Exp. Cell Res.* 61:455–57
420. Wangh, L., Ruiz-Carrillo, A., Allfrey, V. G. 1972. *Arch. Biochem. Biophys.* 150:44–56
421. Warnecke, P., Kruse, K., Harbers, E. 1973. *Biochim. Biophys. Acta* 331:295–304
422. Weinberg, E. S., Birnstiel, M. L., Purdom, D. R., Williamson, R. 1972. *Nature* 240:225–28
423. Weintraub, H. 1974. *Cold Spring Harbor Symp. Quant. Biol.* 38:247–56
424. Wilson, B. G. 1975. *Chromosoma* 51: 213–24
425. Wray, W., Stubblefield, E. Humphrey, R. 1972. *Nature New Biol.* 238:237–38
426. Wu, F. C., Elgin, S. C. R., Hood, L. E. 1973. *Biochemistry* 12:2792–97
427. Wu, J., Hurn, J., Bonner, J. 1972 *J. Mol. Biol.* 64:211–19
428. Yamada, Y., Yasuda, T., Koge, M., Sekiya, J. 1971. *Colloq. Int. C.N.R.S.* 193:137–53
429. Yunis, J. J., Yasmineh, W. G. 1971. *Science* 174:1200–9
430. Zellweger, A., Ryser, U., Braun, R. 1972. *J. Mol. Biol.* 64:681–91
431. Zimmermann, H. -P. 1974. *Cytobiologie* 9:144–61
432. Zimmermann, S. B., Levin, C. J. 1975. *Biochem. Biophys. Res. Commun.* 62:357–61
433. Zirkin, B. R. 1973. *Exp. Cell Res.* 78:394–98
434. Zirkin, B. R., Wolfe, S. L. 1972. *J. Ultrastruct. Res.* 39:496–508
435. Zukowska-Niedzwiedz, A., Toczko, K. 1973. *Acta Biochim. Pol.* 20:351–54
436. Zukowska-Niedzwiedz, A., Toczko, K. 1974. *Bull. Acad. Pol. Sci., Ser. Biol.* 22:81–83

Ann. Rev. Plant Physiol. 1976. 27:71–94

SELF-ASSEMBLY
IN DEVELOPMENT[1]

♦7602

G. Benjamin Bouck
Department of Biological Sciences, University of Illinois at Chicago Circle, Chicago, Illinois 60680

David L. Brown
Department of Biology, University of Ottawa, Ottawa, Ontario, Canada

CONTENTS

INTRODUCTION

Assembly of subunits into larger functional elements is a basic and important property of all living systems. The resulting polymers or macromolecules may be formed through three distinctive routes: *template assembly*—usually involving a

[1]Supported in part by USPHS grant #19537 (G.B.B.) and NRC grant #A6353 (D.L.B.).

master copy and enzymatic addition of new units (e.g. polypeptide, DNA, RNA synthesis); *enzymatic assembly*—characterized by the enzymatic addition of new subunits without a template (e.g. cellulose synthesis); *self-assembly*—recognized as a more or less spontaneous aggregation of subunits. Template assembly is precise, and where accurate selection among dissimilar subunits is necessary, a template is essential. However, the amount of template which can be specified by a genome is finite, and the development of higher levels of organization by template assembly ultimately will demand unacceptably large amounts of informational material. Enzymatic assembly may be utilized when elaborate or cross-linked polymers such as the bacterial cell wall are synthesized and where biochemical modification of subunits is required. Enzymatic activity and self-assembly may often operate coordinately. Self-assembly provides a widely utilized mechanism for organizing subunits during many phases of development. Such assembly is by no means haphazard, but is modulated by the properties of the individual subunits, availability of subunits, or immediate physical and chemical environment among other factors.

It is the purpose of this review (*a*) to examine some of these factors which may control self-assembly at the molecular level and ask if the same principles apply at higher levels of organization; (*b*) to explore the interrelationships among template, enzymatic, and self-assembly in several specific examples; and (*c*) to assess some of the variations on self-assembly and ask if they provide sufficient rationale for approaching larger problems in cell development. Reviews by Caspar & Klug (36) and by Kushner (97) provide earlier summaries of the self-assembly process and its significance in a wide range of systems.

DEFINITIONS AND APPLICATION

Self-assembly is often a loosely used term and encompasses an assortment of completely or partially nontemplate-mediated phenomena. The following characteristics are used as operational definitions for this review:

1. *Self-assembly is a process which involves units capable of assembling into higher orders without participation of DNA or RNA at the subunit by subunit assembly level.* RNA clearly may play a role in viral protein self-assembly and termination (see below) or ribosome self-assembly (110, 147), but here the role of RNA is limited to specific phases of assembly and is not required for general subunit addition.

2. *Self-assembly is rapid under physiological conditions.* A variety of mechanisms —including thermodynamic, kinetic, and physical—associated with the general principles of initiation and nucleation are utilized to insure that assembly occurs in biologically real time (4). Random association, particularly in the initial stages of polymerization, is simply too slow to account for the observed speeds of assembly in many structures. The exact nature of initiation and nucleation is controversial but clearly is a key to understanding much of the basic properties of self-assembly.

3. *Self-assembly is a process whose initiation or rate is sensitive to the presence of specific organic or inorganic molecules, to variations in temperature, pH, pressure, or other factors.* A great many self-assembling polymers of biological importance are transient in appearance and must respond to the physiological state of the cell (e.g.

spindle microtubules in the dividing cell). Such reversible systems respond to exogenously applied physical and chemical stimuli and therefore presumably respond to similar agents in the cell milieu. Similar sensitivities to environmental factors must apply even to irreversibly self-assembled systems. It may be disadvantageous to assemble a polymer (virus head, for example) at an inappropriate stage of development.

The principles of self-assembly apply at many levels of organization and with many variations. The general scheme outlined in Figure 1 illustrates some of the hierarchies of the assembly process. It is apparent that self-assembly is a widespread phenomenon and can provide a rationale for many complex developmental events. Since we will restrict our consideration to those polymers in Figure 1 which are predominently protein, it seems appropriate to examine first the underlying mechanisms of protein folding and then see how the folded protein is itself assembled into a variety of more complex supramolecular entities. These entities will include examples of large polymers initiated and organized in association with specific organization centers (microtubules and bacterial flagellum), representatives of the coordinated timing of self-assembly with proteolytic enzyme activity (collagen), and examples of the role of processed protein or RNA in self-assembly (some virus assembly).

PROTEIN FOLDING

The Nature of the Driving Forces

Polypeptides consisting of linear arrays of sequenced amino acids may fold spontaneously into helical segments (secondary structure) and then pack into globular proteins (tertiary structure) along with nonhelical segments (35). Helical structure in general may be stabilized by the tertiary state (37). There is disagreement as to whether packing occurs during or shortly after the synthesis of the nascent polypeptide chain (66, 136), but for ease of discussion folding will be considered as a separate event from chain growth. The finished protein (native configuration) may be stabilized by a variety of either covalent bonds such as disulfide linkages or noncovalent bonds utilizing polar interactions such as hydrogen bonds and salt links or those utilizing nonpolar interactions such as van der Waal's and hydrophobic bonds. It is an experimentally important property of many proteins that under suitable conditions the covalent or noncovalent bonds of the native protein can be reversibly broken and the native protein denatured to a random coil (141, 155). During the process of denaturation and renaturation to a functional form, the process of folding and the forces driving the assembly of the native protein can be analyzed by physical, chemical, and immunological methods. From these analyses the general mechanisms of folding often can be inferred.

The forces governing most folding are related to selection of the most favorable free energy (i.e. order) of conformation (176, 181). This energy (order) is gained primarily through hydrogen bonds, van der Waal's interactions, and hydrophobicity. Opposed to these ordering forces is the intrinsic entropy of the unfolded

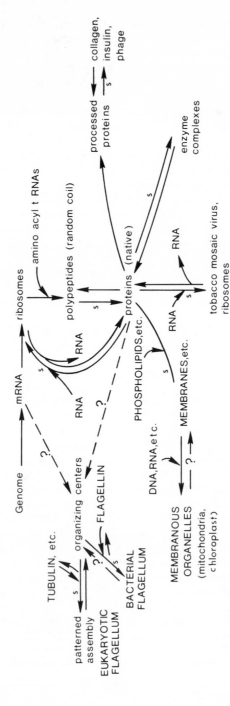

Figure 1 Assembly routes for proteins and higher orders of macromolecules. Self-assembling steps are indicated with letter s.

(more random) state. However, since many folded proteins are characterized by increased entropies and positive enthalpies (potential energy) relative to the unfolded state, some component must randomize during the formation of tertiary structure (35). That component is generally recognized as water molecules in the vicinity of the native protein which are restricted in their rotational freedom relative to bulk water (96, 109). During folding and polymerization of many kinds of biological molecules, some of that restricted water loses its affinity for the protein and becomes less ordered (i.e. has increased entropy) by joining the bulk phase. Nonpolar regions of the protein tend to associate and form many weak hydrophobic bonds (109). It is assumed that water near hydrophobic regions is initially more highly ordered than bulk water, so that decreasing the attraction of water to nonpolar groups results in more disorder and hence overall increased entropy. Although this process is often described as melting of ice-like water next to the protein, this bound water produces an NMR image intermediate between that of bulk water and ice (96, 156). The fact that reagents such as D_2O which tend to favor the attraction of water to itself may cause a more favorable or stable protein conformation (95) lends further support to the role of hydrophobic interactions in protein folding. Furthermore, the expected loss of bound water has been measured directly during polymerization of virus protein (151). To summarize, the positive enthalpies represent the potential energy needed to disrupt the hydrogen bonds of the protein-associated water; positive entropies result from the increased freedom of water molecules released from the protein molecules; and large heat capacities arise from the breakdown of the ordered water as the temperature is increased.

The Nature of Folding

Adequate driving force is not of course sufficient to explain the precise pathway of folding characteristic of many proteins. To a surprising extent the three-dimensional packing of many globular proteins conforms to that of a molecular crystal (37), and the ultimate volume occupied by an amino acid residue may be no more than that occupied in a crystal of the same amino acid. It has been argued in fact that "through simple space-filling requirements the amino acid sequences control the final three-dimensional structure" (128). However, given the myriad rotational possibilities for a polypeptide chain (57a), it is inconceivable that a molecule could seek out with any efficiency the correct three-dimensional conformation on a totally random basis.

Theories on the mechanisms of folding fall into two general categories: (a) thermodynamic considerations, or (b) kinetic mechanisms. According to thermodynamic theory, folding results from the inherent capacity of a polypeptide chain to seek out the most thermodynamically favorable arrangement of polar and nonpolar side chains (47). This allows ultimate attainment of the most energetically favorable state, i.e. that of lowest Gibbs free energy or the global minimum, but frequently requires long time periods to reach equilibrium (4). It should be noted that the prediction of tertiary structure from the known properties of the amino acid residues has received some success (133, 140), and apart from time limitations there are no conceptual difficulties in a thermodynamic solution to the problem of protein folding. The alternative hypothesis (kinetic theory) postulates that the number of possibilities for folding are limited—perhaps many orders of magnitude less than on an equilibrium basis—by nucleation events (e.g. 139). By imposing pathway restrictions, nucleation greatly reduces the number of possible conformations sampled during folding, but by imposing path limitations, it involves more than thermodynamic considerations (which are path independent). Nucleation-initiated self-assembly produces conformations which are not the structures of lowest Gibbs free energy but are in the "lowest free energy of their kinetically accessible structure" (176).

Evidence Favoring Nucleation in Enzyme Folding

In contrast to crystal growth, which is characterized by a slow initial stage of seed formation or achievement of a critical size, nucleation events should be characterized by rapid initial conformational changes followed by slower selection and stabilization of the permissible pathways. Evidence for two sequences of reactions (nucleation and growth) proceeding at different rates would provide strong support for the kinetic theory.

Some of the most compelling evidence in support of this theory are the studies of conformational changes in *Staphylococcus* nuclease. Nuclease has a molecular weight of about 17,000, no disulfide bridges, and can be reversibly denatured by citric acid buffers at low pH (3.2). Renaturation occurs when the enzyme is returned to a neutral or higher pH in the presence of 0.1 M NaCl at room temperature (4). The magnitude of the folding task required of nuclease has been summarized by Anfinsen (4): the polypeptide chain consists of 149 amino acids with 2 rotatable bonds per residue—each bond would be able to assume 4^{149} to 9^{149} different conformations in the folded enzyme.

Conformational changes during renaturation of nuclease can be monitored by stop-flow kinetic analysis using the changes in fluorescence emitted by the tryptophanyl residues of the enzyme (48). First-order rate plots of folding were obtained by subtracting final levels of fluorescence from instantaneous levels of fluorescence. It is clear from such plots that two distinct rates of folding can be observed: k_1 with a mean half time of about 50 msec, and k_2 with a half life of about 350 msec. Arrhenius plots (from which enthalpy values can be calculated) of the two rates as a function of temperature showed strikingly different temperature dependence (48); the slower process was endothermic with an apparent enthalpy of activation of 7.9 kcal/mol. The faster reaction had little or no activation enthalpy. These findings suggest that folding involves an entropically driven nucleation step and a second step involving formation of hydrogen bonds.

Further evidence on the nature of the nucleation process has been obtained by examining the behavior of antibodies to specific portions of the nuclease molecule (136). Antibody produced against folded fragments will inactivate enzyme activity, whereas antibody produced against randomly coiled fragments obtained from cyanogen bromide cleavage will not. The kinetics of antibody inactivation (of nuclease activity) suggested that the fragment containing amino acids 99–149 "flickered" from random to the native state and that 0.02% of fragment 99–149 exists in its native form at any one moment (4, 136). It was postulated that portions of a protein chain that can serve as nucleation sites for folding will be those which can filcker in and out of the conformation that they will occupy in the final protein and that they will form a relatively rigid structure stabilized by cooperative interactions.

Scrutiny of a number of globular proteins revealed the general occurrence of specific regions characterized by β helices or hairpin turns as likely candidates for a nucleation function (175). It was suggested that there may be several such sites in a given globular protein but that each site probably does not involve more than 18 or fewer than 8 amino acids. The higher figure was considered maximum due to time limitations on forming such a region, and the lower figure is indicative of the minimum number of amino acid residues required to form a stable structure (175).

In summary, time restraints impose serious limitations on random folding alone as the mechanism for achieving tertiary structure of globular proteins. There are simply too many possibilities to examine in the limited time available (57a). Consequently there has emerged a growing recognition of the role of nucleation events in reducing the number of conformational pathways which will be searched. Some experimental work supports a role for nucleation, although the precise molecular mechanisms for this process are not well understood.

HIGHER ORDERS OF ASSEMBLY

In the preceding section, the role of nucleation and subsequent growth has been emphasized. From the available evidence it would appear that nucleation may be rapid whereas subsequent folding and bond formation may be slower. By contrast, self-assembly of higher orders of structure frequently involves a slow initial phase (initiation) followed by more rapid polymerization (growth). In this respect these latter assemblies are analogous to crystal growth and, in fact, self-assembly of several systems is visualized as a condensation or crystallization phenomenon. The analogy must be recognized as limited, however, since in organic crystals each unit is a simple atom or molecule while in a protein polymer each unit has its own complex structure which may have many variations. As pointed out by Oosawa & Higashi (117), such flexibility in protein polymers makes possible the delicate regulation of assembly by other molecules. In the following discussion we shall attempt to assess the mechanisms of assembly in a few selected representative higher orders and to assess how self-assembly may be initiated and controlled. We will consider *initiation* in higher order assembly as the counterpart of *nucleation* in protein folding since both processes serve to accelerate the assembly of the polymer. Clearly, kinetic differences may exist (see above) between initiation and protein nucleation even though the two terms have been used interchangeably in different systems. Specific orientation or patterning of the assembling polymers is provided in turn by *organizing centers.*

Collagen Assembly

Collagen is representative of a group of macromolecules which also includes insulin and some viruses in which a series of covalent modifications follow peptide bond formation prior to expression of the normal function of the molecule. Collagen fiber formation involves several steps (65), as follows:

INTRACELLULAR   EXTRACELLULAR

procollagen ⟶ collagen ⟶ collagen ⟶ microfilament ⟶ fiber
polypeptides ⟵ molecule   molecule ⟵   ⟵
(proα)   (super helix   cleaved
                    + registration (super
                    peptides)   helix)

The biochemical pathways for this process are reasonably well known, expecially since the recognition that a precursor molecule (procollagen) is formed before final assembly into collagen fibers (146). The procollagen polypeptide chains (chains) have a molecular weight of about 125,000, which is about 25% higher than the chains of the collagen fiber (21). Three properties of the procollagen chains are recognized as critical to the final assembly into fibers (20, 21):

1. The presence at the N-terminal end of the polypeptide of a pepsin-sensitive segment which contains cystine and tryptophan residues (108). This segment is refereed to as "additional" sequences, "registration" peptides, or "extension" peptides (20).

2. An enzymatically mediated hydroxylation (8) of the polypeptide which apparently confers thermal stability to the molecule (12).

3. The regular distribution of glycine (every third residue) throughout the α chain except in the segment consisting of registration peptides.

Following post-translational hydroxylation, assembly of the collagen fiber begins with the formation of a super helix consisting of three polypeptide (alpha) chains. The chains may be identical or different depending on the organism and tissue (21). It is generally believed that the super helix assembly is mediated through the interactions in the registration peptide (53, 55) which are then stabilized by disulfide cross bridges (54, 107). When aligned in this manner the glycine-rich portions of the chain form a tight triple helix held together in part by hydrogen bonds between hydroxyproline residues (8, 126). There is evidence to suggest that procollagen (triple helix) formation occurs intracellularly within cell compartments of the Golgi apparatus and/or the endoplasmic reticulum (116, 172).

Before further assembly the registration peptides still present in the triple helix are enzymatically cleaved by a procollagen peptidase (93), thereby producing a triple stranded helical collagen molecule of about 300,000 mol wt. Subsequent assembly may involve microfilament formation through the regular stagger and rotation of the collagen molecule (122). These in turn are assembled into the final collagen fibril by staggering of microfilaments to produce the characteristic banding pattern of collagen. The regular stagger appears to be due to the tendency of charged or hydrophobic interactions to occur every 234 residues (76).

Collagen formation illustrates two interesting facets of self-assembly. First, two self-assembly steps, super helix assembly and fiber assembly, are separated by an enzymatic cleavage step. We see here an example of assisted assembly whereby monomer interactions may be enhanced, in this case by registration peptides which do not participate in the final assembled product. The process is similar in a broad sense to the role of special assembly proteins (scaffold proteins) and processed proteins in some viruses and to the allosteric or conformational changes which may operate during flagellar assembly in bacteria (see below). Secondly, collagen assembly is not fully reversible. The reduced ability of α chains to assemble without registration peptides minimizes the opportunities for later mismatching in the final collagen fiber. Also, the spatial separation of intracellular super helix formation from extracellular fiber assembly further ensures an orderly stepwise assembly process (53).

Virus Assembly

An extensive critique of virus assembly is beyond the scope of this review. However, several virus assembly systems provide additional insight into the versatility of the self-assembly processes and will therefore be examined briefly.

SCAFFOLDING AND PROCESSED PROTEINS IN VIRUS ASSEMBLY   An interesting example of coat protein assembly being assisted or "catalyzed" by a second protein, which is later removed, occurs in several viruses (125, 143, 153), including the DNA temperate phage of *Salmonella,* P22. Aptly termed a scaffolding protein, it has been detected in SDS acrylamide gel analysis of proheads in P22 assembly but not in mature virus (87, 88). Table 1 illustrates the polypeptides identified during stages in virus maturation and the estimated number of copies of each protein in the mature virus. P_8 is a major head protein in the prohead stage but is absent shortly after DNA encapsulation. Pulse-chase experiments (34, 87) clearly demonstrate that P_5 label is transferred to mature virus whereas P_8 label remains in the prohead fraction (i.e. is reutilized). This apparent recycling of P_8 provides the most compelling evidence for a scaffold function. It has been suggested therefore that co-polymerization resulting from an interaction between P_5 and P_8 produces the prohead (34, 87). The possibility that P_8 may be primarily involved with DNA encapsulation has not been excluded (34, 88, 161), however, and a definitive role of P_8 in scaffolding must await successful assembly in vitro of proheads from only P_8 and P_5.

A different mechanism for control over polymerization is suggested in capsid formation in the bacteriophage λ (70, 71, 86). Here the major coat protein pE interacts with about 12 copies of another protein pC to produce two products X1 and X2. Peptide maps of tryptic digests of pE, pC, X1, and X2 indicate the four proteins are related. It appears that X2 is a proteolytic cleavage product of X1 and that X1 is a fusion product of pE and pC. While X1 and X2 may appear in the final assembled capsid, pC does not. The function of X1 and X2 in the mature head assembly is unknown, but it may be significant that the icosohedral head has 12 corners and the pC-pE fusion product occurs 12 times in each head (70). The processed proteins X1 and X2 of λ and similar proteins of other viruses (5, 60, 70) appear to be examples of post-translational modifications of proteins prior to or during assembly into larger structures.

Table 1 Phage P22 proteins present during different stages of development[a]

		Mol wt.	No. of copies in mature phage
major proteins	P_8--------------------------------	42,000	0^b
	P_5------P_5------P_5------P_5	55,000	420
	P_9	76,000	16
	P_{26}-----P_{26}	23,000	10
	P_1------P_1 -----P_1	94,000	10
needed for infection not assembly	P_{16}-----P_{16}-----P_{16}-----P_{16}	67,000	6
	P_{20}-----P_{20}-----P_{20}-----P_{20}	50,000	15
	P_x------P_x------P_x------P_x	18,000	20
	P-------P-------P	15,000	10

[a] Adapted from Ref. 34.
[b] 250 copies in prohead only.

RNA-MEDIATED SELF-ASSEMBLY   As the classic example of self-assembly (58, 59), it seems appropriate to consider the assembly of tobacco mosaic virus (TMV) and the closely related virus, cucumber mottle mosaic virus (CMMV). Both viruses consist of a rod-shaped shell of helically coiled protein subunits surrounding a strand of RNA. The assembly pattern for TMV, while controversial in detail, has ·the following general characteristics:

RNA + protein ⇌ RNA – disc + protein ⇌ assembled virus
        (A-protein   (A-protein
        in disc form)   nondisc)

A-protein, so called because of its early extraction by alkali, consists of monomers, trimers, and small amounts of higher aggregates (129). Prolonged incubation of the A-protein in phosphate or pyrophosphate buffer at 20°C produces 20S discs which consist of 34 monomeric units arranged in two adjacent rings (2, 31, 41, 42, 129). A smaller (13S) one-turn disc is formed under similar conditions with CMMV protein (113). Both TMV and CMMV discs bind to the 5' end of the TMV–RNA to produce an initiated rod. Rod growth then proceeds rapidly by addition of subunits (112, 113, 129; Figure 2) or possibly by addition of new discs (30). Assembly rate is independent of the concentration of A-protein (from 7 mg/ml–1.5 mg/ml)

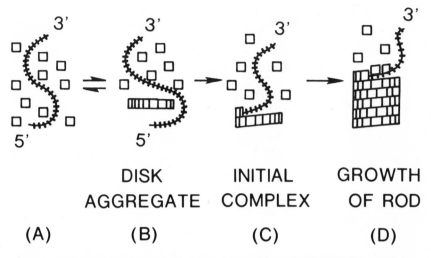

DISK   INITIAL   GROWTH

AGGREGATE   COMPLEX   OF ROD

(A)   (B)   (C)   (D)

Figure 2   Cucumber mottle mosaic virus protein assembly on TMV-RNA. Note initiation complex consisting of RNA and a disc of protein monomers. Final assembly occurs by monomer addition to initiation complex (from 113).

which may be due to the apparent constant amount of protein monomer present at different concentrations of A-protein (129). Growth is terminated in some manner when the end of the intact RNA strand has been reached. Polymerization is endothermic, and the entropic driving force is derived from the release of water during polymerization (98, 99, 151).

A requirement for RNA in TMV and CMMV assembly does not violate the guidelines of self-assembly set forth earlier. RNA does not act as a template throughout assembly but, together with a protein disc, only as an initiator. In its role as initiator TMV-RNA is similar in function to the RNA associated with assembly of the small and large subunit of the ribosome. It is conceivable that in TMV assembly the dislocation [lock washer configuration (31)] postulated to occur after attachment of the disc to RNA may be mediated by disc association to RNA. The helix thus produced can provide a self-perpetuating ramp for the potentially endless addition of new subunits.

Bacterial Flagellum Assembly

The intact bacterial flagellum consists of three principal morphologically distinguishable parts: a complex basal structure attached to the cell membrane and wall; a short hook region which extends beyond the wall; and the long tubular flagellar filament (for general review see 6, 16). The filament is constructed of identical subunits, each consisting of a single polypeptide termed flagellin. The subunits are arranged so that there are less than 11/circumference—resulting in rows skewed from the longitudinal (32, 68, 111). Flagellin monomers [40,000 mol wt or larger in some species (74)] prepared by heat dissociation of isolated filaments will assem-

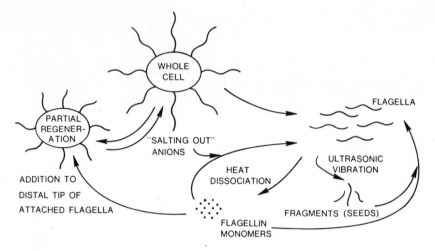

Figure 3 Diagram illustrating various ways bacterial flagellin can assemble from seeds or from monomers alone (adapted from Ref. 63).

ble rapidly (growth stage) both onto seeds consisting of isolated fragments of flagella (1, 7, 102, Figure 3) and also onto the distal ends of flagellar filaments still attached to cell bodies (79). Flagellin monomers also can assemble spontaneously in the absence of seeds in solutions of certain salting-out anions (167). The nonseeded assembly of flagellin in vitro proceeds in two steps: the slow de novo formation of seeds (i.e. initiation complexes) and subsequent more rapid elongation (16). In the presence of salting-out anions, it is estimated that the initiation step involves the association of at least three monomers (167). Generally the formation of an initiation complex is believed to depend on the simultaneous collision of several molecules. In addition, optical rotatory dispersion (92) and circular dichroism (163) analyses suggest that flagellin molecules undergo large conformational changes before or during polymerization. Because of the dual requirements for simultaneous collisions and large conformational changes, under physiological conditions of pH, ionic strength, and temperature the initiation rate is greatly reduced (163). The elongation step is temperature dependent, involves positive enthalpy changes (62 but see 164) and is accompanied by large molar volume increases (63). All these latter properties are indicative of hydrophobic interactions between monomers during polymerization (99).

Purified monomers will assemble onto the distal ends of isolated hooks in vitro (85) and onto in situ hooks of a flagellin-less mutant (77). Thus assembly of bacterial flagella in vivo differs significantly from that observed in vitro in that initiation must involve the binding of monomers to a nonflagellin structure, the basal hook (74). The conditions of assembly are the same as those used for the in vitro assembly of flagellin onto the tips of attached flagella but the efficiency is much lower (77). During purification the hooks progressively lose the ability to initiate assembly, suggesting the presence of some labile factor at the distal end of the hook. It has been suggested that this may be the termination factor for hook elongation, since mutants lacking termination control (with polyhooks) do synthesize flagellin but cannot assemble flagellar filaments (77).

In summary, the bacterial flagellum represents an apparently unique self-assembling system in which the polymer is extracellular and monomers are added distally (46, 78) at the point farthest from the cell body. After initiation, cellular control over assembly must be limited to the production of monomers and their availability at the distal tip rather than the involvement of specific regulatory molecules.

Microtubule Assembly

ASSEMBLY AND DISASSEMBLY OF MICROTUBULE PROTEIN   A wide range of physiological processes in a variety of eukaryotic cells depend on the capacity for microtubules to polymerize and depolymerize in an orderly and controlled manner. The proliferation of papers, recent reviews (9, 43, 73, 105, 114, 131, 177), and major symposia on microtubule organization, assembly, and function provide a dramatic testimonial to the ubiquity of microtubules and the many functions they apparently mediate. Progress in understanding microtubule assembly has come largely through (*a*) application of optical methods to assess the degree of microtubule polymerization in vivo (80, 82); (*b*) analysis of microtubules or microtubule protein binding or responding to several more or less specific drugs and physical factors (cf 177); and (*c*) the discovery that microtubule protein can be extracted from brain tissue and polymerized in vitro (17, 173) relatively easily and hence purified through successive cycles of polymerization and depolymerization under suitable conditions (18, 142). A general scheme of in vitro microtubule assembly incorporating some of the observations to be discussed below is as follows:

Monomers → dimer + additional nontubulin protein(s) ⇌ discs ⇌ microtubule
(tubulin)

The two broad classes of monomers (α tubulin and β tubulin) appear to be similar in composition throughout an evolutionary diverse group of organisms. Amino acid sequencing (103) of tubulins suggests that as with many other biologically important molecules [e.g. insulin (118)] remarkably little change in protein composition has occurred over an extensive evolutionary past. Additional support for the similarity or nonspecificity of tubulin comes from experiments demonstrating that microtubule protein can polymerize on seeds from widely different sources (3, 14, 29). α and β tubulin have been further separated by isoelectric focusing on acrylamide gels into several subspecies (180). Current evidence favors the view that α and β tubulin associate as a heterodimer (cf 179, however) and that the tubulin dimer (mol wt 110,000–120,000) is the stable polymerizable subunit of the microtubule. The general properties of the subunit dimer include (*a*) lateral (MLT) and longitudinal (MLO) binding site(s) for assembly into the microtubule; (*b*) one binding site for colchicine (MC) which may be identical to either site MLT or MLO (19); (*c*) one (26) or two (100) binding site(s) for vinblastine (MV) which is not the same as MC;

(*d*) two (84) binding sites for guanine nucleotides (MG) which are not the same as MC but may [in vitro (13)] or may not [in vivo (27)] be the same as MV; (*e*) limited or no capacity to initiate polymerization by themselves (17); (*f*) capacity for phosphorylation on serine residues on β tubulin (44, 45).

The general finding that the dimer alone cannot initiate microtubule assembly has focused attention recently on other components which, in stoichometric amounts with dimer, do initiate assembly. One such component, identified as a ring or disc (17), or an alternative form, the spiral, consists of α and β tubulin (171) plus additional proteins (170). It is clear that unlike the TMV disc, the microtubule disc or spiral does not initiate assembly as a preformed seed but appears to unwind into longitudinal elements (protofilaments) which may aggregate laterally to form a 13 (usually) protofilament microtubule wall (49, 90). Tubulins associated with the discs are similar to nondisc tubulins except they have reduced or no capacity to bind colchicine (91).

Several proteins associated with discs co-purify with tubulin during successive polymerization-depolymerization cycles, and certain of these may stimulate in vitro assembly (39, 170). One such protein termed TAU (170), which can be separated from disc with 0.1 M NaCl followed by phosphocellulose chromatography, appears to associate directly with tubulin to form spirals or discs. A fraction separated from in vitro-assembled microtubules which contains two high molecular weight microtubule-associated proteins (MAPs) has also been reported to stimulate tubulin dimer assembly. These two proteins, one of which can act as an efficient substrate for cyclic AMP-stimulated phosphorylation by a microtubule-associated protein kinase (144), have been shown to compose the filaments associated with microtubules (39). A precise role for MAPs in stimulating assembly is not known, but their addition may occur after partial or complete microtubule polymerization (39). The sum of these observations suggest that in vitro, accessory protein(s) act in concert with about 34 tubulin molecules to form an initiation complex consisting of a short segment of protofilament. Images suggesting direct incorporation of such protofilaments into a polymerizing microtubule have been published (49).

MICROTUBULE GROWTH   Following initiation, unwound discs, spirals, or dimers are rapidly added to the polymerizing microtubule until in vitro, equilibrium is reached. Assembly of spindles (structurally consisting primarily of microtubules) in vivo is characterized by high enthalpic values suggesting entropic driven polymerization resulting from released water from the assembling units (compare 138, 150). Spindle microtubules are identified by retardation of polarized light, i.e. polymerization has been shown to be proportional to retardation (e.g. 82). The concept that microtubules are in dynamic equilibrium with tubulin dimer (83) has received support from observations of the effect on retardation of heat and pressure (137, 138) and from observations of the effects of exogenously added heterologous tubulin to spindle growth and integrity in lysing cells (33, 81, 127). The concept of dynamic equilibrium helps explain why colchicine, vinblastine, and similar drugs may cause disassembly of labile microtubules such as mitotic microtubules and some cytoplasmic microtubules. Presumably these drugs bind to the unassembled dimer in the tubulin pool, and by occupying the normal assembly sites or by steric hindrance, they prevent these dimers from participating in polymerization. Thus these tubulin molecules are effectively removed from the tubulin pool, and equilibrium shifts towards the disassembled condition (82). By contrast, stable microtubules characteristic of eukaryotic flagella may not be undergoing dynamic exchange, and therefore drugs can only affect new assembly and will have no effect on the intact microtubule (135). Just how flagellar microtubules are stabilized remains to be determined. It seems unlikely, however, that flagella tubulins are biochemically different from other tubulins since under appropriate conditions the tubulin of flagella will bind colchicine (178) and can be disassembled and reutilized for new flagellar growth (15).

Under some conditions tubulin may assemble into structures quite different from microtubules, such as open or spiral sheets (49, 50), partially rolled tubes (61; see also 49 and refs. therein) and macrotubules (e.g. 24, 67, 75, 159, 162). These aberrant forms may represent stages in assembly or altered arrangements of microtubule components. It is probably significant that in most of these cases the protofilament is preserved, and it is the lateral association of protofilaments which appears to be altered (MLT site). From current evidence it would appear, for example, that vinblastine-produced macrotubules (162) are derived by separation of protofilament pairs or a stabilization of protofilament pairs which coil into helices, compact, and thereby form macrotubules (168, 169). These may further aggregate to form crystals (162). This kind of assembly is the reciprocal of normal assembly in which the spiral initiation complex may unwind to form longitudinal protofilaments which are incorporated into the microtubule wall (50). Since so many unrelated factors (e.g. 162) produce apparently similar reorganization of protofilaments into macrotubules, it seems reasonable to assume that the common denominator of these effects is the relatively labile lateral bonding of protofilaments and the inherent tendency of laterally unbonded protofilaments to seek a spiral or ring-like configuration. Vinblastine may substitute for some factors which initiate the linear polymerization (168) but inhibit the normal lateral bonding of protofilaments.

ORGANIZING CENTERS   The presence of rings or discs capable of initiating microtubule polymerization in vitro may be a fortuitous property of either brain microtubules or in vitro microtubule assembly where assembly is random.

The concept of organizing centers for microtubule assembly (119, 124) has been developed to account for the many observations that microtubules rarely (see, however, 11) assemble randomly in vivo. In developing systems, microtubule assembly is under close spatial and temporal regulation (119). Organizing centers may function in this regulation by controlling: (a) initiation, (b) orientation, (c) directionality, and (d) patterning of microtubule polymerization. Microtubules are generally observed to be associated with structures or regions that have been shown in several systems to be the sites of initial microtubule assembly. It is not clear whether this initiation involves specific binding sites for tubulin, conformation changes in tubulin associated with the structures, the presence of specific molecules which activate the assembly process, or a combination of these and other factors.

Organizing centers appear in a variety of forms in cells and are recognized by the fact that microtubules are attached to or on them. The organizing center itself is generally unstructured, but it may be associated with other well-defined material. Despite the general absence of well-defined structure [e.g. the centroplast in *Raphidiophrys* (158) or spindle poles in plant cells (119)], microtubule assembly is initiated in a polarized fashion, and it seems likely that there is a subtle, but still undetected, organization of initiation sites that provides some control over orientation. During the assembly of axonemes in *Raphidiophrys*, for example, microtubules are initiated at the centroplast and grow towards the cell surface, not into or through the centroplast (158). The directionality of assembly is a direct consequence both of the imposed initial orientation and the inherent polarity of assembly of microtubules (see next section).

The function of organizing centers in controlling orientation and directionality is more striking when the amorphous initiating material is localized on a specific structure which permits tubule growth only in one direction. During mitosis, the spindle plaques localized on the intact nuclear envelope in some fungi, for example, apparently initiate continuous spindle microtubules which then extend between plaques on opposite sides of the nucleus (69, 106, 132). The centrosomal spindle plates in diatoms (104, 121) and structured chromosomal kinetochores (120) also fall into this class of organizing centers associated with well-defined structures.

In addition to polymerizing in specific directions in the cell, microtubules often appear in highly ordered patterns. In some cases the pattern is thought to be determined by secondary factors [e.g. intermicrotubule bridges (158)]. However, in some organisms microtubules are assembled initially in the characteristic pattern, followed by the formation of intermicrotubule bridges which stabilize these patterns but are not essential to pattern formation (160). Observations of this latter type have led to the suggestion that the sites of microtubule initiation may be prepatterned on some other cell structure. Detailed studies of the organizing center for cytoplasmic microtubules in the cellular slime mold *Polysphondylium* suggest such a prepatterning (134). In this fungus a disc-shaped, multilayered structure (termed a nucleus-associated body, NAB) appears in interphase cells. The amorphous material believed to function in initiation occurs as discrete nodules (about 16) on the NAB. One or two microtubules terminate on each nodule. In the alga *Ochromonas*, organizing centers also appear to be prepatterned and to exert precise spatial control over microtubule assembly (22, 23). The organizing center material in this organism occurs as regularly spaced aggregates on the lower surface of a fiber (the rhizoplast) which is accurately positioned in the cell. The positioning of the rhizoplast presumably specifies the direction and perhaps orientation of microtubule growth. Once initiated at this structure, microtubules elongate in a posterior direction. Similarly, the basal body roots in the alga *Polytomella* are characteristically positioned in the cell and confer orientation and directionality to assembly (25). The pattern of microtubules is specified at the organizing center, implying that the initiation sites are prepatterned on the organizing center.

Basal bodies differ from the types of organizing centers mentioned above in that they appear to provide at least a partial template. Most of the flagella doublet microtubules are continous with tubules in the organizing center (basal body). The assembly of doublet tubules onto these existing tubules may be homologous to seeded assembly and may not require the initiation step in assembly apparently required of amorphous organizing centers. The demonstration that isolated basal bodies can serve to seed the patterned assembly of chick brain tubulin in vitro (145) strongly supports the many earlier suggestions that basal body microtubules at least partially organize the axoneme microtubules.

Several recent studies have indicated that membranes may also function as organizing centers or as a framework for organizing centers for microtubules. A colchicine-binding protein (148) (presumably tubulin) and tubulin itself (94) have been detected in isolated membranes. In addition, studies of resonance transfer between labeled populations of membranes and tubulin suggest a direct role of membranes in initiating polymerization (10). Thus when fluorescein isothiocyanate (FITC)-labeled membranes isolated from rabbit polymorphonuclear leukocytes are mixed with rhodamine (RITC)-labeled tubulin at low temperature there is no transfer of energy between the labeling chromatophores (i.e. no long-range energy transfer). When the mixture is then incubated at 37°C, resonance transfer between FITC and RITC is detected. The authors conclude from their results that some labeled membrane components can serve as an initiation site for microtubule assembly. These highly suggestive experiments now await evidence of direct polymerization of microtubules on membrane fragments.

The antimitotic herbicide isopropyl N-phenylcarbamate (IPC) appears to have no specific affinity for microtubule protein and yet may have a direct effect on organizing centers in plant cells. The exposure of dividing *Haemanthus* (72) endosperm cells to IPC results in the formation of a multipolar spindle. This unusual effect was confirmed in dividing cells of the alga *Oedogonium* (38) and was shown to result from a fragmentation of the polar spindle organizing centers. IPC also appears to have a direct effect on the organizing centers for cytoplasmic microtubules in the unicell *Ochromonas* (24). *Ochromonas* in the presence of IPC (following treatment with hydrostatic pressure sufficient to depolymerize the existing microtubules) assembles macrotubules (see preceding section) on the rhizoplast organizing center. Exposure of nondividing cells to pressure or IPC alone did not produce macrotubules, but, in the presence of IPC, dividing cells (which normally assemble microtubules) now assemble macrotubules on the mitotic rhizoplast.

The conservative nature of tubulins and their ability to copolymerize with heterologous seeds (e.g. axonemes, 3, 14, 29) suggest that it should be possible to assemble tubules onto organizing centers in vitro. Several successful efforts have verified this assumption. An apparently unstructured organizing center has been isolated from activated surf clam eggs which will polymerize surf clam tubulin into asters in vitro (174). The isolated basal body apparatus from *Chlamydomonas* assembles chick brain tubulin principally by distal addition to the basal body tubules (145). In addition some microtubules assemble on a structure between the two basal bodies (145) that in vivo is an apparent initiation site for cytoplasmic microtubules

(130). The basal body rootlets in *Polytomella,* which provide in vivo organizing centers for large numbers of cytoplasmic microtubles (25), will also function as assembly sites for brain tubulin in vitro (149). This general approach using non-specific tubulin offers promising possibilities for assaying the presence of polymerization-competent organizing centers in vitro and for dissecting some of the different functions that organizing centers may perform in vivo.

The occurrence of organizing centers is not conspicuously common in other self-assembly systems, but one would predict that structures with functions similar to the organizing centers for microtubules would be found in systems where spatial regulation is important. For example, the distribution of flagella on bacteria may be species specific (101) and may be considered to be regulated by an organizing center, the flagellar hook. The flagellar hook (*a*) functions in initiation of flagellar assembly (74); (*b*) provides orientation since flagellin only assembles on the distal tip of the hook (77); (*c*) in conjunction with the inherent polarity of the flagellum does confer directionality of growth (79); and (*d*) dictates the pattern of flagella on the cell since flagella do not form in cells lacking hooks (182).

APPARENT COMMON MECHANISMS OF SELF-ASSEMBLY IN HIGHER ORDERS

It is evident even from a consideration of these few reasonably well characterized self-assembly systems that some generalizations emerge: (*a*) subunits may be dramatically or subtly modified during or before assembly; (*b*) accessory molecules in addition to the repeating subunits may be present and required for polymer assembly; and (*c*) the assembly process appears to follow similar thermodynamic principles in a wide variety of systems.

Subunit Modification

Among the preassembly subunit modifications examined above are those involving removal of specific portions of subunits (collagen molecule) and the production of new subunits through cleavage and fusion of other molecules (bacteriophage λ). The apparent purpose of these relatively conspicuous modifications would appear to be to impose restraints on the reversibility of subunit assembly (53). Extensively modified proteins are essentially irreversibly polymerized or if depolymerized, cannot return to the original subunit pool.

In addition to these more or less dramatic changes in composition, subtle conformational changes may also occur in subunits during polymerization. Changes in circular dichroism (CD), optical rotatory dispersion (ORD), and intrinsic fluorescence (IF) have shown that during some polymerizations [e.g. TMV (166) and bacterial flagella (92, 163)] that the amount of protein α helix increases relative to β helix and random coil. In bacterial flagella these changes have been interpreted to suggest conformational changes may be requisite to subunit addition (6), but it is not entirely clear whether such changes precede polymerization, i.e. produce an activated monomer. Observed CD changes in microtubule tubulin at different temperatures (165) are difficult to interpret in terms of polymerization, but it is of interest that α helix structure is lost in subunits under denaturing conditions and that the loss can be prevented by various nucleotides, colchicine, and vinblastine. It would be consistent with these observations to expect tubulin CD changes during polymerization to be similar to those observed with flagellin and TMV protein although such measurements have not yet been made.

Conformational changes identified during bacterial flagellin and TMV polymerization might be attributable to the general finding that polymerization in many self-assembling systems is entropically driven and is accompanied by hydrophobic interactions within the subunits (98). Presumably such hydrophobic interactions would result in some rearrangements of subunit conformations and give rise to observed changes in CD. However, only limited hydrophobic interactions (or change in cohesive water associated with protein subunits) is apparently required to promote polymerization in some polymers as in the large subunit of glutamate dehydrogenase (157). Therefore CD changes might be expected to be small during polymerization mediated by hydrophobic interactions. Since the conformational changes observed in TMV and bacteria flagella are of a larger order, it seems probable that these changes may reflect protein-protein interactions during polymerization.

Accessory Molecules

That accessory molecules may frequently implement, catalyze, or co-polymerize with assembling polymers is of interest in considering possible mechanisms of the control of self-assembly. Accessory molecules may assume many forms such as: (a) the RNA of TMV, which initiates and terminates virus assembly (30, 42); (b) the recycling polypeptide which may serve to scaffold head protein in P22 (70, 71); (c) anions in in vitro flagellin assembly (167); and)d) the several proteins (MAPs, 145, TAU, 171 factors) which have been implicated in tubulin assembly in vitro. Interest in accessory proteins centers on their effects on assembly per se and on their possible regulatory role in polymerization-depolymerization in vivo. It seems clear, however, at least in the examples discussed above, that there is no accessory molecule common to all these systems and therefore presumably diverse regulatory mechanisms.

In vitro polymerization of microtubules may be inhibited or stimulated by divalent cations depending on concentration. Polymerization is inhibited by Ca^{2+} in millimolar concentration [its removal by specific chelators was in fact the key to the first successful polyme. zation in vitro (173)], while in micromolar concentrations Ca^{2+} may substitute for Mg^{2+} under some conditions (115). Ca^{2+} does not appear to exert its effect directly on the tubulin dimer, as there appears to be no specific binding site for Ca^{2+} (152). An alternative site of action may be through mediation of the activities of some other cofactor such as protein kinase or cyclic AMP (64). Protein kinases catalyze addition or removal of phosphoryl groups utilizing nucleotides as donors or acceptors (154). Protein kinases may be associated with microtubule protein although there is little current agreement on which fraction becomes phosphorylated or what might be its significance for assembly. Recent experiments suggest that a cAMP-stimulated phosphorylation of a high molecular weight protein, but not the 6S dimer, can occur in vitro (144). Other evidence indicates that the 6S protein (β tubulin) may also be phosphorylated in vivo, but at different sites than when phosphorylated in vitro (44, 45). Current evidence suggests the protein kinase is not associated with the tubulin molecule itself but with one or more of the accessory proteins (MAPs, TAU, etc). It remains to be determined whether these protein kinases play a direct role in microtubule assembly, but it is probably significant that the degree of microtubule phosphorylation changes during different phases of the cell cycle of HeLa cells (123). Such changes may reflect differences in amounts of polymerized or unpolymerized microtubule protein. The possibility of a specific inhibitor for assembly must also be considered (28, 29, 52).

The occasional differences in response of the in vivo and in vitro polymers to the same factors serve as a reminder that the in vitro assemblies are performed under highly artificial conditions, and thus far use only brain tubulin. Furthermore, unlike virus assembly or flagellin assembly, to date there is no assay available to test the functionality of in vitro assembled microtubules. For these reasons the role of accessory molecules in microtubule assembly must be interpreted with caution. Nonetheless it is clear that microtubule polymerization can be affected by a large variety of intrinsic and extrinsic factors. This may be important in the sensitive regulation of transient polymers.

Other kinds of potential regulators operate in different assembly systems. In the assembly of the tetrameric lactic dehydrogenase (LDH), the choice of subunits appears to operate on a random basis (51). Thus the availability, i.e. the rate of synthesis, of monomeric units determines which of the five potential isozymes is actually assembled. In other cases, such as tail assembly in bacteriophage T4, the availability of monomers is not limiting (89), but interactions between subunits occur in a sequential manner governed perhaps by conformational changes which must occur before the next sequential step can be initiated. In phage T3–infected cells, assembly of a modified subunit in host RNA polymerase results in greatly altered enzyme activity (40).

Unifying Principles in these Higher Order Self-Assembly Systems

Regardless of the specific molecules involved, the nature of processing, and the presence or absence of different accessory molecules, there appear to be some fundamental similarities in the basic mechanisms of higher order self-assembly. 1. In TMV, tubulin, and probably flagellin a critical concentration of subunit is required before assembly can be initiated. Such requirements have been considered analogous to phase transitions (115) because an abrupt change in the physical state (monomer-polymer) is related to concentration and temperature. 2. Assembly is in general a two-step reaction characterized by nucleation events or by an initiation step followed by growth or elongation. Nucleation of protein folding and initiation of higher order assembly both accomplish the same end (accelerate assembly) but are not entirely homologous (see section on protein folding). The growth step is generally considered not to be of the cooperative kind which assumes that the free energy for the formation of a bond is dependent on the number of bonds previously formed (98), but rather to be one of *linear condensation polymerization* (57) in which the free energy of bond formation is independent of the number of bonds previously formed. Thus the chemical reactivity of a combining site is completely independent of the length of the chain of which it is a terminus. Current views favor linear condensation polymerization as the probable mechanism for polymerization, although compelling direct evidence of condensation polymerization awaits further study. 3. The general role of hydrophobic interaction at every level of self-assembly is striking. As recently summarized (99, 138), widely diverse self-assembly systems are generally characterized by high heat capacities, positive enthalopies, and positive entropies during polymerization. Such findings lend strong support to the proposal that the release of water is a basic mechanism in the driving force for polymerization. 4. Finally, to a remarkable degree polar growth is a general characteristic of tubular polymers, e.g. TMV, microtubules, phage tails, and bacterial flagella. The mechanics for polar growth are not well understood, and polar growth can often be overridden if the concentration of subunit is sufficiently high (18). Nonetheless the general property of polarity is a striking and consistent property of those higher ordered systems which have identifiable ends. Polarity is of course a basic property of all developing cellular systems. Its manifestations at the molecular and supramolecular level suggest the assembling cell components are already predisposed toward still higher levels of organization.

Literature Cited

1. Abram, D., Koffler, H. 1964. *J. Mol. Biol.* 9:168–85
2. Adiarte, A. L., Vogel, D., Jaenicke, R. 1975. *Biochem. Biophys. Res. Commun.* 63:432–40
3. Allen, C., Borisy, G. G. 1974. *J. Mol. Biol.* 90:381–402
4. Anfinsen, C. B. 1973. *Science* 181:223–30
5. Apte, B. N., Zipser, D. 1973. *Proc. Natl. Acad. Sci. USA* 70:2969–73
6. Asakura, S. 1970. *Adv. Biophys.* 1:99–155
7. Asakura, S., Eguchi, G., Iino, T. 1964. *J. Mol. Biol.* 10:42–56
8. Bailey, A. J., Robins, S. P., Balian, G. 1974. *Nature* 251:105–9
9. Bardele, C. F. 1973. *Cytobiologie* 7:442–88
10. Becker, J. S., Oliver, J. M., Berlin, R. D. 1975. *Nature* 254:152–54
11. Behnke, O. 1971. *Int. Rev. Exp. Pathol.* 9:1–91
12. Berg, R. A., Prockop, D. J. 1973. *Biochemistry* 12:3395–3401
13. Berry, R. W., Shelanski, M. L. 1972. *J. Mol. Biol.* 71:71–80
14. Binder, L. I., Dentler, W. L., Rosenbaum, J. L. 1975. *Proc. Natl. Acad. Sci. USA* 72:1122–26
15. Bloodgood, R. A. 1974. *Cytobios* 9:142–61
16. Bode, W. 1973. *Angew. Chem. Int. Ed.* 12:683–93
17. Borisy, G. G., Olmsted, J. B. 1972. *Science* 177:1196–97
18. Borisy, G. G., Olmsted, J. B., Marcum, J. M., Allen, C. 1974. *Fed. Proc.* 33:167–73
19. Borisy, G. G., Taylor, E. 1967. *J. Cell Biol.* 34:525–33
20. Bornstein, P. 1974. *J. Supramol. Struct.* 2:108–20
21. Bornstein, P. 1974. *Ann. Rev. Biochem.* 43:567–603
22. Bouck, G. B., Brown, D. L. 1973. *J. Cell Biol.* 56:340–59
23. Brown, D. L., Bouck, G. B. 1973. *J. Cell Biol.* 56:360–78
24. Ibid. 1974. 61:514–36
25. Brown, D. L., Massalski, A., Patenaude, R. 1976. *J. Cell Biol.* In press
26. Bryan, J. 1972. *Biochemistry* 11:2611–16
27. Bryan, J. 1974. *Fed. Proc.* 33:152–57
28. Burns, R. G. 1973. *Exp. Cell Res.* 81:285–92
29. Burns, R. G., Starling, D. 1974. *J. Cell Sci.* 14:411–19
30. Butler, P. J. G. 1974. *J. Mol. Biol.* 82:333–41
31. Butler, P. J. G., Klug, A. 1971. *Nature* 229:47–50

32. Calladine, C. R. 1975. *Nature* 255: 121–24
33. Cande, W. Z., Snyder, J., Smith, D., Summers, K., McIntosh, J. R. 1974. *Proc. Natl. Acad. Sci. USA* 71:1559–63
34. Casjens, S., King, J. 1974. *J. Supramol. Struct.* 2:202–24
35. Caspar, D. L. D. 1963. *Adv. Protein Chem.* 18:37–121
36. Caspar, D. L. D., Klug, A. 1962. *Cold Spring Harbor Symp. Quant. Biol.* 27:1–24
37. Chothia, C. 1975. *Nature* 254:304–8
38. Coss, R. A., Pickett-Heaps, J. D. 1974. *J. Cell Biol.* 63:84–98
39. Dentler, W. L., Granett, S., Rosenbaum, J. L. 1975. *J. Cell Biol.* 65:237–41
40. Dharmgrongartama, B., Mahadik, S. P., Srinivasan, P. R. 1973. *Proc. Natl. Acad. Sci. USA* 70:2845–49
41. Durham, A. C. H., Finch, J. T., Klug, A. 1971. *Nature* 229:37–42
42. Durham, A. C. H., Klug, A. 1971. *Nature* 229:42–46
43. Dustin, P. 1974. *Arch. Biol.* 85:263–88
44. Eipper, B. A. 1974. *J. Biol. Chem.* 249:1398–1406
45. Ibid, 1407–16
46. Emerson, S. U., Tokuyasu, K., Simon, M. 1970. *Science* 169:190–92
47. Epstein, C. J., Goldberger, R. F., Anfinsen, C. B. 1963. *Cold Spring Harbor Symp. Quant. Biol.* 28:439–49
48. Epstein, H. F., Schechter, A. N., Chen, R. F., Anfinsen, C. B. 1971. *J. Mol. Biol.* 60:499–508
49. Erickson, H. P. 1974. *J. Supramol. Struct.* 2:393–411
50. Erickson, H. P. 1974. *J. Cell Biol.* 60:153–67
51. Everse, J., Kaplan, N. O. 1973. *Adv. Enzymol.* 37:61–133
52. Farrell, K. W., Burns, R. G. 1975. *J. Cell Sci.* 17:669–81
53. Fessler, J. H. 1974. *J. Supramol. Struct.* 2:99–102
54. Fessler, J. H., Tandberg, W. D. 1975. *J. Supramol. Struct.* 3:17–23
55. Fessler, L. I., Burgeson, R. E., Morris, N. P., Fessler, J. H. 1973. *Proc. Natl. Acad. Sci. USA* 70:2993–96
56. Fessler, L. I., Rudd, C., Fessler, J. H. 1974. *J. Supramol. Struct.* 2:103–7
57. Flory, P. J. 1969. *Statistical Mechanics of Chain Molecules.* New York: Wiley. 432pp.
57a. Flory, P. J. 1975. *Science* 188:1268–76
58. Fraenkel-Conrat, H. 1970. *Ann. Rev. Microbiol.* 24:463–78
59. Fraenkel-Conrat, H., Williams, R. C. 1955. *Proc. Natl. Acad. Sci.* 41:690–98
60. Friedmann, T. 1974. *Proc. Natl. Acad. Sci. USA* 71:257–59
61. Gaskin, F., Litman, D. J., Cantor, C. R., Shelanski, M. L. 1975. *J. Supramol. Struct.* 3:39–50
62. Gerber, B. R., Asakura, S., Oosawa, F. 1973. *J. Mol. Biol.* 74:467–87
63. Gerber, B. R., Noguchi, H. 1967. *J. Mol. Biol.* 26:197–210
64. Gillespie, E. 1971. *J. Cell Biol.* 50:544–49
65. Grant, M. E., Prockop, D. J. 1972. *N. Engl. J. Med.* 286:194–99
66. Hamlin, J., Zabin, I. 1972. *Proc. Natl. Acad. Sci.* 69:412–16
67. Hanzely, L., Olah, L. V. 1973. *Cytologia* 38:623–33
68. Harris, W. F. 1974. *J. Theor. Biol.* 47:295–308
69. Heath, I. B. 1974. *J. Cell Biol.* 60:204–20
70. Hendrix, R. W., Casjens, S. R. 1974. *J. Supramol. Struct.* 2:329–36
71. Hendrix, R. W., Casjens, S. R. 1974. *Proc. Natl. Acad. Sci. USA* 71:1451–55
72. Hepler, P. K., Jackson, W. T. 1969. *J. Cell Sci* 5:727–33
73. Hepler, P. K., Palevitz, B. A. 1974. *Ann. Rev. Plant Physiol.* 25:309–62
74. Hilmen, M., Silverman, M., Simon, M. 1974. *J. Supramol. Struct.* 2:360–71
75. Hinkley, R. E., Samson, F. E. 1972. *J. Cell Biol.* 53:258–63
76. Hulmes, D. J. S., Miller, A., Parry, D. A. D., Piez, K. A., Woodhead-Galloway, J. 1973. *J. Mol. Biol.* 79:137–48
77. Iino, T. 1974. *J. Supramol. Struct.* 2:372–84
78. Iino, T. 1969. *J. Gen. Microbiol.* 56:227–39
79. Iino, T., Suzuki, H., Yamaguchi, S. 1972. *Nature New Biol.* 237:238–40
80. Inoue, S. 1959. *Rev. Mod. Phys.* 31:402–8
81. Inoue, S., Borisy, G. G., Kiehart, D. P. 1974. *J. Cell Biol.* 62:175–84
82. Inoue, S., Fuseler, J., Salmon, E. D., Ellis, G. W. 1975. *Biophys. J.* 15:725–44
83. Inoue, S., Sato, H. 1967. *J. Gen. Physiol.* 50:259–92
84. Jacobs, M., Smith, H., Taylor, E. W. 1974. *J. Mol. Biol.* 89:455–68
85. Kagawa, H., Asakura, S., Iino, T. 1973. *J. Bacteriol.* 113:1474–81
86. Kaiser, D., Syvanen, M., Masuda, T. 1974. *J. Supramol. Struct.* 2:318–28
87. Kibuchi, Y., King, J. 1975. *J. Supramol. Struct.* 3:24–38

88. King, J., Casjens, S. R. 1974. *Nature* 251:112–19
89. King, J., Lenk, E. V., Botstein, D. 1973. *J. Mol. Biol.* 80:697–731
90. Kirschner, M. W., Williams, R. C. 1974. *J. Supramol. Struct.* 2:412–28
91. Kirschner, M. W., Williams, R. C., Weingarten, M., Gerhart, J. C. 1974. *Proc. Natl. Acad. Sci.* 71:1159–63
92. Klein, D., Foster, J. F., Koffler, H. 1969. *Biochem. Biophys. Res. Commun.* 36:844–50
93. Kohn, L. D., Isersky, C., Zupnik, J., Lenaers, A., Lee, G., Lapiere, C. M. 1974. *Proc. Natl. Acad. Sci. USA* 71:40–44
94. Kornguth, S. E., Sunderland, E. 1975. *Biochim. Biophys. Acta* 393:100–14
95. Kresheck, G. C., Schneider, H., Scheraga, H. A. 1965. *J. Phys. Chem.* 69:3132–44
96. Kuntz, I. D., Kauzmann, W. 1974. *Adv. Protein Chem.* 28:239–345
97. Kushner, D. J. 1969. *Bacteriol. Rev.* 33:302–45
98. Lauffer, M. A. 1971. *Subunits In Biological Systems, Part A*, ed. S. N. Timasheff, G. D. Fasman, 149–99. New York: Dekker
99. Lauffer, M. A. 1975. *Entropy-Driven Processes in Biology.* New York: Springer-Verlag. 264 pp.
100. Lee, J. C., Harrison, D., Timasheff, S. N. 1975. *Biophys. J.* 15:75A (Abstr.)
101. Leifson, E. 1960. *An Atlas of Bacterial Flagellation.* New York: Academic
102. Lowy, J., McDonough, M. W. 1964. *Nature* 204:125–27
103. Luduena, R. F., Woodward, D. O. 1973. *Proc. Natl. Acad. Sci. USA* 70:3594–98
104. Manton, I., Kowallik, K., Von Stosch, H. A. 1970. *J. Cell Sci.* 6:131–57
105. Margulis, L. 1973. *Int. Rev. Cytol.* 34:333–61
106. Moens, P. B., Rapport, E. 1971. *J. Cell Biol.* 50:344–61
107. Monson, J. M., Bornstein, P. 1973. *Proc. Natl. Acad. Sci. USA* 70:3521–25
108. Murphy, W. H., von der Mark, K., McEneany, L. S. G., Bornstein, P. 1975. *Biochemistry* 14:3243–50
109. Nemethy, G., Scheraga, H. A. 1962. *J. Phys. Chem.* 66:1773–89
110. Nomura, M. 1970. *Bacteriol. Rev.* 34:228–77
111. O'Brien, E. J., Bennett, P. M. 1972. *J. Mol. Biol.* 70:133–52
112. Ohno, T., Inoue, H., Okada, Y. 1972. *Proc. Natl. Acad. Sci.* 69:3680–83

113. Ohno, T., Okada, Y., Nonomura, Y., Inoue, H. 1975. *J. Biochem.* 77:313–19
114. Olmsted, J. B., Borisy, G. G. 1973. *Ann. Rev. Biochem.* 42:507–40
115. Olmsted, J. B., Marcum, J. M., Johnson, K. A., Allen, C., Borisy, G. G. 1974. *J. Supramol. Struct.* 2:429–50
116. Olsen, B. R., Prockop, D. J. 1974. *Proc. Natl. Acad. Sci. USA* 71:2033–37
117. Oosawa, F., Higashi, S. 1967. *Progr. Theor. Biol.* 1:79–164
118. Peterson, T. L. 1975. *J. Biol. Chem.* 250:5183–91
119. Pickett-Heaps, J. D. 1969. *Cytobios* 1:257–80
120. Ibid 1972. 5:59–77
121. Pickett-Heaps, J. D., McDonald, K. L., Tippit, D. H. 1975. *Protoplasma* 86:205–42
122. Piez, K. A., Miller, A. 1974. *J. Supramol. Struct.* 2:121–37
123. Piras, R., Piras, M. M. 1975. *Proc. Natl. Acad. Sci. USA* 72:1161–65
124. Porter, K. R. 1966. *Principles of Biomolecular Organization*, ed. G. E. Wolstenholme, M. O'Connor, 308–45. Boston: Little, Brown
125. Onorato, L., Showe, M. K. 1975. *J. Mol. Biol.* 92:395–412
126. Ramachandran, G. N., Bansal, M., Bhatnagar, R. S. 1973. *Biochim. Biophys. Acta* 322:166–71
127. Rebhun, L. I., Rosenbaum, J. L., Lefebvre, P., Smith, G. 1974. *Nature* 249:113–15
128. Richards, F. M. 1974. *J. Mol. Biol.* 82:1–14
129. Richards, K. E., Williams, R. C. 1973. *Biochemistry* 12:4574–81
130. Ringo, D. L. 1967. *J. Cell Biol.* 33:543–71
131. Roberts, K. 1974. *Progr. Biophys. Mol. Biol.* 22:373–419
132. Robinow, C. F., Marak, J. 1966. *J. Cell Biol.* 29:129–51
133. Robson, B. 1974. *Biochem. J.* 141:853–68
134. Roos, U. P. 1975. *J. Cell Sci.* 18:315–26
135. Rosenbaum, J. L., Moulder, J. E., Ringo, D. L. 1969. *J. Cell Biol.* 41:600–19
136. Sachs, D. H., Schechter, A. N., Eastlake, A., Anfinsen, C. B. 1972. *Proc. Natl. Acad. Sci. USA* 69:3790–94
137. Salmon, E. D. 1975. *J. Cell Biol.* 65:603–14
138. Ibid. 66:114–27
139. Sanchez, I. C. 1974. *Reviews in Macromolecular Chemistry*, ed. G. B. Butler, K. F. O'Driscoll, M. Shen, 2:113–48. New York: Dekker

140. Scheraga, H. A. 1974. In *Current Topics In Biochemistry 1973*, ed. C. B. Anfinsen, A. N. Schechter. New York: Academic
141. Sela, M., White, F. H., Anfinsen, C. B. 1957. *Science* 125:691–92
142. Shelanski, M. L., Gaskin, F., Cantor, C. R. 1973. *Proc. Natl. Acad. Sci. USA* 70:765–68
143. Showe, M. K., Black, L. W. 1973. *Nature* 242:70–75
144. Sloboda, R. D., Rudolph, S. A., Rosenbaum, J. L., Greengard, P. 1975. *Proc. Natl. Acad. Sci. USA* 72:177–81
145. Snell, W. J., Dentler, W. L., Haimo, L. T., Binder, L. I., Rosenbaum, J. L. 1974. *Science* 185:357–60
146. Speakman, P. J. 1971. *Nature* 229:241–43
147. Spirin, A. S. 1973. *Subunits in Biological Systems*, Part B, ed. G. D. Fasman, S. N. Timasheff, 71–120. New York: Dekker. 373 pp.
148. Stadler, J., Franke, W. W. 1974. *J. Cell Biol.* 60:297–303
149. Stearns, M., Connolly, J., Brown, D. L. 1976. *Science* 191:189–91
150. Stephens, R. E. 1973. *J. Cell Biol.* 57:133–47
151. Stevens, C. L., Lauffer, M. A. 1965. *Biochemistry* 4:31–37
152. Straprans, I., Kenney, W. C., Dirksen, E. R. 1975. *Biochem. Biophys. Res. Commun.* 62:92–97
153. Studier, W. F. 1973. *J. Mol. Biol.* 79:237–48
154. Taborsky, G. 1974. *Adv. Protein Chem.* 28:1–210
155. Tanford, C. 1968. *Adv. Protein Chem.* 23:121–282
156. Tanford, C. 1973. *The Hydrophobic Effect*. New York: Wiley. 200 pp.
157. Thusius, D., Dessen, P., Jallon, J. M. 1975. *J. Mol. Biol.* 92:413–32
158. Tilney, L. G. 1971. *J. Cell Biol.* 51:837–54
159. Tilney, L. G., Porter, K. R. 1967. *J. Cell Biol.* 34:327–43
160. Tucker, J. B. 1970. *J. Cell Sci.* 7:793–805

161. Tye, B. K., Botstein, D. 1974. *J. Supramol. Struct.* 2:225–38
162. Tyson, G. E., Bulger, R. E. 1973. *Z. Zellforsch. Mikrosk. Anat.* 141:443–58
163. Uratani, Y., Asakura, S., Imahori, K. 1972. *J. Mol. Biol.* 67:85–98
164. Valdes, R., Ackers, G. K. 1974. *Biochem. Biophys. Res. Commun.* 60:1403–9
165. Ventilla, M., Cantor, C. R., Shelanski, M. L. 1971. *Biochemistry* 11:1554–61
166. Vogel, D., Jaenicke, R. 1974. *Eur. J. Biochem.* 41:607–15
167. Wakabayashi, K., Hotani, H., Asakura, S. 1969. *Biochim. Biophys. Acta* 175:195–203
168. Warfield, R. K. N., Bouck, G. B. 1974. *Science* 186:1219–21
169. Warfield, R. K. N., Bouck, G. B. 1975. *J. Mol. Biol.* 93:117–20
170. Weingarten, M. D., Lockwood, A. H., Hwo, S. Y., Kirschner, M. W. 1975. *Proc. Natl. Acad. Sci. USA* 72:1858–62
171. Weingarten, M. D., Suter, M. M., Littman, D. R., Kirschner, M. W. 1974. *Biochemistry* 13:5529–37
172. Weinstock, M., Leblond, C. P. 1974. *J. Cell Biol.* 60:92–127
173. Weisenberg, R. C. 1972. *Science* 177:1104–5
174. Weisenberg, R. C., Rosenfeld, A. C. 1975. *J. Cell Biol.* 64:146–58
175. Wetlaufer, D. B. 1973. *Proc. Natl. Acad. Sci.* 70:697–701
176. Wetlaufer, D. B., Ristow, S. 1973. *Ann. Rev. Biochem.* 42:135–58
177. Wilson, L., Bryan, J. 1974. *Adv. Cell Mol. Biol.* 3
178. Wilson, L., Meza, I. 1973. *J. Cell Biol.* 58:709–19
179. Witman, G., Carlson, K., Berliner, J., Rosenbaum, J. 1972. *J. Cell Biol.* 54:507–39
180. Witman, G., Carlson, K., Rosenbaum, J. 1972. *J. Cell Biol.* 54:540–55
181. Wu, T. T., Fitch, W. M., Margoliash, E. 1974. *Ann. Rev. Biochem.* 43:539–66
182. Yamaguchi, S., Iino, T., Horiguchi, T., Ohta, K. 1972. *J. Gen. Microbiol.* 70:59

Ann. Rev. Plant Physiol. 1976. 27:95–117

MOBILIZATION OF STORAGE PROTEINS OF SEEDS[1]

❖7603

Floyd M. Ashton

Department of Botany, University of California, Davis, California 95616

CONTENTS

INTRODUCTION

During germination the seed rapidly changes from a quiescent state to a dynamic state. Metabolism increases rapidly. The substrate for this rapid metabolism is known as storage reserves. The largest amounts of these storage reserves are usually

[1]Abbreviations used: ABA (abscisic acid); BA (6-benzylaminopurine); BAEE (α-N-benzoyl-L-arginine ethyl ester); BAPA (α-N-benzoyl-L-arginine β-nitroanilide); BTEE (N-benzoyl-L-tyrosine ethyl ester); DFP (diisopropylfluorophosphate); EDTA (ethylenediaminetetraacetic acid); GA (gibberellic acid); IAA (indole-3-acetic acid); TAME (β-tosyl-L-arginine methyl ester); TCA (trichloroacetic acid).

found in the endosperm of monocots or cotyledons of dicots; however, other organs may also be involved. These storage reserves consist of lipids, proteins, and carbohydrates. During germination they are hydrolyzed and the products used by the axis for the synthesis of protoplasm, structural components, and subsequent growth. The initial energy required for the metabolic processes and growth is also derived from these storage reserves. Although all three types of storage reserves occur in most seeds, the relative concentration of each varies considerably among various species.

The storage proteins of seeds are found primarily in subcellular organelles called protein bodies. It is generally agreed that the storage protein is hydrolyzed to amino acids by proteolytic enzymes. The amino acids may remain in the storage tissue but most are translocated to the developing axis tissues. They are used for the synthesis of various enzymes and structural proteins. Some of the amino acids may also undergo deamination. These products may then be used for the synthesis of non-nitrogen containing compounds or further metabolized to yield energy.

Although the author is unaware of any recent review primarily devoted to this topic, the reader will find substantive information from the following sources (3, 4, 29, 49, 76, 112).

This review is concerned with the mobilization of storage protein of seeds during germination. Particular emphasis will be given to the three major components involved: the protein body, the storage protein, and the proteolytic enzymes, including their subcellular localization, respective changes during germination, and control mechanisms.

PROTEIN BODIES

The bulk of the storage protein of most seeds is located in distinct organelles which are most often referred to as protein bodies in current literature. Other terms such as protein granule, protein vacuole, aleurone body, aleurone vacuole, and aleurone grain are also frequently used.

Altschul et al (4) presented an historical case for the use of the term "aleurone grains" for these subcellular bodies. However, the fact that they occur in many tissues other than the aleurone layer of monocot seeds has resulted in a decrease in the use of this ambiguous term.

Protein Body Distribution

Protein bodies are found in haploid, diploid, and triploid storage tissues of seeds and in the axis (Altschul et al 4). Most monocots have either triploid storage tissue (the endosperm) or diploid storage tissue (the perisperm). Both of these may contain protein bodies. In some species the protein bodies may occur throughout the endosperm while in others they may be restricted to the outer layer (the aleurone layer). Most dicots do not have special storage tissues and most of the protein bodies are located within a part of the embryo, the cotyledons (Esau 36). The axes of both monocots (47, 48, 93–95, 97, 110) and dicots (63, 148) also contain protein bodies. In gymnosperms, haploid storage tissue derived from the megagametophyte and the embryos contain protein bodies (Cecich 23).

Protein Body Structure and Composition

Protein bodies are spherical or oval organelles that contain storage protein and other substances bound by a single limiting membrane. This single membrane is often difficult to see in many photomicrographs. Ultrastructural studies have shown that all protein bodies are not alike. They vary in internal structure and size. Diameters have been reported from 0.1 μm to 22 μm; however, the average is 1.5 μm to 8 μm. The simplest protein bodies have a granular or homogeneous matrix without subunits (110, 113). However, some have characteristic ultrastructure; for example, clumps of fine filaments in kidney beans (*Phaseolus vulgaris*) (97) and granular fine structure of individual particles of 100 Å diameter in wheat (*Triticum vulgare*) (18). Other protein bodies are somewhat more highly structured with a concentric pattern of light and dark layers (62, 83, 109). In some cases a dense core also may be present (62, 109), or the layers may be located mainly toward the periphery of the protein bodies (57, 83, 98). In rice (*Oryza sativa*) the electron dense layers appear to be composed of minute granules approximately 150 Å in diameter (83).

The most highly structured protein bodies have one or more subunits embedded within the finely granular proteinaceous matrix. Rost (110) has used the types of subunits present to categorize angiosperm protein bodies into three groups: Group 1, protein bodies without subunits; Group 2, protein bodies with globoid subunit; Group 3, protein bodies with globoid and crystalloid subunits.

The *crystalloid* is a crystalline protein deposit. Crystalloids isolated from hemp (*Cannabis sativa*) are roughly spherical but somewhat angular (St. Angelo et al 124). The surface appears pebbly, as if composed of subunits. Solubilized crystalloid and edesten solutions give very similar images, polygonal-shaped units as small as 80 Å. Freeze-etched replicas of barley (*Hordeum vulgare*) protein bodies show crystalloids with a hexagonal crystal structure with a lattice period of 130 Å (Buttrose 19). The freeze-etched protein bodies of squash (*Cucurbita maxima*) have crystalloids with concentric fracture surfaces (Lott & Vollmer 71).

The *globoid* consists of storage phosphate compounds. The major compound is phytin, an isoluble Ca, Mg salt of inositol hexaphosphoric acid (Lui & Altschul 73). The globoid is very brittle; therefore, it is not penetrated well by fixatives and resins used in electron microscopy and tends to shatter when cut. This often leaves a hole in the section or small fragments of globoid material around the globoid area. Isolated globoids viewed with a light microscope are regular, round bodies which refract light strongly (Suvorov et al 129). Freeze-etched protein bodies have globoids with rough, structureless fracture faces (19). Lott et al (70) and Lott & Vollmer (71) have further divided the globoid of squash into two parts: a globoid crystal, which corresponds to what others have called the globoid, and a soft globoid, an electron translucent area surrounding the globoid crystal. This is termed soft because it often smears in freeze-etch preparations. Also some authors have identified a membrane surrounding the globoid (19, 61, 129).

The major components of protein bodies are storage proteins, located in the matrix and crystalloid, and phytin, located in the globoid. In addition, Poux (107) has shown the existence of soluble K phytate in the proteinaceous matrix of cucumber (*Cucumis sativus*) and flax (*Linum usitatissimum*). Several other substances have been reported to be present in protein bodies. These have been found by chemical analysis of purified protein body pellets and histochemical or energy dispersive X-ray analysis of thin sections. Inorganic elements other than those reported to be associated with phytin (P, Ca, Mg, K) are Mn (111, 119), Cu (111), Na (130), S (69), and Cl (69). Mn, Cu, and Na were found in protein body pellets by chemical analysis, whereas the S and Cl were detected in the proteinaceous region using X-ray analysis of thin sections. In one study where Mn was detected, the Mn was considered to be part of the storage protein molecule (111). One atom of Mn was present in each molecule of conarachin, a storage protein of peanuts (*Arachis hypogaea*). Lipids have also been reported to be present in protein bodies (55, 84, 134); however, these may very well be contaminants except for the membrane phospholipids (134). RNA has also been found in protein bodies (31, 113, 144, 145), although one investigator reported no evidence of RNA (86).

Chemical analysis of globoids isolated from protein bodies have suggested that in addition to phytin, protein, phospholipids, RNA, oxalic acid, K, and Mn may also be components of globoids (119, 129). Using cytochemical methods on barley aleurone tissue, Jacobsen et al (55) found lipid present in the globoid and an unknown substance in the crystalloid which stained green with toluidine blue.

Enzymatic activity of acid proteases and acid phosphatases have been found in protein bodies isolated from ungerminated seeds. These are discussed in the section on Enzymes. More details on the proteins found in protein bodies may be found in the section on Storage Proteins of Seeds.

Protein Body Fate

Several ultrastructural studies on protein body fate during seed germination have been reported. The theory that protein bodies give rise to the cell's central vacuole was advanced as early as 1908 by Guillermond (41). Later investigators who have supported this theory are Dengler (30), Jones (60), Lott & Vollmer (72), Srivastava & Paulson (122), and Davis (28). Additional indirect evidence has been given by Klein & Ben-Shaul (63), Nieuwdorp & Buys (94), Öpik (96), Paleg & Hyde (102), Rost (110), Yoo (148). Protein body degradation apparently starts either within the protein mass or at the periphery of the protein mass. When it starts within the protein mass it appears as electron negative areas in the form of general dissolution or internal cavities. When it starts at the periphery the initial electron negative areas are adjacent to the limiting membrane. The internal type of degradation suggests that the proteolytic enzymes originate within the proteinaceous mass whereas peripheral degradation suggests that the proteolytic enzymes are associated with the limiting membrane or originate outside the protein body.

INTERNAL DEGRADATION AND FUSION   The pattern of protein body fate most commonly reported is swelling of the organelle, followed by internal degradation of protein, then fusion of vacuoles, partially degraded protein masses, and/or protein bodies.

In several species, the contents of individual protein bodies appear to be degraded leaving vacuoles which may then fuse. In pea (*Pisum sativum*) cotyledons, the protein contents appear clumped or vacuolated indicating internal breakdown of the protein body (Bain & Mercer 11). In barley (*Hordeum vulgare*) aleurone cells, internal cavities enlarge at the expense of the protein matrix which dissolves in about 8 days (van der Eb & Nieuwdorp 138). In barley aleurone cells treated with GA_3, breakdown is much faster (Jones 58–60). Protein bodies first swell to a maximum size, then decrease in volume, become vacuolated, and then swell again after protein and phytin are mostly depleted. After 24 hr the protein bodies are reduced to vacuoles which become the large central vacuole. In pea embryo radicles, Yoo (148) states that the protein contents are degraded, leaving vacuoles. In lettuce (*Lactuca sativa*) embryos the protein bodies swell, the matrix disperses, and the protein body becomes a vacuole which may fuse with others to form the central vacuole (Srivastava & Paulson 122).

Fusion of protein bodies or of incompletely degraded protein bodies is sometimes described. In the perisperm and embryo of three *Yucca* species and in the embryo of a fourth species of *Yucca,* coalescence of protein bodies followed by breakdown and disappearance of the masses occurs (Horner & Arnott 47). In *Pisum arvense* cotyledons, the protein bodies swell and fuse to form large aggregate bodies which then disintegrate (Smith & Flinn 120). In soybean (*Glycine max*) cotyledons, protein bodies become more granular, and the limiting membrane disappears. The bodies eventually become irregular and sometimes coalesce into a single mass (Tombs 134). Protein bodies of peanut cotyledons swell and develop cavities; some fuse. The protein bodies then assume a loose spongy structure and aggregate in the center of the cell. This loose mass disintegrates into numerous fragments which disappear as germination proceeds (Bagley et al 8). In broadbean (*Vicia faba*) cotyledons also, dispersal of protein occurs in some protein bodies while others coalesce. After 15 days the cells are highly vacuolate, but proteinaceous material is often still seen within the vacuole (Briarty et al 16). Protein bodies in kidney bean cotyledons swell and become more diffuse. These then fuse and are gradually "replaced by vacuoles" (Öpik 96). In GA-treated barley aleurone cells, protein bodies coalesce and give rise to vacuoles which occupy most of the cell volume (Paleg & Hyde 102).

In squash cotyledons, protein body breakdown has been described as a process whereby during hydration protein bodies swell and become fluid-irregular masses which fuse (Davis 28). Fusion continues as the protein contents become randomly dispersed until a large empty central vacuole remains. Swollen but intact protein bodies are seen from 0 to 2 days but rarely at 3 days. Large proteinaceous masses, formed by the fusion of two or more protein bodies, are seen as early as 2 days and as late as 5 days. Vacuoles containing amorphous protein material are seen at 4 days and persist beyond 7 days. The greatest ultrastructural changes occur at 3 to 4 days. The crystalloid seems to disappear into the matrix at an early point in hydrolysis. Digestion of the globoid occurs more slowly. The phytin crystals become granular and dissolution usually appears to start at the center outward leaving a ring of granular material. These partially digested globoids may be seen in the central vacuole even after the protein has mostly dispersed. Khokhlova (61) describes a somewhat different but highly ordered degradation process in squash cotyledons. Protein bodies swell and sometimes fuse. The globoid contents do not swell but the globoid membrane does, leaving an electron permeable region lying along the globoid periphery. This zone disappears as the globoid phytin disintegrates into thread-like formations evenly distributed throughout the globoid area. The cavities develop within the matrix and increase in size until the matrix disappears leaving the crystalloid and globoid within the vacuole formed. The crystalloid next disappears. The globoid, which is now greatly enlarged and may have thread-like contents throughout or in the center, finally also disappears. Some investigations have dealt mainly with the later stages of protein body degradation in squash cotyledons (Lott & Vollmer 72). The protein bodies become a series of large aqueous vaculoes containing irregularly shaped pieces of proteinaceous material. The protein eventually disappears, and the vacuoles fuse to form the central vacuole of mesophyll cells.

PERIPHERAL DEGRADATION AND FUSION   Peripheral degradation proceeds from the protein body periphery inward rather than internally. In the perisperm of *Yucca schidigera,* degradation begins by erosion at the periphery and also internally, followed by generalized dissolution until the protein body becomes a network, and eventually only a vacuole remains (Horner & Arnott 47). In the embryo of *Clarkia rubicunda,* explored by Dengler (30), cavities appear at the periphery and internally. These enlarge until only a vacuole remains which may fuse with others forming a single large central vacuole. In the embryo of yellow foxtail (*Setaria lutescens*), studied by Rost (110), degradation begins in many locations at the protein body periphery. Vesicles appear along the margin of the degraded areas. Finally an empty vacuole remains, several of which may fuse to form larger vacuoles. Similar vesicles were seen in the degradation of corn protein bodies by Mollenhauer & Totten (85).

SUBUNIT DEGRADATION   Most investigations deal with the general process of protein body breakdown. However, several investigations, such as that of Khokhlova (61) and Davis (28), mentioned above, specifically discuss the breakdown of the globoid and crystalloid subunits also. Lott & Vollmer (72), using freeze-etched tissue, state that the first change in squash cotyledon protein bodies is the appearance of small pieces of material in the proteinaceous matrix. These have the same texture as the soft globoid, the electron permeable region surrounding the globoid. This soft globoid-like material becomes widely distributed throughout the matrix. However, by the second day of germination this material is seen less frequently and degradation of the globoid crystal has begun. This may occur in two ways: from the outside toward the center or by internal pitting. The pitted regions increase in size and number and fuse. The soft globoid may be present or absent during globoid crystal degradation. In lettuce remains of globoids can be seen as rings long after the matrix is degraded. Crystalloids may dissolve or remain intact for a long while (Srivastava & Paulson 122). In *Yucca schidigera* perisperm, the globoid and crystalloid disappear as the protein body network breaks up. In the perisperm of three other *Yucca* species, the large protein masses contain large birefringent spheroids which may be aggregations of globoids. These disappear shortly after, but details of their breakdown have not been observed (Horner & Arnott 48). In barley scutellum after 3 days, the globoids have a granular periphery and possibly a dense core. These are still present in the protein vacuoles after 10 days of germination (Nieuwdorp & Buys 94). In barley aleurone cells after 10 to 12 hr exposure to GA_3, Jones (60) observed that the globoids appear to be filled with spherical vesicle-like units without membranes. The phytin globoid is substantially depleted after 24 hr of treatment.

STORAGE PROTEINS OF SEEDS

Several reviews have been written on plant proteins that include information on seed proteins (15, 25, 92, 123), as well as two restricted to seed proteins (4, 79). The proceedings of two symposia on seed proteins have also been published (3, 54). In spite of the very significant advances that have been made in protein chemistry over the past several years, relatively little progress has been made on the chemistry of seed proteins. As in the past, much of the recent research on seed proteins has been oriented toward their use as food for man. In general, these are only of peripheral value to an understanding of the mobilization of storage seed proteins.

Osborne's studies (100) in the early 1900s resulted in the classification of plant protein of the basis of their solubilities in water and various aqueous solutions. This classification is still widely used. Proteins soluble in water are referred to as albumins; those insoluble in water but soluble in dilute salt solutions, globulins; those insoluble in the above solutions but soluble in weak acidic or basic solutions, glutelins; those insoluble in the above solutions but soluble in 70 to 80% enthanol, prolamines. In most seeds, except those of Granineae, the principal storage proteins are globulins. In the commonly grown cereals except rice, 40 to 60% of the seed protein consists of prolamines and 20 to 40% glutelins. Albumins and globulins are also present in cereal seeds. Mossé (87) has reviewed the extensive literature on the protein constituents of cereal grains. Additional information on the relative amounts of these four fractions of proteins in seeds of various species can be found in the aforementioned reviews.

The nomenclature for the storage proteins found in seeds dates to the early work of Osborne (101). The storage proteins from seeds of each species, genera, or family were given different names; for example, edestin for hemp, cucurbitin for Cucurbitacease, and legumin and vicilin of legumes. These names are still in common usage.

In general, studies on the formation of storage proteins of seeds during embryogenesis and the mobilization of these during germination have been carried out by different investigators. However, both types of studies require that the storage protein be rigorously purified and defined. Ultimately such study will require amino acid sequence and perhaps secondary structure and subunit interactions of the storage proteins.

Much of the recent research on the storage proteins in seeds has involved refined isolation, purification, and characterization techniques. Basically these methods take advantage of differential solubility, molecular charge and size, and immuno-chemical responses of the proteins being resolved. The preparation of pure storage proteins from seeds which is homogenous by standard criteria has been very difficult. Millerd (79) recently reviewed the various purification procedures which have been used, the problems encountered, and some precautions or modifications that may be beneficial. She was particularly critical of extraction of globulins by dilute salt solutions, followed by dialysis precipitations, and finally isoelectric precipitation. She points out that in precipitation of the desired salt-extracted globulin by dialysis, considerable amounts of other protein species will be trapped in the precipitate which may be difficult to remove by isoelectric precipitation. She writes favorably of a new electophoretic method using cellulose acetate membranes, described by Blagrove & Gillespie (14), superior because of its speed, resolution, and potential ease of quantitation. As for an assay, she discusses the very specific and sensitive antigen-antibody technique and notes that purified storage-protein antigens have been prepared from soybean (21), peanuts (27), peas (81, 82), and broadbeans (80). It should be pointed out, however, that undoubtedly it will not be possible to isolate, purify, and characterize all storage proteins by a specific set of procedures any more than one can do this with enzymes.

Millerd (79) suggests that seeds harvested from the parent plant prior to the onset of dehydration may be the ideal starting material for the purification of storage proteins because of possible changes induced by drying. However, she is viewing the storage protein as the product formed during embryogenesis. The use of protein bodies isolated from ungerminated seeds would seem to be the ideal starting material in experiments designed to isolate pure storage proteins for those interested in storage protein mobilization studies.

Early studies using ultracentrifuge and free electrophoresis methods on crystal-lized globulins suggested that the seeds of many species contain only one or two major storage proteins (4). Recent research, using a wide variety of techniques, has tended to support this concept. However, each of these major storage proteins may contain a number of subunits. In soybean seeds, Koshiyama (65) reported the presence of two proteins (7S and 11S), and Hill & Breidenbach (46) detected three different protein fractions (2.2S, 7.5S, and 11.8S). Their (46) data also suggested that the 7.5S protein contained three subunits and the 11.8S protein contained 5 or 6 subunits. Catsimpoolis et al (20, 22) had previously shown that the ~11S fraction purified from soybeans contained 6 subunits. Thanh et al (133) determined that a 7S globulin from soybeans contained 5 subunits. Grant & Lawrence (39) reported that legumin and vicilin from peas contained 6 and 4 subunits, respectively. Basha's data (12), also using peas, suggest 5 subunits for both legumin and vicilin. The vicilin of vetch has been reported to contain 6 subunits (136). Legumin purified from broadbean seeds appears to have 3 subunits (9, 80). Vicilin of broadbean seeds has been reported to contain 4 subunits (10). Three N-terminal residues from legumin of broadbean seeds were found to be leucine, glycine, and threonine (9, 137). Four N-terminal residues from vicilin of broadbean seeds were found to be leucine, threonine, serine, and lysine. The above reports suggest that the legumin and vicilin from various species may not be identical. Two storage proteins (8S and 11.3S) isolated from seeds of mung bean (*Phaseolus aureus*) by Ericson & Chrispeels (35) have been suggested to contain 4 and 3 subunits, respectively. Arachin and conarachin of peanut seeds may contain 4 and 2 subunits, respectively (27).

The subunits or polypeptide chains that are contained in the native storage protein are probably not present in a 1:1 ratio. Bailey & Boulter (9) have proposed that broadbean legumin is made of three distinct polypeptide chains with molecular weights of 56,000, 42,000, and 23,000 in molar ratios of 1:3:6, respectively, whereas Vaintraub (137) has suggested that vetch (*Vicia sativa*) legumin is also made of three distinct subunits with molecular weights of about 37,000, 32,600, and 24,300 in molar ratios of 4:2:6, respectively.

Accumulating evidence suggests that some storage proteins are glycoproteins. Bailey & Boulter (9) determined that the legumin they purified from broadbean seeds contained 0.1% neutral sugars. Pusztai & Watt (108) purified a glycoprotein from kidney bean seeds that contained mannose and glucosamine. The two proteins isolated and purified from seeds or protein bodies of mung bean by Ericson & Chrispeels (35) were shown to be glycoproteins. The 11.3S protein contained 0.1% glucosamine and the 8S protein contained 0.2% glucosamine and 1% mannose. The legumin and vicilin purified from peas were found to contain carbohydrates (12). Legumin contained 0.1% glucosamine and 1.25% neutral sugars (glucose and mannose) while vicilin contained 0.2% glucosamine and 0.3% mannose. Thanh et al (133) suggested that all 5 subunits of a 7S globulin of soybean seeds were glycoproteins.

PROTEOLYTIC ENZYMES

Proteolytic enzymes involved in the mobilization of protein reserves of seeds during germination may be classified as endopeptidases or exopeptidases depending on whether they hydrolyze internal peptide bonds of a polypeptide or terminal peptide bonds. The proteolytic enzymes that attack the terminal peptide bonds may be referred to as carboxypeptidases or aminopeptidases, depending upon which end of the molecule they act. Furthermore, some of these terminal peptidases hydrolyze only relatively small molecules rather than the large proteins. Specific dipeptidases that only hydrolyze dipeptides are also present in germinating seeds.

Ryan (112) and Dechary (29) recently reviewed plant proteolytic enzymes and their inhibitors. These reviews include a discussion of proteolytic enzymes involved in seed germination as well as other proteolytic enzymes of plants.

Endopeptidases

Many workers have shown that endopeptidases are present in both ungerminated and germinating seeds. However, only a limited number of the early investigators conducted time-course studies during germination. As early as 1936, Mounfield (88) showed that the endopeptidase activity of germinating wheat seeds remains relatively constant for the first 2 days, increases rapidly from 2 to 4 days, and continues to increase from 4 to 7 days at a slower rate. Mounfield used edestin as a substrate where other workers used casein (66, 67, 149) or gelatin (106, 132) for their time-course studies. Other early time-course studies conducted prior to 1960 presented several different patterns of endopeptidase activity development during germination: no change in peanuts (66) and peas (149), an increase in lima beans (*Phaseolus lunatus*) (67), an increase followed by a decrease in soybeans (132), and an increase followed by a decrease and a second increase in lettuce (106). In the latter case with lettuce, two endopeptidases were thought to be involved. Several time-course studies of endopeptidase activity during germination have been conducted since 1960 (37, 40, 42, 44, 45, 103, 104, 121, 142, 146, 147). These usually showed an increase in endopeptidase activity during germination; in some studies this increase was followed by a decrease. A delay of 1 to 2 days in the initiation of the increase has often been reported.

A serious limitation to progress in research on the mobilization of storage protein in seeds has been the lack of adequate endopeptidase assays. Most assay procedures have involved the removal of nonhydrolyzed proteins by TCA precipitation, followed by measurement of an increase in absorption at 280 nm, increase in amino groups with ninhydrin, or increase in tyrosine by Lowry assay. These methods do not measure total endopeptidase activity, they lack the desired specificity, and adequate sensitivity is often lacking because of high backgrounds. Furthermore, inappropriate substrates are often used because hydrolysis of the native storage protein of the species being studied cannot be detected by these methods. Investigators frequently use substrates of animal origin (casein, hemoglobin, gelatin) or a storage protein from another species. Synthetic substrates have also been used; some of these have a colorless chromophore attached which develop a color when hydrolysis occurs. Azoproteins are based on this same principle; although azocasein has been used, apparently azo-storage proteins have not been used. Occasionally marked differences in the time-course of endopeptidase activity development have been observed when different substrates or different methods have been used to detect the products of hydrolysis, such as 280 nm vs ninhydrin. The following newer methods may overcome some of these problems. Peterson (105) adopted a procedure of Lin et al (68) in studies on proteolytic activity of leaves. This procedure involves the methylation of the free amino groups in casein and it is claimed that it measures all proteolytic cleavages with a much reduced background. A method described by Spencer & Spencer (121) appears to offer unusual promise in sensitivity and substrate specificity. It involves the release of 1-anilino-8-napthalenesulfonate which was previously bound to internal hydropholic sites of pumpkin seed globulin. Davis (28) used ^{14}C-labeled protein bodies isolated from seeds of a squash plant previously treated with $^{14}CO_2$. Haissig & Schipper (41a) used a radiometric assay based in the hydrolysis of ^{125}I-bovine serum albumin.

PROPERTIES OF ENDOPEPTIDASES   An acid endopeptidase (pH optimum 3.6) from sorghum (*Sorghum vulgare*) endosperm of 5- to 6-day-old plants has been prepared in crystalline form (37). It had a molecular weight of about 80,000 and an apparent K_m of 0.76 mM and 0.19 mM using bovine serum albumin and N,N-dimethylalbumin as substrates, respectively. The endopeptidase did not require serine or cysteine (sulfhydryl) at the active site and had no metal ion requirement. The endosperm from ungerminated seeds contained no endopeptidase activity but the activity increased up to 5 days of germination. Subsequent substrate specificity studies (38) using synthetic peptides and pancreatic ribonuclease A as substrates revealed rather narrow specificity requirements. The endopeptidase specifically cleaves the peptide linkages involving the α-carboxyl group of either aspartic acid or glutamic acid with the release of the acyl portion of the acidic amino acids.

Enari & Mikola (34) reported that germinating barley seeds contain several endopeptidases with pH optima ranging from 3.9 to 9. The main component is a sulfhydryl endopeptidase with a pH optimum of 3.9. In addition there are sulfhydryl endopeptidases with higher pH optima and possibly three metal-activated endopeptidases with pH optima at 6 to 9. However, the metal-activated endopeptidases are quite low in activity relative to the sulfhydryl endopeptidases.

A number of years ago Irving & Fontaine (54a) purified arachain from ungerminated peanut seeds and considered it to be a trypsin-like enzyme. Recently Cameron & Mazelis (19a) also purified this enzyme but their results suggested that it was not a trypsin-like enzyme. They reported that it hydrolyzed a large number of dipeptides, BAPA, and BAEE but it had essentially no activity toward casein, dimethyl casein, or bovine serum albumin. TAME and BTEE, specific substrates for trypsin and chymotrypsin, respectively, were hydrolyzed only 0.3% and 14% by the peanut enzyme relative to trypsin and chymotrypsin, respectively. The pH optimum for the hydrolysis of BAPA was 8.1 and for BAEE 7.5. The K_m was 10 μM for BAPA and 110 μM for BAEE. The energy of activation was calculated to be 10 kilocalories with BAPA. The $S_{20,w}$ value was 6.20. Mainguy et al (74) isolated and purified an endopeptidase from cotyledons of 6-day-old peanut seedlings that degraded BAPA. It had a molecular weight of about 60,000, temperature optimum between 25° and 36°C, and its pH optimum was 7.4. Inhibitor experiments showed that it does not have sulfhydryl groups at its active site nor does it respond to trypsin inhibitors, but it is inactivated by DFP. It was therefore concluded that it is a serine-type endopeptidase.

Beevers (13) detected endopeptidase activity in cotyledons of germinating pea seeds. Using casein, he found two pH optima at 5.5 and 7.0, suggesting two different endopeptidases. Using BAPA, a broad pH optimum of 7 to 8 was found. Since the pH 7 optimum of casein hydrolysis was relatively sharp a third endopeptidase is suggested. Differences between BAPA and casein hydrolysis by barley endopeptidases have also been reported (17, 56).

LOCALIZATION OF ENDOPEPTIDASES   The early work on endopeptidases of ungerminated and germinating seeds was conducted with homogenates without any concern for their localization. Consequently it was assumed that they were soluble enzymes of the cytoplasm. However, subsequent research has indicated a localization of at least some of these enzymes. Localization has been approached using: 1. isolated aleurone layers; 2. differential sucrose gradient separation of organelles; 3. gelatin-film substrate methods; and 4. isolated protein bodies. Most of the work has been conducted with isolated protein bodies. However, since the stability of the protein body in the isolating media decreases rapidly as germination proceeds, such studies have usually been limited to ungerminated seeds.

Yatsu & Jacks (143) found that all of the endopeptidase activity of ungerminated cotton (*Gossypium hirsutum*) seed cotyledons was in the protein bodies. Perhaps two endopeptidases are present since two pH optima were reported, pH 1 to 2 and 3 to 4. They use hemoglobin as the substrate. Using protein bodies isolated from ungerminated barley seeds, Ory & Henningsen (98) demonstrated the presence of an acid endopeptidase as well as a acid phosphatase that hydrolyzed sodium phytate. The endopeptidase hydrolyzed BAPA as well as gelatin. An acid endopeptidase has also been reported to be present in protein bodies of hemp seed which hydrolyzes hemoglobin and edestin (125). Upon purification, this enzyme was found to have a pH optimum of 3.4 with hemoglobin, a temperature optimum of 50°C, a Michaelis-Menten constant of 0.44×10^{-4} M, and a V_{max} of 0.742 (127). It was not a sulfhydryl or serine enzyme, and they concluded that it resembled cathepsin D, an enzyme found in the lysosomes of mammalian tissue. Acid endopeptidases have also been reported to be present in protein bodies of sunflower (*Helianthus annuus*) seeds (116), peas (75), and vetch (64).

Koroleva et al (64) demonstrated that the cotyledons of ungerminated vetch seeds not only contain two endopeptidases in the protein bodies but the cytoplasmic fraction contains two different endopeptidases which are probably absent from the protein bodies. These were differentiated by pH optimum values. The pH optima for the protein body endopeptidases were 3.8 and 7.2, whereas those of the cytoplasm were 4.8 and 5.8. Casein was used as the substrate.

In studies on the nature of gibberellic acid (GA₃) induced endopeptidases secreted by separated aleurone layers of barley, Sundblom & Nikola (128) reported that four different endopeptidases can be demonstrated. The principal one is a labile sulfhydryl enzyme with a pH optimum of 3.9. Two other sulfhydryl enzymes with a pH optimum of 5 and 6.5 and a metal activated endopeptidase with a pH optimum of 7.0 are also secreted. Gelatin was used as the substrate.

In a series of three papers (89–91), Nakano & Asahi reported on studies concerned with endopeptidases in the cotyledons of germinating pea seeds. Using differential sucrose gradient centrifugation techniques, they demonstrated the presence of at least one soluble endopeptidase and at least one membrane-bound endopeptidase. The membrane containing the endopeptidase activity was not the endoplasmic reticulum. The membrane-bound endopeptidase was heat stable (60°C for 60 min), whereas the soluble endopeptidase was heat labile. Both enzymes had pH optima of 6 and 8. Casein was used as the substrate.

Using a histochemical technique (gelatin-film substrate), Yomo & Taylor (146) detected the presence of endopeptidase activity in the cotyledons of germinating kidney bean seeds at the fifth day of germination. Some endopeptidase activity was found throughout the cotyledons except for the surface 2 to 3 layers of cells and in a layer several cells thick around the vascular bundles. The highest level of endopeptidase activity was found in a layer of cells surrounding the "endopeptidase-inactive cells" near the vascular bundles. These findings are in agreement with those of previous workers who have reported that the endopeptidase activity does not start in the cells nearest the vascular bundles (8, 26, 96) or near the epidermis (96). However, their (146) hypothesis: "only special cells in a cotyledon can produce protease, and other cells acquire the enzyme through intercellular spaces or cell walls, . . ." appears to be highly speculative. In localization studies of endopeptidase activity in cotyledons of mung bean by the gelatin-film technique, Harris & Chrispeels (42) reported that low levels of endopeptidase activity were found throughout the cotyledons after 24 hr of inhibition. After 48 to 60 hr a marked increase in activity was observed in cells farthest from the vascular bundles. A wave of endopeptidase activity moved progressively through the cotyledons toward the vascular bundles leaving behind areas devoid of stored reserves and low in endopeptidase activity. Since the membrane of the protein body remained intact, they considered that the protein body might be undergoing autolysis. Although the incubation of isolated protein bodies from ungerminated seeds resulted in the release of amino acids, the specific amino acids released did not correspond to the amino acid composition of the storage protein. Hydrolysis of the storage protein present in the protein bodies was greatly accelerated by the addition of extracts from cotyledons of 4-day-old seedlings. They suggested that new enzymatic activities not present in the protein bodies of ungerminated seeds must be activated or synthesized and possibly added to the protein bodies before storage protein breakdown can begin.

Harris & Chrispeels (42) assayed a protein body preparation and a cytoplasmic fraction from ungerminated seeds for several enzymes which might be involved in the degradation of storage proteins. The protein bodies contained all, or nearly all, of the carboxypeptidase, endopeptidase(s) (gelatin or casein as substrate), α-mannosidase, and N-acetyl-β-glucosaminidase. The cytoplasm contained all, or most, of the leucine aminopeptidase and trypsin-like activity (BAPA as a substrate).

An acid endopeptidase has been isolated from ungerminated seeds of hemp (126) that appears to be associated with some lipid material. It was suggested that this lipid material was the phospholipid membrane that surrounds the protein body.

Protein bodies and spherosomes isolated from whole grain, aleurone layers, and embryos of ungerminated sorghum (*Sorghum bicolor*) seeds have been shown to contain several hydrolases including endopeptidase activity (1, 2). The endopeptidase activity associated with the protein bodies was relatively insoluble whereas the endopeptidase activity associated with the spherosome was quite soluble. The other hydrolases associated with the protein bodies were also relatively insoluble. These authors (2) therefore conclude that while the protein bodies possess a variety of acid hydrolase activities, they cannot be considered analogous to animal lysosomes (32). The spherosomes are similar to animal lysosomes in several respects, however, but they also have a storage function for protein, phosphorus, and metals. Adams & Novellie (2) also reported that sorghum protein bodies undergo rapid protein autolysis in vitro, releasing α-amino nitrogen for at least 24 hr. Spherosomes act similarly but rapid protein autolysis proceeds for only 4 hr. They therefore conclude that there would not necessarily be a requirement for de novo synthesis of an endopeptidase during the early stages of germination of sorghum.

Endopeptidases have been isolated from seeds that can be classified according to the four major types of proteinases as suggested by Hartley (43): namely, serine proteinases, sulfhydryl proteinases, metalloproteinases, and acid proteinases. Although most of them appear to hydrolyze a variety of proteins, some of them have unusual substrate specificities. They have pH optimum ranging from 3.4 to 9.0. Some have been found to associate with protein bodies, others appear to be soluble enzymes of the cytoplasm, while a few have been reported to be associated with membranes. Most seeds contain more than one endopeptidase. Although many of them are undoubtedly involved with storage protein breakdown, some of them may have entirely different roles, e.g. protein turnover.

Exopeptidases

Amino-, carboxy-, and di-peptidase activities have been detected in ungerminated and germinating seeds. The role that these enzymes play in the mobilization of protein reserves is beginning to become apparent. However, certain ones that are found in nonprotein storage organs as well as storage organs may be involved more in protein turnover than in storage protein hydrolysis. At our current state of knowledge this distinction is not readily made. It is generally assumed that the insoluble storage proteins in seeds are first hydrolyzed to soluble peptides by endopeptidases during germination and the soluble peptides are then hydrolyzed to amino acids by various peptidases (78).

AMINOPEPTIDASES   Mikola & Kolehmainen (78) concluded that germinating barley seedlings contained eight different peptidases with pH optima ranging from pH 4.8 to pH 8.6. Three of these are considered to be aminopeptidases that act on aminoacyl-β-napthylamides as well as dipeptides and tripeptides. Their pH optima range from 5.8 to 6.5 with hydrolysis of di- and tri-peptides. Two of the eight peptidases are characterized by their relatively high pH optima, pH 7.8 and 8.6, Ala-Gly and Leu-Try, respectively. These two peptidases also hydrolyze the tripeptide Leu-Gly-Gly. The remaining three peptidases are classified as carboxypeptidases and will be discussed later. The three aminoacyl-β-napthylamidases and two Ala-Gly/Leu-Try peptidases are present in the aleurone layers and scutella but totally absent from the endosperm. During germination these five peptidases show no change in activity in the aleurone layers, but in scutella the Ala-Gly/Leu-Tri peptidases increase in activity whereas the aminoacyl-β-napthylamidase activity remains constant. These results, plus the fact that at least two-thirds of the total reserve protein in barley seeds is located in the endosperm and the pH of the endosperm during germination is considered to be 5.0 to 5.2, cause the authors to suggest that these five enzymes play a lesser role in the mobilization of storage protein than the carboxypeptidases. Although these studies were conducted on crude extracts, one of these peptidases was purified about 670-fold and partially characterized (Sapanen & Mikola 115). This was the pH 8.6/Leu-Try peptidase referred to above. They considered the enzyme to be very similar to mammalian leucine aminopeptidase (EC3.4.1.1) since both have a sedimentation constant of 12.75, molecular weight about 260,000. Furthermore, their enzyme required Mg^{2+} and Mn^{2+} for stabilization (and probably activation). However, their enzyme was inactivated in the absence of reducing sulfhydryl compounds whereas mammalian leucine aminopeptidase does not have this requirement and pH optima of these two enzymes are quite different. Therefore, although this enzyme may be similar to mammalian leucine aminopeptidase it is not identical.

Salmia & Mikola (114) also demonstrated the presence of two peptidases from ungerminated seeds and germinating seedlings of Scots pine (*Pinus sylvestris*). These two enzymes appear to be similar, if not identical, to ones isolated from barley (78, 115), namely: Leu-Try (pH 8.6) and Ala-Gly (pH 7.8). The activity of these two enzymes increased two to threefold during the early stages of germination in both the endosperm and seedling tissue and then decreased. Although the increase in activity coincided with the rapid mobilization of reserve protein, the fact that they increased in the seedling tissue as well as the storage tissue (endosperm) during germination led the authors to question their specific role in the mobilization of reserve storage protein.

In a series of papers, Ashton and associates (5–7, 131, 135) reported studies concerned with the peptidases of germinating squash seeds. Evidence has been presented indicating that there are at least three peptidases present in the cotyledons of squash at 3 days after the initiation of germination (5). All three have been purified and characterized (5–7). One appears to be similar to mammalian leucine aminopeptidase, the second one is also an aminopeptidase, but pH optimum, metal ion requirements, and substrate specificity clearly distinguish it from the leucine aminopeptidase (5,6). The third peptidase of squash cotyledons is a dipeptidase and will be discussed later. The aminopeptidase was purified about 500-fold (7). This enzyme required a free amino group next to the bond cleaved, exhibited a low rate of hydrolysis of L-amino acid amides, and did not cleave dipeptides, carboxypeptidase substrates, or endopeptidase substrates. The relative hydrolysis of triglycine, tetraglycine, pentaglycine, and polyglycine was 100, 95, 27, and 0, respectively. Therefore, it was referred to as an amino-oligopeptidase. The pH optimum was 8.0 with triglycine as the substrate and there did not appear to be a metal ion requirement. The K_m for triglycine was 7.3 X 10^{-3}M at pH 7.6. Certain characteristics of the leucine aminopeptidase of squash cotyledons can be derived by comparing the data from the aminopeptidase paper (7) and the original paper (5). The leucine aminopeptidase was not prepared entirely free of the aminopeptidase. The leucine aminopeptidase had a pH optimum of 7.0, was activated by Mg^{2+} and Mn^{2+}, and inhibited by EDTA. Wall (141) has also demonstrated leucine aminopeptidase activity in seeds of several species and/or cultivars of the genus *Cucurbita*.

Elleman (33) detected the presence of three peptidases from pea seeds that had been surface sterilized and soaked in water overnight. One was proline specific and was referred to as proline iminopeptidase. The other two hydrolyzed β-naphthylamides of primary amino acids. These were considered to be true aminopeptidases since they required the presence of a free amino group and hydrolyzed the amide bond of amino acid amides, dipeptides, and oligopeptidases from the N-terminal end. The addition of actinomycin D (RNA synthesis inhibitor) and cyclohexamide (protein synthesis inhibitor) to the inhibition solution did not alter the development of the activity of these enzymes during germination. Therefore, Elleman concluded that these enzymes were present in the seeds in an active form and their increase during germination was not a result of de novo synthesis.

CARBOXYPEPTIDASES   Three of the eight peptidases isolated from germinating barley seedlings by Mikola & Kolehmainen (78) were considered to be carboxypeptidases. They had pH optima of 4.8, 5.2, and 5.7. They were present in the aleurone layers, endosperm, and scutella. Their activity increased in all three of these tissues during germination; however, the increase in the aleurone layer was relatively small. The absence of the aminopeptidases in the endosperm of barley, plus the favorable pH of the endosperm for the activity of carboxypeptidases, suggests that they may play a significant role in storage protein mobilization in this species.

Ihle & Dure (50–53) isolated a carboxypeptidase from cotyledons of cotton seedlings. The enzyme has been purified 2000-fold and has a molecular weight of 85,000. It hydrolyzes several ester substrates, polypeptides, and denatured proteins, apparently from the COOH-terminal end. Di- and tripeptides are hydrolyzed very slowly, if at all. It has no metal requirement and is not inhibited by sulfhydryl antagonists; however, it is inhibited by DFP. They conclude that it has a "serine protease" type of hydrolytic mechanism.

DIPEPTIDASES   A dipeptidase has been purified about 2000-fold from cotyledons of 3-day-old germinating squash seedlings (Ashton & Dahmen 6). This enzyme appeared to be specific for L-dipeptide hydrolysis. Although L-leucylglycine was hydrolyzed most rapidly, 12 other L-dipeptides were also hydrolyzed. D-dipeptides, tripeptides, amino acid amides, chloroacetyldipeptides, tripeptide amides, and proteins were not hydrolyzed by this dipeptidase. Mg^{2+} and Mn^{2+} increased the activity of the dialyzed enzyme 20 to 25%; however, EDTA alone had little effect. Therefore, its metal ion requirements are not clear. It had a broad pH optimum between 8.0 and 8.5 and was quite stable to high temperature.

Control Of Proteolytic Enzymes

The control of proteolytic enzyme activity, the resulting storage protein mobilization, and protein body changes during germination present a very challenging problem. Not only do there appear to be several proteolytic enzymes in most germinating seeds, but many of them seem to increase at the same time that synthetic enzyme activities are also increasing. Why don't the proteolytic enzymes hydrolyze the synthetic enzymes? This question as well as the ordered mobilization of storage proteins during germination mandate control mechanisms for the proteolytic enzymes. All proteolytic enzymes of germinating seeds are probably not controlled in the same way. Some of the control mechanisms which have been suggested include: hormonal control of de novo synthesis, endogenous inhibitors, zymogens, compartmentation, pH, substrate specificity, and end product inhibition. Although most control studies have involved endopeptidases, a few have been related to exopeptidases.

Perhaps the most widely considered mechanism for the control of endopeptidase activity in germinating seeds is hormonal control of de novo synthesis. The hormone is usually considered to originate in the embryonic axis and be translocated to the storage tissue. In general, it is not unlike the widely studied GA induced de novo synthesis of amylase in barley (140). However, as discussed by Mayer & Shain (76), the production of α-amylase is not the primary response to GA. Likewise, the responses of proteolytic enzymes to hormones are probably not their primary response. Furthermore, the hormones are not specific for a single enzyme and the specific hormones required to induce the de novo synthesis of enzymes vary from species to species: GA for barley and cytokinin for squash. It would appear that some species are limiting in one hormone whereas others require a different hormone for the de novo synthesis of certain enzymes. It has been suggested that a degree of control of de novo synthesis of a dipeptidase in squash cotyledons is affected through four endogenous hormones acting in concert (135).

Studies with peas have shown that the axis influences the activity of certain enzymes in the cotyledons during germination, as well as other metabolic reactions (139, 149). Guardiola & Sutcliffe (40) studied the effects of removing the shoot or whole axis 4 to 5 days after initiation of germination on the levels of total protein and TCA-soluble nitrogen, as well as endopeptidase activity in cotyledons of peas during germination. They concluded that control of protein hydrolysis in pea cotyledons is not mediated through the level of protease enzymes or the amount of soluble nitrogen compounds accumulated. Although protease activity seemed to be controlled by the shoot and closely linked to senescence of the cotyledons, protein hydrolysis and transport of nitrogen to the axis was affected by both the shoot and root. The shoot appeared to exert independent control on protease activity and nitrogen transport.

Penner & Ashton (103, 104) studied the hormonal control of endopeptidase activity in squash cotyledons and found that the activity increased in the cotyledons during the third day and then decreased in intact seeds. The presence of the embryonic axis during the first 32 hours of germination was a prerequisite for the development of maximum proteolytic activity. The presence of a cytokinin in the culture solution could reproduce the effect of the embryonic axis, but other hormones did not induce this increase. The presence of 6-methylpurine, a kinetin inhibitor (24), inhibited endopeptidase activity development and BA partly reversed this inhibition. They concluded that the synthesis of an endopeptidase in the cotyledons of squash seedlings is hormonally controlled by the embryonic axis that the hormone involved appears to be a cytokinin.

During the first 2 days of germination the dipeptidase activity of squash cotyledons remained unchanged and then rapidly increased during the next 3 days (Sze & Ashton 131, Tsay & Ashton 135). Removal of the axis reduced, but did not eliminate, the increase in the dipeptidase activity of the cotyledons. When cycloheximide was added to the seeds at the beginning of germination, dipeptidase was inhibited up to 74% at 5 days. When cycloheximide was added to cotyledons of 3-day-old seedlings, inhibition of the increase in dipeptidase activity was almost immediate. This and other data presented suggest that more than one enzyme is responsible for the dipeptidase activity measured, but that at least one of these enzymes is synthesized de novo and that its synthesis is under the control of the axis. Additional research on this problem has shown that the dipeptidase is synthesized de novo as evidenced by ^{14}C-leucine incorporation into the purified enzyme molecule and other data (53, 56). In studies on hormonal control of the development of this dipeptidase in cotyledons during germination, intact seeds and distal-half cotyledons were treated with GA, BA, IAA, or ABA. The data suggested that all four of these hormones act in concert to control the biosynthesis of a dipeptidase. Cytokinins and GA act as stimulants, auxins act as stimulant or inhibitor (depending on concentration), and ABA acts as an inhibitor.

In a series of papers, Ihle & Dure (50–53) reported on a very interesting relationship between embryogenesis and seed germination in regard to the development of a carboxypeptidase in the cotyledons of cotton seedlings. Their usual substrate, BAEE, is not hydrolyzed by extract of cotyledons from germinating cotton seedlings for the first 24 hr of germination; subsequently the activity develops. The addition of cycloheximide to the cotyledons stops the development of the enzyme activity and the incorporation of ^{14}C-amino acids into enzyme; however, actinomycin D has no effect. Therefore, the enzyme appears to be synthesized de novo; however, mRNA does not seem to be limiting. When the source of the mRNA was investigated they found that it was transcribed during embryogenesis on the parent plant at the time when the embryo obtained about two-thirds of its final size.

In studies on the hydrolysis of endosperm protein in corn (*Zea mays*), Harvey & Oaks (44, 45) have shown that degradation of zein (in protein bodies) and glutelin (in cytoplasmic matrix) begins during the second day of germination and proceeds most rapidly between 3 and 8 days. In general, the rate of breakdown of both storage proteins was similar; however, between 40 and 80 hr glutelin was degraded more rapidly than zein. Although there were no qualitative differences in the pattern of protein breakdown between the endosperm from intact seeds and excised endosperms, the embryos of the germinating seeds appeared to retard protease production and protein hydrolysis. This is in contrast to most studies with dicots and barley which have been shown to require the axis for maximum storage protein hydrolysis in the cotyledons or endosperm. The time course of endopeptidase activity development paralleled protein hydrolysis, essentially zero until day-2, increased rapidly between day-2 and day-8, declined rapidly between day-8 and day-11. The enzyme had a pH optimum of 3.8 and also degraded gliadin, edestin, and bovine serum albumin. Since cycloheximide inhibited the development of the endopeptidase activity and disappearance of the protein reserves, the enzyme was considered to be synthesized de novo.

Oota et al (99) suggested that the products of hydrolysis may inhibit further hydrolysis in excised kidney bean cotyledons. However, Guardiola & Sutcliffe (40) did not consider this conclusion valid nor come to this conclusion from their data with peas because the level of soluble nitrogen compounds in excised cotyledons was not higher than in cotyledons from intact seedlings. More recent work by Yomo & Varner (147), which measured amino acids rather than soluble nitrogen, reported higher amounts of amino acids in excised cotyledons than in cotyledons from intact pea plants. They also found that the endopeptidase activity increased in attached cotyledons as the storage protein declined; however, the activity did not increase in excised cotyledons. Excised cotyledons placed in a casein hydrolysate solution developed less endopeptidase activity than those placed in water. They suggested that the accumulation of amino acids regulates endopeptidase activity.

A considerable amount of research has been conducted on proteinase inhibitors from plant material, especially seeds. Most of these are proteinaceous and inhibit proteinases of animal or microbial origin. They usually have trypsin-like or chymotrypsin-like specificities. Although it is attractive to consider that they have a role in the control of proteolytic enzymes of plant origin, essentially all such studies have been negative (29, 112). The trypsin and chymotrypsin inhibitors have usually been shown to be noninhibitory to proteolytic enzymes of plant origin. Ryan (112) suggests that they may play a role in plant protection against microorganisms and insects. However, Shain & Mayer (117, 118) reported the presence of a proteinase inhibitor in lettuce seeds that inhibits an endogenous proteinase. The inhibitor decreases during germination with a corresponding increase in proteinase activity. Extracts from ungerminated barley seeds have been shown to contain a proteinase inhibitor that inhibits a barley endopeptidase (77). The inhibitor appears to disappear early in germination and before endopeptidase activity begins to increase. In the purification of an aminopeptidase (7) and a dipeptidase (6), unusual increase in the percent recovery of these two enzymes was observed; this was attributed to the removal of an inhibitor.

Substrate specificities offer an attractive mechanism for the control of proteolytic enzyme action on proteins of seeds. In fact, it may be the primary reason for the lack of hydrolysis of synthetic enzymes during germination; however, compartmentation may also be involved. Although a variety of substrate specificities have been demonstrated for proteolytic enzymes of germinating seeds, data on their physiological significance is largely lacking. All four basic types of proteinases have been demonstrated to be present in ungerminated and/or germinating seeds, namely, acid-, sulfhydryl-, serine-, and metallo-endopeptidases. In addition to these general substrate specificities, others have been enumerated previously in the section on Endopeptidases. The specificities of several carboxypeptidases, aminopeptidases, and other peptidases of seeds have also been described (112). However, until we can develop an in vitro system using native storage protein of a given species as the substrate, add the endo- and exo-peptidases of that species sequentially, and determine the products formed after the addition of each enzyme, the physiological significance of substrate specificity as a control mechanism will remain obscure.

Although a number of proteolytic enzymes of animals have been shown to be zymogens, this has not been unequivocally shown for proteolytic enzymes of higher plants (49). However, the rapid increase in the proteolytic activity in germinating seeds suggests that zymogens may be the origin of some of these enzymes.

Compartmentation of an acid proteinase and the storage protein in the protein body appears to provide a control mechanism which would favor the rapid hydrolysis of storage protein and protect the cytoplasmic proteins from attack. Should the acid proteinase come in contact with proteins of cytoplasm during protein body rupture and/or fusion, it would have a much reduced activity because of the higher pH. Therefore, a compartmented pH control mechanism can be visualized. However, it is also interesting to note that Koroleva et al (64) found an endopeptidase associated with the protein body which had a pH optimum of 7.2.

CONCLUDING REMARKS

Although considerable progress has been made during the last decade on the mobilization of storage protein in germinating seeds, a clear understanding of the entire process has not been achieved. In general, our understanding of the structural changes which occur in the protein body during germination is relatively advanced. However, our knowledge of the physiology and biochemistry of the process is inadequate. A critical examination of the literature shows that we do not know with *certainty* the complete structure of the substrate, whether one or several enzymes are involved or in most instances their control mechanisms, and the nature of any intermediate products. What we do know can be briefly summarized as follows: (*a*) the substrate is a protein and it probably contains several subunits; (*b*) ungerminated and germinating seeds contain several proteolytic enzymes and at least one is present in the protein body; (*c*) amino acids are the final product; and (*d*) certain of the enzymes appear to have one or more control mechanisms. Our knowledge of the nature of the storage protein(s) is slowly increasing; however, ultimately we need to know the complete molecular structure. Although many proteolytic enzymes have been isolated from ungerminated and germinating seeds, the ones actually involved in the hydrolysis of storage protein or its intermediate hydrolytic products are often speculative because storage protein of the species under study is rarely used as the substrate for these enzymes. Some enzymes are probably involved in protein turnover and may have no role in storage protein hydrolysis. The acid endopeptidase found in protein bodies of many species is undoubtedly involved in storage protein hydrolysis; however, it is not generally known whether the products are amino acids or peptides. If they are peptides, other peptidases would be required for their hydrolysis to amino acids. Although it is conceivable that the protein body acid endopeptidase or the carboxypeptidase reported for one species is responsible for the complete hydrolysis of storage protein to amino acids, the author favors a multiple enzyme system hypothesis. It would appear that it is essential that specific control mechanisms be present for the storage protein hydrolytic enzymes to prevent their degradation of structural and functional proteins as well as their interference with protein turnover. Since the amount of research being conducted on this problem is relatively meager, a clear understanding of the complete process will probably not be available in the foreseeable future.

ACKNOWLEDGMENTS

The author wishes to thank Melanie E. Davis for her assistance on the protein body section. A major portion of the research by the author reported in this review was supported by grants from the National Science Foundation.

Literature Cited

1. Adams, C. A., Novellie, L. 1975. *Plant Physiol.* 55:1–6
2. Ibid, 7–11
3. Altschul, A. M., Talluto, K. F., Sharar, B. A., Eds. 1963. *Proc. Seed Protein Conf., New Orleans.* Southern Utilization Res. Dev. Div., USDA. 292 pp.
4. Altschul, A. M., Yatsu, L. Y., Ory, R. L., Engleman, E. M. 1966. *Ann. Rev. Plant Physiol.* 17:113–36
5. Ashton, F. M., Dahmen, W. J. 1967. *Phytochemistry* 6:641–53
6. Ibid, 1215–25
7. Ibid 1968. 7:189–97
8. Bagley, B. W., Cherry, J. H., Rollins, M. L., Altshul, A. M. 1963. *Am. J. Bot.* 50:523–32
9. Bailey, C. J., Boulter, D. 1970. *Eur. J. Biochem.* 17:460–66
10. Bailey, C. J., Boulter, D. 1972. *Phytochemistry* 11:59–64
11. Bain, J. M., Mercer, F. V. 1966. *Aust. J. Biol. Sci.* 19:69–84
12. Basha, S. M. M. 1974. *Protein metabolism in cotyledons of Pisum sativum L. during seed development and germination.* PhD thesis. Univ. Oklahoma, Norman. 79 pp.
13. Beevers, L. 1968. *Phytochemistry* 7:1837–44
14. Blagrove, R. J., Gillespie, J. M. 1975. *Aust. J. Plant Physiol.* 2:13–27
15. Boulter, D. 1973. In *Phytochemistry,* ed. L. P. Miller, 2:30–60
16. Briarty, L. G., Coult, D. A., Boulter, D. 1970. *J. Exp. Bot.* 21:513–24
17. Burger, W. C., Siegelman, H. W. 1966. *Physiol. Plant.* 19:1089–93
18. Buttrose, M. S. 1963. *Aust. J. Biol. Sci.* 16:768–74
19. Buttorse, M. S. 1971. *Planta* 96:13–26
19a. Cameron, E. C., Mazelis, M. 1971. *Plant Physiol.* 48:278–81
20. Catsimpoolas, N., Campbell, T. G., Meyer, E. W. 1969. *Arch. Biochem. Biophys.* 131:577–86
21. Catsimpoolas, N., Meyer, E. W. 1968. *Arch. Biochem. Biophys.* 125:742–50
22. Catsimpoolas, N., Rogers, D. A., Circle, S. J., Meyer, E. W. 1967. *Cereal Chem.* 44:631–37
23. Cecich, R. 1974. *Am. J. Bot.* 61: Suppl., p. 5
24. Chen, H. -R., Galston, A. W. 1965. *Plant Cell Physiol.* 6:365–70
25. Danielson, C. E. 1956. *Ann. Rev. Plant Physiol.* 7:215–36
26. Danjo, T., Shida, S. 1970. *Bull. Fac. Agric. Univ. Miyazaki* 17:209–20
27. Daussant, J., Neucere, N. J., Yatsu, L. Y. 1969. *Plant Physiol.* 44:471–79
28. Davis, M. E. 1974. *In vivo and in vitro breakdown of Cucurbita seed protein bodies.* MS thesis. Univ. California, Davis. 86 pp.
29. Dechary, J. M. 1970. *Econ. Bot.* 24:113–22
30. Dengler, R. E. 1967. *Histochemistry and ultrastructure of the embryo axis of Clarkia during seed maturation and germination.* PhD thesis. Univ. California, Davis. 118 pp.
31. Diekert, J. W., Snowden, J. E. Jr., Moore, A. T., Heinzelman, D. C., Altschul, A. M. 1962. *J. Food Sci.* 27:321–25
32. Dingle, J. T., Fell, H. B. 1969. *Lysosomes in Biology and Pathology.* Amsterdam: North-Holland. 668 pp.
33. Elleman, T. C. 1974. *Biochem. J.* 141:113–18
34. Enari, T.-M., Mikola, J. 1967. *Proc. 11th Congr. Evr. Brewery Conv., Madrid,* 9–16
35. Ericson, M. C., Chrispeels, M. J. 1973. *Plant Physiol.* 52:98–104
36. Esau, K. 1967. *Plant Anatomy.* New York: Wiley. 767 pp.
37. Garg, G. K., Virupaksha, T. K. 1970. *Eur. J. Biochem.* 17:4–12
38. Ibid, 13–18
39. Grant, D. R., Lawrence, J. M. 1964. *Arch. Biochem. Biophys.* 108:552–61
40. Guardiola, J. L., Sutcliffe, J. F. 1971. *Ann. Bot.* 35:791–807
41. Guillermond, A. 1908. *Arch. Anat. Microsc. Morphol. Exp.* 10:141–226
41a. Haissig, B. E., Schipper, A. L. 1975. *Biochem. Biophys. Res. Commun.* 63:57–61
42. Harris, N., Chrispeels, M. J. 1975. *Plant Physiol.* 56:292–99
43. Hartley, B. S. 1960. *Ann. Rev. Biochem.* 29:45–72
44. Harvey, B. M. R., Oaks, A. 1974. *Plant Physiol.* 53:449–52
45. Ibid, 453–57
46. Hill, J. E., Breidenbach, R. W. 1974. *Plant Physiol* 53:742–46
47. Horner, H. T. Jr., Arnott, H. J. 1965. *Am. J. Bot.* 52:1027–38
48. Horner, H. T. Jr., Arnott, H. J. 1966. *Bot. Gaz.* 127:48–64
49. Huffaker, R. C., Peterson, L. W. 1974. *Ann. Rev. Plant Physiol.* 25:363–92
50. Ihle, J. N., Dure, L. 1969. *Biochem. Biophys. Res. Commun.* 36:705–10

51. Ihle, J. N., Dure, L. S. 1972. *J. Biol. Chem.* 247:5034–40
52. Ibid, 5041–47
53. Ibid, 5048–55
54. Inglett, G. E., Ed. 1972. *Symp. Seed Proteins.* Westport, Conn: AVI. 320 pp.
54a. Irving, G. W. Jr., Fontaine, T. D. 1945. *Arch. Biochem.* 6:351–64
55. Jacobsen, J. V., Knox, R. B., Pyliotis, N. A. 1971. *Planta* 101:189–209
56. Jacobsen, J. V., Varner, J. E. 1967. *Plant Physiol.* 42:1596–1600
57. Jennings, A. C., Morton, R. K., Palk, B. A. 1963. *Aust. J. Biol. Sci.* 16:366–74
58. Jones, R. L. 1969. *Planta* 85:359–75
59. Ibid. 87:119–33
60. Ibid. 88:73–86
61. Khokhlova, V. A. 1971. *Sov. Plant Physiol.* (Engl. transl.) 18:855–61
62. Khoo, V., Wolf, M. J. 1970. *Am. J. Bot.* 57:1042–50
63. Klein, S., Ben-Shaul, Y. 1966. *Can. J. Bot.* 44:331–40
64. Koroleva, T. N., Alekseeva, M. V., Shutov, A. D., Vaintraub, I. A. 1973. *Sov. Plant Physiol.* (Engl. transl.) 20:650–53
65. Koshiyama, I. 1972. *Agric. Biol. Chem.* 36:62–67
66. Kudryashova, N. A. 1960. *Tr. Gl. Bot. Sada, Akad. Nauk SSSR* 7:93
67. Kudryashova, N. A. 1960. *Soobsch. Mosk. Otd. Vses. Bot. Ova.* p. 83
68. Lin, Y., Means, G. E., Feeney, R. E. 1969. *J. Biol. Chem.* 244:789–93
69. Lott, J. N. A. 1975. *Plant Physiol.* 55:913–16
70. Lott, J. N. A., Larson, P. L., Darley, J. 1971. *Can. J. Bot.* 49:1777–82
71. Lott, J. N. A., Vollmer, C. M. 1973. *Can. J. Bot.* 51:687–88
72. Lott, J. N. A., Vollmer, C. M. 1973. *Protoplasma* 78:255–71
73. Lui, N. S. T., Altschul, A. M. 1967. *Arch. Biochem. Biophys.* 121:678–84
74. Mainguy, P. N. R., VanHuystee, R. B., Hayden, D. B. 1972. *Can. J. Bot.* 50:2189–95
75. Matile, Ph. 1968. *Z. Pflanzenphysiol.* 58:365–68
76. Mayer, A. M., Shain, Y. 1974. *Ann. Rev. Plant Physiol.* 25:167–93
77. Mikola, J., Enari, T.-M. 1970. *J. Inst. Brew.* 76:182–88
78. Mikola, J., Kolehmainen, L. 1972. *Planta* 104:167–77
79. Millerd, A. 1975. *Ann. Rev. Plant Physiol.* 26:53–72
80. Millerd, A., Simon, M., Stern, H. 1971. *Plant Physiol.* 48:419–25
81. Millerd, A., Spencer, D. 1974. *Aust. J. Plant Physiol.* 1:331–41
82. Millerd, A., Spencer, D., Dudman, W. F., Stiller, M. 1975. *Aust. J. Plant Physiol.* 2:51–59
83. Mitsuda, H., Murakami, K., Kusano, T., Yasumoto, K. 1969. *Arch. Biochem. Biophys.* 130:678–80
84. Mitsuda, H., Yasumoto, K., Murakami, K., Kusano, T., Kishida, H. 1967. *Agric. Biol. Chem.* 31:293–300
85. Mollenhauer, H. H., Totten, C. 1971. *J. Cell Biol.* 48:387–94
86. Morris, G. F. I., Thurman, D. A., Boulter, D. 1970. *Phytochemistry* 9:1707–14
87. Mossé, J. 1968. In *Progres en chimie agricole et alimentaire,* 47–81. Paris: Hermann
88. Mounfield, J. D. 1936. *Biochem. J.* 30:1778–86
89. Nakano, M., Asahi, T. 1972. *Plant Cell Physiol.* 13:101–10
90. Ibid 1974. 15:331–40
91. Nakano, M., Asahi, T. 1974. *Agric. Biol. Chem.* 38:219–21
92. Nelson, O. E. 1969. *Adv. Agron.* 21:171–94
93. Nieuwdorp, P. J. 1963. *Acta Bot. Neerl.* 13:295–301
94. Nieuwdorp, P. J., Buys, M. C. 1964. *Acta Bot. Neerl.* 13:559–65
95. Nougarède, A., Pilet, P. E. 1964. *C. R. Acad. Sci. Paris* 258:2641–44
96. Öpik, H. 1966. *J. Exp. Bot.* 17:427–39
97. Öpik, H. 1972. *Planta* 102:61–72
98. Ory, R. L., Henningsen, K. W. 1969. *Plant Physiol.* 44:1488–98
99. Oota, J., Fujii, R., Sunobe, Y. 1956. *Physiol. Plant.* 9:38–50
100. Osborne, T. B. 1908. *Science* 28:417–27
101. Osborne, T. B. 1924. *The Vegetable Proteins.* New York: Longmans, Green 151 pp.
102. Paleg, L. G., Hyde, B. 1964. *Plant Physiol.* 39:673–80
103. Penner, D., Ashton, F. M. 1966. *Nature* 212:935–36
104. Penner, D., Ashton, F. M. 1967. *Plant Physiol.* 42:791–96
105. Peterson, L. W. 1974. *Proteolytic enzymes on the synthesis and degradation of ribulose 1,5-diphosphate carboxylase in primary barley leaves.* PhD dissertation. Univ. California, Davis. 93 pp.
106. Poljakoff-Mayber, A. 1953. *Palestine J. Bot.* 6:101–06
107. Poux, N. 1965. *J. Microsc.* 4:771–82
108. Pusztai, A., Watt, W. B. 1970. *Biochim. Biophys. Acta* 207:413–31
109. Rost, T. L. 1971. *Protoplasma* 73:475–79
110. Rost, T. L. 1972. *Am. J. Bot.* 59:607–16

111. Rozacky, E. E. 1969. *Diss. Abstr. Int. B* 29 (12,pt 1):4519B
112. Ryan, C. A. 1973. *Ann. Rev. Plant Physiol.* 24:173–96
113. Saio, K., Watanabe, T. 1966. *Agric. Biol. Chem.* 30:1133–38
114. Salmia, M. A., Mikola, J. J. 1975. *Physiol. Plant.* 33:261–65
115. Sapanen, T., Mikola, J. 1975. *Plant Physiol.* 55:809–14
116. Schnarrenberger, C., Oeser, A., Tolbert, N. E. 1972. *Planta* 104:185–94
117. Shain, Y., Mayer, A. M. 1965. *Physiol. Plant.* 18:853–59
118. Shain, Y., Mayer, A. M. 1968. *Phytochemistry* 7:1491–98
119. Sharma, C. B., Dieckert, J. W. 1975. *Physiol. Plant.* 33:1–7
120. Smith, D. L., Flinn, A. M. 1967. *Planta* 74:72–85
121. Spencer, P. W., Spencer, R. D. 1974. *Plant Physiol.* 54:925–30
122. Srivastava, L. M., Paulson, R. E. 1968. *Can. J. Bot.* 46:1447–53
123. Stahmann, M. A. 1963. *Ann. Rev. Plant Physiol.* 14:137–58
124. St. Angelo, A. J., Yatsu, L. Y., Altschul, A. M. 1968. *Arch. Biochem. Biophys.* 124:199–205
125. St. Angelo, A. J., Ory, R. L., Hansen, H. J. 1969. *Phytochemistry* 8:1135–38
126. Ibid, 1873–77
127. Ibid 1970. 9:1933–38
128. Sundblom, N., Nikola, J. 1972. *Physiol. Plant.* 27:281–84
129. Suvorov, V. I., Buzulukova, N. P., Sobolev, A. M., Sveshnikova, I. N. 1970. *Sov. Plant Physiol.* (Engl. transl.) 17:1020–27
130. Suvorov, V. I., Sobolev, A. M. 1972. *Sov. Plant Physiol.* (Engl. transl.) 19:486–89
131. Sze, H., Ashton, F. M. 1971. *Phytochemistry* 10:2935–42
132. Tazawa, Y., Hirokawa, T. 1956. *J. Biochem.* 43:785–95
133. Thanh, V. H., Kazuyoshi, O., Shibaski, K. 1975. *Plant Physiol.* 56:19–22
134. Tombs, M. P. 1967. *Plant Physiol.* 42:797–813
135. Tsay, R., Ashton, F. M. 1974. *Phytochemistry* 13:1759–63
136. Vaintraub, I. A., Shutov, A. D. 1972. *Dokl. Akad. Nauk SSSR* 203:1200–3
137. Vaintraub, I. A., Tuen, N. T. 1971. *Mol. Biol.* 5:59–68
138. van der Eb, A. A., Nieuwdorp, P. J. 1967. *Acta Bot. Neerl.* 15:690–99
139. Varner, J. E., Balce, L. V., Huang, R. C. 1963. *Plant Physiol.* 38:89–92
140. Varner, J. E., Chandra, G. R. 1964. *Proc. Natl. Acad. Sci. USA* 52:100–6
141. Wall, J. R. 1969. *Southwest Nat.* 14:141–48
142. Wiley, L., Ashton, F. M. 1967. *Physiol. Plant.* 20:688–96
143. Yatsu, L. Y., Jacks, T. Y. 1968. *Arch. Biochem. Biophys.* 124:466–71
144. Yokoyama, Z., Mori, T., Matsushita, S. 1972. *Agric. Biol. Chem.* 36:33–41
145. Ibid, 2237–40
146. Yomo, H., Taylor, M. P. 1973. *Planta* 112:35–43
147. Yomo, H., Varner, J. E. 1973. *Plant Physiol.* 51:708–13
148. Yoo, B. Y. 1970. *J. Cell Biol.* 45:158–71
149. Young, J. L., Varner, J. E. 1959. *Arch. Biochem. Biophys.* 84:71–78

Ann. Rev. Plant Physiol. 1976. 27:119–32

PLANT RNA POLYMERASES ❖7604

C. T. Duda
Department of Biology, Wayne State University, Detroit, Michigan 48202

CONTENTS

Several enzymes capable of catalyzing the incorporation of nucleoside monophosphates into a ribonucleic acid (RNA) polymer have been isolated and characterized from a variety of higher plants. The most widely studied enzyme requires the presence of a polydeoxynucleotide for activity and catalyzes the formation of an RNA molecule with a base composition complementary to the added template (ribonucleoside triphosphate: RNA nucleotidyl transferase, EC 2.7.7.6 or DNA-dependent RNA polymerase). DNA-dependent RNA polymerase thus functions in the initial step of the process by which the genetic information encoded in the cellular DNA is expressed. Other enzymes which synthesize a heteroribonucleic acid polymer have been found to occur in some plants; however, they exclusively utilize an RNA template for the synthesis of a complementary product. Homoribonucleic acid polymers can also be synthesized by plant enzymes utilizing RNA as template and/or primer. The biological significance of the DNA-independent RNA polymerases has as yet not been determined. This article deals with the aforementioned RNA polymerases, describing some of their properties and possible function in cellular RNA metabolism. Since space is limited, the discussion will center on solubilized plant polymerases and I refer the reader to selected articles dealing with chromatin-bound plant polymerases (6, 7, 35, 37, 38, 45, 51, 62, 93, 95).

A number of review articles on RNA polymerases from prokaryotes (3, 15, 17) and nonplant eukaryotes (6, 7, 18, 36, 47) have been published which should be consulted if the reader wishes to carry out a more extensive comparison with these polymerases than is presented here.

ISOLATION OF PLANT DNA-DEPENDENT RNA POLYMERASES

A detailed procedure for the extraction of DNA-dependent RNA polymerases from maize which may "... serve as a model for the reader's own research pursuits" has been published (59).

Extraction and Solubilization

The various methods that have been employed for the extraction of RNA polymerase from plant tissue can be broadly classified into three categories: (a) isolation of chromatin under low salt conditions with subsequent treatment under moderately high to high salt conditions for removal of DNA free enzyme (28, 41, 46, 54, 65, 76, 80, 94); (b) homogenization of the plant tissue under moderately high salt conditions yielding an enzyme partially dependent on added DNA for maximal activity (31, 33, 44, 48); and (c) homogenization under low salt conditions yielding a polymerase dependent upon exogenous DNA for maximal RNA synthesis (24, 35, 56, 59, 61, 83, 85, 89, 92). Isolation of chloroplast polymerase does not fall into one of these categories as a low salt homogenization and low salt treatment were necessary for the removal of the enzyme from its endogenous template complex (9).

Initial cellular disruption can be accomplished with a number of different mechanical devices (rotating blades or crushers with frozen or fresh tissue). Sonication has been used routinely in the purification of polymerases from cauliflower (83), peas (33, 85), soybeans (44, 54), and wheat germ (48) with no apparent generation of artifacts such as those observed with fungi (36). Sonication should not be used in the preparation of chloroplast polymerases since the enzyme is extremely sensitive to this treatment (10). One study (85) does point to a possible problem generated by sonication: disruption of organelles which remain intact under less vigorous treatment. In this case, the addition of the phenolic absorbent Polyclar AT (57) was required for maintenance of enzyme activity (loss of specifically polymerase II was evident). Polyclar has also proved useful in isolation procedures not involving sonication (24, 76; Duda and Kahl unpublished; see also 35). The addition of a protease inhibitor (29, 44, 54, 56), an antioxidant (29) and/or antifoaming agent (24, 28) to the extraction medium should also be explored.

Separation of Multiple Forms

The chromatography of solubilized plant RNA polymerase activity on DEAE-cellulose or DEAE-Sephadex has revealed multiple forms of the enzyme (Table 1). The enzymes are eluted from the column using an increasing salt gradient and classified by a number indicative of the order of their elution from the ion exchanger (after Roeder & Rutter, 81). Thus the nomenclature of multiple plant polymerases has been uniform between the different labs [see (7, 18, 47) for nomenclature of other eukaryotic polymerases].

The initial separation of plant polymerases on DEAE-cellulose as compared to DEAE-Sephadex may not yield the same number of peaks of activity or enzymes with similar properties (Table 1, cauliflower, peas, soybeans). Since most labs employ the cellulose ion exchanger, comparison is not very meaningful and the differences may be due to extraction or tissue variation. A detailed study using animal tissue as a source of enzyme indicates that activity migrating as a single peak on DEAE-cellulose can be separated into two peaks of activity, with different properties, on DEAE-Sephadex (86, 87). That single peaks of activity separated on DEAE-cellulose can be composed of polymerases with different properties has also been shown to occur in plants (8, 44, 92). Separation into two differing activities was accomplished by glycerol gradient centrifugation (44, 92), phosphocellulose (4) or QAE-Sephadex (8) chromatography. In the maize report, template studies indicated the duality of activity even in the DEAE-cellulose peak (92).

In all plant polymerase extracts but one, the elution of the nucleolar enzyme precedes that of the nucleoplasmic activity (see following section and 81). The situation is reversed in coconut (64, 65). Removal of the polymerase from chromatin by high salt extraction (2M NaCl) was given as the reason for the altered elution pattern (7). However, high salt extraction (1 M NaCl) of chromatin from lentil roots does not alter the usual elution pattern (94). Furthermore, enzyme preparations which have undergone $(NH_4)_2SO_4$ precipitation do not show such altered elution patterns. An alteration in structure or conformation of coconut polymerase by 2 M NaCl has not been shown.

Localization and Function

The localization of at least four of the multiple DNA-dependent RNA polymerases from higher plants has been established. Three appear to be of nuclear origin (39, 41, 50, 54, 79, 80) and one can be isolated from purified chloroplasts (9). No definitive studies on the intraorganelle distribution of the three nuclear enzymes have been performed. However, two or three species of RNA polymerase can be solubilized from plant chromatin (8, 39, 54, 80, 94). One preliminary report dealing with a nucleolar enzyme has appeared (50); however, contamination by a nucleoplasmic enzyme is indicated.

Present data indicate the following role for the three nuclear polymerases, designated I, II, and III, in cellular RNA synthesis. Polymerase I [RII in coconut (8)] synthesizes a RNA polymer rich in G + C bases (70) which can be effectively competed against by cellular ribosomal RNA in DNA-RNA hybridization experiments (64). Polymerase II [RI in coconut (8)] appears to synthesize a nonribosomal RNA, since cellular ribosomal RNA will not compete with the in vitro product for DNA hybridization sites (64). Polymerase III synthesizes at least two species of RNA in vitro, the major product resembles transfer RNA while the minor species is more ribosomal in nature (8). The foregoing product analyses represent initial

Table 1 Chromatographic separation and properties of plant DNA-dependent RNA polymerases

Source of Enzyme	Chromatographic Properties[a]	Salt Optima (mM)[b]			References
		Mn²⁺	Mg²⁺	NH₄⁺	
Cauliflower	D–C, KCl				
inflorescence	I (0.09)	1	10		
	II (0.15)	(One-step elution, contains			31
	III (0.22)	activities I, II, III)			
Cauliflower	D–S, (NH₄)₂SO₄				
inflorescence	I (0.18)	2	5	35	84
	II (0.32)	2	5		
Coconut	D–C, KCl				
endosperm	I (0.10)	2 (1.6×)	8	200 (KCl)	
chromatin	II (0.20)	2	10 (2.5×)	200 (KCl)	8, 68
	III (0.35)				
Jerusalem	D–C, (NH₄)₂SO₄				
artichoke tuber	I (0.125)	1.25	2.5	inhibition	35
	II (0.30)	1.25 (2×)	2.5	inhibition	
Lentil	D–S, (NH₄)₂SO₄				
roots	Ia (wash)				
chromatin	Ib (0.125)	1	2 (1.1×)	30	94
	II (0.25)	1 (1.3×)	3	30	
	III (0.50)				
Maize	D–C, Tris				
shoots	II (0.47)	5 (1.5×)	25	100	89
	D–C, (NH₄)₂SO₄				
	II (0.35)	5	10	100	59
Maize	D–C, (NH₄)₂SO₄				
leaf	I (0.08)	8	25 (2.5×)	inhibition	92
(nuclear)	IIa (0.18)	8	25 (2.5×)	inhibition	
	IIb (0.22)				
Maize	D–C, (NH₄)₂SO₄				
leaf	I (0.21)	8	10–40 (5×)	inhibition	9
(chloroplast)					
Parsley	D–C, (NH₄)₂SO₄				
cell culture	I (0.15)				
	II (0.25)	5 (4×)	10		56
Pea	D–S, (NH₄)₂SO₄				
buds	I (0.10)	2 (1×)	15	100	85
	II (0.23)	2 (3×)	10	100	
Pea	D–C, (NH₄)₂SO₄				
seedling	I (0.10)	1	2 (1.2×)	inhibition	33
	II (0.14)	1 (2.6×)	2	50	
Soybean	D–C, (NH₄)₂SO₄				
hypocotyl	I (0.15)	5 (1.2×)	30	100	44
	II (0.28)	5	20 (1.3×)	100	
	III (0.33)				
	IV (0.41)				
Soybean	D–C, KCl				
hypocotyl	I (0.27)	1.5	3 (1×)	none	80,
chromatin	II (0.35)	2.0 (1.3×)	5	none	79
	III (D–S, KCl, 0.5M)				
Soybean	D–C, (NH₄)₂SO₄				
hypocotyl	I (0.09)	1		200 (KCl)	37, 54
chromatin	II (0.18)		10	400 (KCl)	

Table 1   (Continued)

Source of Enzyme	Chromatographic Properties[a]	Salt Optima (mM)[b]			References
		Mn^{2+}	Mg^{2+}	NH$_4$$^+$	
Sugar beet					
root	D–S, (NH$_4$)$_2$SO$_4$				
chromatin	I (0.18)	1.25 (2×)	10	50	28
Sugar beet	D–C, Tris				
root	II (0.5)	4.5 (2.4×)	10	50	24,
				200 (KCl)	C. T. Duda, G. Kahl
					unpublished data
Wheat					
leaf	D–C, Tris				
	I (0.4)				
	II (0.5)	3.4	18 (5×)		75
Wheat	D–C, (NH$_4$)$_2$SO$_4$				
germ	I (0.11)	1 (2×)	5	none	48
	II (0.22)	1 (1.3×)	15	125	

[a] Separation of multiple polymerase activities was accomplished on DEAE-cellulose (D–C) or DEAE-Sephadex (D–S) employing a linear gradient of KCL, (NH$_4$)$_2$SO$_4$ or Tris (see also section on Isolation); nomenclature (I–IV) refers to the order of elution from these ion exchangers. Figures in parenthesis indicate the molarity of the salt required for the elution of the various enzyme activities.

[b] Parentheses indicate that the enzyme exhibited maximal activity in the presence of this divalent metal ion and the figure the degree of stimulation above that exhibited in the presence of the other metal, example coconut polymerase I is 1.6× more active in the presence of Mn^{2+} than in the presence of Mg^{2+}.

data, but they indicate that plant polymerases I, II, and III perform similar if not identical functions as their counterparts isolated from other eukaryotes (7, 18, 47, and references therein).

Reports on the relative proportions of polymerases I and II, in quantitative terms, within the cell (nucleus) are conflicting. Purified chromatin appears to be enriched in polymerase I (28, 37–39, 54, 80), while crude chromatin reflects the relative levels of polymerase I and II in isolated nuclei (39, 80). However, a large amount of the cellular polymerase II activity can be detected in the postnuclear supernatant (39, 54). It can be said, in general, that there is significantly more polymerase II activity in the cell (nucleus) than polymerase I (see refs. Table 1). Other species of RNA polymerase (III and IV) have not been studied in enough detail to make a quantitative comparison with I and II.

PROPERTIES OF DNA-DEPENDENT RNA POLYMERASES

In general, plant polymerases exhibit similar pH and temperature optima, and require the presence of four nucleoside triphosphates for maximal activity [see (9, 92) for polymerases which show a high temperature optima].

Metal Ion and Ionic Strength Optima

The divalent metal ion and ionic strength optima for the different polymerases are summarized in Table 1. Caution should be exercised when viewing this table; metal ion and ionic strength optima were not determined under similar assay conditions in the various labs. The condition and concentration of the template varied (heat

denatured or native, homologous or heterologous), metal ion optima were determined under low or high salt conditions, while ionic strength optima were determined in the presence of Mn^{2+}, Mg^{2+} or Mn^{2+} plus Mg^{2+}. It has been shown that
ionic strength optima vary with the divalent metal cation (85), and the metal ion
optimum varies with the ionic strength of the assay medium (97). These varying
assay conditions may be responsible for the variations in the relative efficiencies
(as well as in concentration optima) of these two divalent metal cations (Mg^{2+} and
Mn^{2+}) in stimulating the same enzymatic activity extracted from the same taxonomic species but prepared in different labs (compare maize, pea, soybean). Similarly, lack of agreement concerning the stimulating effect of high ionic strength (and
ionic strength optima) may be accounted for by varying assay conditions or even
related to the purity of the enzyme (see 9, 56, 69). Even with these variables, a
pattern in regards to salt conditions of the assay does emerge. The nucleolar en-
zyme(s) (polymerase I) is equally stimulated by Mn^{2+} or Mg^{2+} and prefers a low
ionic strength (Mg^{2+} is slightly more stimulatory). On the other hand, the nucleoplasmic enzyme(s) (polymerase II) shows optimal activity in the presence of Mn^{2+}
and prefers high ionic strength. High ionic strength assays show a greater stimulation by Mn^{2+} than Mg^{2+} for polymerases I and II. If more emphasis is going to be
placed on the differences in salt optima between the various polymerase isozymes
and on the differences between taxonomic plant species, then a more uniform
method of determining (and reporting) these salt optima will have to be adopted. I
suggest that divalent cation optima be determined under low [10mM $(NH_4)_2SO_4$]
and high ionic strength [100mM $(NH_4)_2SO_4$] and that ionic strength optima be
determined in the presence of optimal concentrations of Mn^{2+} or Mg^{2+}. Furthermore, listing optimal assay conditions in the order in which they were determined
may be of benefit to those working in other labs (see also 59).

Product analysis of the Mn^{2+} and Mg^{2+} stimulated reactions with chromatin
bound polymerase I of soybean (71) and with DEAE-cellulose purified polymerase
II of sugar beet (Duda and Kahl, unpublished results) indicate that similar regions
of the DNA template are being copied under differing metal ion stimulation. As yet
there appears to be no correlation between metal ion and specificity of template
binding for any of the multiple polymerases. Although the studies with coconut
polymerases indicate a specificity in template transcription, the products of a
Mn^{2+} or Mg^{2+} stimulated reaction for one isozyme were not compared (8, 64).

Template Preference

Purified polymerases show an absolute requirement for a DNA template. Most
investigators have used calf thymus DNA as template; however, some enzymes have
shown a preference for a homologous DNA template (31, 68, 77, 92). In general,
the nucleolar polymerase(s) uses native DNA whereas the nucleoplasmic enzyme(s)
exhibits higher activity with denatured DNA as template. Does this relate to the
finding that polymerase I appears to be strongly bound to endogenous chromatin
template (28, 37, 39, 54)? Asymmetric transcription of DNA (mixed heteropolymer)
by a plant polymerase has not been shown. However, selective transcription of a

DNA template is indicated from the work with maize and coconut enzymes (8, 14, 64).

Maize polymerase II was shown to be a mixture of two activities: one (IIa) which preferred denatured DNA and another (IIb) which preferred native DNA. Soybean polymerase II was likewise shown to be a mixture of two activities (IIa and IIb); IIa was found to be more sensitive to α-amanitin (see following section) then IIb (44). Is there a correlation between template preference (i.e. heat denatured versus native DNA) and sensitivity to α-amanitin? Polymerase IIa of maize and soybean (assuming they represent the same activity) prefers denatured DNA and is sensitive (80% inhibition) to α-amanitin, while IIb is less sensitive (35% inhibition) to this drug and prefers native DNA. Drug and template studies will have to be done using enzyme from the same tissue for this question to be answered. Interestingly, polymerase I prefers native DNA and is insensitive to inhibition by α-amanitin.

It is becoming increasingly apparent that studies on template specificity have to include characterization of the DNA as to size and the presence of single-stranded breaks (7, 16, 18, 47). For example, yeast polymerases, and apparently eukaryotic polymerases in general, cannot transcribe intact double helical DNA (22). Single-stranded gaps are required for initiation (see also 16, 19) but synthesis can continue into a duplex structure. Such a scheme would form a DNA-RNA hybrid of the 5'-terminus (22) which would be resistant to ribonuclease digestion. Plant polymerases appear to form such a product using maize enzyme (89, 90) and sugar beet enzyme (Duda, unpublished data). Template problems are indicated in the work with the chloroplast enzyme (9). The enzyme shows a preference for denatured over native DNA and for maize DNA over that of calf thymus; however, the degree of preference varies from one DNA preparation to another (of maize chloroplast and nuclear DNA).

Inhibitors of Polymerization

It is generally accepted (but not always reported) that plant polymerases are inhibited by actinomycin D and inorganic pyrophosphate [see Peller (74a) for discussion of the necessity of removing the pyrophosphate formed during polymerization from an in vitro reaction]. As already mentioned, RNA synthesis by polymerase I is resistant to added α-amanitin (55), while polymerase II is sensitive to this drug (see 1, 4, and refs. in Table 1). However, partial sensitivity of polymerase I to α-amanitin inhibition (8–30%) has been noted (44, 64, 80, 85, 92) with enzyme from a variety of plants and may be a general characteristic of plant polymerase I or indicate the presence of another species of enzyme. Polymerase III from coconut (8), polymerases III and IV from soybean (44), the soluble polymerases from wheat (75), as well as the chloroplast polymerase of maize and wheat (9, 76) are also insensitive to α-amanitin. However, Rizzo & Cherry (79) have reported that their soybean polymerase III is completely sensitive to low concentrations of α-amanitin. Sensitivity of animal cell RNA polymerase III to high concentrations of α-amanitin (50% inhibition of 20 μg/ml) has been reported (86). At this time it is difficult to say what constitutes a high concentration of α-amanitin for inhibition of plant polymerases. Polymerase II from different plants varied in the degree of sensitivity to this drug, all the way from the pea enzyme which was inhibited 93% at a concentration of 0.13 μg/ml (85) to the soybean enzyme (IIa + IIb) which required a concentration of 50 μg/ml to yield a 90% inhibition in activity (44). The mechanism of inhibition by α-amanitin of plant polymerases has not been investigated.

Rifamycin SV or its derivative rifampicin has been shown not to inhibit plant polymerases (see refs. in Table 1, also 1, 4, 50, 76) in the greatest majority of cases. The exceptions are soybean polymerase III (44, 78) and IV (44), and all three polymerases of coconut endosperm (8). From the coconut studies it appears that rifampicin binds to the enzyme, thus inhibiting its activity (64). Inhibition can be reversed or prevented by the addition of a protein factor isolated from coconut chromatin. It should be noted that even though eukaryotic nuclear polymerases are generally resistant to rifampicin, a sensitivity to other rifamycin derivatives has been shown (23, 63, 96). Cyloheximide has no effect on soybean polymerases I and II (44) nor maize enzyme (50). Streptovaricin and streptolydigin do not inhibit the soluble wheat polymerase (75).

Subunit Structure and Molecular Weight

Analysis of purified plant polymerases by electrophoresis on SDS polyacrylamide gels indicates that they are composed of several polypeptide subunits. The three polymerases of coconut endosperm are all composed of four subunits (a, b, c, d) in the ratio of 1:2:1:2. The a-subunit is the same size for polymerases I, II, and III: 180,000; the b-subunit is the same for I and II: 150,000, but different for III: 112,000; the c- and d-subunits are different for all enzymes: I – 95,000 and 80,000, II – 69,000 and 42,000, III – 50,000 and 40,000 (8, 32). Maize nuclear enzyme (IIa) contains polypetides with molecular weights of 180,000, 160,000, 35,000, 25,000, 20,000 and 17,000 (40, 69, 88). Maize chloroplast polymerase is also composed of six subunits: 180,000, 140,000, 100,000, 95,000, 85,000, 40,000 (98). Wheat germ polymerase II yields five bands on SDS gels: A-220,000; A'-170,000; B-140,000; C-45,000; and D-40,000 (49). The authors suggest that the A' band may have arisen from the A subunit by proteolytic cleavage [see (99) and (43) for a similar suggestion regarding rat liver and calf thymus, and blue-green algae, respectively]. Use of proteolysis inhibitors, as suggested in an earlier section, would appear to be mandatory in these types of studies. Parsley polymerase II was also separated into three large subunits (200,000, 180,000, 140,000) as well as four smaller polypeptides (43,000, 26,000, 25,000, 16,000). In this case no proteolytic conversion of subunits was indicated; instead it was suggested that the enzyme peak may be composed of two different forms with a high molecular weight subunit composition: 180,000 + 140,000 and 200,000 + 140,000 (56). It would appear that plant polymerases, like those of other organisms, consist of two large subunits and a variable number of smaller subunits. Molecular weight estimates (using glycerol gradients) of cauliflower polymerase I [400,000 (85)], soybean polymerase II [16S (44) and 650,000 — six subunits (74; Cherry, personal communication)], and sugar beet polymerase II [460,000 (Duda and Kahl, unpublished data)] also indicate that other plant polymerases are large molecules. A purified RNA polymerase of wheat leaf appears to contain a single polypeptide (65,000 molecular weight); however, it is not known if the active form of the enzyme consists of the monomer or of an aggregate (75).

Modification of Polymerase Activity

A factor which specifically enhances the ability of polymerases to transcribe native (but not denatured) DNA has been isolated from maize (40) and coconut (64, 65). The maize factor was identified late in the purification scheme for polymerase II and may have been part of the enzyme complex of a previous purification step. Indeed its loss may have been responsible for the conversion of an enzyme preferring native DNA to an enzyme preferring denatured DNA (see ref. 92 and above). It is of interest to note that such a factor can also be separated from purified rat liver polymerase I (34). At least two factors have been isolated from coconut endosperm chromatin independently of the RNA polymerases (64, 65). Factor B (molecular weight 76,000) stimulates the activity of all three coconut polymerases with native eukaryotic DNA (but not denatured or λ-phage DNA) by binding to the enzyme or enzyme-DNA complex and acting as an initiator factor (64). Coconut factor B also stimulates the activity of chicken erythrocyte polymerases (58), suggesting that it may play a similar role in transcription by other eukaryotic polymerases. Factor C seems to facilitate the release of RNA from the DNA template and the reinitiation of new RNA synthesis, thereby acting as a termination factor (64). The puzzling thing about the coconut polymerases is their inability to synthesize RNA in the absence of factor B with either native or denatured DNA (68). Only the ability to transcribe native DNA is diminished with the loss of factor from maize polymerase II; activity with denatured DNA does not change (40). Furthermore, though most polymerases utilize either native DNA or denatured DNA more efficiently, they do show a substantial degree of activity in the presence of the less preferred template; this is not so for the coconut polymerases. Further studies are required before the various factors can be assigned an exact role in the initiation, elongation, and/or termination of RNA synthesis.

The observed changes in ribonucleic acid biosynthesis resulting from hormone treatment (52) have recently been extended to include changes in the activity of purified RNA polymerases (1, 39, 41, 78, 94). An increase in the activity of polymerase I (39, 41, 94) and polymerase II (1) was observed as a result of an in vivo auxin treatment of the tissue before enzyme extraction and purification. It appears that auxin brings about an increase in the specific activity of the polymerase I molecule (94; 37, 39) while increasing the number and specific activity of polymerase II molecules (1). In addition, recent studies suggest that auxin can interact with some acceptor protein (factor) and stimulate RNA synthesis by purified polymerases (42, 66, 67). Mondal et al have suggested that purified coconut auxin-acceptor protein complex binds to the DNA (not the polymerase-factor B complex) and causes coconut polymerase II to transcribe a portion of DNA not transcribed in its absence (66, 67). Changes in polymerase activities with development have also been observed (79, 91). Inhibitor studies indicate that fully elongated soybean cells contain mainly polymerase II, the elongating cells about equal quantities of polymerase I and II, and the meristematic region more polymerase II than I in addition to containing a new polymerase (III) not detectable in as large amounts in the other regions (79). Using a crude enzyme preparation, Stout et al (91) reported an increase in maize soluble polymerase after illumination of darkgrown seedlings. Similarly, using suspension of maize plastids, Hardin et al (40) reported an increase in RNA polymerase activity with illumination. However, no difference in activity could be detected using purified chloroplast polymerase from 2- and 6-hour illuminated tissue. The washing or aging of a plant storage tissue (51, 98), sugar beet, was reported to cause an increase in extractable RNA polymerase (24, 26, 28).

DNA-INDEPENDENT RNA POLYMERASES

RNA-Dependent RNA Polymerase

It now appears that not all cellular RNA is synthesized by DNA-dependent RNA polymerase, at least this is what the data from two labs indicate (2, 21, 27). An RNA-dependent RNA polymerase can be extracted from chinese cabbage (2) and tobacco (27) leaves, in both instances from healthy tissue (although it is interesting to note that infection by a virus caused this enzyme activity to increase). The purified enzymes prefer RNA to DNA [cabbage enzyme 3:1 (2), tobacco enzyme exclusively (Duda, unpublished results)], exhibit greater activity in the presence of Mg^{2+} than Mn^{2+}, and are completely dependent upon the presence of four nucleoside triphosphates for activity. The product of the in vitro reaction is double-stranded RNA, complementary to the added template. The molecular weight of the template-free native enzyme was estimated as 160,000 in both studies. The tobacco enzyme as isolated with its endogenous template synthesizes a low molecular weight double-stranded RNA. The presence of the above described enzyme in healthy tobacco leaves has recently been confirmed (20, 30). Furthermore, low molecular weight double-stranded RNA has been found in healthy tobacco tissue (53). The cellular location or role of RNA-dependent RNA polymerase has not been determined. Its small size [excluding the wheat enzyme (75); also see following discussion] and preference for an RNA template would say it is not a new type of DNA-dependent enzyme. The large amount of activity would argue against it being a subunit of a DNA-dependent enzyme; however, this possibility cannot be excluded. The similarity of the tobacco enzyme to tobacco mosaic viral replicase, in size and biochemical characteristics, has been noted (100) and is presently being investigated in the author's lab.

On Homopolymer Synthesis

Homopolymer synthesis by maize DNA-dependent RNA polymerase II and cauliflower polymerase I have been reported (5, 84, respectively). The maize enzyme requires single-stranded DNA for poly(A) production and can synthesize this homopolymer in the presence or absence of other nucleoside triphosphates. Homopolymer and heteropolymer synthesis are inhibited by α-amanitin, indicating that both products may be formed by the same polymerases (4, 5). On the other hand, cauliflower polymerase I (not II) synthesizes a purine polyribonucleotide in the presence of one substrate, requiring Mn^{2+} and a template (84). The template can be DNA (native or denatured), a pyrimidine polyribonucleotide or a pyrimidine polydeoxyribonucleotide.

Ribohomopolymer synthesis can also be accomplished by enzymes shown not to be DNA-dependent RNA polymerases. Mans and co-workers have described an enzyme which synthesizes a poly(A) sequence (80 to 200 AMP moities) from the 3'-hydroxyl terminus of either ribo- or deoxyligomers (60, and references therein). A molecular weight of about 65,000 was estimated by sucrose density gradient analysis. In view of the work done with the aforementioned enzyme, the DNA-dependent enzyme of Polya (75) should be reexamined. It, too, has a molecular weight of 65,000 and in a less purified state exhibits a high degree of poly(A) synthesis [59% of the activity with the other triphosphates (76)]. Though the enzymes differ in other respects (aggregation, sensitivity of product to ribonuclease), comparative studies under identical conditions are indicated. A poly(U) polymerase which requires Mn^{2+} (not Mg^{2+}) and a polynucleotide for activity has been purified from tobacco leaves (13). The enzyme is highly specific for UTP and is inhibited by other ribonucleoside triphosphates. An approximate molecular weight of 40,000 was reported. Tobacco leaves also appear to contain poly(A), poly(G), and poly(C) polymerase activity as well as the above-mentioned poly(U) polymerase (11). A poly(U) synthesizing activity utilizing UDP as substrate has also been purified from tobacco leaves (12). The enzyme exhibits the characteristics of a polynucleotide phosphorylase and has an approximate molecular weight of 150,000. Not to be outdone by another plant, DNA-dependent polymerase can be extracted from tobacco (11, 82).

The above-mentioned homopolymer synthesizing enzymes have been isolated from the soluble phase of plant homogenates, and their contribution to a presumed DNA-dependent polymerase isolated from a soluble fraction should be determined. Use of chromatin as a source of DNA-dependent polymerase also has its problems, as homopolymer activity (DNA-dependent) has been reported to be present in this fraction (25) and also on chromatin isolated by the Huang & Bonner method (46; Duda, unpublished finding).

CONCLUDING REMARKS

The chromatin-nuclei experiments of the '60s have now become the multiple polymerase studies of the '70s. For the most part, these studies have centered on proving the existence of multiple forms of DNA-dependent polymerase and determining some of their physical and biochemical properties. The intracellular localization has been determined with a fair degree of certainty. Difficult as it was to accumulate this information, the hard part is still ahead; namely, determining the role of the different polymerases in cellular RNA synthesis. The present factor boom may be beneficial in this regard. At the moment it points to the existence within the cell of proteins capable of modifying polymerase activity. The observations that factors can be removed during isolation reduces the probability that the purified polymerases represent the complete enzyme as it functions in vivo. Furthermore, it questions the existence of multiple polymerases, since removal of a factor or subunit could change the chromatographic characteristics of the enzyme. However, the differential response to divalent ions and ionic strength, and the differing subunit compositions of the multiple polymerases isolated from a single tissue, plus the initial report that different forms of polymerase synthesize different classes of RNA, support the presence of polymerase isozymes within a cell. It is obvious that confirmation of the proposed functional specificity of the various polymerases requires that greater emphasis be placed on analyzing the transcription products and comparing them with their in vivo counterparts.

DNA-dependent enzymes are not the only RNA synthesizing activities in plant cells. RNA-dependent RNA polymerase and the full spectrum of ribohomopolymerases have been isolated from a variety of plants. In view of the reports that both polymerase I and II can synthesize homopolymers, as can a subunit of *E. coli* (72, 73) polymerase, the existence of these activities (DNA-independent enzymes) as separate enzymes within the cell remains in question. They may in fact represent subunits of the more complex DNA-dependent enzymes. Whatever, these activities are considerable and should be considered as possible contaminants in preparations of the DNA-dependent polymerases.

Literature Cited

1. Arens, M. Q., Stout, E. R. 1972. *Plant Physiol.* 50:640-41
2. Astier-Manifacier, S., Cornuet, P. 1971. *Biochim. Biophys. Acta* 232:484–93
3. Bautz, K. F. 1972. *Progr. Nucleic Acid Res. Mol. Biol.* 12:129–57
4. Benson, R. H. 1971. *Plant Physiol.* 47:Suppl. 36, 1–52
5. Benson, R. H., Mans, R. J. 1972. *Fed. Proc.* 31 (2):427 (Abstr.)
6. Biswas, B. B. 1974. *Sub-Cell. Biochem.* 3:27–38
7. Biswas, B. B., Ganguly, A., Das, A. 1975. *Progr. Nucleic Acid Res. Mol. Biol.* 15:145–84
8. Biswas, B. B., Mondal, H., Ganguly, A., Das, A., Mandal, R. K. 1974. In *Control of Transcription,* ed. B. B. Biswas, R. K. Mandal, A. Stevens, W. E. Cohn, 279–93. New York: Plenum. 423 pp
9. Bottomley, W., Smith, H. J., Bogorad, L. 1971. *Proc. Natl. Acad. Sci. USA* 68:2412–16
10. Bottomley, W., Spencer, D., Wheeler, A. M., Whitfield, P. R. 1971. *Arch. Biochem. Biophys.* 143:269–75
11. Brishammar, S., Juntti, N. 1974. *Arch. Biochem. Biophys.* 164:218–23
12. Ibid, 224–32
13. Brishammar, S., Juntti, N. 1975. *Biochim. Biophys. Acta* 383:351–58
14. Brooks, R. R., Mans, R. J. 1973. *Biochem. Biophys. Res. Commun.* 52: 608–13
15. Burgess, R. R. 1971. *Ann. Rev. Biochem.* 40:711–40
16. Butterworth, P. H. W., Flint, S. J., Chesterton, C. J. See Ref. 8, 269–78
17. Chamberlin, M. J. 1974. In *The Enzymes,* ed. P. D. Boyer, 10:333–74. New York: Academic. 886 pp.
18. Chambon, P. See Ref. 17, 261–331
19. Chambon, P., Mandel, J. L., Gissinger, F., Kedinger, C., Gross-Bellard, M., Hossenlopp, P. 1974. See Ref. 8, 257–68
20. Clerx-van Haaster, Weening, C. J., Bol, J. F. 1975. *3rd Int. Congr. Virology, Madrid*
21. Cornuet, P., Astier-Manifacier, S. 1971. *Ann. Phytopathol.* 3:27–35
22. Dezélée, S., Sentenac, A., Fromageot, P. 1974. *J. Biol. Chem.* 249:5971–77
23. Di Mauro, E., Mezinna, M. 1974. *Arch Biochem. Biophys.* 164:765–68
24. Duda, C. T. 1969. *Ribonucleic acid polymerases of sugar beet tissue.* PhD thesis. Purdue Univ., Lafayette, Ind. 129 pp.
25. Duda, C. T., Cherry, J. H. 1971. *J. Biol. Chem.* 246:2487–93
26. Duda, C. T., Cherry, J. H. 1971. *Plant Physiol.* 47:262–68
27. Duda, C. T., Zaitlin, M., Siegel, A. 1973. *Biochim. Biophys. Acta* 319:62–71
28. Dunham, V. L., Cherry, J. H. 1973. *Phytochemistry* 12:1897–1902
29. Eccleshall, R., Criddle, R. S. 1974. *Arch. Biochem. Biophys.* 164:602–18

30. Fraenkel-Conrat, H. 1975. *Properties and Replication of Infectious RNA Agents of Plants.* Bordeaux, Sept. 18–22
31. Fukasawa, H., Mori, K. 1974. *Plant Sci. Lett.* 2:391–96
32. Ganguly, A., Das, A., Mondal, H., Mandal, R. K., Biswas, B. B. 1973. *FEBS Lett.* 34:27–30
33. Glicklich, D., Jendrisak, J. J., Becker, W. M. 1974. *Plant Physiol.* 54:356–59
34. Goldberg, M., Perriard, J., Hager, G., Hallick, R. B., Rutter, W. J. 1974. See Ref. 8, 241–56
35. Gore, J. R., Ingle, J. 1974. *Biochem. J.* 143:107–13
36. Griffin, D. H., Timberlake, W., Cheney, J., Horgen, P. A. 1975. In *Isozymes I— Molecular Structure,* ed. C. L. Market, 69–87. New York: Academic. 856 pp.
37. Guilfoyle, T. J., Hanson, J. B. 1973. *Plant Physiol.* 51:1022–25
38. Ibid 1974. 53:110–13
39. Guilfoyle, T. J., Lin, C. Y., Chen, Y. M., Nagao, R. T., Key, J. L. 1975. *Proc. Natl. Acad. Sci. USA.* 72:69–72
40. Hardin, J. W., Apel, K., Smith, J., Bogorad, L. See Ref. 36, 55–67
41. Hardin, J. W., Cherry, J. H. 1972. *Biochem. Biophys. Res. Commun.* 48:299–305
42. Hardin, J. W., Cherry, J. H., Morré, D. J., Lembi, C. A. 1972. *Proc. Natl. Acad. Sci. USA* 69:3146–50
43. Herzfeld, F., Rath, N. 1974. *Biochim. Biophys. Acta* 374:431–37
44. Horgen, P. A., Key, J. L. 1973. *Biochim. Biophys. Acta* 294:227–35
45. Hou, G. C., Pillay, D. T. N., 1975. *Phytochemistry* 14:403–7
46. Huang, R. C., Bonner, J. 1962. *Proc. Natl. Acad. Sci. USA* 48:1216–22
47. Jacob, S. T. 1973. *Progr. Nucleic Acid Res. Mol. Biol.* 13:93–126
48. Jendrisak, J., Becker, W. M. 1973. *Biochim. Biophys. Acta* 319:48–54
49. Jendrisak, J., Becker, W. M. 1974. *Biochem. J.* 139:771–77
50. Jones, A. H., Stout, E. R. 1973. *Plant Physiol.* 51:Suppl. 38, 1–70
51. Kahl, G. 1974. *Bot. Rev.* 40:263–314
52. Key, J. L. 1969. *Ann. Rev. Plant Physiol.* 20:449–74
53. Lewandowski, L. J., Kimball, P. C., Knight, C. A. 1971. *J. Virol.* 8:809–12
54. Lin, C. Y., Guilfoyle, T. J., Chen, Y. M., Nagao, R. T., Key, J. L. 1974. *Biochem. Biophys. Res. Commun.* 60:498–506
55. Lindell, T. J., Weinberg, F., Morris, P. W., Roeder, R. G., Rutter, W. J. 1970. *Science* 170:447–49
56. Link, G., Richter, G. 1975. *Biochim. Biophys. Acta* 395:337–46
57. Loomis, W. D. 1969. *Methods Enzymol.* 13:555–63
58. Mandal, R. K., Mazumber, H. K., Biswas, B. B. See Ref. 8, 295–302
59. Mans, R. J. 1973. *Methods Mol. Biol.* 4:93–125
60. Mans, R. J., Huff, N. J. 1975. *J. Biol. Chem.* 250:3672–78
61. Mans, R. J., Novelli, G. D. 1964. *Biochim. Biophys. Acta* 91:186–88
62. Mazus, B., Buchowicz, J. 1972. *Phytochemistry* 11:2443–46
63. Meilhac, M., Tysper, Z., Chambon, P. 1972. *Eur. J. Biochem.* 28:291–300
64. Mondal, H., Ganguly, A., Das, A., Mandal, R. K., Biswas, B. B. 1972. *Eur. J. Biochem.* 28:143–50
65. Mondal, H., Mandal, R. K., Biswas, B. B. 1970. *Biochem. Biophys. Res. Commun.* 40:1194–1200
66. Ibid 1972. 49:306–11
67. Mondal, H., Mandal, R. K., Biswas, B. B. 1972. *Nature NB* 40:111–13
68. Mondal, H., Mandal, R. K., Biswas, B. B. 1972. *Eur. J. Biochem.* 25:463–70
69. Mullinix, K. P., Strain, G. C., Bogorad, L. 1973. *Proc. Natl. Acad. Sci. USA* 70:2386–90
70. Nagao, R. T., Lin, C. Y., Key, J. L. 1974. *Plant Physiol.* 53:Suppl. 37, 1–75
71. Nagao, R. T., Lin, C. Y., Murray, M. G., Key, J. L. 1973. *Plant Physiol.* 51:Suppl. 39, 1–70
72. Ohasa, S., Tsugita, A. 1972. *Nature NB* 240:35–38
73. Ohasa, S., Tsugita, A., Mii, S. 1972. *Nature NB* 240:39–41
74. Pedersen, K., Cherry, J. H. 1974. *Plant Physiol.* 53:Suppl. 38, 1–75
74a. Peller, L. 1975. *Biochem. Biophys. Res. Commun.* 63:912–16
75. Polya, G. M. 1973. *Arch. Biochem. Biophys.* 155:125–35
76. Polya, G. M., Jagendorf, A. T. 1971. *Arch. Biochem. Biophys.* 146:635–48
77. Ibid, 649–57
78. Rizzo, P. J., Cherry, J. H. 1973. *Plant Physiol.* 51:Suppl. 38, 1–70
79. Ibid 1975. 55:574–77
80. Rizzo, P. J., Cherry, J. H., Pedersen, K., Dunham, V. L. 1974. *Plant Physiol.* 54:349–55
81. Roeder, R. G., Rutter, W. J. 1969. *Nature* 224:234–37
82. Sachar, R. C. 1968. *Biochim. Biophys. Acta* 169:58–66
83. Sasaki, R., Goto, H., Arima, K., Sasaki, Y. 1974. *Biochim. Biophys. Acta* 366:435–42

84. Sasaki, Y., Goto, H., Wake, T., Sasaki, R. 1974. *Biochim. Biophys. Acta* 366: 443–53
85. Sasaki, Y., Sasaki, R., Hashizume, T., Yamada, Y. 1973. *Biochem. Biophys. Res. Commun.* 50:785–92
86. Schwartz, L. B., Sklar, V. E. F., Jaehning, J. A., Weinmann, R., Roeder, R. G. 1974. *J. Biol. Chem.* 249:5889–97
87. Seifart, K. H., Benecke, B. J. 1975. *Eur. J. Biochem.* 53:293–300
88. Smith, H. J., Bogorad, L. 1974. *Proc. Natl. Acad. Sci. USA* 71:4839–42
89. Stout, E. R., Mans, R. J. 1967. *Biochim. Biophys. Acta* 134:327–36
90. Stout, E. R., Mans, R. J. 1968. *Plant Physiol.* 43:405–10
91. Stout, E. R., Parenti, R., Mans, R. J. 1967. *Biochem. Biophys. Res. Commun.* 29:322–26

92. Strain, G. C., Mullinix, K. P., Bogorad, L. 1971. *Proc. Natl. Acad. Sci. USA* 68:2647–51
93. Surzycki, S. J. 1969. *Proc. Natl. Acad. Sci. USA* 63:1327–34
94. Teissere, M., Penon, P., Richard, J. 1973. *FEBS Lett.* 30:65–70
95. Tewari, K. K., Wildman, S. G. 1969. *Biochim. Biophys. Acta* 186:358–72
96. Tsai, M., Saunders, G. F. 1973. *Proc. Natl. Acad. Sci. USA* 70:2072–76
97. Tsai, M., Saunders, G. F. 1974. *Biochim. Biophys. Acta* 366:61–69
98. Van Steveninck, R. F. M. 1975. *Ann. Rev. Plant Physiol.* 26:273–58
99. Weaver, R. F., Blatti, S. P., Rutter, W. J. 1971. *Proc. Natl. Acad. Sci. USA* 68:2994–99
100. Zaitlin, M., Duda, C. T., Petti, M. A. 1973. *Virology* 53:300–11

Ann. Rev. Plant Physiol. 1976. 27:133–57

THE ORGANIZATION AND REGULATION OF ELECTRON TRANSPORT IN PLANT MITOCHONDRIA

♦7605

J. M. Palmer

Department of Botany, Imperial College of Science and Technology, University of London, London SW7 2BB, England

CONTENTS

INTRODUCTION

The recent general acceptance that ATP synthesis may be coupled to electron transport by a system similar to that proposed by Mitchell when he formulated the chemiosmotic theory (96) has resulted in a broadening of the scope of research into the functioning of mitochondria from many sources. Research on plant mitochondria has benefited from this change of emphasis and from the growing interest in the properties of mitochondria isolated from microorganisms (88). The introduction of new techniques has also made it possible to determine the nature, behavior, and location of the members of the respiratory chain more precisely. In this review I shall discuss advances made in this field, particularly with respect to the organization and interaction of the NADH dehydrogenase systems. I shall also speculate on the metabolic regulation and significance of these enzynes,

CRITERIA FOR THE ASSESSMENT OF MITOCHONDRIAL PURITY AND INTEGRITY

It has always been considered more difficult to isolate mitochondria from plant tissue than from animal tissue. This is due to three main factors: (a) the difficulty of breaking the tough cell wall without damaging the organelle; (b) the difficulty of controlling the pH because the vacuoles of many plants contain large amounts of organic acids; and (c) the accumulation of potentially damaging compounds such as metal ions or the oxidation products of polyphenols such as quinones or tannins. These difficulties have led to the belief that many of the results obtained using plant mitochondria are due to artifacts induced during isolation (105). These problems are aggravated by the diversity of plant material from which mitochondria are isolated and the lack of an accepted standard method of isolation. Most workers have solved the problems in different ways, making it difficult to compare data from different laboratories. These problems become more significant when investigating the operation of branched electron transport pathways (16, 56) or attempting to identify the physical location of enzymes with respect to the structure of the organelle (28, 33, 40, 111). It is therefore essential that criteria are developed to establish the quality of isolated mitochondria, especially with respect to the degree of contamination and structural damage.

Bonner (20) has emphasized the importance of defining minimal criteria which mitochondria must meet if they are to be judged acceptable with respect to purity and integrity. These original criteria include (a) negligible endogenous respiration; (b) a low State-4 respiration rate [note that the metabolic states used in this review are as defined by Chance & Williams (24)]; (c) a rapid State-3 respiration rate; (d) a high pyridine nucleotide to cytochrome c ratio; and (e) no response of malate oxidation to exogenous NAD^+. These criteria are basically those used to assess mammalian mitochondria and are not necessarily applicable to plant mitochondria. Condition a is easily achieved if the mitochondria are carefully washed. Conditions b and c have very little meaning since terms such as high and low are not absolute values. It might seem to be more useful to use the respiratory control ratio, which is the ratio of the State-3 to State-4 respiratory rates. This parameter measures the degree of control that the phosphorylating system can exert over the electron transport system and is frequently used as a sensitive indicator for success of isolation. This criterion was developed with mammalian mitochondria and appears to be valid only if the mitochondria have a respiratory chain arranged in a linear sequence. We know this is not the case in plant mitochondria. In mung bean

(*Phaseolus aureus*) mitochondria it has been calculated that all of the electron flow during State-3 respiration is mediated by the cyanide-sensitive oxidase, whereas the State-4 respiration rate is mediated by both the cyanide-sensitive and resistant oxidases (2, 3); similar observations have been obtained using mitochondria from *Neurospora crassa* (44). Thus part of State-4 respiration is mediated by a separate nonphosphorylating electron transport chain which was not operating under State-3 conditions. Therefore a high State-4 is not necessarily indicative of badly produced mitochondria. The State-4 respiration rate also depends on the nature of the substrate used; it is slow with malate and faster with succinate (62). When malate is supplied as the substrate the State-4 rate is not linear but is slowest immediately after the ADP becomes depleted and then gradually increases in velocity (J. M. Palmer, unpublished results); the initial slow rate is related to the presence of oxaloacetate. Other authors have noticed the same phenomenon (58, 83) (this phenomenon will be discussed more fully in a later section). Thus it is difficult to know which is the true State-4 rate.

The final criteria *d* and *e* are designed to check that the inner membrane of the mitochondrion has not been made permeable to endogenous NAD^+. The suggestion that the permeability of the inner membrane to NAD^+ can be directly tested (criterion *e*) by seeing if the oxidation of malate is stimulated by exogenous NAD^+ is invalid in the light of the observation that there is an externally located NADH dehydrogenase and malic enzyme (28, 33, 40, 111). Thus it can be seen that the traditional criteria of mitochondrial quality are questionable when applied to plant mitochondria and a new set is necessary.

In early publications it was claimed that the traditional methods of isolation yielded very high grade mitochondria (11, 14). However, in recent years it has been suggested that these methods result in preparations heavily contaminated with microsomes and "other cytochrome *b*-containing organelles" and that further purification on a sucrose density gradient is advisory (40, 78) or even mandatory for serious research (12). Recent results of Douce et al (40) show that the biochemical activity of several types of plant mitochondria improved markedly if they were purified by passage through a sucrose density gradient. Earlier studies of Baker et al (4) using density gradients had shown the heterogeneous nature of unpurified preparations, but their data failed to show enhanced biochemical activity following purification. My own unpublished data are similar to those obtained by Baker et al (4), and recent data published by Pomeroy (115) also fail to show that there is any great biochemical benefit to be derived from purifying the mitochondria using density gradients. Thus I feel that the problem of microsomal contamination may not be so widespread as suggested by Douce et al (40). However, the use of density gradients has reminded us of the heterogeneity of mitochondrial preparations which may prove to be more difficult to sort out than a simple matter of microsomal contamination.

METHODS FOR ASSESSING PURITY   Direct examination using the electron microscope is one technique, but it is not rapid nor easily applied. Lambowitz & Bonner (78) describe two assays which provide a rapid, but probably insensitive, check for microsomal contamination. The first test is to assay for high redox potential *b*-type cytochromes which can be reduced by ascorbate under aerobic conditions in the presence of cyanide (118). None of the *b*-type cytochromes of the mitochondria are reduced under these conditions while a *b*-type cytochrome with an α absorption peak at 558 nm associated with the microsomes is extensively reduced. The problem with this technique is that there appears to be a variation in the cytochrome content of microsomes from different tissue (118). The second method is to test for the presence of an antimycin A insensitive NADPH-cytochrome *c* reductase which is present in the microsomal system and may not be present in the mitochondrial membranes.

METHODS FOR ASSESSING INTEGRITY   All the techniques currently employed use indirect methods to determine the apparent permeability of the mitochondrial membrane to various reagents. One method is to measure the permeability of the inner membrane to NADH by measuring the rate at which exogenous NADH can be oxidized by oxaloacetate, using the malate dehydrogenase situated in the matrix of the mitochondrion (110). It is also possible to measure the permeability of the inner membrane to ferricyanide by determining the antimycin A insensitivity of the succinate-ferricyanide reductase (110). However, the simplest and perhaps the most sensitive test for mitochondrial integrity is to determine the level of succinate-cytochrome *c* reductase (39), which is very low in intact organelles and can be increased dramatically if the organelles are damaged by osmotic swelling. Whether the rate of reduction of exogenous cytochrome *c* is limited by the permeability of the outer membrane to cytochrome *c* (39) or by the inability of exogenous cytochrome *c* to interact with the endogenous cytochrome *c* on the inner membrane (110) has yet to be decided. Whatever the answer, the assay does provide a sensitive parameter of mitochondrial integrity.

THE ORGANIZATION OF THE ELECTRON TRANSPORT CHAIN

The organization of the respiratory chain in plant mitochondria appears to be more complex than that believed to operate in mammalian mitochondria. The classic illustration of this complexity is the presence of the cyanide-resistant oxidase (61); more recent experiments show that the organization of the NADH dehydrogenase may also be more complex (16, 28, 33, 40, 111).

Possible Components of the Respiratory Chain

A discussion of this aspect of the problem appears in most reviews concerning plant mitochondria and this is no exception. Ikuma (61) has reviewed the literature up until 1971 and covered the early work concerning the kinetic behavior of the various components.

FLAVOPROTEINS   The study of flavoproteins is technically more difficult than the study of cytochromes, and consequently considerable confusion exists with respect to the involvement of flavoproteins in the respiratory chain of both plant and animal mitochondria. The study of animal and yeast mitochondria (20, 22, 50) has shown that the flavoproteins may give both fluorescence and absorption changes when they undergo redox changes; the ratio of the change in fluorescence compared with the change in absorption (designated as the FA ratio) was found to be different for each flavoprotein. Storey (126) has used the FA ratio to characterize the flavoproteins in mung bean mitochondria. He found evidence for four distinguishable species of flavoproteins involved in electron transport. Two had high redox potentials and could be reduced directly by succinate in the presence of an uncoupling agent. The redox potential of the succinate/fumarate couple used as the substrate was estimated to be in the region of -8 mV (77). These two high potential flavoproteins could be distinguished from each other by their FA ratio. One was highly absorbant with an $FA = 0$ and is called Fp_{ha}, and the other was more highly fluorescent with an $FA = 1.4$ and is referred to as Fp_{hf}; in both cases the subscript h refers to the high redox potential. The remaining two flavoproteins appeared to have low redox potentials because they could only be reduced by succinate under conditions when energy conservation was present and reversed electron transport could occur. These two low potential flavoproteins could also be distinguished from each other by their FA ratio; one was highly absorbant with an $FA = 0$ and the other was very highly fluorescent with an $FA = 3.8$. The highly fluorescent species was only slowly reduced by the reversed electron flow from succinate and its redox state appeared to be closely related to that of the endogenous pyridine nucleotide pool; this component is designated Fp_{lf} and is thought to be analogous to the highly fluorescent flavoprotein Fp_L which is a component involved in the oxidation of reduced α lipoic acid in animal mitochondria (20). The other low potential component was rapidly reduced by reversed electron flow from succinate and was reduced by malate via an amytal sensitive pathway. This has been designated Fp_M (126) or more recently Fp_{la} (128), and it is thought that this flavoprotein may be the equivalent of the flavoprotein Fp_{DI} of the NADH dehydrogenase in mammalian mitochondria (20).

The behavior of the two high potential flavoproteins is very difficult to understand and cannot be readily equated with any component in the mammalian system. The concentration of the high potential components is high in skunk cabbage (*Symplocarpus foetidus*) mitochondria, and their behavior has been studied extensively in this tissue (46). Neither Fp_{hf} nor Fp_{ha} could be definitely identified as the counterpart of the flavoprotein associated with the succinic dehydrogenase in animal mitochondria. Many workers have observed that the flavoproteins remain in a relatively oxidized state in the presence of inhibitors of cytochrome oxidase (8, 19, 46, 132). Thus these components have been closely implicated with the operation of the cyanide-resistant oxidase. Studies using antimycin A to block the conventional electron transport chain and m-chlorobenzhydroxamic acid (120) to inhibit the cyanide-resistant oxidase indicated that Fp_{ha} appeared to have a role on the main respiratory chain between the ubiquinone and cytochrome b and the Fp_{hf} appeared to be a member of the cyanide-resistant electron transport system (46, 61).

The development of the anaerobic titration technique (43) made it possible to determine the midpoint potential (E_m). Using this technique with skunk cabbage mitochondria, it was possible to detect five flavoprotein components with $E_{m7.2}$

values of $+170$, $+110$, $+20$, -70 and -155 mV (128). These E_m values are considerably higher than those characteristic of the flavoprotein from animal mitochondria, which vary between -45 and -220 mV (47), and yeast, which vary between $+50$ and -320 mV (128). It has proved difficult to relate the flavoprotein species identified from E_m measurements with those identified from FA ratio measurements. It would seem that Fp_{lf} could have an $E_{m7.2} = -155$ mV, Fp_{la} (Fp_M) may have $E_{m7.2} = -70$ or $+20$ mV. The flavoprotein with $E_{m7.2} = +110$ mV represents 50% of the total flavoprotein in skunk cabbage mitochondria and may be equated with Fp_{ha}. The redox titration failed to show the existence of a fluorescent flavoprotein with a high E_m value (i.e. Fp_{hf}). It is now considered that the kinetic changes previously allocated to this component represent interference from changes associated with Fp_{lf} (128). This possibility raises the problem of how a flavoprotein with such a low E_m value (-155 mV) can have a role in the cyanide-resistant oxidase which is traditionally thought to branch from the main chain somewhere between the first and second sites of phosphorylation (56). It may be possible that the alternative oxidase may be able to interact directly with the NADH dehydrogenase, resulting in the bypass of the first site of phosphorylation (17, 80). The metabolic role of the very high potential flavoprotein (Fp_{vha}) is not known; its $E_{m7.2}$ of $+170$ mV is very close to that of the cytochrome a [$+190$ mV (42)]. Recently Storey (131) suggested that this flavoprotein may not be a member of the respiratory chain but acted together with cytochrome b_{566} as part of an enzymic sequence mediating the hydroxylating reactions required for the biosynthesis of ubiquinone. Plant mitochondria do not appear to contain the flavoproteins associated with the oxidation of fatty acids (29, 30, 60, 126).

It is clear that there is much more to be learned about the flavoproteins, and it is likely to prove to be even more complex when we begin to identify the flavoproteins associated with the external membrane (117) and those associated with the multiple NADH dehydrogenases (16, 40).

IRON-SULFUR PROTEINS   Much has been learned in recent years concerning the role and nature of iron-sulfur proteins in animal and yeast mitochondria (6, 99, 109, 121). Little is known concerning the role of iron-sulfur proteins in plant mitochondria. Their presence has been deduced from the observation that inhibitors such as rotenone and piericidin A, which are traditionally assumed to inhibit at the level of the iron-sulfur components in the NADH dehydrogenase, inhibit respiration in plant mitochondria. Schonbaum et al (120) were the first to publish an electron paramagnetic resonance (EPR) spectrum obtained using plant mitochondria. This showed a clear signal at $g = 2.0$ and 1.94, which is characteristic of iron-sulfur proteins (6, 99). Cammack & Palmer (17) have also examined the iron-sulfur proteins in Jerusalem artichoke (*Helianthus tuberosus*) and *Arum maculatum* spadix mitochondria using EPR techniques. These studies suggested that the NADH-ubiquinone reductase segment of the respiratory chain contained at least three distinguishable iron-sulfur centers. Two of these correspond closely to iron-sulfur centers N-1 ($g = 2.02$; 1.93) and N-2 ($g = 2.05$; 1.92) found in animal mitochondria (99, 101). A third signal at $g = 2.10$; 1.87 seen at temperatures below 20°K may be the counterpart of centers N-3 and N-4, although it was not possible to resolve the two centers as is possible with animal or yeast mitochondria (99). Preliminary redox titrations (R. Cammack and J. M. Palmer, unpublished data) showed that the E_m values of centers N-1 and N-2 of the NADH dehydrogenase in plant mitochondria were approximately the same as those reported for the animal counterparts [i.e. –300 mv and –20 mv, respectively (99, 101)]. The EPR spectrum of arum spadix submitochondrial particles showed an intense signal at $g = 1.93$ that was tentatively identified as center N-1 of the NADH dehydrogenase (109). Subsequent studies (R. Cammack and J. M. Palmer, in preparation) indicate that this initial interpretation was probably incorrect. As the arum spadix matured the rate of respiration of the isolated mitochondria rose and the cyanide-resistant pathway developed (65, 81). Our EPR studies showed that during this developmental sequence the signals characteristic of centers N-1, N-2 and (N-3 + N-4) of the NADH dehydrogenase declined and the single signal at $g = 1.93$ developed. Attempts to characterize this signal suggested that it was due to the iron-sulfur centers associated with the succinic dehydrogenase. Redox titrations showed that the signal was produced by two different components, one detectable at 77°K with an $E_m = -10$ mV. This signal completely disappeared below 12°K; when the temperature was decreased to below 25°K, a second signal appeared which had an $E_m = -230$ mV. These centers appear to correspond closely to the iron-sulfur centers S-1 and S-2 associated with the succinic dehydrogenase in animal mitochondria (102). In addition to the centers S-1 and S-2, we detected a high potential iron protein (Hipip) similar to the center S-3 reported to be present in animal mitochondria (64, 100, 103). The term high potential iron protein is used to describe a group of iron-sulfur proteins which have a detectable EPR spectrum in the oxidized rather than reduced form (104). The signal associated with the Hipip component disappeared at temperatures above 30°K and had a g(av) above 2.0, whereas the S-1 and S-2 had EPR signals with g(av) near 1.96. In addition to the centers N-1, N-2, (N-3 + N-4), S-1, S-2, and S-3, plant mitochondria also appeared to contain another signal from nonheme iron. This signal appeared to come from a ferric ion which may have been bound to a protein via a linkage other than that characteristic of iron-sulfur proteins because the EPR spectrum could be detected at unusually high temperatures.

Much has been written recently concerning the possible role of a nonheme iron protein in mediating electron transport via the cyanide-resistant oxidase (7, 13, 36, 61, 93, 120). The identification of such a component depends on the observation that the alternative oxidase was specifically inhibited by chelating agents such as α,α'-dipyridyl, thiocyanate, 8-hydroxyquinoline, and hydroxamic acids. However, most of these reagents, other than the hydroxamic acids, have been found to inhibit the normal electron transport chain at concentrations only slightly higher than those needed to block the cyanide-resistant oxidase (2). Bendall & Bonner (7) reported a powerful synergism between thiocyanate and antimycin A and concluded that this supported the existence of an auto-oxidizable iron-sulfur protein as the oxidase. Although these observations have been confirmed (106), it is possible to reach the conclusion that the site of action of thiocyanate was at the level of the succinic dehydrogenase and not at the oxidase.

It is debatable whether iron chelating agents such as α,α'-dipyridyl or 8-hydroxyquinoline can remove the iron from iron-sulfur proteins. Studies on soluble ferredoxins showed that the iron only reacted very slowly with chelating agents unless the protein was first denatured (91). Thus it seems unlikely that the iron of membrane bound iron-sulfur proteins would be accessible to chelating agents. Therefore, if a nonheme iron protein is acting as the alternative oxidase and is sensitive to iron chelating agents, the iron would have to be in a different conformation from that found in the classical iron-sulfur centers so far investigated (104). Chemical analysis of plant mitochondria showed that there is a 1:1 stoichiometry between the nonheme iron and acid labile sulfur (36); it is also apparent that arum spadix mitochondria, which contain a powerful cyanide-resistant oxidase, contain less iron and sulfur than do potato mitochondria which have no cyanide-resistant oxidase. From these data Dizengremel et al (36) concluded that potato mitochondria contain the cyanide-resistant oxidase but that it is not active. This conclusion would only be true if the possession of equal amounts of iron and sulfur meant that the mitochondria contained equal amounts of the various types of iron-sulfur proteins. This is clearly not so, either on the basis of data already published (17) or that discussed earlier in this section. Thus the data of Dizengremel et al (36) could be used equally to argue against the role of an iron-sulfur protein in the cyanide-resistant oxidase. This does not mean to say that an iron-sulfur protein may not have a role in mediating cyanide-resistant electron transport, but prudence is required when interpreting the data and much more work needs to be done.

Further details of the operation of the cyanide-resistant oxidase can be found in a comprehensive review by Henry & Nyns (56).

UBIQUINONE   The ubiquinone component of mung bean mitochondria has been shown to be UQ_{10} (i.e. ubiquinone with 10 isoprenyl residues in the side chain) (9). Kinetic measurements and redox titrations are not easy to carry out on the ubiquinone because its absorption bands are in the ultraviolet region of the spectrum and are therefore prone to interference from many other compounds. Kinetic observations suggested that the ubiquinone accepted electrons from succinic dehydrogenase (134) and transferred them to the cytochrome chain, a role similar to that suggested for the ubiquinone in animal mitochondria (48, 76). When exogenous NADH was used as the substrate there was a lag before the reduction of the ubiquinone began, and it has been suggested that ubiquinone may act as a storage pool for reducing equivalents entering the respiratory chain on the substrate side of the second site of ATP synthesis (127). Kinetic evidence also suggested that when succinate was the electron donor the ubiquinone acted on the substrate side of the flavoprotein Fp_{ha} (134). This is a controversial but interesting position for the flavoprotein because of the possible role of the ubiquinone (137) and flavoprotein (134) in acting as the branch point for the cyanide-resistant oxidase, and because it has a bearing on how the changeover from a two-electron to a one-electron carrier may be achieved.

Redox potential measurements (130) showed that the ubiquinone may exist as two pools. The main pool, which appeared active in mediating electron transport, had an $E_m = +70$ mV which was close to that determined for the ubiquinone in animal mitochondria (136). The second smaller pool had an $E_m = -12$ mV. Storey (130) speculated that this pool may function in close association with cytochrome b_{566}. There is evidence from studies with beef heart mitochondria for the existence of dual respiratory chains utilizing separate pools of ubiquinone associated with different species of cytochrome b (97).

b-TYPE CYTOCHROMES   The b-type cytochromes have been studied intensively during the past 5 years (140), and as a result of these studies the apparent role of these cytochromes has become even more confusing. This reflects the level of ignorance we have concerning the role of these cytochromes. It was originally believed that animal mitochondria contained a single cytochrome b_{562} while plant mitochondria contained three components: b_{557}, b_{560}, and b_{566} (10, 18). In this review the cytochromes are identified by the position of their α absorption peak at room temperature, in line with the recommendation of the IUB Nomenclature subcommittee. This can lead to some confusion because some recent papers (61) used the position of the α peak at 77°K, which is moved 2-3 nm towards the blue end of the spectrum. It is now thought that there are at least two and possibly three b-type cytochromes in animal mitochondria (18, 45). One of these cytochromes has a single α absorption peak at 562 nm and an $E_m = +40$ mV and appears to behave as a simple electron carrier and is often referred to as cytochrome b_K. Two other α absorption peaks, observed at 558 and 566 nm, were originally thought to belong to a single cytochrome b with a double α peak [this is not unique; cytochrome c has a double α peak (20, 70) and the microsomal b-type cytochromes also have double α peaks (118)]. This cytochrome was believed to have the unique characteristic of changing its E_m from –30 mV in uncoupled mitochondria to +245 mV in mitochondria energized by the addition of ATP (25). These data were interpreted as showing that b_{566} had an $E_m = -30$ mV and that a high energy form $b_{566}\sim$I, formed in the presence of ATP, had an $E_m = +245$ mV. This cytochrome b was believed to be closely related to the process of energy transduction and was named cytochrome b_T. There is now considerable doubt concerning this interpretation, and it appears that cytochrome b_{566} may not be as unique as was first thought. The double α peak attributed to this cytochrome may actually belong to two cytochromes with single peaks at 558 and 566 nm (57, 140). Other data suggest that b_{562} may also become more reduced in the presence of ATP. It is now apparent that the increased reducibility of all three b-type cytochromes in the presence of ATP may not be due to an increase in the E_m, but due to reversed electron transport or the abolition of an accessibility barrier for the transfer of redox equivalents between the substrate and the cytochrome (85, 140, 141).

Original studies on plant mitochondria showed the presence of three b-type cytochromes with α bands at 557, 560, and 566 nm (10, 20, 61, 82). Lambowitz & Bonner (78) have shown that plant mitochondria may contain two extra b-type cytochromes both with α absorption bands close to 558 nm. One of the new species could be reduced by reversed electron flow from succinate and the other could only be reduced by dithionite; thus there appear to be four cytochromes that can be reduced by natural donors. Redox titrations (42, 78) have shown that b_{557} and b_{560} have relatively high redox potentials of +75 and +45 mV respectively, while b_{565} and b_{558} have relatively low potentials of –75 and between –70 and –105 mV respectively.

Kinetic studies have shown that these cytochromes behave in a complex manner. Cytochrome b_{560} appears to be the easiest to understand. It is readily reduced under anaerobic conditions by NADH, succinate, and ascorbate plus N,N'-tetramethylphenylenediamine (TMPD) and rapidly reoxidized by oxygen with a half time of 8 msec (124). This rate of oxidation is approximately ten times faster than the rate of oxidation of cytochrome b in animal mitochondria (21), and there is no clear gap in the kinetic behaviour of b_{560} and cytochrome c, suggesting a close functional relationship between the two components.

The kinetic behavior of cytochrome b_{557} appears to be more complex. It can be reduced extensively by succinate under anaerobic conditions but it is only partially reduced by ascorbate plus TMPD (124), even though the E_m of b_{557} is more positive than b_{560}; this suggests the presence of an accessibility barrier preventing the establishment of an equilibrium between the TMPD and b_{557}. The kinetic behavior of b_{557} in presence of inhibitors is even more strange. Succinate will extensively reduce b_{557} immediately anaerobiosis sets in. If, however, azide is added to block the cytochrome oxidase, then b_{557} remains oxidized even under anaerobic conditions, induced by the activity of the alternative oxidase (125). The half time for the reoxidation of b_{557} (500 msec) is much slower than b_{560} (8 msec) and is comparable with that of the ubiquinones and flavoproteins (124), suggesting a kinetic relationship with these components.

The response of cytochrome b_{566} has been found to be even more complex. Because the E_m of b_{566} is –70 mV and the actual redox potential of the succinate/fumarate couple used as the donor is only –8 mV (77) succinate can only reduce this cytochrome under conditions which encourage reversed electron flow; even then only 20% of the total b_{566} can be reduced at anaerobiosis. Neither exogenous nor endogenous NADH, which are much stronger reducing agents than succinate, can reduce any more cytochrome b_{566} than can succinate. The addition of phenazine methosulfate, a redox mediator which aids the establishment of a redox equilibrium between redox components, allows NADH to reduce twice as much b_{566}. This suggests that an accessibility barrier exists between NADH and cytochrome b_{566} (78).

The addition of antimycin A greatly modifies the behavior of cytochrome b_{566}. Succinate will reduce virtually no b_{566} under anaerobic conditions in the presence of weak acid uncouplers. If, however, antimycin A is added, succinate can reduce nearly all the b_{566} in the presence of uncouplers under aerobic conditions. When the antimycin A treated mitochondria become anaerobic, then b_{566} becomes slowly reoxidized (77, 129). The full explanation of these phenomena is not known. The apparent change of redox poise between succinate/fumarate and b_{566}, under aerobic conditions in the presence of antimycin A and an uncoupling agent, can be interpreted as an apparent change in the E_m of cytochrome b_{566} from –70 to approximately +40 mV (77, 129). How this change in E_m is achieved is not known, but it could be the result of antimycin A binding the b_{566}. The reoxidation appears to be a response to the change in redox poise of other components of the electron transport chain. Storey originally suggested that the reoxidation of the reduced b_{566} depended on the redox poise of cytochrome c_{549} (129). When c_{549} became reduced under anaerobic conditions, the b_{566} became oxidized. Lambowitz & Bonner (77) questioned that conclusion because they could find no apparent kinetic relationship between the rate of reduction of c_{549} and the rate of oxidation of b_{566}. They suggested that the redox poise of some other component, such as an unidentified iron-sulfur protein, may have been the regulating factor. A similar suggestion has been made for the behavior of cytochrome b in animal mitochondria (5, 119). In his most recent paper concerning this phenomenon, Storey (131) showed that at least part of the reoxidation of b_{566} appeared to be synchronous with the reduction of c_{549} during the onset of anaerobiosis. He also observed that a flavoprotein underwent reduction synchronously with the oxidation of b_{566} and suggested that the redox poise of the flavoprotein may regulate the behavior of cytochrome b_{566}. Storey has equated this flavoprotein with the component which has the very high redox potential of +170 mV.

It seems clear that the rate of electron transfer from succinate to b_{566} may be dependent on the redox poise of another component in the respiratory chain. This could form the basis for an important physiological control mechanism which could regulate and integrate the rate of electron flow from different substrates entering the respiratory chain at different points. There is direct evidence that the redox poise of cytochrome c_1 in animal mitochondria may regulate the rate at which electrons can be transferred from succinate to cytochrome b (135).

In many respects cytochrome b_{566} appears to be the counterpart of cytochrome b_T in animal mitochondria. However, it has never been possible to show that energization of the organelle alters the E_m of this component (42, 79). In plant mitochondria the increased reducibility of b_{566} induced by ATP has been accounted for by reversed electron flow. The fact that cytochrome b_{566} does not show significant alterations in its E_m may be due to the fact that the mediators used during the redox titration can establish an equilibrium directly with the b_{566}. Recent evidence has been obtained to suggest that the change in E_m of cytochrome b_T in animal mitochondria is only apparent, and it is really only the result of reversed electron flow. If the concentration of redox mediators is increased, a better equilibrium appears to be established and the alteration in the E_m seems to disappear (141). Thus the study of plant mitochondria has made a direct contribution to our understanding of how all mitochondria may function, and I am sure this will happen more frequently in the future than it has done in the past.

c- AND a-TYPE CYTOCHROMES   Little new information has been forthcoming concerning these components since they were last reviewed in these volumes (20, 61), and it is therefore unnecessary to discuss the function of these at present.

One of the main aims of studying the components of the respiratory chain is to make it possible to draw up a scheme to represent the sequence of reactions involved in electron transport. Many schemes have been presented over the past few years

(46, 61, 130, 132–134); these are all slightly different and there is very little value in my adding another comprehensive scheme to this list. We probably understand most about the organization of the cyanide-sensitive succinic oxidase system which seems, in the light of present data, to be mediated by the following linear sequence:

$$\text{succinate} : \text{dehydrogenase} : \text{Fe-S} : \text{UQ} : Fp_{ha} : b_{557} : b_{560} : c_{549} : c_{547} : a : a_3 : O_2$$

In the past few years we have begun to learn some facts concerning the operation and organization of the NADH dehydrogenase systems in plant mitochondria. These have not been widely discussed in previous reviews and it seems profitable to spend the rest of this review discussing some of the data that are relevant to understanding the organization of the NADH dehydrogenases.

Organization of the NADH Dehydrogenase Systems

There are two basic differences between plant and animal mitochondria which form the basis for this discussion. Plant mitochondria always oxidize exogenous NADH (31) and frequently oxidize malate in the absence of a system for the removal of oxaloacetate (28, 61, 62); in general, animal mitochondria are unable to carry out similar processes.

OXIDATION OF EXOGENOUS NADH   Intact animal mitochondria cannot oxidize exogenous NADH (86), and isotopic studies showed that external NADH could not traverse the inner membrane of animal mitochondria (51, 75). This compartmentation allows the pyridine nucleotide in the cytosol and matrix of the mitochondrion to adopt different redox poises (23, 72).

The ability of plant mitochondria to oxidize exogenous NADH was originally thought to be due to the NADH entering the matrix space and being oxidized by the internal dehydrogenase (53, 54, 71, 87). Thus plant mitochondria were considered to be more "leaky" than animal mitochondria (61), a property often thought to be an artifact induced during isolation (54, 105). Evidence now shows that exogenous and endogenous NADH may be oxidized by different NADH dehydrogenase systems. Cunningham (31) observed that exogenous NADH was oxidized most rapidly by intact mitochondria and that the P/O ratio obtained with exogenous NADH was lower than that obtained with endogenous NADH. He proposed that exogenous NADH was oxidized by a dehydrogenase which bypassed the normal flavoprotein responsible for the oxidation of endogenous NADH and coupled to ATP synthesis. Many observations are now available to substantiate this view. Divalent metal ions stimulate the oxidation of exogenous NADH but have no direct effect on the rate of oxidation of endogenous NADH (27, 53, 94, 95, 109). Compounds such as amytal, rotenone, and piericidin A, which are reasonably effective at inhibiting the oxidation of endogenous NADH, have no effect on the oxidation of exogenous NADH (28, 63, 94). Thus the NADH dehydrogenase responsible for the oxidation of exogenous NADH appears to bypass the first site of ATP synthesis and the rotenone sensitive site; both properties are associated with the iron-sulfur protein components of the internal NADH dehydrogenase (109). Since the oxidation of exogenous and endogenous NADH are equally sensitive to inhibition by antimycin A (28, 94), electrons from both dehydrogenase systems appear to share a common pathway from the level of ubiquinone to oxygen.

If the exogenous and endogenous NADH are oxidized by different dehydrogenases, this removes the necessity for the inner membrane to be permeable to NADH. The dehydrogenase responsible for the oxidation of exogenous NADH could be located on the outer surface of the inner membrane similar to the external NADH dehydrogenase found in mitochondria from yeast (138) and *Neurospora crassa* (139). Potassium ferricyanide has proved to be a useful electron acceptor when investigating the physical location of components of the electron transport chain. Ferricyanide has an E_m of +360 mV and can theoretically accept electrons from any component in the respiratory chain. However, ferricyanide is a hydrophilic anion and cannot cross the inner membrane of the mitochondrion (74) and can only accept electrons from components that are situated on the outer surface of the inner membrane. The outer membrane of the mitochondrion does not appear to be a permeability barrier for the passage of ferricyanide (37). In mammalian mitochondria the first component in the respiratory sequence known to be accessible to ferricyanide is cytochrome c (116), and the reduction of ferricyanide is observed to be sensitive to antimycin A. If, however, a component such as an external NADH dehydrogenase is located on the outer surface of the inner membrane, then electrons will be donated to ferricyanide from a component before the antimycin A block, and a component of the ferricyanide reductase will be resistant to antimycin A. A diagramatic illustration of such a situation is shown in figure 1.

Using this technique, Palmer & Passam (111) showed that there was an externally located NADH dehydrogenase in Jerusalem artichoke mitochondria. It was assumed that this result provided evidence that the distribution of NADH dehydrogenases in plant mitochondria was similar to that described in microorganisms (138, 139). However, there is a major weakness in this argument since the use of ferricyanide fails to differentiate between the NADH dehydrogenase associated with the electron transport chain and enzymes which may be associated with the outer membrane (40, 109) and do not normally provide reducing equivalents to the respiratory chain. Douce et al (40) have isolated the outer membrane from mung bean mitochondria and have shown that it contains an NADH-ferricyanide reductase. This dehydrogenase differs from the NADH dehydrogenase associated with the respiratory chain by being specific for the 4α hydrogen of the NADH. The dehydrogenases of the inner membrane are specific for the 4β hydrogen of NADH (40, 138). Douce et al (40) criticized the work carried out by Von Jagow & Klingenberg using yeast (138) on the basis that they had not differentiated between the NADH-ferricyanide reductase associated with the outer membrane and that associated with the inner membrane. This criticism may have been unwarranted because all of the NADH-ferricyanide reductase in yeast was reported to be specific for the 4β hydrogen of NADH (138). However, their criticism may be valid if applied to the previous work carried out with plant mitochondria (28, 111). Douce et al (40) also observed that in mung bean mitochondria most of the NADH-ferricyanide reductase was

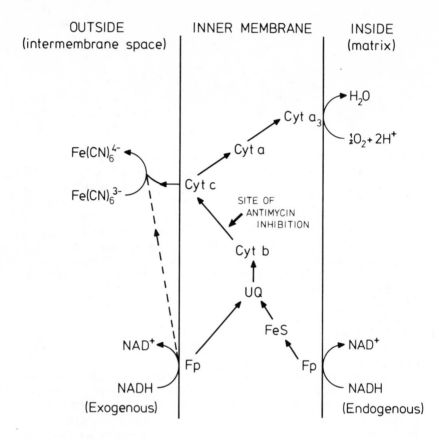

OUTSIDE
(intermembrane space)

INNER MEMBRANE

INSIDE
(matrix)

Figure 1 Diagram showing the sites at which ferricyanide is thought to be able to accept electrons from endogenous and exogenous NADH. The topographical distribution of the components of the respiratory chain is after Racker (116). The reduction of ferricyanide can be seen to be sensitive to antimycin A when endogenous NADH is the electron donor and resistant to antimycin A when exogenous NADH is the donor because electrons can be donated directly from the flavoprotein to the ferricyanide.

sensitive to antimycin A, a result which was different from those already obtained using mitochondria from yeast (138) or Jerusalem artichoke (111). Since they stated that NADH could not cross the inner membrane, they had to conclude that the antimycin A sensitive component of the ferricyanide reduction was a property of the external dehydrogenase. They suggested that the flavoprotein component of the external NADH dehydrogenase was associated with the outer face of the inner membrane in such a way that it was accessible to NADH and not to ferricyanide. It is impossible to distinguish between this situation and one in which the mitochondria were permeable to NADH and not ferricyanide.

Oxidation on the outer membrane   The dehydrogenase associated with the outer membrane does not normally contribute reducing equivalents to the respiratory chain. However, if cytochrome c is added, the dehydrogenase will catalyze an antimycin A resistant NADH-cytochrome c reductase by means of a flavoprotein and cytochrome b_{555} (40). If the mitochondria are suitably damaged, the cytochrome c reduced by this enzyme can be oxidized by the cytochrome oxidase on the inner membrane, resulting in an antimycin A resistant, cyanide-sensitive oxygen consumption (54, 109). The antimycin A insensitive NADH-cytochrome c reductase, catalyzed by this enzyme system associated with the outer membrane, has been observed to be stimulated by lowering the osmolarity of the suspending medium (109). Thus cytochrome c may have to cross the outer membrane (39) before it can accept electrons from this dehydrogenase, and this may be considered to be evidence that the outer membrane has anisotropic properties.

Oxidation on the inner membrane   All the evidence suggests that exogenous NADH is oxidized by a dehydrogenase system associated with the inner membrane of the mitochondrion. Evidence obtained from the use of ferricyanide as a nonpenetrating electron acceptor suggests, but does not prove conclusively, that the dehydrogenase is located on the outer surface of the inner membrane. We know very little concerning the components involved in mediating the flow of electrons from exogenous NADH to ubiquinone. Douce et al (40) have suggested that an easily soluble flavoprotein may be involved. The lack of coupled phosphorylation and rotenone sensitivity, both factors closely related to the iron-sulfur centers of the NADH dehydrogenases (109), suggest that iron-sulfur proteins may not be closely associated with this external dehydrogenase.

The operation of the external dehydrogenase is dependent on divalent cations. Ethyleneglycol-bis (β-aminoethyl ether) N,N'-tetraacetic acid (EGTA)) has been observed to inhibit specifically the oxidation of exogenous NADH; this inhibition can be reversed by adding calcium (27). Many authors have noted the dependency of NADH oxidation on divalent ions (55, 59, 94, 95). The explanations for this stimulation have been varied, including the promotion of uptake of NADH (53, 54) and the removal of respiratory control by the ions interacting with a high energy state (94). Other authors have suggested that the flavoprotein associated with the oxidation of exogenous NADH had a requirement for a divalent metal ion (11, 95). Coleman & Palmer (27) found that the exogenous NADH oxidase was dependent on added calcium while the NADH-ferricyanide reductase was not. Accepting that the NADH-ferricyanide reductase was not all due to the dehydrogenase associated with the outer membrane, it seems that calcium may be involved in allowing electrons to flow from the flavoprotein to the respiratory chain. Thus calcium may be involved in binding the flavoprotein dehydrogenase to the oxidase. There is evidence to suggest that the exogenous NADH dehydrogenase can be removed easily from the membrane (40, 138).

Association of the malic enzyme with the exogenous NADH dehydrogenase   The metabolic role of this external NADH dehydrogenase is not known. It seems reasonable to suggest that it plays a role in oxidizing the NADH present in the cytosol. There is no direct counterpart in animal mitochondria where it is suggested that cytosolic NADH is oxidized indirectly by substrate based shuttle systems (26). In Jerusalem artichoke tissue there is clear evidence that some of the NAD^+-linked malic enzyme, known to be present in plant mitochondria (89, 90), appears to be located in the intermembrane space and supplies reducing equivalents to the external NADH dehydrogenase (28). Day & Wiskich (33, 34) have contested the interpretation of these data and have suggested that all the NAD^+-linked dehydrogenases were located in the matrix and reducing equivalents reached the external dehydrogenase by means of a transmembrane transhydrogenase. They claimed this enzyme could only transfer reducing equivalents in an outward direction. However, the theory of Day & Wiskich (33, 34) fails to explain why the products of malate oxidation were oxaloacetate and pyruvate when the internal dehydrogenase was operational and only pyruvate when the external enzyme was operational (28). Thus I still feel that at least some malic enzyme is located outside the inner membrane. Recent data suggest that the malic enzyme may have a metabolic role in decarboxylating C_4 acids during photosynthesis (68).

Regulation of oxidation by the external dehydrogenase   Since the $NAD^+/NADH$ ratio plays an important role in regulating the activity and direction of metabolism in both the cytosol and mitochondrial matrix, it seems essential that some mechanism should exist in order to regulate the rate at which the internal and external dehydrogenases work. It would also be preferable that the regulatory mechanism should be more specific than merely control by the phosphate potential which has an overall controlling effect on the rate of oxidation along all branches of the respiratory chain.

Alteration of the calcium concentration is one possible control mechanism. The activity of the external dehydrogenase depends on the concentration of calcium in the intermembrane space which in turn is in equilibrium with the calcium in the cytosol. Thus any alteration of the calcium concentration in the cytosol, possibly brought about by calcium accumulation in the mitochondria, will reduce the rate of oxidation of NADH in the cytosol and as a result indirectly reduce the rate of glycolysis. The presence of organic acids has also been observed to influence the rate of NADH oxidation. High concentrations of citrate can inhibit the oxidation of external NADH by removing calcium (R. C. Cowley and J. M. Palmer, unpublished data). Succinate also inhibits the oxidation of NADH (107). In this case it is not caused by the chelation of calcium since the inhibitory effect of succinate can be reversed by adding malonate. This inhibition may be the result of electrons from succinate altering the redox poise of a component in the respiratory chain so that electrons cannot flow from the NADH dehydrogenase. Similar suggestions have been made for the regulation of electron flow in animal mitochondria (52, 135).

OXIDATION OF ENDOGENOUS NADH   Evidence presented in the preceding section suggests that endogenous NADH is oxidized by a dehydrogenase which is sensitive to piericidin A or rotenone and coupled to the first site of ATP synthesis. However, the situation is more complex than this and there is evidence that in yeast mitochondria, extracted from cells in the logarithmic growth phase, it is possible to oxidize endogenous NADH by a dehydrogenase which is sensitive to piericidin A and not coupled to the first site of ATP synthesis (69, 98, 99, 109).

Evidence for a piericidin A resistant NADH dehydrogenase   Brunton & Palmer (16) reported the existence of a piericidin A resistant pathway for the oxidation of endogenous NADH in wheat mitochondria. Since no exogenous NAD^+ was present during the assay, it seems unlikely that the piericidin A resistant, antimycin A sensitive, malate-ferricyanide reductase, reported to be present in these mito-chondria, could be the result of oxidation taking place via the "masked" external flavoprotein described by Douce et al (40). From the studies of Brunton & Palmer (16) it seemed that there were two dehydrogenases capable of oxidizing endogenous NADH; one was sensitive to piericidin A and coupled to the synthesis of ATP, the other was apparently capable of synthesizing ATP until piericidin A was added, when it appeared to bypass both the piericidin A sensitive site and the site of ATP synthesis. The metabolic significance of the multiplicity of the internal NADH dehydrogenases is not known, except that they appear to be closely related to different NAD^+-linked dehydrogenases.

Regulation of electron flow through the piericidin A sensitive dehydrogenase   Recent observations concerning the response of plant mitochondria to adenine nucleotides and weak acid uncoupling agents (41, 84) have lead to observations which indicated that the relative flow of electrons along the piericidin A resistant and sensitive dehydrogenases may be influenced by the concentration of AMP in the cytosol (122). AMP stimulated the oxidation of endogenous NADH in uncoupled mitochon-dria. The stimulation appeared to be the result of AMP lowering an apparent accessibility barrier between the endogenous pyridine nucleotide pool and cyto-chrome *b,* which enhanced the flow of electrons along the phosphorylating, pierici-din A sensitive dehydrogenase. Thus the presence of AMP diverted electrons along the phosphorylating dehydrogenase which would increase the efficiency of ATP synthesis. Adenine nucleotides enter animal mitochondria by means of a specific translocator which exchanges internal ATP for external ADP (73). An adenine nucleotide translocator also appears to be present in plant mitochondria, but its properties appear to be slightly different from those characteristic of the translocator in animal mitochondria. The translocator in plant mitochondria has been reported to be relatively insensitive to atractyloside (66, 67, 112–114), which inhibits translo-cation in animal mitochondria, but was inhibited normally by bongkrekic acid (114). AMP does not appear to be readily translocated into the matrix of animal mito-chondria (73). If AMP cannot enter plant mitochondria then it must be able to regulate the relative flow along the internal NADH dehydrogenases from the outer compartment of the mitochondrion. This may be achieved by AMP interacting with the outer extremity of the proton pumping loop of the NADH dehydrogenase as envisaged in the organization of the respiratory chain necessary for the chemiosmotic coupling of ATP synthesis (96). The observation that AMP stimulated the uncoupled rate of electron transport in the presence of sufficient bongkrekic acid to inhibit the translocator (122) provides direct experimental evidence for the above theory. This may be an ideal control mechanism whereby AMP in the cytosol can activate the phosphorylating internal NADH dehydrogenase and thus increase the supply of ATP.

RELATIONSHIP BETWEEN THE NADH DEHYDROGENASES OF THE RESPIRATORY CHAIN AND THE SOLUBLE NAD$^+$-LINKED DEHYDROGENASES

The observation that the oxidation of different NAD$^+$-linked substrates respond differently to the addition of piericidin A and oxaloacetate (16) indicated that different substrates may supply NADH to different internal dehydrogenases. There have been many reports that oxaloacetate is a potent inhibitor of electron transport (1, 38, 142). Douce & Bonner (38) reported that in mung bean mitochondria the inhibition of oxygen uptake resulting from the addition of oxaloacetate was transient; the inhibition was caused by the reversal of malic dehydrogenase, rather than the respiratory chain, oxidizing the NADH. When all the oxaloacetate had been removed respiration recovered. They found the oxidation of malate was affected in the same way as other NAD$^+$-linked substrates and concluded that the malate oxidation was catalyzed by an NAD$^+$-linked malic enzyme. Brunton & Palmer (16), using wheat mitochondria, were unable to repeat this result and observed that oxaloacetate caused a high, but transient, inhibition of the oxidation of most NAD$^+$-linked substrates except malate which was only partially inhibited. The proportion of malate oxidation resistant to inhibition by oxaloacetate was assumed to be catalyzed by the malic enzyme. The NADH produced by the malic enzyme was preferentially oxidized by the NADH dehydrogenase and was not readily available for oxidation by the reversal of the malic dehydrogenase in the presence of oxaloacetate. Thus it appeared that the internal malic enzyme and malate dehydrogenase acted as if they existed in different compartments of the matrix of the mitochondrion. Evidence for the compartmentation of enzymes in the matrix of rat liver mitochondria has recently been published (92).

Piericidin A caused a very powerful but transient inhibition of malate oxidation (16), the recovered rate being quite insensitive to further additions of piericidin A. The duration of the transient inhibition caused by piericidin A was related to the length of time oxidation had proceeded before piericidin A was added. The phase of complete inhibition in the presence of piericidin A could be completely removed if glutamate and glutamate oxaloacetate transaminase were added to remove the oxaloacetate (108). Thus the duration of the piericidin A induced inhibition was apparently related to the level of oxaloacetate present in the assay medium. If oxaloacetate was added to mitochondria oxidizing malate in the presence of piericidin A, it resulted in a complete but transient inhibition of oxygen uptake, similar to that observed with other NAD^+-linked substrates (16). Thus the addition of piericidin A had altered the metabolism so that the NADH produced by the malic enzyme could be preferentially oxidized by reversal of the malate dehydrogenase rather than by the NADH dehydrogenase. One explanation of such data (16) could be that the malic enzyme is closely related to the piericidin A sensitive NADH dehydrogenase in one compartment, while the malate dehydrogenase is closely associated with the NADH dehydrogenase which can bypass the piericidin A sensitive site in another compartment. When piericidin A was added, the NADH produced by the malic enzyme could not be oxidized by the NADH dehydrogenase normally associated closely with it and consequently the NADH could only be oxidized by the dehydrogenase closely associated with the malate dehydrogenase in the neighboring compartment, and as a result it was available for oxidation by oxaloacetate.

I do not consider the different compartments as being structural compartments separated by a membrane, but as kinetic compartments in which the two different dehydrogenases occupy different areas on the surface of the inner membrane. The traditionally soluble malate dehydrogenase and malic enzymes would then have to be located in some way close to the appropriate flavoprotein on the surface of the inner membrane. The data of Brunton & Palmer (16) do not necessarily conflict with those of Douce & Bonner (38), who found that oxaloacetate inhibited malate oxidation in the absence of piericidin A. Douce & Bonner (38) carried out their experiments under State-4 conditions, which would minimize the operation of the phosphorylating, piericidin A sensitive dehydrogenase associated with the malic enzyme and result in the NADH produced by the malic enzyme being oxidized by the nonphosphorylating dehydrogenase associated with the malate dehydrogenase. This phenomenon can also provide an explanation of the nonlinear State-4 rates obtained with malate (see earlier in this review and 58, 83).

The apparent physical separation of the malic enzyme and malic dehydrogenase allows them to be independently regulated by altering the activity of the relative NADH dehydrogenase, thus preventing the uncontrolled conversion of two moles of malate to one mole of pyruvate and one mole of oxaloacetate which would subsequently form one mole of citrate and lead to a depletion of the Krebs cycle intermediates within the matrix of the mitochondrion.

The observation that the sensitivity of the rate of oxidation of a number of NAD^+-linked substrates to both piericidin A and oxaloacetate varied has led to the suggestion that the Krebs cycle dehydrogenases may be organized in some sort of functional unit around the NADH dehydrogenases (15, 16). This theory needs more investigation before its validity is accepted; the suggestion that the Krebs cycle enzymes may be organized into a functional unit is not new (123) and has several operational advantages. Evidence from other sources is also available to support the concept that there may be structural relationships between soluble enzyme systems. Davies & Teixeira (32) have recently studied the synthesis of glutamate in plant mitochondria and showed that isocitrate was more efficient than malate as a hydrogen donor for this reaction. Assuming that NADH was the coenzyme responsible for transferring the reducing equivalents between the two enzymes, they considered that there may be a special link between the glutamate dehydrogenase and isocitrate dehydrogenase and that there must have been some form of control which determined whether the NADH was made available for oxidation by the respiratory chain or for the synthesis of glutamate.

An integrated scheme showing the possible organization of the NADH dehydrogenases and their relationship to the NAD⁺-linked dehydrogenases is shown in figure 2.

POSSIBLE METABOLIC SIGNIFICANCE OF INHIBITOR RESISTANT OXIDATION IN PLANT MITOCHONDRIA

In a few cases such as the aroid spadices the inhibitor resistant electron transport is apparently directly related to thermogenic metabolism (56, 93). However, in many tissues there is no such correlation and the existence of inhibitor resistant, nonphosphorylating electron transport pathways appears wasteful if the mitochondrion is simply considered as the powerhouse of the cell. If, on the other hand, the role of

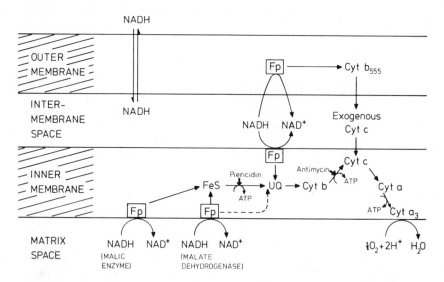

Figure 2 Diagramatic representation of how the NADH dehydrogenase systems may be organized. The dehydrogenase associated with the outer membrane can catalyze an antimycin A resistant oxidation of NADH in the presence of exogenous cytochrome *c* which theoretically has an ADP:O ratio of 1.0. The dehydrogenase associated with the outer surface of the inner membrane catalyzes piericidin A resistant, antimycin A sensitive oxidation with an ADP:O ration of 2.0. Both of the internal dehydrogenases can catalyze a piericidin A sensitive oxidation of endogenous NADH with an ADP:O ratio of 3.0. However, in the presence of piericidin A the dehydrogenase associated with the malate dehydrogenase is apparently able to donate electrons directly to the ubiquinone.

the mitochondrion was not simply to supply ATP but to play a part in the metabolism of carbon compounds, producing carbon skeletons for biosynthetic purposes, there may be an advantage in having a nonphosphorylating electron transport chain to enable this role to be fulfilled in the presence of a high level of ATP, which in plants may be maintained by the process of photosynthesis. The presence of an internally located malic enzyme and malate dehydrogenase may be considered necessary to enable the mitochondria to bring about the interconversion of organic acids. The scheme in figure 3 shows a modified Krebs cycle which could oxidize any of the Krebs cycle intermediates without the necessity of supplying pyruvate from glycolysis. This cycle could also interconvert malate into any other Krebs cycle

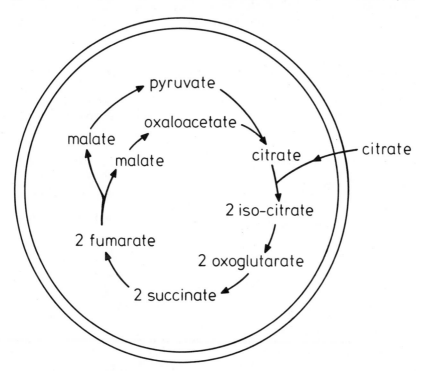

Figure 3   A modified form of the Krebs cycle drawn to show the oxidation of citrate without the necessity to supply pyruvate from glycolysis. This scheme is made possible because of the presence of both the malic enzyme and malate dehydrogenase in the matrix of plant mitochondria. Such a scheme provides a possible pathway for the oxidation of organic acids known to be present in high levels in plant cells. If malate is supplied from the cytosol rather than citrate, it is possible to remove all the keto acids such as pyruvate, oxaloacetate, and oxoglutarate from the mitochondria into the cytosol to provide precursors for biosynthetic purposes. To enable this to occur the NAD^+-linked dehydrogenases would not have to be allosterically regulated by adenine nucleotides, and the resultant NADH would have to be oxidized by a nonphosphorylating electron transport chain.

intermediate which could then be totally removed from the mitochondrion without interrupting the cycle or requiring the participation of anaplerotic reactions to replenish catalytic intermediates. This role could be fulfilled in the presence of a high phosphate potential by using the nonphosphorylating electron transport system to oxidize the NADH produced. It would also be necessary that the activity of the Krebs cycle NAD^+-linked dehydrogenases are not allosterically regulated by the adenine nucleotide level. This situation does appear to hold for the isocitrate dehydrogenase isolated from plants which is not affected by AMP or ATP (35, 49).

Whether plant mitochondria have such a complex electron transport chain to enable them to undertake such a role in biosynthesis is pure speculation but is open to experimental test, and I hope that by the time the subject is next reviewed in this journal some answers will be available.

ACKNOWLEDGMENTS

I wish to acknowledge financial support from the Science Research Council, the Royal Society, and the Central Research Fund, University of London, which enabled me to carry out some of the experimental work described in this review. I would also like to thank Mrs. Jill Farmer for help in preparing and typing the script.

Literature Cited

1. Avron, M., Biale, J. B. 1957. *J. Biol. Chem.* 225:699–708
2. Bahr, J. T., Bonner, W. D. 1973. *J. Biol. Chem.* 248:3441–45
3. Ibid, 3446–50
4. Baker, J. E., Elfvin, L. G., Biale, J. B., Honda, S. I. 1968. *Plant Physiol.* 43:2001–22
5. Baum, H., Rieske, J. S., Silman, H. I., Lipton, S. H. 1967. *Proc. Natl. Acad. Sci. USA* 57:798
6. Beinert, H., Heinen, W., Palmer, G. 1962. *Brookhaven Symp. Biol.* 15:229–65
7. Bendall, D. S., Bonner, W. D. 1971. *Plant Physiol.* 47:236–45
8. Bendall, D. S., Bonner, W. D., Plesnicar, M. 1967. *Fed. Proc.* 26:731
9. Beyer, R. E., Peters, G. A., Ikuma, H. 1968. *Plant Physiol.* 43:1395–1400
10. Bonner, W. D. 1961. *Haematin Enzymes,* ed. J. E. Falk, R. Lemberg, R. K. Morton, 479–97. London: Pergamon
11. Bonner, W. D. 1965. *Plant Biochemistry,* ed. J. Bonner, J. E. Varner, 89–123. New York: Academic
12. Bonner, W. D. 1974. *Experimental Plant Physiology,* ed. A. San Pietro, 125–33. St. Louis: Mosby
13. Bonner, W. D., Christensen, E. L., Bahr, J. T. 1972. *Biochemistry and Biophysics of Mitochondrial Membranes,* ed. G. F. Azzone, E. Carafoli, A. L. Lehninger, E. Quagliariello, N. Siliprandi, 113–19. New York: Academic
14. Bonner, W. D., Plesnicar, M. 1967. *Nature* 214:616–17
15. Brunton, C. J. 1975. *Malate Oxidation and Electron Transport Pathways in Isolated Cereal Mitochondria.* PhD thesis. Univ. London. 205 pp.
16. Brunton, C. J., Palmer, J. M. 1973. *Eur. J. Biochem.* 39:283–91
17. Cammack, R., Palmer, J. M. 1973. *Ann. NY Acad. Sci.* 222:816–23
18. Chance, B. 1952. *Nature* 169:215–21
19. Chance, B., Bonner, W. D. 1965. *Plant Physiol.* 40:1198–1204
20. Chance, B., Bonner, W. D., Storey, B. T. 1968. *Ann. Rev. Plant Physiol.* 19:295–320
21. Chance, B., DeVault, D., Legallais, V., Mela, L., Yonetani, T. 1967. *Nobel Symposium 5. Fast Reactions and Primary Processes in Chemical Kinetics,* ed. S. Claesson, 437–68. New York: Interscience
22. Chance, B. et al 1967. *Proc. Natl. Acad. Sci. USA* 57:1498–1505
23. Chance, B., Thorell, B. 1959. *J. Biol. Chem.* 234:3044–50
24. Chance, B., Williams, G. R. 1956. *Adv. Enzymol.* 17:65–134
25. Chance, B., Wilson, D. F., Dutton,

P. L., Erecinska, M. 1970. *Proc. Natl. Acad. Sci. USA* 66:1175–82
26. Chappell, J. B. 1969. *Br. Med. Bull.* 24:150–69
27. Coleman, J. O. D., Palmer, J. M. 1971. *FEBS Lett.* 17:203–8
28. Coleman, J. O. D., Palmer, J. M. 1972. *Eur. J. Biochem.* 26:499–509
29. Cooper, T. G., Beevers, H. 1969. *J. Biol. Chem.* 244:3507–13
30. Ibid, 3514–20
31. Cunningham, W. P. 1964. *Plant Physiol.* 39:699–703
32. Davies, D. D., Teixeira, A. N. 1975. *Phytochemistry* 14:647–56
33. Day, D. A., Wiskich, J. T. 1974. *Plant Physiol.* 53:104–9
34. Ibid. 54:360–63
35. Dennis, D. T. 1969. *Biochim. Biophys. Acta* 191:719–21
36. Dizengremel, P., Chauveau, M., Lance, C. 1973. *C. R. Acad. Sci. Paris* Ser. D 277:239–42
37. Douce, R. 1975. *Passage of Ferricyanide and Cytochrome c Through the Outer Membrane of Intact Plant Mitochondria.* Presented at 12th Int. Bot. Congr., Leningrad
38. Douce, R., Bonner, W. D. 1972. *Biochem. Biophys. Res. Commun.* 47:619–24
39. Douce, R., Christensen, E. L., Bonner, W. D. 1972. *Biochim. Biophys. Acta* 275:148–60
40. Douce, R., Mannella, C. A., Bonner, W. D. 1973. *Biochim. Biophys. Acta* 292:105–16
41. Drury, R. E., McCollum, J. P., Garrison, S. A., Dickinson, D. B. 1968. *Phytochemistry* 7:2071–81
42. Dutton, P. L., Storey, B. T. 1971. *Plant Physiol.* 47:282–88
43. Dutton, P. L., Wilson, D. F. 1974. *Biochim. Biophys. Acta* 346:165–212
44. Edwards, D. L., Rosenberg, E., Maroney, P. A. 1974. *J. Biol. Chem.* 249:3551–56
45. Erecinska, M., Oshino, R., Oshino, N., Chance, B. 1973. *Arch. Biochem. Biophys.* 157:431–45
46. Erecinska, M., Storey, B. T. 1970. *Plant Physiol.* 46:618–24
47. Erecinska, M., Wilson, D. F., Mukai, Y., Chance, B. 1971. *Biochem. Biophys. Res. Commun.* 41:386–92
48. Ernster, L., Lee, I.-Y., Norling, B., Persson, B. 1969. *Eur. J. Biochem.* 9:299–310
49. Fox, G. F., Davies, D. D. 1967. *Biochem. J.* 105:729–34

50. Garland, P. B., Chance, B., Ernster, L., Lee, C. P., Wang, D. 1967. *Proc. Natl. Acad. Sci. USA* 58:1696–1702
51. Greenspan, M. D., Purvis, J. L. 1965. *Biochim. Biophys. Acta* 99:191–94
52. Gutman, M., Kearney, E. B., Singer, T. P. 1973. *Biochemistry* 10:4763–70
53. Hackett, D. P. 1961. *Plant Physiol.* 36:445–52
54. Hanson, J. B., Hodges, T. K. 1967. *Curr. Top. Bioenerg.* 2:65–98
55. Hanson, J. B., Malhotra, S. S., Stoner, C. D. 1965. *Plant Physiol.* 40:1033–40
56. Henry, M. F., Nyns, E. J. 1975. *Sub-Cell Biochem.* 4:1–65
57. Higuti, T., Mizuno, S., Muraoka, S. 1975. *Biochim. Biophys. Acta* 396:36–47
58. Hobson, G. E. 1970. *Phytochemistry* 9:2257–63
59. Honda, S. I., Robertson, R. N., Gregory, J. M. 1958. *Aust. J. Biol. Sci.* 11:1–12
60. Hutton, D., Stumpf, P. K. 1969. *Plant Physiol.* 44:508–16
61. Ikuma, H. 1972. *Ann. Rev. Plant Physiol.* 23:419–36
62. Ikuma, H., Bonner, W. D. 1967. *Plant Physiol.* 42:67–75
63. Ibid, 1535–44
64. Ingledew, W. J., Ohnishi, T. 1975. *FEBS Lett.* 54:167–71
65. James, W. O., Beevers, H. 1950. *New Phytol.* 49:353
66. Jung, D. W., Hanson, J. B. 1973. *Biochim. Biophys. Acta* 325:189–92
67. Jung, D. W., Hanson, J. B. 1975. *Arch. Biochem. Biophys.* 168:358–68
68. Kagawa, T., Hatch, M. D. 1975. *Arch. Biochem. Biophys.* 167:687–96
69. Katz, R. 1971. *FEBS Lett.* 12:153–56
70. Keilin, D., Hartree, E. F. 1949. *Nature* 164:254–59
71. Kenefick, D., Hanson, J. B. 1966. *Plant Physiol.* 41:1601–9
72. Klingenberg, M. 1963. *Fed. Proc.* 22:527
73. Klingenberg, M. 1970. *Essays in Biochemistry,* ed. P. N. Campbell, F. Dickens, 6:119. London: Academic
74. Klingenberg, M. 1970. *Eur. J. Biochem.* 13:247–52
75. Klingenberg, M., Pfaff, E. 1966. *The Regulation of Metabolic Processes in Mitochondria,* ed. J. M. Tager, S. Papa, E. Quagliariello, E. C. Slater, 180–201. Amsterdam: Elsevier
76. Kroger, A., Klingenberg, M. 1967. *Curr. Top. Bioenerg.,* ed. D. R. Sanadi, 2:151–93. New York: Academic
77. Lambowitz, A. M., Bonner, W. D.

1973. *Biochem. Biophys. Res. Commun.* 52:703–11
78. Lambowitz, A. M., Bonner, W. D. 1974. *J. Biol. Chem.* 249:2428–40
79. Lambowitz, A. M., Bonner, W. D., Wikström, M. K. F. 1974. *Proc. Natl. Acad. Sci. USA* 71:1183–87
80. Lambowitz, A. M., Smith, E. W., Slayman, C. W. 1972. *J. Biol. Chem.* 247:4859–65
81. Lance, C. 1974. *Plant Sci. Lett.* 2:165–71
82. Lance, C., Bonner, W. D. 1968. *Plant Physiol.* 43:756–66
83. Lance, C., Hobson, G. E., Young, R. E., Biale, J. B. 1967. *Plant Physiol.* 42: 471–78
84. Laties, G. G. 1973. *Biochemistry* 12:3350–55
85. Lee, I.-Y., Slater, E. C. 1972. *Biochim. Biophys. Acta* 283:223–33
86. Lehninger, A. L. 1955. Harvey Lectures 1953–54:176–216. New York: Academic
87. Lieberman, M., Baker, J. E. 1965. *Ann. Rev. Plant. Physiol.* 16:343–82
88. Lloyd, D. 1974. *The Mitochondria of Microorganisms.* London: Academic. 553 pp.
89. Macrae, A. R. 1971. *Phytochemistry* 10:2343–47
90. Macrae, A. R., Moorhouse, R. 1970. *Eur. J. Biochem.* 16:96–102
91. Malkin, R. 1973. *Iron-Sulfur Proteins,* ed. W. Lovenberg, 2:1–26. New York: Academic
92. Matlib, M. A., O'Brien, P. J. 1975. *Arch. Biochem. Biophys.* 167:193–202
93. Meeuse, B. J. D. 1975. *Ann. Rev. Plant Physiol.* 26:117–26
94. Miller, R. J., Dumford, S. W., Koeppe, D. E., Hanson, J. B. 1970. *Plant Physiol.* 45:649–53
95. Miller, R. J., Koeppe, D. E. 1971. *Plant Physiol.* 47:832–35
96. Mitchell, P. 1966. *Biol. Rev. Cambridge Philos. Soc.* 41:445–502
97. Norling, B., Nelson, B. D., Nordenbrand, K., Ernster, L. 1972. *Biochim. Biophys. Acta* 275:18–32
98. Ohnishi, T. 1972. *FEBS Lett.* 24:305–9
99. Ohnishi, T. 1973. *Biochim. Biophys. Acta* 301:105–28
100. Ohnishi, T., Ingledew, W. J., Shiraishi, S. 1975. *Biochem. Biophys. Res. Commun.* 63:894–99
101. Ohnishi, T., Leigh, J. S., Ragan, C. I., Racker, E. 1974. *Biochem. Biophys. Res. Commun.* 56:775–82
102. Ohnishi, T., Leigh, J. S., Winter, D. B.,

Lim, J., King, T. E. 1974. *Biochem. Biophys. Res. Commun.* 61:1026–35
103. Ohnishi, T., Winter, D. B., Lim, J., King, T. E. 1974. *Biochem. Biophys. Res. Commun.* 61:1017–25
104. Orme-Johnson, W. H. 1973. *Ann. Rev. Biochem.* 42:159–204
105. Packer, L., Murakami, S., Mehard, C. W. 1970. *Ann. Rev. Plant Physiol.* 21:271–304
106. Palmer, J. M. 1972. *Phytochemistry* 11:2957–61
107. Palmer, J. M. 1975. *Identification and Regulation of NADH Dehydrogenases in Plant Mitochondria.* Presented at 12th Int. Bot. Congr., Leningrad
108. Palmer, J. M., Arron, G. P. 1976. *J. Exp. Bot.* In press
109. Palmer, J. M., Coleman, J. O. D. 1974. *Horizons Biochem. Biophys.* 1:220–60
110. Palmer, J. M., Kirk, B. I. 1974. *Biochem. J.* 140:79–86
111. Palmer, J. M., Passam, H. C. 1971. *Biochem. J.* 122:16–17p
112. Passam, H. C., Coleman, J. O. D. 1975. *J. Exp. Bot.* 26:536–43
113. Passam, H. C., Palmer, J. M. 1973. *Biochim. Biophys. Acta* 305:80–87
114. Passam, H. C., Souverijn, J. H. M., Kemp, A. 1973. *Biochim. Biophys. Acta* 305:88–94
115. Pomeroy, M. K. 1975. *Plant Physiol.* 55:51–58
116. Racker, E. 1970. *Essays Biochem.* 6:1
117. Raw, I., Molinari, R., Ferreira do Amaral, D., Mahler, H. R. 1958. *J. Biol. Chem.* 233:225–33
118. Rich, P. R., Bendall, D. S. 1975. *Eur. J. Biochem.* 55:333–41
119. Rieske, J. S. 1971. *Arch. Biochem. Biophys.* 145:179–93
120. Schonbaum, G. R., Bonner, W. D., Storey, B. T., Bahr, J. T. 1971. *Plant Physiol.* 47:124–28
121. Singer, T. P., Gutman, M., Massey, V. 1973. *Iron-sulfur Proteins,* ed. W. Lovenberg, 1:225–300. New York: Academic
122. Sotthibandhu, R., Palmer, J. M. 1975. *Biochem. J.* 152:637–45
123. Srere, P. A. 1972. *Energy Metabolism and the Regulation of Metabolic Processes,* ed. M. A. Mehlman, R. W. Hanson, 79–92. New York: Academic
124. Storey, B. T. 1969. *Plant Physiol.* 44:413–21
125. Ibid 1970. 45:447–54
126. Ibid. 46:13–20
127. Ibid, 625–30
128. Ibid 1971. 48:493–97

129. Storey, B. T. 1972. *Biochim. Biophys. Acta* 267:48–64
130. Ibid 1973. 292:592–603
131. Storey, B. T. 1974. *Plant Physiol.* 53:840–45
132. Storey, B. T., Bahr, J. T. 1969. *Plant Physiol.* 44:115–25
133. Ibid, 126–34
134. Ibid 1972. 50:95–102
135. Trumpower, B. L., Katki, A. 1975. *Biochem. Biophys. Res. Commun.* 65:16–23
136. Urban, P. F., Klingenberg, M. 1969. *Eur. J. Biochem.* 9:519–25
137. Von Jagow, G., Bohrer, C. 1975. *Biochim. Biophys. Acta* 387:409–24
138. Von Jagow, G., Klingenberg, M. 1970. *Eur. J. Biochem.* 12:583–92
139. Weiss, H., Von Jagow, G., Klingenberg, M., Bucher, T. 1970. *Eur. J. Biochem.* 14:75–82
140. Wikström, M. K. F. 1973. *Biochim. Biophys. Acta* 301:155–93
141. Wikström, M. K. F., Lambowitz, A. M. 1974. *FEBS Lett.* 40:149–53
142. Wiskich, J. T., Young, R. E., Biale, J. B. 1964. *Plant Physiol.* 39:312–22

Ann. Rev. Plant Physiol. 1976. 27:159–79

BIOLOGICAL RHYTHMS AND PHYSIOLOGICAL TIMING[1]

❖7606

William S. Hillman

Biology Department, Brookhaven National Laboratory, Upton, New York 11973

CONTENTS

INTRODUCTION

In the 26 years since the start of this series, biological rhythmicity has become respectable. This must be gratifying to those investigators whose early work was often received with the suspicion accorded to parapsychology, but it is not without disadvantages. Chief among these is the volume of literature that makes it no longer reasonable to attempt treating the entire field in a single article.

[1]Review prepared at Brookhaven National Laboratory under the auspices of the US Energy Research and Development Administration. By acceptance of the article, the publisher and/or recipient acknowledges the US Government's right to retain a nonexclusive, royalty-free license in and to any copyright concerning this paper.

For the reader with little background, Sweeney's (134) lucid book provides an effective introduction, primarily on plants. Bünning's (19) monograph is an important classical treatment, repeatedly revised. The wide range of articles in the Aschoff (1) symposium makes it a valuable baseline for considering all work in the past decade, although other useful symposia and reviews have appeared more recently (89, 126). In the present series, the stimulating if impenetrable chapter by Cumming & Wagner (30) may well be the last with any comprehensiveness. Most recently, Queiroz (113) examined selected topics, with no implication of completeness. The same approach has been adopted below. The topics considered, largely but not exclusively in higher plants, include questions of basic mechanism, the cell cycle, photosynthesis, intermediary metabolism, and photoperiodism.

This chapter deals either with circadian rhythms—those in which the "free-running" period (under constant conditions) is of the order of 24 hr—or with others that may be related. As used here, the term rhythms simply denotes oscillations with properties not directly reflecting environmental fluctuations. This deliberately broad usage thus includes oscillations that persist under constant conditions for tens of cycles with those that damp after one or two, and those that are entrainable by external signals to a wide range of frequencies with those having a narrow resonance range. It also bypasses the question of whether even oscillations that, under apparently constant conditions, are self-sustained and maintain no invariable phase relationship to any known geophysical periodicity, might nevertheless still result from frequency-transformation by the organism of some such input (14). More rigorous definitions are often used (1, 126). However, the many instances of properties between extreme persistence or precision on the one hand and extreme lability on the other make it at least reasonable, without compelling contrary evidence, to treat all circadian oscillations conforming to the broad definition as in some sense related. As to endogeny of the basic time-keeping function, it is assumed in all that follows, with no further attention to possible geophysical frequency transformations.

GENERAL PROPERTIES, MODELS, AND MECHANISMS

Many important phenomena can best be considered in terms of models and mechanisms of circadian rhythmicity proposed in the recent literature, and the kind of data used in evaluating them. Among the properties with which such proposals must deal, the most important are probably: (a) the fact of oscillation itself, together with the length of the free-running period; (b) the temperature compensation (Q_{10} near 1.0) of that period length over a wide range of constant temperatures; (c) the susceptibility to, and manner of, resetting of the phase by light and darkness; and (d) phase resetting by other inputs, including temperature changes and chemical agents. Of these four categories, a is perhaps easiest and b the hardest to explain, while c and d provide the greatest opportunity for comparing various proposals.

Rhythmicity and Feedback

Oscillations—rhythmicity itself—can in principle result from any of a wide variety of feedback systems. The origin of circadian period length (though not its mechanism) is generally explained by the selective advantage of conforming to the day/night cycle. Again in principle, it is easy to achieve any desired period length by choosing appropriate rate constants (103) or by introducing "delay blocks" in a feedback model (73). But proponents of specific mechanisms must find ways of obtaining relatively slow oscillations from known biochemical processes, most of which are rapid. Suggestions as to how this may occur include dilution, compartmentation, limitation by diffusion, or the accumulation and destruction of critical substances (103). Two examples of ways of dealing with this problem may be cited.

According to Pavlidis (101, 103), interacting oscillators with short period lengths could result in overall oscillations with longer periods. This suggestion has been at least partially confirmed by Jacklet & Geronimo (72) in work on a rhythm in the compound action potential of the isolated eye of *Aplysia*. As the number of neuronal cells is surgically reduced towards a critical number, progressively shorter circadian periods occur; below the critical number, much shorter period lengths (though still of the order of hours) are observed.

A cellular mechanism proposed by Ehret and co-workers invokes genetic feedback. Transcription of unique, long polycistronic DNA components (chronons)—with transcription, and possibly translation and expression, of each successive cistron being a prerequisite for transcription of the next—continues to the end, then starts at the beginning again. Slowing to circadian dimensions arises through the many diffusion steps and compartmentation, e.g. between the transcription of each cistron (37). While so far there is no evidence uniquely demanding, rather than merely consistent with, such a mechanism, it is one of the best developed in biochemical terms.

Temperature Compensation, Membranes, and Lipids

The problem of temperature compensation is dealt with unconvincingly by most proposed mechanisms. Abstract models, again, need merely postulate appropriate networks of reactions with differing temperature optima. When the question is faced more squarely, as by Pavlidis and co-workers (102, 104), it forces some challenging proposals, such as the existence of enzymes whose active forms decrease in concentration with increasing temperature. The chronon mechanism depends for temperature compensation either on its many diffusion steps or, in an ad hoc though testable variation, on the activity of qualitatively different but temporally equivalent chronons at different temperatures (38).

Because of the difficulty of explaining temperature compensation of the period length, particular interest attaches to a recent idea on the possible role of membranes in the clock mechanism. As will appear later, the suggestion in general terms is not new, and there is perhaps better evidence for it, on the whole, than for genetic mechanisms. The specific proposal of Njus et al (97) envisions mutual interaction of a membrane and a solute, with the membrane assuming two (at least) possible states—active transport or passive "leakiness"—with respect to the solute. These states reflect changed orientations of specific transport structures within the membrane as a result of the response of these structures to the solute concentration (closing the feedback loop). The outstanding point in the present context is that if the physical properties—specifically, the liquidity—of the membrane are rate limiting for the reorientation of the transport structures, then temperature compensation becomes a consequence of the known temperature adaptation of membrane lipids; in several systems, the relative proportion of various lipids changes with temperature in such a manner as to maintain an essentially constant phase state (98, 153). Whether specific forms of the proposed mechanism survive rigorous testing remains to be seen. But the linking of temperature compensation to known biochemistry rather than to ad hoc or unspecific suggestions may represent a major advance.

Light Resetting and Basic Mechanisms

Susceptibility to phase resetting by light and darkness is, almost by definition, a property of circadian rhythms in all unicells and plants and in many animal phenomena. Certain processes in animals with complex nervous systems, however, may involve clocks that are spatially separate (as indicated by surgery) from the site of photoreception, and in which resetting thus occurs through synaptic or other inputs. Such "type II" (141) clocks are of no direct concern here, except that what is known of their properties strengthens the view of circadian timekeeping as a function of membrane-solute interactions.

The responses of the more widespread type I rhythms to light have been studied in numerous organisms, often in terms of phase-response curves. These are produced by giving a single light pulse to a system oscillating in darkness, then waiting for a new steady state. The effect of the pulse in advancing or delaying some phase marker of the rhythm can then be plotted as a function of the original time, in terms of the rhythm itself, when the pulse was given. Not only are similar curves observed in a variety of organisms, but phenomena as different as *Drosophila* pupal eclosion and *Lemna* flowering and CO_2 output respond to successions of light pulses in a manner suggesting the operation in both species of rhythmic timers having similar, though not identical, phase-response curves (61, 106). Yet the tempting conclusion that such similarities point to common mechanisms is probably unjustified, as some theoretical and experimental studies by Winfree (154, 155) suggest.

When resetting experiments on *Drosophila* eclosion are conducted by varying both the phase (timing) and length of the light pulses, the total response to both variables can be represented by a surface resembling a corkscrew or spiral staircase. Examination of this surface suggests that pulses having a critical combination of timing and length should put the rhythm into a "singular state" in which it no longer oscillates, or does so abnormally, and that the effects of pulses with values differing from the critical fall into two distinct classes. Such predictions are experimentally verified (154). There is evidence that other systems, for example the *Kalanchoë* petal rhythm, also exhibit such properties (41). Even though singularities are predicted by several mathematical models (41, 102, 103), such apparently fundamental characteristics, with no obvious selective advantages attributable to evolutionary convergence, might seem irresistable evidence for a common basic mechanism. But work with a very different system challenges any such optimistic view.

Oscillations in yeast glycolysis occur in cell-free or intact systems and can be followed by changes in NADH fluorescence (25); perturbations such as ADP addition elicit phase-response curves similar to those of circadian rhythms (112). Winfree found that varying both time and duration of a pulse of oxygenated buffer generates a resetting surface with the now familiar corkscrew shape (though with quantitatively different parameters), and the predicted singularities are again experimentally demonstrable (155). Yet the period lengths here are of the order of 30 sec, and there is no reason to suppose that "the particulars of chemical machinery" (155) are the same as those in circadian systems. Thus many, if not all, of those formal aspects of resetting that have so interested students of rhythms may be consequences of relatively abstract features of the systems—of their organization, not their components. The similar behavior of rhythms in various organisms does not necessarily argue for a common biochemistry (156, 157).

Resetting and Period Modification by Chemicals

If quantitative aspects of resetting convey less about basic mechanisms than meets the eye, the same pessimistic assessment need not be made of chemical effects on rhythms, at least in a qualitative sense. For one thing, there are surprisingly few such effects, provided the criteria are understood. It is useful in such studies to distinguish between a particular manifestation of rhythmicity and the (assumed) underlying oscillation—as it is often put, between "the hands on the clock" and "the clock" itself. Such distinctions are complicated by the nontrivial question of whether a system may have more than one clock, as well as by the eventual necessity of finding processes that are both manifestations of clock action and part of the clock—for example, the flux of the ion in a membrane-ion mechanism (see also 157). Merely inhibiting oscillations in a given process does not of itself imply inhibition of the underlying timer, particularly if the process can be restarted in the same phase relationship to other events as before inhibition. Also, effects on the amplitude of oscillations are not, without additional evidence, indicative of effects on a clock; steady state changes in phase or free-running period length must be sought for. On these criteria, relatively few effective chemicals have been found. Recent investigations have used cycloheximide, actinomycin D, ethanol, deuterium oxide, and various ions and ionophores, as well as respiratory inhibitors and anaerobiosis.

During the 1960s, several investigations involved inhibitors of RNA and protein synthesis, but with little success. In one of the few exceptions, Feldman found that cycloheximide lengthens the free-running period of the phototactic rhythm in *Euglena* (45). In both *Euglena* and *Neurospora* rhythms, the period lengthening by cycloheximide is smaller than its inhibition of protein synthesis, and there is an interesting parallel between cycloheximide effects and temperature. On the assumption that protein synthesis has an overall Q_{10} of about 2, a given reduction in protein synthesis has approximately the same effect on period length whether it is brought about by cycloheximide or lowering the temperature. In *Neurospora,* strain and media effects on temperature sensitivity of period length are paralleled in cycloheximide sensitivity (46, 47). These results are among the few at present that argue for a significant role of protein synthesis in the clock.

In *Acetabularia* as in many systems, several inhibitors of RNA or protein synthesis have no effect on rhythm phase or period (137). However, actinomycin D causes the disappearance of photosynthetic rhythmicity in intact and not in enucleate plants (143). The latter observation, together with a second "*Acetabularia* paradox" in which rhythmicity, though persistent in enucleate plants, nevertheless is phase determined by the nucleus in transplantation experiments, has been interpreted by Sweeney (136) in terms of a membrane-solute feedback mechanism for rhythmicity.

Indeed, most work with chemical agents seems consistent with the hypothesis that rhythmic timing is a function of membrane activity; some of the relevant data are not even that recent. Ethanol effects are generally interpreted as due to action on membranes, and an ethanol-induced increase in period length from 27.5 to 32.8 hr in *Phaseolus* leaf movements was reported in 1960 (78). Since then, similar results have been obtained on the endogenous tidal rhythmicity of isopods (43), while pulses of ethanol in the transpiration stream cause phase shifts in *Phaseolus* (23). The *Phaseolus* system can also be reset by temporary wilting (22), by pulses of K^+ ion, and by exposures for several hours to valinomycin (22), a substance known to complex K^+ (49). In the isolated eye of *Aplysia*, K^+ pulses give a phase-response curve (44) similar to that for light pulses (71), although there is no such close parallel in *Phaseolus*, in which K^+ causes phase advances only, no delays (23).

Related observations are not confined to multicellular organisms. In *Gonyaulax*, perhaps the unicell studied most carefully, a circadian rhythm in K^+ content, in this case unaffected by external pulses of high K^+ or Na^+, occurs even under conditions in which the photosynthetic rhythm is suppressed. Pulses of ethanol reset the bioluminescence rhythm in much the same manner as does light, while valinomycin negates ethanol effects on both bioluminescence and K^+ content (135).

Heavy water (D_2O) lengthens the free-running period of circadian rhythms in unicells (16), plants (21, 87) and animals (42, 133). Oscillations of greater than circadian frequency are similarly affected, including cardiac pacemakers in invertebrates (42) and oscillatory water uptake and transpiration in *Avena* (13). Such effects, like those of ethanol and K^+, can be ascribed to action on the "ionic balance across the cellular membrane" (42), whether the membrane in question be neuronal, stomatal, or some other. In this connection, Pittendrigh et al (108), using the *Drosophila* eclosion rhythm, tested the hypothesis that D_2O "diminishes the apparent temperature." The free-running period length was less affected by D_2O than was the phase relationship to an entraining light/dark cycle, paralleling the relative temperature sensitivity of the two parameters. A more critical test has been made (88) using the *Gonyaulax* bioluminescence rhythm. Under conditions in which a decrease in temperature (from 22° to 16°) actually shortens period length, D_2O still lengthens it, thus acting as a nonspecific braking agent rather than to imitate lower temperature.

Additional support for a membrane hypothesis of biological oscillations can be found in reports of period lengthening by Li^+ ions, both in the circadian rhythms of excised *Kalanchoë* flower petal movements and the activity of the small mammal Meriones (39), as well as in short-term oscillations of *Avena* transpiration (12). The latter are not affected when Li^+ is given to the roots of intact plants, but only when it is taken up by excised tops.

More on Membranes

The kind of evidence summarized above makes membrane hypotheses of biological rhythmicity appear increasingly attractive; certainly, mutual interactions of membranes and solutes can provide feedback systems of the required complexity (35, 50, 97, 136). In addition, several manifestations of rhythmic timing in plants may involve changes in membrane properties. In *Chenopodium* seedlings, there is a rhythm of betacyanin leakage into the medium (144). In *Lemna perpusilla,* in which photoperiodic timing involves a circadian rhythm (61), the inhibition of flowering by exposure to distilled water for short periods during long nights shows much the same timing as inhibition by light (53, 54). The most extensive work of this kind is that of Satter, Galston and collaborators (114, 118–122) on the rhythmic nyctinastic movements of *Albizzia* and *Samanea* leaflets, the pulvinar K^+ fluxes associated with and probably responsible for them, and the changes in membrane potentials that may in turn control K^+ movements. Phytochrome also plays a role in these phenomena. Pulvinar K^+ distribution may depend on an oscillation between an active transport phase and a "leaky" phase of the membranes, as indicated by differential sensitivities of the two phases, although the effects of sucrose are apparently contradictory to those of temperature and respiratory inhibitors. The work on nyctinasty provides support for a tension-relaxation mechanism of the kind proposed some time ago by Bünning (19) and resting on membrane properties (121). Although the rhythm of *Kalanchoë* petal movement is not affected by valinomycin, nonactin, or K^+ ions, plasmolytic studies and flame spectrophotometry do provide evidence for K^+-related turgor changes (127) in this system as well.

It would be unwise to conclude without recommending caution on what this discussion has termed "membrane hypotheses." First, since membranes are currently the focus of much work and speculation, one should be wary of the bandwagon effect, as real in science as in politics. Second, and more concretely, "evidence consistent with" is not as conclusive as "evidence for," or even better, "against." Unfortunately, most of the work on membranes and rhythms, or any other basic mechanism, seems to be only of the first kind. Predictions that would critically distinguish, for example, between "membrane hypotheses" and "transcription-translation hypotheses" are lacking. Without them, while many important phenomena may be discovered, the mechanism of a cellular clock or clocks—provided they exist (157)—will remain undefined.

THE MITOTIC CYCLE

Circadian rhythmicity in cell division occurs in cultured and intact tissues of animals (57, 94, 138) and in eukaryotic microorganisms (34–36, 38). Experimental and theoretical studies of noncircadian mitotic oscillations have also been carried out in the acellular slime-mold *Physarum,* in which populations initially in different phases can be mixed (77, 115, 142). None of this literature will be considered here, except for an important generalization, the circadian-infradian rule, also referred to as the "G-E-T" effect because it has been demonstrated in the unicells *Gonyaulax, Euglena,* and *Tetrahymena* (36, 38). It states that a eukaryotic cell is incapable of circadian outputs while its generation time is ultradian—substantially shorter than circadian. It can produce circadian outputs when, due to nutrition, temperature, or other factors, cell division is closed to the infradian mode—with generation time greater than circadian—or in the nondividing condition. So far, this rule appears to hold in all known systems, although the basis for implications that it somehow constitutes specific evidence for the chronon mechanism is not obvious.

One should also use caution in applying the circadian-infradian rule to multicellular organisms. While mitotic cycles in many tissues are often ultradian, it does not follow that they may not be controlled or gated by a circadian timer. What the rule suggests is simply that such circadian timing would be expected to arise not in the rapidly dividing cells themselves, but elsewhere in the organism. However, detailed considerations of the possible significance of the rule in multicellular organisms are not to be found in the literature.

It will not have escaped the reader that so far nothing has been said in this section of higher plants. In spite of much lore about optimal times of day for obtaining mitotic figures, there is very little real information. All the earlier work (see references in 5, 15) was performed under ill-defined conditions. Chandler (26) found that the diurnal mitotic rhythm in *Allium* roots described in earlier reports did not occur in constant temperature darkness. Similarly, Brown (15) observed "mitotic waves" only in roots of *Pisum* seedlings grown in diurnally fluctuating environments, not in strictly constant conditions.

The only extensive study in recent years, that of Mäkinen (84) on *Allium,* is flawed by anecdotal presentation and less than rigorous procedures. For instance, a rhythm in mitotic frequency, with two peaks per 24 hr, was observed in onion seedlings at 21° in "continuous light." The light was indeed continuous, as far as the fluorescent source was concerned, but "during the day the seedlings were also exposed to dim daylight," making it impossible to know whether the rhythmicity might have been simply imposed by quality changes. A similar rhythm was observed in continuous darkness. Again, however, details of sampling, safelights if any, and so forth, are not given, so it is not clear that the darkness was in fact total, not interrupted by brief light exposures or other signals.

Bishop & Klein (5) reported that *Allium* roots in constant-temperature darkness showed a damping rhythm with four mitotic maxima and minima per 24 hr with timing dependent on the time of seed imbibition, but without statistical treatments of small differences. Subsequently, they (6) reported on effects of continuous white light and other light treatments, with admittedly "semiquantitative" results. The mitotic cycle in *Lemna perpusilla* fronds is apparently not synchronized by either long or short photoperiods (52). Diurnal changes in nuclear size in *Allium* bulb scale epidermis have been observed (4) but under incompletely controlled conditions. Frolova & Khallak (48) determined mitotic indices in callus cultures of several species grown in constant temperature darkness, and concluded that *Nicotiana* and *Crepis* showed two peaks in 24 hr while *Pisum* showed only one. However, the data on these tissues seem similar to those on three others, including *Vicia,* described (with justice) as showing no clear relationships.

A well designed and statistically rigorous study on diurnal mitotic periodicities in *Allium,* that of Zeiger & Cardemil (159) on stomatal differentiation in cotyledons, unfortunately does not bear on endogeny since it was conducted under a cycle of light and temperature. Of several epidermal cell populations studied, the one involved in asymmetrical divisions displayed two daily peaks 12 hr apart while the one involved in asymmetrical divisions showed only a single one at a different time. Cell populations having different phase relationships to the external conditions clearly coexist even in the same area of cotyledon. King (80) has reported that after several days' exposure to alternating temperatures, *Chenopodium rubrum* seedlings show an oscillation in mitotic index persisting for at least 80 hr in continuous light and constant temperature, with a period of about 20 hr. Evidence that this oscillation, like several others in the same plant, is initiated and controlled only by alternating temperatures rather than light and darkness, raises the question of whether it can be regarded as a circadian rhythm in the usual sense.

In summary, considering the degree to which other mechanisms controlling the cell cycle in higher plants are beginning to be understood, a critical study of the role of circadian rhythmicity is obviously overdue, and should at least address itself to conditions initiating the oscillations, zeitgebers, and persistence under truly constant conditions.

METABOLISM

Though it could include many chemical changes, this discussion will concentrate on aspects of photosynthesis and respiration supplying structural materials and energy to other processes.

Photosynthesis and Related Processes

Considering the significance of light for both photosynthesis and rhythmicity, the dearth of information on their interactions is remarkable. Enough is nevertheless known to invalidate the assumption, still generally widespread, that light necessarily affects photosynthesis and its immediate sequelae solely through the known chloroplast reactions.

Stomatal opening in several plants is affected by a circadian rhythm responsive to phase shifting by light and darkness (86; additional references in 27). The major osmotic role of K^+ in stomatal turgor changes (69) suggests that at least some of the work on nyctinastic leaf movements described earlier (121) might also be relevant here.

Many investigations suggesting the likelihood of rhythmic changes in photosynthesis have in fact been performed only to study processes such as product translocation (105) or the synthesis of amino acids (131) under daily light/dark conditions, and were not intended to determine whether the diurnal fluctuations have an endogenous component. However, seedlings of *Chenopodium rubrum* germinated in light and fluctuating temperatures, then placed in constant temperature darkness, unequivocally exhibit rhythms, in phase, of both photosynthetic capacity and chlorophyll *a* content, with period lengths of about 21 hr (27). Pallas et al (99) report clear-cut rhythms in photosynthesis and carbon dioxide compensation in peanuts (*Arachis hypogaea*) maintained in continuous light, with the expected susceptibility to resetting by intercalated dark periods. In succulents, of course, oscillations in CO_2 compensation under constant conditions are related to the well-known rhythmic properties of crassulacean acid metabolism (CAM) (74, 95, 113), but the results on peanuts, as well as on *Coffea* (74), suggest that circadian changes in CO_2 compensation are not confined to CAM plants.

Photosynthetic rhythms are well documented in the microorganisms *Gonyaulax* and *Euglena* and in the large unicell *Acetabularia*, all three of which are being used in seeking the biochemical controls involved. In spite of earlier positive results, the *Gonyaulax* rhythm apparently does not involve changes in the activity of ribulose bisphosphate carboxylase (24). The same is true in *Euglena*, which also fails to show oscillations in Hill reaction and photosystem I activity; the activity of glyceralde-hyde-3-phosphate dehydrogenase in *Euglena*, however, undergoes changes parallel to those in photosynthetic capacity (150).

The role of rhythms in the integration and modulation of photosynthetic pathways remains to be explored. While Steer's work on the fate of photosynthetically fixed carbon in *Capsicum* leaves is not directly relevant, the results warrant speculation and indicate some possible approaches. The diurnal periodicity in amino acid synthesis (131) apparently depends on the timing of pyruvate kinase activation and resultant increased synthesis of carbon skeletons; that activation can be ascribed to an increased supply of ammonium, which in turn depends on the timing of nitrate reductase activity (132). The several daily peaks in the latter are affected in different ways by previous and current light exposures, and one light effect (of several possible) may be exerted by the entrainment of a metabolic rhythm. Indeed, Cohen & Cumming (28) describe a rhythm in nitrate reductase activity in *C. rubrum* seedlings, and suggest that the situation may be widespread in higher plants. These results, taken together, challenge the widely received view (e.g. 3) that the role of light in regulating nitrogen metabolism is solely or even primarily photosynthetic, offering points of departure for further work.

Respiratory Gas Exchange

Since much of the work to be discussed has followed CO_2 output rather than O_2 uptake, the term "respiratory" here is loosely used. The extensive data recently reviewed (95, 113) on rhythmicity of CO_2 output in CAM plants such as *Kalanchoë* will not be discussed further, except to point out that success has replaced earlier failures to demonstrate entrainment by light acting through phytochrome in *Bryophyllum fedtschenkoi* (152).

Rhythmicity in CO_2 output that is presumably not CAM-dependent has been reported in *C. rubrum* seedlings (27), peanut plants (99), and in *Lemna perpusilla* (60–63), while rhythmic O_2 uptake has been followed in *L. gibba* (90–93) and in onion (*Allium*) (17). Only the *Lemna* systems have been explored to any degree, but the *Allium* results are the most striking: they were obtained on dry, dormant seeds and apparently without any concomitant release of CO_2. However, before pursuing what would certainly be the major significance of these observations for proposed mechanisms of circadian rhythmicity (17), it would be well to have additional confirmation.

The O_2 uptake rate of *Lemna gibba* plants, measured at intervals of 3–4 hr by Warburg respirometry in darkness, oscillates with circadian periodicity after transfer from short days to continuous light. The oscillation damps after several days and can be reset by the "light-on" signal at the end of a dark period, perhaps involving phytochrome. Uptake at different times during the rhythm is differentially sensitive to azide, while respiratory quotient is constant throughout, indicating parallel CO_2 changes (90–93). Aspects of metabolism other than gas exchange in this system will be discussed later.

The CO_2 output of axenic *L. perpusilla* cultures growing heterotrophically has been followed by continuous monitoring. After transfer from continuous dim red light (which suppresses oscillation) to darkness, circadian oscillations persist for 2 to 4 cycles; entrainment characteristics and the responses to skeleton photoperiods also reflect the operation of a circadian timer (61, 63). Most of the work, however, has been conducted under entrainment by dim light schedules. The phase relationships between CO_2 output patterns and schedules involving various wavelengths depend on the succession of phytochrome-Pfr levels induced (60). The patterns obtained under standard schedules are altered by various nitrogen sources, organic and inorganic, with the differences interpretable as changes in phytochrome response, timing properties, or both (62, 63). These differences probably reflect changes, mediated through modified levels of related amino acids, in the proportions of the several reactions contributing to overall CO_2 flux; in effect, different reactions may be "displayed" under the different circumstances. While the primary purpose of this work remains the development of parameters relevant to photoperiodism (64, 65; see later), the results also bear on the roles of phytochrome and timing reactions in the integration of metabolism and may be relevant to pathways in photorespiration.

The timing of the respiratory climacteric in the inflorescence of the aroid *Sauromatum* may be gated by a circadian timer. No clear climacteric at all occurs under continuous light. The event takes place roughly 36 hr after an initial 1 hr dark period followed by a second one 24 hr later, but the lag period is longer (42 hr or more) if the time between the two dark periods is either more or less than 24 hr (18).

Intermediary Metabolism and Energy

In the *L. gibba* system described earler, the output of $^{14}CO_2$ from glucose-1-^{14}C oscillated in the same manner as O_2 uptake, while output from 2- or 6-labeled glucose was almost constant, suggesting that the rhythm in O_2 uptake depends on the pentose phosphate pathway. Damping oscillations in glyceraldehyde-3-phosphate dehydrogenase were observed, with the NAD- and NADP-dependent enzyme activities changing in opposite directions. The most clear cut circadian oscillation of all was that in acid phosphatase activity, which persisted undamped for at least 72 hr in continuous light (93).

The recent work of Wagner and associates on *C. rubrum* (31, 32, 145–149) is the most comprehensive study in any higher plant of free-running oscillations in various intermediates and enzyme systems. Levels and activities measured, mostly at 3 hr intervals but more frequently in some series, include: reduced and oxidized NAD and NADP; AMP, ADP, and ATP; adenylate kinase; both types of glyceraldehyde-

3-phosphate dehydrogenase; and malate, glutamate, glucose-6-phosphate and glu-conate-6-phosphate dehydrogenases. In continuous darkness after an initial period of fluctuating light and temperature, most of these show free-running period lengths of 12 to 15 hr (about 30 hr for adenylate kinase). According to calculations per-formed using three-point moving averages, these changes interact to give circadian oscillations—with 21 to 24 hr periodicities—in energy charge (148), calculated as $(ATP) + 0.5 (ADP)$ divided by $(ATP) + (ADP) + (AMP)$, as well as in the ratios of reduced to oxidized pyridine nucleotides (146). In addition, phytochrome effects are detectable on a number of these entities and their interactions, and shorter frequency components, with period lengths of 4 to 5 and 9 to 15 hr, can be observed as well. The overall interpretation is that "the adenylate system of the cell is the basic component of endogenous time measurement" (149), a concept close to one advanced earlier by Jones (76) on the basis of observations in a number of plant and animal systems. Nevertheless, in spite of the massive amounts of data, it remains unclear to this reviewer why the oscillation in energy charge need be regarded as the basis, rather than simply another manifestation, of endogenous rhythmicity.

Elegant results related to those on *C. rubrum* have been obtained on *Neurospora*. The bd mutant, in which a circadian rhythm controls the alteration of conidiating and nonconidiating bands of growth, shows correlated changes in NAD/NADH and NADP/NADPH ratios (11) and in energy charge (33), with the latter reflecting oscillations in AMP levels. These changes are not simply reflections of the changed morphology; they occur at the growing front and are not permanent characteristics of the different bands. They might result from periodic changes in the degree of coupling of mitochondrial phosphorylation, but the investigators are far more hesi-tant in deciding whether they are parts or manifestations of a "clock." Rhythmic changes in the activities of several enzymes also occur in the "band" strain of *Neurospora* (66), while even strains without conidiation rhythms exhibit circadian oscillations in nucleic acid content (85) and CO_2 output (158; M. L. Sargent, personal communication). Rhythms in the CO_2 output of several other fungi have been reported, with a clear circadian character at least in the case of *Coniophora* strains (129).

Purposes and Procedures: A Critique

Conceptual and technical problems common to all rhythm work may be aggravated when dealing with metabolism. Experiments on rhythms have at least three distinct purposes. These are: 1. to demonstrate the existence of a rhythm or rhythms; 2. to describe the components of a rhythm in detail; or 3. to determine the relationship of a rhythm and another process such as photoperiodism. What is perhaps not as clear as it might be to either readers or writers of the literature is that the same type of experiment is not necessarily optimal for all three purposes. This commonplace observation can be crucial in a context of extended analytical procedures and the increased random variation often observable when (especially) plants and microor-ganisms free run.

Some guidance is afforded by a valuable overstatement that can be called, with the appropriate apologies, Pittendrigh's Principle: if you can't automate it, don't study it. Neither counsel of despair nor confession of sloth, the Principle emphasizes that the most informative properties of rhythms, such as degree of persistence, free-running period, or phase-relationship to entraining elements, can only be studied adequately through data obtained with high frequency over numerous cycles and relatively free of subjective error. To the Principle, still in the spirit of useful exaggeration, may be added a Qualification: or if you must, at least entrain it!

Both Principle and Qualification can reasonably be defied, but not ignored. Defiance means estimating the alternative to automation in sheer labor and appropriate data reduction, which may be acceptable (though the literature suggests that it is rarely actually accepted), and recognizing the increased noise and possible loss of synchrony in free-running systems. Of course, for the first purpose enumerated, the Qualification is on occasion untenable, since the major single criterion of circadian rhythmicity is persistence without entrainment. Even here, however, demonstrations of the limits of entrainability to various frequencies have their place, as do estimates of the free-running period through changed phase relationships to different frequencies (106).

If automation remains impossible, the value of entrainment for the remaining purposes—describing components and relationships—is even greater. Indeed, it may be essential and not merely useful. For if a significant degree of asynchrony occurs under free-run conditions, the features of interest may not be stable enough to describe. The objection that entrainment may obscure effects evident in free runs, or impose others that would be absent, has force only if the frequency and reliability of free-run data provide the necessary resolving power. Even then, entrainment to different frequencies might provide more reliable information at lower cost, particularly if it can be maintained with signals of small energy and duration rather than extended periods of bright light or temperature differences. Of two major groups currently examining rhythms in plant metabolism, that of Wagner (149) works largely with free runs and that of Queiroz (113) with entrained systems; while both have provided important observations, some of those of the former seem vulnerable to questions about resolving power and significance. Full acceptance of the alternatives to automation and entrainment, as in the work of Delmer & Brody (33) on *Neurospora,* is rare indeed.

PHOTOPERIODIC TIMING

There is no more confusing literature than that on the relationship between circadian rhythmicity and photoperiodism. The chief single difficulty is to reduce both concepts and results to forms at once easy to grasp and fully expressive of the data; an analogy, though merely that, is to modeling the molecular features underlying protein specificity. A more tractable problem is that superficially similar investigations may be directed at different questions, while questions that appear to differ may do so largely in verbal terms for which critical experimental distinctions are lacking. Some of the more frequent questions are listed below, with brief answers, and then followed by explanations of those answers in terms of some recent papers.

1. Does circadian rhythmicity (cr) ever play a major role in photoperiodic time measurement (ptm)? Yes. 2. Does ptm in all organisms depend on cr? Probably not.

3. Does ptm ever depend solely on cr? Unknown; perhaps not. 4. Given a role of cr in ptm, is the rhythm in question the same one that controls other cr-dependent processes in the organism? Not necessarily. 5. Given a role of cr, is more than a single rhythm involved in ptm itself? No clear evidence; the question *may* be largely verbal.

On Circadian Rhythmicity as the Unique Basis of Photoperiodic Timing

The first three questions can be examined together. The involvement of circadian rhythmicity in photoperiodic timing is evident in what follows, in recent reviews (20, 29, 56, 75) and in papers on *Chenopodium* (139), *Glycine* (128), *Pharbitis* (100, 125, 130) and *Lemna gibba* (96) not considered further. Evidence against such involvement has been advanced for two insects. All sorts of experiments with the aphid *Megoura* support the hypothesis of a "dark period hourglass" without oscillatory properties (83). Less complete but still negative is the observation that in the pink boll-worm *Pectinophora*, red light incapable of synchronizing any of that insect's known rhythms is nevertheless photoperiodically effective in controlling diapause (110). Hence photoperiodism probably does not absolutely require circadian rhythmicity, and some organisms may achieve the one without employing the other.

The concept of circadian rhythmicity as the sole photoperiodic timer may be satisfactory only for systems that have not been studied sufficiently. In *Pharbitis,* for instance, evidence for rhythmic timing stands with equally strong evidence for the additional participation of a nonoscillatory dark period timer (56). While the flowering response of *Chenopodium* seedlings to many combinations of light and dark durations can be explained by circadian timing, on either of two reasonably explicit models (8, 81) there is probably an additional role of phytchrome-Pfr disappearance, a role not related to the phasing of a clock (82). In *Xanthium,* of course, many data have always suggested the participation (or exclusive function) of a dark period hourglass, and complex experiments are necessary to demonstrate circadian rhythmicity (116, 117).

Perhaps the most comperehensive model of photoperiodic timing yet devised, developed by Beck (2) from Truman's (141) proposal for the timing of pupal eclosion in the moth *Antheraea,* incorporates both circadian and noncircadian (hourglass) elements. The model describes not only the control of diapause in the European corn-borer *Ostrinia,* but, with relatively simple changes in parameters, all the common responses observed among insects, including long-, short-, and intermediate-day types. No physiological meaning has been attached to any of the parameters used, but the successful combination of circadian and noncircadian timers should encourage its use in connection with plant systems as well.

Does the Same Rhythm Control Photoperiodic Timing and Other Processes?

This question becomes central with a search for processes that, as "hands on the clock," might supplement inferences from end results such as flowering with direct photoperiodic effects on rhythmic processes in real time. Leaf movements are often chosen for such work out of respect for Pittendrigh's Principle and from established evidence of circadian timing. The clearest positive results are undoubtedly those on *Coleus* obtained by Halaban (51), who compared the timing of that portion of the dark period sensitive to light interruptions with that of the daily minimum in leaf position. Both responded to changes in the length of the main light period in the same way, remaining a constant time apart, thus suggesting that the same timer was involved. Brest et al (9) reported that leaf movements in *Glycine* (Biloxi soybean) also seemed expressive of the flowering response to various light regimes, although the direction of movement rather than leaf position was the significant indicator. Light interruptions that affected flowering did not necessarily affect leaf movement, as noted also by Halaban in *Coleus,* and as might be expected on the hypothesis (see later) that light plays a dual role in photoperiodism.

Surprisingly, the ineffectiveness on leaf movements of light intensities effective on flowering serves Salisbury & Denney (116, 117) as evidence that the two do not depend on the same timer in *Xanthium.* However, their work also provides a firmer basis, including the lack of a constant time interval between various leaf positions and the period sensitive to light interruptions, to suggest that two different timers, both circadian, are involved. A similar conclusion on *Pharbitis* is reached by Bollig (7), since the rhythms of leaf movement and of photoperiodic sensitivity failed to maintain a constant relation both under entraining conditions and following the phase shift due to a 6 hr light pulse. Despite the complexities of these and other (70) investigations, and the dissimilarities among them, the case that circadian timing in photoperiodism is not always expressive of a single "master clock" in an organism seems strong. Nevertheless, the perhaps ill-fated search for "hands" on that clock suggests that indicators of photoperiodic timing—processes apparently timed in the same way as some aspect of photoperiodism—might be used directly as tools for further analysis regardless of the timer(s) involved. For this purpose, processes easier to define biochemically than the turgor and growth changes underlying leaf movements would help. So far, if one excludes the interesting notion, based on relatively few data, that long-day, short-day, and day-neutral plants differ in the way in which various light regimes entrain a rhythm of amylase activity (55), the only such indicator is CO_2 output in the *Lemna perpusilla* system described earlier. Its response, and that of flowering, to darkness preceding skeleton photoperiods, implicates a circadian timer in both processes (61). In a test analogous to that with leaf movement in *Coleus,* the daily output maximum on certain media serves as an indicator of photoperiodic timing that may reflect both circadian and noncircadian elements (64, 65).

Although the appropriate tests parallel to flowering have not been done, a reading of recent papers suggests other possible photoperiodic indicators. These include a change in the level of free serine during the dark period in *Lemna perpusilla* (79), a change that may be related to the fact that CO_2 output as a photoperiodic indicator is modifiable through nitrogen metabolism (64, 65). In addition, rhythms of nucleic acid synthesis (140) as well as many other processes (147) in *Chenopodium* could be tested for photoperiodic timing, although, unlike the rhythm in flowering response, some result from germination in fluctuating temperatures are not reset by darkness (80, 145).

Does Photoperiodic Timing Involve More than One Rhythm?

In Bünning's original hypothesis, light affects both the phasing of a rhythm and, depending on whether it falls into a particular phase of that rhythm, the photoperiodically controlled process (flowering, diapause) itself. Thus light is viewed as having a dual role, conceivably two separate roles, exerted in relation to a single oscillation. Pittendrigh (107) calls this an "external coincidence" hypothesis—it depends on how an external (light) input coincides with a specific phase of the rhythm—and distinguishes it from "internal coincidence" hypotheses in which the light schedule acts by driving two (or more) internal rhythms into a particular phase relationship with each other.

Hamner and associates (56, 67, 68) use internal coincidence concepts originating in the insect literature (2, 56, 107) to interpret results with *Pharbitis* and other plants. They propose that one of two oscillators whose phase relationship determines the response is reset by "dawn" (or "light-on") signals, and the other by "dusk" ("light-off"). A major support for such hypotheses in both insects (124) and plants is that the responses to successions of various light and dark durations may give maxima, minima, and slopes that relate relatively independently to the beginnings and ends of the light periods. It is not obvious, however, that such results require a two-oscillator hypothesis rather than merely being consistent with it, particularly since defining the proposed dawn and dusk signals is admittedly difficult (56).

In *Chenopodium* seedlings, photoperiodic responses that could be interpreted in terms of dawn and dusk signals with effectiveness on their respective oscillators modified by light period duration (81) are also consistent with a one-oscillator model in which phase is set solely by a light-on signal (8). In several photoperiodic and behavioral systems, the effects of full light periods can be imitated, except in narrow ranges, by skeleton photoperiods in which light pulses occupy the locations of dawn and dusk. Although each such "pulse," 0.25 to several hours long, in principle presents both a dawn and dusk signal, the results can nevertheless be interpreted with a relatively simple single oscillator model (106, 125). On the other hand, the powerful model by Beck (2), an originator of internal coincidence concepts, depends on the relationship between two timing systems that are themselves, in turn, much more than simple oscillators.

Such examples suffice to show that the recent literature abounds in hypotheses consistent with the data but, on the face of it, inconsistent with each other, or at least strikingly different. Of course, aspects of the photoperiodic timing mechanism may differ between organisms. And some of the hypotheses may well reduce to the same basic structure. But here, as in the search for biochemical "clock" mechanisms, there is a need for experiments that will reject, or at least distinguish between, various proposals. Easier said than done, of course, but again as in basic clock investigations, the formal analysis of photoperiodism—based solely on relating an end response to light and darkness in a simple on-or-off manner—may have reached its limits. In this context, the proposition that photoperiodic timing involves more than one rhythm is surely unproved.

Two attempts to go beyond formal analysis have recently appeared. Saunders (123) found that diapause in the progeny of the wasp *Nasonia* kept in darkness can be controlled in a manner analogous to its normal photoperiodic response by temperature cycles—by the number of hours in 24 spent at 23° rather than 13°C. The conclusion, however, that the results demonstrate internal coincidence "since a specific temperature-sensitive phase seems unlikely" is hardly warranted. In plants —which undergo environmental regulation similar in many regards to that in insects—nothing is more likely, nor better established in the older literature (59) than the idea that the processes normally associated with light or darkness in photoperiodism may have different temperature sensitivities. Analysis of *Kalanchoë* petal movement by the Johnsson-Karlsson feedback model (31) suggests that both light and high temperature pulses may indeed affect the same sensitive phase in that system (40). Nor do the results most resembling those on *Nasonia*, the elimination of continuous light injury to *Lycopersicon* (tomato) by fluctuating temperatures (58), require the postulation of two oscillators instead of the simpler idea that temperature changes can nonspecifically force some degree of synchrony on processes normally synchronized by other means. Surely not every treatment other than light that has effects with timing similar to those of light—such as leaching on *Lemna perpusilla* (53, 54)—demonstrates internal coincidence, unless that hypothesis is to be reduced to a meaningless generality.

A different approach to the possibility that several rhythmic processes participate in photoperiodism is to locate and describe them in concrete terms. A promising beginning, with seedlings and adult plants of *Chenopodium*, has been made by King (80). Complex manipulations including temperature changes, glucose treatments, and leaf removal provide evidence for at least two distinct rhythms. One, possibly related to mitosis, is in the apex, and another in the leaf. Both probably affect the flowering response, although only one of them, that in the leaf, appears to be a typical circadian oscillation in that its phase is controlled by light and darkness.

CONCLUDING REMARKS

The omission here of many aspects of rhythmicity because of space limitation may be just as well, for, as in the aspects discussed, phenomena seem easier to come by than principles, mechanisms, and analytical approaches. However, two additional areas deserve mention.

First, evidence of endogenous circannual rhythms is good in animals with complex nervous systems (references in 10) but less convincing in plants (134). Brock (10) has followed free-running changes, with period lengths of 379 to 411 days, in the development of the marine cnidarian *Campanularia*, which possesses only a simple nerve net. Colonies with different histories cultured together remain out of phase, reinforcing the view that the oscillations are truly endogenous. Similarly critical work on seed germination and other plant processes is needed.

The relationship, if any, of circadian rhythmicity to life span and aging has attracted little attention since the plant investigations of Went and associates (58,

151), but two reports from Pittendrigh's laboratory suggest that it merits more. Among *Drosophila* populations held at 25°C in continuous light or under the three different *light*:dark cycles *12*:12, *13.5*:13.5 or *10.5*:10.5, longevity was greatest under the 24 hr periodicity (111). A quite different study on *Mesocricetus* (golden hamster) and two species of deermouse showed that the free-running activity rhythms become shorter as the animals age (109). Both studies imply a role of circadian rhythmicity in the optimal functioning of living systems, apart from any relationship to specific processes such as reproduction.

So for a moral to this undulating and even knotty tale, perhaps the following will do. Biologists have long since learned to ask "what?" with sufficient precision to get detailed molecular answers, while few investigations of any process are complete without an answer to "where?" in commensurate ultrastructural terms; the obvious third question, requiring answers in all complexity yet down to the same levels, is "when?"

Literature Cited

1. Aschoff, J., Ed. 1965. *Circadian Clocks.* Amsterdam: North-Holland. 479 pp.
2. Beck, S. D. 1974. *J. Comp. Physiol.* 90:275–310
3. Beevers, L., Hageman, R. H. 1969. *Ann. Rev. Plant Physiol.* 20:495–522
4. Biebl, R. 1974. *Protoplasma* 81:3–15
5. Bishop, R. C., Klein, R. M. 1971. *Can. J. Genet. Cytol.* 13:597–99
6. Ibid 1973. 15:667–70
7. Bollig, I. *Z. Pflanzenphysiol.* In press
8. Bollig, I., Chandrashekaran, M. K., Engelmann, W., Johnsonn, A. *Int. J. Chronobiol.* In press
9. Brest, D. E., Hoshizaki, T., Hamner, K. C. 1971. *Plant Physiol.* 47:676–81
10. Brock, M. A. 1975. *Comp. Biochem. Physiol.* 51A:377–98
11. Brody, S., Harris, S. 1973. *Science* 180:495–500
12. Brogardh, T., Johnsson, A. 1974. *Z. Naturforsch.* 29c:298–300
13. Brogardh, T., Johnsson, A. 1974. *Physiol. Plant.* 31:112–18
14. Brown, F. A. Jr., Hastings, J. W., Palmer, J. D. 1970. *The Biological Clock: Two Views.* London, New York: Academic. 94 pp.
15. Brown, R. 1951. *J. Exp. Bot.* 2:96–110
16. Bruce, V. G., Pittendrigh, C. S. 1960. *J. Cell. Comp. Physiol.* 56:25–31
17. Bryant, T. R. 1972. *Science* 178:634–36
18. Buggeln, R. G., Meeuse, B. J. D., Klima, J. R. 1971. *Can. J. Bot.* 49:1025–31
19. Bünning, E. 1964. *The Physiological Clock.* New York: Springer-Verlag. 145 pp.
20. Bünning, E. 1969. *Photochem. Photobiol.* 9:219–28
21. Bünning, E., Baltes, J. 1963. *Naturwissenschaften* 50:622
22. Bünning, E., Moser, I. 1972. *Proc. Natl. Acad. Sci. USA* 69:2732–33
23. Ibid 1973. 70:3387–89
24. Bush, K. H., Sweeney, B. M. 1972. *Plant Physiol.* 50:446–51
25. Chance, B., Estabrook, R. W., Ghosh, A. 1964. *Proc. Natl. Acad. Sci. USA* 51:1244–51
26. Chandler, A. C. Jr. 1957. *Biol. Bull.* 112:305–12
27. Chia-Looi, A., Cumming, B. G. 1972. *Can. J. Bot.* 50:2219–26
28. Cohen, A. S., Cumming, B. G. 1974. *Can. J. Bot.* 52:2351–60
29. Cumming, B. G. 1972. *Proc. Int. Symp. Circadian Rhythmicity Wageningen 1971,* 33–85. Wageningen, The Netherlands: Centre for Scientific Documentation
30. Cumming, B. G., Wagner, E. 1968. *Ann. Rev. Plant Physiol.* 19:381–416
31. Deitzer, G. F., Haertle, U., Wagner, E. 1974. *J. Interdiscip. Cycle Res.* 5: 187–98
32. Deitzer, G. F., Kempf, O., Fischer, S., Wagner, E. 1974. *Planta* 117:29–41
33. Delmer, D. P., Brody, S. 1975. *J. Bacteriol.* 121:548–53
34. Edmunds, L. N. Jr. 1976. In *Les Cycles Cellulaires et Leur Blocage Chez Plusiers Protistes,* 53–67. Paris: Coll. Int. C.N.R.S.
35. Edmunds, L. N. Jr., Cirillo, V. P. 1974. *Int. J. Chronobiol.* 2:233–46

36. Ehret, C. F. 1974. *Adv. Biol. Med. Phys.* 15:47–77
37. Ehret, C. F., Trucco, E. 1967. *J. Theor. Biol.* 15:240–62
38. Ehret, C. F., Wille, J. J. 1970. *Photobiology of Microorganisms,* ed. P. Halldal, 369–416. London: Wiley-Interscience
39. Engelmann, W. 1973. *Z. Naturforsch.* 28c:733–36
40. Engelmann, W., Eger, I., Johnsson, A., Karlsson, H. G. 1974. *Int. J. Chronobiol.* 2:347–58
41. Engelmann, W., Karlsson, H. G., Johnsson, A. 1973. *Int. J. Chronobiol.* 1:147–56
42. Enright, J. T. 1971. *Z. Vgl. Physiol.* 72:1–16
43. Ibid. 75:332–46
44. Eskin, A. 1972. *J. Comp. Physiol.* 80:353–76
45. Feldman, J. F. 1967. *Proc. Natl. Acad. Sci. USA* 57:1080–87
46. Feldman, J. F. 1973. *Behavioral Genetics: Simple Systems,* ed. J. R. Wilson, 166–87. Boulder: Colo. Assoc. Univ. Press
47. Feldman, J. F., Stevens, S. B. 1973. *Behavior of Microorganisms,* ed. A. Perez-Miravete, 297–301. London: Plenum
48. Frolova, L. V., Khallak, K. I. 1974. *Tsitologiya* 16:377–81
49. Grell, E., Funck, T., Sauter, H. 1973. *Eur. J. Biochem.* 34:415–24
50. Hahn, H. S., Ortoleva, P. J., Ross, J. 1973. *J. Theor. Biol.* 41:503–21
51. Halaban, R. 1968. *Plant Physiol.* 43:1894–98
52. Ibid 1972. 50:308–10
53. Halaban, R., Hillman, W. S. 1970. *Plant Physiol.* 46:641–44
54. Ibid 1971. 48:760–64
55. Halberg, J., Halberg, E., Halberg, F., Olson, L. C. 1973. *Int. J. Chronobiol.* 1:81–90
56. Hamner, K. C., Hoshizaki, T. 1974. *BioScience* 24:407–14
57. Hardeland, R., Homann, D., Rensing, R. 1973. *J. Interdiscip. Cycle Res.* 4:89–118
58. Hillman, W. S. 1956. *Am. J. Bot.* 43:89–96
59. Hillman, W. S. 1962. *The Physiology of Flowering.* New York: Holt, Rinehart & Winston. 164 pp.
60. Hillman, W. S. 1971. *Plant Physiol.* 48:770–74
61. Ibid 1972. 49:907–11
62. Hillman, W. S. 1974. *Am. J. Bot.* 61 (5, Suppl):28 (Abstr.)
63. Hillman, W. S. 1975. *Photochem. Photobiol.* 21:39–47
64. Hillman, W. S. 1976. *Proc. Natl. Acad. Sci. USA* 73:501–4
65. Hillman, W. S. *Light and Plant Development,* Proc. 22nd Easter Sch. Agric. Sci., Univ. Nottingham, ed. H. Smith. London: Butterworths. In press
66. Hochberg, M. L., Sargent, M. L. 1974. *J. Bacteriol.* 120:1164–75
67. Hoshizaki, T., Brest, D. E., Hamner, K. C. 1974. *Plant Physiol.* 53:176–79
68. Hoshizaki, T., Hamner, K. C. 1974. *Int. J. Chronobiol.* 2:35–38
69. Hsiao, T. C. 1973. *Ann. Rev. Plant Physiol.* 24:519–70
70. Ioffe, A. A. 1968. *Dokl. Bot. Sci.* 180:92–94. Transl. of *Dokl. Akad. Nauk, SSSR* 180:496–98, May 1968
71. Jacklet, J. W. 1974. *J. Comp. Physiol.* 90:33–45
72. Jacklet, J. W., Geronimo, J. 1971. *Science* 174:299–302
73. Johnsson, A., Karlsson, H. G. 1972. *J. Theor. Biol.* 36:153–74
74. Jones, M. B., Mansfield, T. A. 1972. *Planta* 103:134–46
75. Jones, M. B., Mansfield, T. A. 1975. *Sci. Progr.* 62:103–25
76. Jones, P. C. T. 1972. *J. Theor. Biol.* 34:1–13
77. Kauffman, S. 1974. *Bull. Math. Biol.* 36:171–82
78. Keller, S. 1960. *Z. Bot.* 48:32–57
79. Khudairi, A. K., Hemberg, T. 1974. *J. Exp. Bot.* 25:740–44
80. King, R. W. 1975. *Can. J. Bot.* 53:2631–38
81. King, R. W., Cumming, B. G. 1972. *Planta* 103:281–301
82. Ibid. 108:39–57
83. Lees, A. D. 1973. *J. Insect Physiol.* 19:2279–2316
84. Mäkinen, Y. 1963. *Ann. Bot. Soc. Zool. Bot. Fenn. "Vanamo"* 34(6):1–61
85. Martens, C. L., Sargent, M. L. 1974. *J. Bacteriol.* 117:1210–15
86. Martin, E. S., Meidner, H. 1972. *New Phytol.* 71:1045–54
87. Maurer, A., Engelmann, W. 1974. *Z. Naturforsch.* 29c:36–38
88. McDaniel, M., Sulzman, F. M., Hastings, J. W. 1974. *Proc. Natl. Acad. Sci. USA* 71:4389–91
89. Menaker, M., Ed. 1971. *Biochronometry.* Washington: Natl. Acad. Sci. 662 pp.
90. Miyata, H., 1970. *Plant Cell Physiol.* 11:293–301
91. Ibid 1971. 12:517–24
92. Ibid, 969–77
93. Miyata, H., Yamamoto, Y. 1969. *Plant Cell Physiol.* 10:875–89

94. Moller, Y., Larsen, J. K., Faber, M. 1974. *Cell Tissue Kinet.* 7:231–39
95. Morel, C., Queiroz, O. 1974. *J. Interdiscip. Cycle Res.* 5:206–16
96. Nakashima, H. 1968. *Plant Cell Physiol.* 9:247–57
97. Njus, D., Sulzman, F. M., Hastings, J. W. 1974. *Nature* 248:116–20
98. Nozawa, Y., Iida, H., Fukushima, H., Ohki, K., Ohnishi, S. 1974. *Biochim. Biophys. Acta* 367:134–47
99. Pallas, J. S. Jr., Samish, Y. B., Willmer, C. M. 1974. *Plant Physiol.* 53:907–11
100. Paraska, J. R., Spector, C. 1974. *Physiol. Plant.* 32:62–65
101. Pavlidis, T. 1969. *J. Theor. Biol.* 22:418–36
102. Pavlidis, T. 1971. See Ref. 89, 110–16
103. Pavlidis, T. 1973. *Biological Oscillators: Their Mathematical Analysis.* New York: Academic. 207 pp.
104. Pavlidis, T., Kauzmann, W. 1969. *Arch. Biochem. Biophys.* 132:338–48
105. Pearson, C. J. 1974. *Planta* 119:59–70
106. Pittendrigh, C. S. 1966. *Z. Pflanzenphysiol.* 54:275–307
107. Pittendrigh, C. S. 1972. *Proc. Natl. Acad. Sci. USA* 69:2734–37
108. Pittendrigh, C. S., Caldarola, P. C., Cosbey, E. S. 1973. *Proc. Natl. Acad. Sci. USA* 70:2037–41
109. Pittendrigh, C. S., Daan, S. 1974. *Science* 186:548–50
110. Pittendrigh, C. S., Minis, D. H. 1971. See Ref. 89, 212–50
111. Pittendrigh, C. S., Minis, D. H. 1972. *Proc. Natl. Acad. Sci. USA* 69:1537–39
112. Pye, E. K. 1969. *Can. J. Bot.* 42:271–85
113. Queiroz, O. 1974. *Ann. Rev. Plant Physiol.* 25:115–34
114. Racusen, R., Satter, R. L. 1975. *Nature* 255:408–510
115. Rusch, H. P., Sachsemaier, W., Berens, K., Gruter, V. 1966. *J. Cell Biol.* 31:204–9
116. Salisbury, F. B., Denney, A. 1971. See Ref. 89, 292–310
117. Salisbury, F. B., Denney, A. 1974. See ref. 126, pp. 679–686
118. Satter, R. L., Applewhite, P. B., Chaudri, J., Galston, A. W. *Photochem. Photobiol.* Submitted
119. Satter, R. L., Applewhite, P. B., Galston, A. W. 1974. *Plant Physiol.* 54:280–85
120. Satter, R. L., Galston, A. W. 1971. *Science* 174:518–20
121. Satter, R. L., Galston, A. W. 1973. *BioScience* 23:407–16
122. Satter, R. L., Geballe, G. T., Applewhite, P. B., Galston, A. W. 1974. *J. Gen. Physiol.* 64:413–30
123. Saunders, D. S. 1973. *Science* 181:358–60
124. Saunders, D. S. 1974. *J. Insect Physiol.* 20:77–88
125. Saunders, D. S. 1974. *J. Comp. Physiol.* 97:97–112
126. Scheving, L. D., Halberg, F., Pauly, J. E., Eds. 1974. *Chronobiology.* Tokyo: Igaku Shoin. 784 pp.
127. Schrempf, M. 1975. *Eigenschaften und Lokalisation des Photorezeptors für Phasenverschiebendes Störlicht bei der Blutenblattbewegung von Kalanchoë Blossfeldiana (v. Poelln.).* Dissertation. Univ. Tübingen, Germany. 62 pp.
128. Sirohi, G. S. 1974. *Indian J. Exp. Biol.* 12:272–74
129. Smith, R. S. 1973. *Can. J. Bot.* 51: 701–10
130. Spector, C., Paraska, J. R. 1973. *Physiol. Plant.* 29:402–5
131. Steer, B. T. 1973. *Plant Physiol.* 51:744–48
132. Ibid 1974. 54:758–65
133. Suter, R. B., Rawson, K. S. 1968. *Science* 160:1011–14
134. Sweeney, B. M. 1969. *Rhythmic Phenomena in Plants.* London, New York: Academic. 147 pp.
135. Sweeney, B. M. 1974. *Plant Physiol.* 53:337–42
136. Sweeney, B. M. 1974. *Int. J. Chronobiol.* 2:25–33
137. Sweeney, B. M., Tuffli, C. F., Rubin, R. H. 1967. *J. Gen. Physiol.* 50:647–59
138. Taguchi, Y. H., Tabachnick, J. 1974. *Arch. Dermatol. Forsch.* 249:167–77
139. Teltscherova, L., Opatrna, J., Pleskotova, D. 1974. *Biol. Plant.* 16:341–47
140. Teltscherova, L., Pleskotova, D. 1973. *Biol. Plant.* 15:419–26
141. Truman, J. W. 1972. *Proc. Int. Symp. Circadian Rhythmicity Wageningen 1971,* 111–35. Wageningen, The Netherlands: Cent. Sci. Doc.
142. Tyson, J., Kauffman, S. 1975. *J. Math. Biol.* 1:289–310
143. Vanden Driessche, T. 1971. See Ref. 89, 612–22
144. Wagner, E., Cumming, B. G. 1970. *Can. J. Bot.* 48:1–18
145. Wagner, E., Frosch, S. 1971. *Can. J. Bot.* 49:1981–85
146. Wagner, E., Frosch, S. 1974. *J. Interdiscip. Cycle Res.* 5:231–39
147. Wagner, E., Frosch, S., Deitzer, G. F. 1974. *J. Interdiscip. Cycle Res.* 5: 240–46

148. Wagner, E., Strobele, L., Frosch, S. 1974. *J. Interdiscip. Cycle Res.* 5:77–88
149. Wagner, E., Tetzner, J., Haertle, U., Deitzer, G. F. 1974. *Ber. Dtsch. Bot. Ges.* 87:291–302
150. Walther, W. G., Edmunds, L. N. Jr. 1973. *Plant Physiol.* 51:250–58
151. Went, F. W. 1959. *Photoperiodism and Related Phenomena in Plants and Animals,* ed. R. B. Withdrow, 551–64. Washington: Am. Assoc. Adv. Sci.
152. Wilkins, M. B. *Light and Plant Development.* Proc. 22nd Easter Sch. Agric. Sci. Univ. Nottingham, ed. H. Smith. London: Butterworths. In press
153. Wilson, J. M., Crawford, R. M. M.

1974. *New Phytol.* 73:805–20
154. Winfree, A. T. 1970. *J. Theor. Biol.* 28:327–74
155. Winfree, A. T. 1972. *Arch. Biochem. Biophys.* 149:388–401
156. Winfree, A. T. 1974. *J. Math. Biol.* 1:73–95
157. Winfree, A. T. 1975. *Nature* 253: 315–19
158. Woodward, D. O., Sargent, M. L. 1973. *Behavior of Microorganisms,* ed. A. Perez-Miravete, 282–96. London: Plenum
159. Zeiger, E., Cardemil, L. 1973. *Dev. Biol.* 32:179–88

Ann. Rev. Plant Physiol. 1976. 27:181–205

REGULATORY ASPECTS OF PHOTOSYNTHETIC CARBON METABOLISM[1]

✦7607

Grahame J. Kelly and Erwin Latzko

Abteilung Chemische Pflanzenphysiologie, Technische Universität München, 8050 Weihenstephan, West Germany

Martin Gibbs

Institute for Photobiology of Cells and Organelles, Brandeis University, Waltham, Massachusetts 02154

CONTENTS

[1]Abbreviations used: CAM (Crassulacean acid metabolism); DTT (dithiothreitol); FDP (fructose-1,6-diphosphate); G3P (glyceraldehyde-3-phosphate); PEP (phosphoenolpyruvate); PGA (3-phosphoglycerate); RuDP (ribulose-1,5-diphosphate); SDP (sedoheptulose-1,7-diphosphate).

181

INTRODUCTION

Research on the carbon metabolism of photosynthesis has proceeded with vigor during the last 5 years in the aftermath of the discoveries of C_4 metabolism (100, 122, 135) and photorespiration (79). Special attention has been devoted to detailing the metabolic sequences of these two processes and their interplay with the Calvin cycle of CO_2 fixation. In addition, properties and distribution of the enzymes involved in photosynthetic carbon metabolism have been more closely examined with a view to identifying those with important regulatory functions in CO_2 fixation. This review presents the current state of knowledge on the flow of carbon during photosynthesis and will consider how those regulatory properties so far identified for enzymes of carbon metabolism relate to the movement of carbon. Most of the examined literature follows that reviewed earlier in these volumes by Black (29) on CO_2 fixation, Preiss & Kosuge (188) on the regulatory properties of enzymes, Tolbert (222) concerning the role of peroxisomes in photorespiration, and Heber (103) on the movement of metabolites between chloroplasts and the cytoplasm.

AUTOCATALYSIS AND PHOTOSYNTHETIC CO_2 FIXATION

Uniqueness of the Calvin Cycle

For plants to grow, net fixation of CO_2 into organic matter is essential, and the only known series of reactions capable of achieving this end is the Calvin cycle (20, 230, Figure 1). Unfortunately, the primary importance of the ability of the photosynthetic CO_2 fixation mechanism to support growth has, in recent years, received second place to the nature of the first compounds observed after feeding $^{14}CO_2$ in the light; the nature of these compounds depends of course on which carboxylating enzymes with their substrates are in the path of the $^{14}CO_2$. In some plants PGA was the first labeled compound detected (20) while in others labeled 4C acids, mainly malate and aspartate, were initially observed (32, 135), and although it cannot be denied that the identification of PGA was vital to the elucidation of the Calvin cycle, it does not follow that the appearance of some other compound as the first radioac-

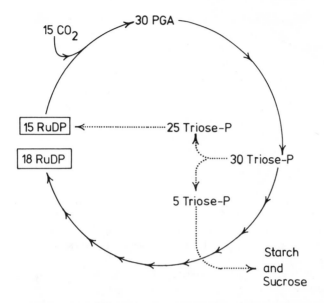

Figure 1   Autocatalytic nature of the Calvin cycle of CO_2 fixation. Carboxylation of 15 RuDP produces 30 PGA which are reduced to 30 triose phosphate. These 30 triose phosphate can be rearranged into 18 RuDP by the enzymes of the Calvin cycle, thus permitting three extra CO_2 acceptor (RuDP) molecules to be formed from the incorporated CO_2. Dotted lines show that reduced carbon can be utilized for starch and sucrose formation after a steady-state level of RuDP sufficient for photosynthesis has been attained. Adapted from Walker (230).

tive product indicates an alternative to this cycle. Any CO_2 fixation mechanism permitting growth must be an autocatalytic sequence able to generate more CO_2 acceptor than was present initially. In a recent report, Walker (230) has clearly differentiated between the Calvin cycle and C_4 metabolism on this basis and concluded that while the Calvin cycle is autocatalytic the C_4 pathway is not. Comparison of the Calvin cycle (Figure 1) and any of the three variations of the C_4 pathway (Figure 2) makes this point: in each case 15 molecules of CO_2 combine with 15 molecules of acceptor, but while the reactions of the Calvin cycle allow the possibility of synthesizing three extra molecules of acceptor (RuDP) from the fixed CO_2, those of the C_4 pathway do not permit increase in the number of CO_2 acceptor (PEP) molecules. The uniqueness of the Calvin cycle as the only presently known pathway for the net incorporation of CO_2 for growth is a prerequisite for a realistic interpretation of much of the current literature on photosynthetic carbon metabolism.

Possible Alternatives to the Calvin Cycle

It remains possible that other autocatalytic pathways for CO_2 fixation exist. A direct reduction of CO_2 to formate, shown feasible in an aerobic bacterium (110), is the basis of an interesting proposal to explain the distribution of label in organic acids obtained from *Vicia faba* leaves fed $^{14}CO_2$ in the light (129); however, the reduction of CO_2 to formate in leaves has not been directly demonstrated. Net CO_2 fixation by a reductive carboxylic acid cycle has been proposed for the green photosynthetic bacterium *Chlorobium thiosulfatophilum* (36), and although activity of citrate lyase, a key enzyme of this cycle, has not been detected (24), labeling data consistent with operation of the cycle has again been reported (208). RuDP carboxylase, originally believed absent from this organism (36), has since been shown to be present (218), hence there is no longer reason to suspect that the Calvin cycle is absent.

THE CALVIN CYCLE

The path of carbon in the Calvin cycle remains virtually unchanged from that outlined in the 1950s (20). Continuing studies, particularly of the individual enzymes, are rapidly removing the few lingering problems preventing its unqualified acceptance. An early observation causing concern was the asymmetric distribution of radioactivity in hexose phosphates formed from triose phosphates during photosynthesis in $^{14}CO_2$ (87), but this effect has since been attributed to the reversibility of the transketolase reaction and the influence of a triose phosphate pool (19); the latter could be enhanced by the easier transport of triose phosphates, in comparison to hexose phosphates, between chloroplasts and the cytoplasm (107). Low activities of the diphosphatases for FDP and SDP were also inconsistent with operation of the cycle (147), but the FDPase activity has now been shown sufficient to support CO_2 fixation (83), and there are indications that high SDPase activities will also be confirmed; activations by the sulfhydryl reducing agent DTT (6, 203) and reduced ferredoxin (203) were recently reported for this enzyme. The disparity between the apparent low affinity of RuDP carboxylase in vitro for CO_2 and the over 20-fold higher affinity of whole leaves and isolated chloroplasts for CO_2 (see 188) no longer exists; an original report by Bahr & Jensen (13) that RuDP carboxylase freshly released from broken chloroplasts had a K_m for CO_2 of 11 to 18 μM, similar to the level of CO_2 in air, has been confirmed in other laboratories (12, 31, 159), and although a recent estimate places the true K_m closer to 50 μM, the large amount of carboxylase activity detected was nevertheless sufficient to account for normal rates of photosynthesis by leaves in air (154).

Regulatory Properties of Enzymes of the Calvin Cycle

RIBULOSE-1,5-DIPHOSPHATE CARBOXYLASE   The kinetic and structural properties of RuDP carboxylase are beginning to be correlated and a rather intricate picture is emerging. The enzyme from higher plants is composed of eight large subunits, shown by kinetic (173) and immunological (93, 172) studies to contain the catalytic site for RuDP and CO_2, and eight small subunits to which Mg^{2+} binds (172). The enzymes from *Chlorella* (156) and *Euglena* (163) are structurally very similar but that from a blue-green alga consists of eight large subunits only (219), an interesting result from the evolutionary standpoint since in higher plants the large subunit, but not the small subunit, is synthesized in chloroplasts (94). Bacterial enzymes are even smaller; the *Rhodospirillum rubrum* enzyme is composed of just two large subunits (217).

Reports by Chu & Bassham (46) and Tabita & McFadden (215) that RuDP carboxylase can be inhibited by low concentrations of 6-P-gluconate have been followed by a number of experiments showing that the effects of this and other sugar phosphates on the enzyme activity depend very much on the composition of reaction mixtures and the order of addition of components (47–49, 216); this situation may explain why some metabolites such as fructose-6-P had effects in certain earlier investigations (34) but not in others (48). The 6-P-gluconate inhibition was only seen when this substance was added after or simultaneously with the substrate RuDP (47); if present during a preincubation it activated the enzyme (34, 47). FDP and NADPH had similar effects, except in the latter case no inhibition was observed (48). *Chlorella* RuDP carboxylase responded similarly to 6-P-gluconate (156). A pertinent question is whether the effects of 6-P-gluconate can be physiologically important since only traces of this substance have been detected in chloroplasts (see 46). Nevertheless, 6-P-gluconate is proving a valuable tool for elucidation of the properties of RuDP carboxylase.

Chu & Bassham (49), in an attempt to explain observed regulatory phenomena, have proposed that RuDP carboxylase contains four regulatory sites in addition to the catalytic sites, and have suggested that activation by Mg^{2+} and bicarbonate during preincubation (23, 47, 186, 216), complimented by effectors such as 6-P-gluconate, NADPH, and FDP, prevents binding of RuDP to a regulatory site; when RuDP binds to this site enzyme activity is much reduced and the affinity for CO_2 is lowered. How these sites relate to the subunit structure of the enzyme is not yet clear, but there is some proclivity towards the demonstration by Kwok & Wildman (140) that binding of RuDP is associated with a considerable enzyme conformational change which is complete after only four of the eight available RuDP binding sites have been occupied. It may be that these four sites are always occupied in vivo even in the dark, since considerable levels of RuDP have been reported in leaves and chloroplasts in darkness (114, 141, 148).

3-PHOSPHOGLYCERATE KINASE   Unlike most kinases, PGA kinase catalyzes a freely reversible reaction. Chloroplast PGA kinase is more active in the direction of photosynthesis when the extent of phosphorylation of the adenylate pool, expressed as energy charge, is high (178). Therefore, the apparent inhibition by ADP of PGA utilization in chloroplast extracts (155) is compatible with regulation by energy charge (179). ATP levels (50, 102) and energy charge (166) are reported to increase upon illumination of chloroplasts, thus favoring the phosphorylation of PGA during photosynthesis (178).

GLYCERALDEHYDE-3-PHOSPHATE DEHYDROGENASE   The reductive step in the Calvin cycle is catalyzed by chloroplast G3P dehydrogenase. Interpretation of results from studies of this enzyme have been complicated by the interference of Tris buffer which forms complexes with triose phosphates in reaction mixtures (204), by the extreme sensitivity of the enzyme to sulfonated polystyrene, a possible contaminant of resins used in the preparation of substrates (K. Pawlizki et al, in preparation), and by the tendency of the spinach leaf enzyme to aggregate (164, 191). Nevertheless, it is clear that the protomeric enzyme has a molecular weight of about 140,000 and catalyzes a reversible reaction with either NAD(H) or NADP(H) as coenzyme (164, 189–191, 226). Activation of the NADP(H)-linked activity following incubation of the enzyme with NADP(H) or ATP (170, 190, 191) appears to be related to the dissociation of the aggregated enzyme into active protomers, but the significance of this phenomenon is questionable since it has been reported only for dilute solutions of the spinach leaf enzyme. The mechanism of the reported light activation of the enzyme in vivo (240) remains unclear, although involvement of sulfhydryl groups is a real possibility (170).

Studies with inhibitors of protein synthesis (40) and the effects of far-red light (41) have led to the proposal (40) that the cytoplasmic G3P dehydrogenase is a precursor for the synthesis of chloroplast G3P dehydrogenase; if this is true then the precursor enzyme must be considerably modified since McGowan & Gibbs (164) have shown that the pea chloroplast and cytoplasmic G3P dehydrogenases are immunologically quite distinct. The possession of two types of subunits by the chloroplast enzyme (181) could be related to these observations.

Although the NADP(H)-linked activity of chloroplast G3P dehydrogenase from higher plants is seldom more than two to four times the NAD(H)-linked activity (191, 235), the enzyme from photosynthetic microorganisms is reported to be proportionately more active with NADP(H): in *Anacystis* the NADP(H)-linked activity of the partially purified enzyme was 50 times that with NAD(H) (112), while Pupillo (189) found the enzymes from *Euglena* and *Ochromonas* were active only with NADP(H). On the other hand, NADP-linked activity has now been detected in a nonphotosynthetic *Pseudomonas* grown gluconeogenically (174).

FRUCTOSE DIPHOSPHATASE   Reported activities of FDPase in chloroplasts do not greatly exceed the rate of CO_2 fixation (83, 149), hence the regulatory properties of this enzyme are more likely to influence the rate of photosynthesis. Following the leads of Preiss et al (187), who showed that increased Mg^{2+} levels lowered the pH optimum, and Buchanan et al (35), who reported activation by reduced ferredoxin or DTT, recent investigators (16, 74, 83) have confirmed that Mg^{2+}, DTT, and the substrate FDP all activate the enzyme, especially at suboptimal pH values; the activity responds to the concentration of FDP in a sigmoid fashion. The observed effects are consistent with full activity of the enzyme in the light when the Mg^{2+} concentration (18, 109, 137) and pH (108) in the chloroplast stroma are believed to rise considerably, but no activity in the dark (16). The requirement of a small protein factor and reduced ferredoxin for activation of FDPase (35) has not been reported since, and in at least one case significant activation by reduced ferredoxin was not found (74). However, there is recent evidence that SDPase is similarly activated (203); it seems important that the nature of the small molecular weight component be identified in order to examine its role.

RIBULOSE-5-PHOSPHATE KINASE   The CO_2 acceptor RuDP is generated from ribulose-5-P by a kinase which is rapidly activated in vivo by light (10). This activation is proposed to be mediated by a photoproduced reductant and is analogous to the in vitro activation by DTT observed earlier (146). Inhibition of the enzyme from microorganisms by AMP (1; see 188) indicated regulation by energy charge, and although similar regulation of the pea leaf enzyme was not initially observed (5), energy charge regulation of the spinach leaf enzyme was recently detected in experiments utilizing a different assay procedure (150).

OTHER ENZYMES   Calvin cycle enzymes involved in the rearrangement of triose phosphates to ribulose-5-P have, apart from FDPase and SDPase, received little attention in recent years. Separation of some of these, including triose-P isomerase (3), FDP aldolase (8) and ribose-5-P isomerase (4), from their cytoplasmic counterparts has been achieved by Anderson and co-workers. In these cases the properties of each chloroplast enzyme were similar to those of the same enzyme from the cytoplasm, as with PGA kinase (179); the strong inhibition of triose-P isomerase by the photorespiratory intermediate P-glycolate (3) deserves attention.

Studies with Isolated Chloroplasts and Chloroplast Extracts

POTENTIAL ACTIVITY OF RIBULOSE-1,5-DIPHOSPHATE CARBOXYLASE   Measurements of RuDP carboxylase activity in chloroplast extracts have substantiated the belief that all CO_2 fixed during photosynthesis is incorporated by this enzyme. In initial experiments much attention was given to the affinity of the carboxylase for CO_2, and although low K_m values indicating high affinities were reported, these were sometimes (13, 31) but not always (12) a consequence, at least in part, of rather low maximum velocities. In a comprehensive study Lilley & Walker (154), questioning the recent restriction of emphasis to enzyme affinity, reinvestigated the affinity and potential activity of RuDP carboxylase in chloroplast extracts using an improved assay. They concluded that the maximum velocity for CO_2 fixation by the carboxylase in either intact chloroplasts or chloroplast extracts approaches 1000 μmoles per mg chlorophyll per hr, severalfold higher than CO_2 fixation by intact leaves. These authors suggest that this value has been underestimated previously with resultant errors in K_m values, and even though the correct K_m for CO_2 of around 50 μM is about five times the concentration of CO_2 in air, the maximum velocity is so high that carboxylation in air levels of CO_2 would still be sufficient to account for observed rates of leaf photosynthesis. Leaf photosynthesis certainly can be increased, however, by CO_2 levels greater than that in air. The low amount of CO_2 normally encountered in air and the diffusive resistance of the leaf to CO_2 clearly limit photosynthesis (167, see 154). This implies, at the biochemical level, that the availability of CO_2 for RuDP carboxylase in the chloroplast limits turnover of the Calvin cycle and prevents the full potential of the Calvin cycle enzymes from being utilized during steady state photosynthesis. With this in mind, the recorded rapid accumulation of bicarbonate by intact chloroplasts (232), the facilitation of this process by a light-induced increase in the stromal pH (108), and the enigmatic presence of carbonic anhydrase (184), which may protect against sudden localized pH changes accompanying these proton and CO_2 movements (113), appear of no small consequence.

In the past, high rates of CO_2 fixation by isolated chloroplasts have been correlated with the retention of the somewhat fragile outer double envelopes (see 86). However, autocatalytic CO_2 fixation by the Calvin cycle has now been demonstrated in reconstituted chloroplast systems (22, 231), leading to the provocative conclusion (22) that a high concentration of soluble chloroplast components in the vicinity of chlorophyll is more important than an intact chloroplast envelope for high rates of CO_2 fixation.

THE INDUCTION PHENOMENON   Turner, Black & Gibbs (223) originally reported a considerable lag in CO_2 fixation following illumination of isolated chloroplasts in the presence of an ample supply of CO_2. This phenomenon, since observed with a reconstituted chloroplast system (231), is believed to reflect the time needed to build up levels of Calvin cycle intermediates, including RuDP (148). Even after a period of photosynthesis, Robinson et al (195) found that levels of RuDP in chloroplasts were little more than sufficient for CO_2 fixation. On the other hand, an appreciable level of RuDP is maintained in leaves (141) and chloroplasts (114, 148) in darkness; this may prime a quick response to the onset of illumination. Such RuDP is maintained in the dark despite the presence of CO_2, thus indicating that RuDP carboxylase is inactive in the dark but activated in the light (229, see 188). The most popular contender as activator is Mg^{2+}, which upon illumination moves into the chloroplast stroma in a counterexchange with protons which move into the thylakoids (18, 109, 137) and which has been shown to activate RuDP carboxylase in a reconstituted chloroplast system (152). This and other effects no doubt contribute to recovery from the lag period; the increased stromal pH resulting from proton movement into the thylakoids could increase the affinity of RuDP carboxylase for CO_2 (31), the combination of increased stromal pH and Mg^{2+} concentration would ensure full activity of FDPase (16), and high activity of this and other enzymes of the Calvin cycle may in addition be facilitated by light activation involving reductive processes. Several enzymes activated in vivo upon illumination are activated by DTT in vitro, and evidence that DTT replaces a natural modulator associated with the photosynthetic electron transport chain has been pursued vigorously by Anderson (7).

C_4 METABOLISM

Probably no reports have stimulated more of the research from the last few years on the carbon metabolism of photosynthesis than those (100, 122, 135) initiating the C_4 pathway of photosynthesis. As originally proposed by Hatch & Slack (100), this pathway would have constituted an autocatalytic cycle utilizing a transcarboxylation from a 4C acid (produced from PEP carboxylation) to an acceptor, thus forming a compound from which additional PEP could be synthesized. However, the transcarboxylation has never been found. Consequently the C_4 pathway of photosynthesis may be considered something of a misnomer since, as presently envisaged (29, Figure 2), plants utilizing this pathway rely completely on the Calvin cycle for net fixation of CO_2 (139, 230).

The C_4 pathway (Figure 2), which varies somewhat from plant to plant, basically involves carboxylation of PEP in the cytoplasm of mesophyll cells to form 4C products which move as either malate or aspartate to bundle-sheath cells where decarboxylation occurs, the CO_2 being fixed by the Calvin cycle while the 3C product is returned to the mesophyll for regeneration of the CO_2 acceptor PEP. Figure 2 is similar to Figure 1 in the review by Black (29), except that there are now three recognized decarboxylation enzymes: NADP-linked malic enzyme, PEP carboxykinase (29), and NAD-linked malic enzyme recently found to have high activity in bundle-sheath mitochondria of certain C_4 plants which had annoyingly low levels of the first two enzymes (98). Enzyme distribution studies of several C_4 plants have continued to give results consistent with the scheme in Figure 2 (42, 72, 99, 138, see 29). Nevertheless, not all workers concur with this scheme. A characteristic of C_4 plants is that, although all chloroplasts are capable of forming starch (143), under normal conditions only bundle-sheath chloroplasts do so. Coombs (56) has suggested that the Calvin cycle operates in mesophyll chloroplasts while bundle-sheath chloroplasts play a major role in storing transitory starch. Enzymes of sucrose and starch synthesis have been demonstrated in both mesophyll and bundle-sheath cells in C_4 grasses (38, 70), adding credibility to this more straightforward scheme. However, evidence for the Calvin cycle in mesophyll chloroplasts is not abundant.

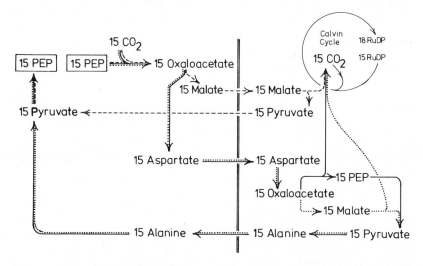

Figure 2 Absence of autocatalysis in the C_4 pathway. None of the three pathways shown permit increase in the number of molecules of CO_2 acceptor (PEP). The vertical line represents the boundary between mesophyll cells (left) and bundle-sheath cells (right). Pathways are distinguished according to the enzyme catalyzing the decarboxylation reaction: _ _ _, NADP-linked malic enzyme; ____, PEP carboxykinase (see 29); . . . . , NAD-linked malic enzyme (98).

Mesophyll cells (199) and chloroplasts (118) have been shown capable of photosynthetically reducing PGA to triose phosphates, but CO_2 fixation was not observed in either case, although it should be remembered that it is difficult to isolate chloroplasts able to fix CO_2 from C_4 grasses, except from very young leaves (175). A basic consideration is whether mesophyll cells contain RuDP carboxylase, and although in most investigations no significant activity was detected (42, 72, 138; see also 29; cf 37, 185), the complex structural (93, 172, 173) and kinetic (49) properties of this enzyme may not be unrelated to the predominance of negative results.

Substantial incorporation of CO_2 into 4C acids through PEP carboxylation occurs also in CAM plants (see 29) and most probably parts of C_3 plants (71). In this review these plants, along with C_4 plants, are considered to possess C_4 metabolism; the C_4 pathway is regarded as a special case of C_4 metabolism involving movement of carbon between mesophyll and bundle-sheath cells. The distinctive arrangement of mesophyll and bundle-sheath cells, termed a Kranz anatomy, is usually associated with C_4 plants (29), although a recent demonstration that most features of the C_4 pathway occur in *Suaeda monoica* which, however, lacks a Kranz anatomy (207), questions the validity of this correlation. Clearly, separation of plants into distinct C_3 and C_4 categories is not a simple task.

Flow of Carbon in C_4 Metabolism

PHOSPHOENOLPYRUVATE CARBOXYLATION   The carboxylation of PEP in both C_4 and CAM plants, catalyzed by PEP carboxylase, is believed to occur in the cytoplasm (88, 118) although there are reports of the enzyme associated with chloroplasts (193, 202, 224). Coombs et al (60) have confirmed that bicarbonate and not CO_2 is the substrate for the enzyme from C_4 plants (61); the K_m for bicarbonate was 2 mM (58). The enzymes from C_3, C_4, and CAM plants have very different K_m values for PEP and Mg^{2+}, and contrasting maximum velocities (221), but the K_m values may have to be reevaluated in light of the elegant analysis by Miziorko et al (168) on the relationship between PEP and Mg^{2+} in the enzyme reaction (the K_m of the spinach enzyme for the substrate MgPEP was only 10 μM) and the study by Mukerji (169) showing that the activity with low Mg^{2+} levels can be higher than would be predicted from earlier data (58, 221). PEP carboxylase from C_4 plants showed allosteric kinetics (58), including regulation by glucose-6-P (58, 91), triose phosphates, and PGA (57); the enzyme from dark-grown plants was less sensitive to glucose-6-P (91). Activity increased with energy charge, consistent with a role in the C_4 pathway (59). In CAM plants malate accumulated during the night is a possible feedback inhibitor of the carboxylase (134). It is interesting that P-glycolate was a potent inhibitor of the enzyme from a C_3 plant (168).

THE TRANSFER OF CARBON   The product of PEP carboxylation is oxaloacetate which is reduced to malate in mesophyll chloroplasts by NADP-linked malate dehydrogenase (101, 200) or converted by a transaminase (99) to aspartate in the cytoplasm; the activities of both these enzymes are increased in illuminated plants. Kennedy & Laetsch (127) have shown that both these compounds can be formed by one plant (in this case *Portulaca oleracea*) making the terms "malate former" and "aspartate former" (see 29) of questionable value. In fact, *Portulaca* also rapidly forms labeled alanine, presumably from pyruvate, during photosynthesis in $^{14}CO_2$, but the origin of the pyruvate is not yet understood (128).

DECARBOXYLATION   4C acids transported to bundle-sheath cells of C_4 plants may be decarboxylated through one of three enzyme systems (Figure 2). Decarboxylation of malate, catalyzed by NADP-linked malic enzyme in chloroplasts, is linked to formation of NADPH which must compensate for reported deficiencies of photosynthetically generated NADPH in these chloroplasts (76, 139, 176). Isolated strands of bundle-sheath cells have been shown capable of decarboxylating malate and fixing CO_2, including that released from the malate, into intermediates of the Calvin cycle (44, 68, 76, 224). The activity of NADP-linked malic enzyme in vivo is remarkably increased by illumination (115). Aspartate transported to bundle-sheath cells is converted in mitochondria to oxaloacetate (99) which may be decarboxylated by ATP-linked PEP carboxykinase (see 29) or first reduced to malate and then decarboxylated by NAD-linked malic enzyme in mitochondria (98). Kagawa & Hatch (119) observed that formation of pyruvate and CO_2 from aspartate occurred at high rates with mitochondria only from C_4 plants with high NAD-linked malic enzyme activity. Apparently it is not a prerequisite for the C_4 pathway that the decarboxylation takes place in bundle-sheath chloroplasts. Furthermore, if CO_2 produced in mitochondria can be used by the Calvin cycle in these cells, then so also should CO_2 from the atmosphere be available to the Calvin cycle since there exist in leaves of C_4 plants free spaces through which CO_2 could diffuse to bundle-sheath cells (143).

Decarboxylation in CAM plants may be catalyzed in the light by either NADP-linked malic enzyme, PEP carboxykinase (67), or NAD-linked malic enzyme (P. Dittrich, personal communication). A postillumination burst of CO_2, thought to be a remnant of this process, was recently reported (64). The affinity of NADP-linked malic enzyme for malate decreases with lower temperatures such as occur at night, thus favoring malate accumulation at this time (33). Garnier-Dardart & Queiroz (84) propose that the allosteric regulatory properties of this enzyme contribute to the circadian pattern of CAM metabolism seen in these plants.

REGENERATION OF PHOSPHOENOLPYRUVATE   The 3C compounds remaining from the decarboxylation of 4C acids in the bundle sheath are believed to follow the pathways shown in Figure 2 (29, 99) and eventually appear in the mesophyll as pyruvate from which PEP is regenerated by pyruvate P_i dikinase (101) in chloroplasts (118). This enzyme, recently purified from maize leaves (213), is light activated in vivo (101). Evidence that PEP regeneration uses photosynthetically generated ATP, the formation of which depends on a Hill oxidant such as oxaloacetate (200) or PGA (199), has recently been obtained with isolated mesophyll cells (111).

The Primary CO_2 Acceptor: Ribulose-1,5-diphosphate or Phosphoenolpyruvate?

Perhaps a misleading feature of C_4 metabolism is the rapid appearance of radioactive label from $^{14}CO_2$ in 4C products derived from PEP carboxylation, creating the illusion that PEP is the primary CO_2 acceptor. This labeling pattern can be expected when PEP carboxylase activities are high, as detected in C_4 and CAM plants (29), the marine alga *Ulva* (121) and even in parts of C_3 plants (71), or when growth conditions favor increases in either the enzyme activity, as seen in CAM plants (192) and halophytes (233), or the level of PEP, as seems likely in algae (69, 92). Even in C_4 plants growth conditions can influence the extent of this phenomenon; Grishina et al (95) found the predominance of label in 4C compounds lasted for over 10 min in maize plants under blue light and a high level of oxygen. In many experiments where 4C compounds were labeled, subsequent appearance of label in intermediates of the Calvin cycle was observed and often attributed to loss, in the form of CO_2, of that carbon originally fixed by PEP carboxylase followed by refixation of this CO_2 by the Calvin cycle while PEP was regenerated from the 3C compound remaining (29). The possibility that the PEP may instead have been generated from PGA supplied from the Calvin cycle received little attention; such a scheme would in effect make PEP carboxylation a secondary one and completely dependent on the Calvin cycle. However, at the grassroots level, supply of PEP from the Calvin cycle is not only possible but essential: comparison of Figures 1 and 2 demonstrates that such a connection must exist for the plant to grow. Indeed, the distribution of label in malate obtained from photosynthesizing maize leaves was compatible with PEP being derived from PGA supplied by the Calvin cycle (142) in a manner reminiscent of that proposed earlier for a CAM plant (32). More recent results with maize leaves (225) argue against PEP originating from the Calvin cycle under the experimental conditions employed but do not prohibit the possibility that PEP may be derived from the Calvin cycle under other conditions. Laber et al (141) observed that RuDP (but not PEP) accumulated in illuminated maize leaves in the absence of CO_2. Uptake of CO_2 subsequently introduced was correlated with a parallel decrease in the level of RuDP and increases in the levels of PGA and PEP even though the appearance of label in 4C acids indicated PEP utilization; clearly additional PEP must have originated from the Calvin cycle. The 4C acids were considered a means of storing CO_2, a conclusion independently reached from other studies with maize leaves (63, 82). The central importance of RuDP carboxylase in maize leaves has been emphasized by experiments showing that the rise in the activity of this enzyme in certain mutants was parallel to the rise in CO_2 fixation (45), and mutants without the enzyme soon ceased to fix CO_2 although ample levels of PEP carboxylase were present (171). The inhibition by oxygen of CO_2 fixation into 4C compounds in maize leaves (211) is also consistent with RuDP carboxylase being essential for the supply of PEP since CO_2 fixation in bundle-sheath cells is more sensitive to oxygen than that in mesophyll cells (43). Finally, the only chloroplasts isolated from a C_4 plant (maize) and capable of CO_2 fixation fixed CO_2 exclusively through RuDP carboxylase (175).

With respect to CAM plants, the proposal of Bradbeer, Ranson & Stiller (32) that PEP (which is carboxylated for the purpose of malate accumulation) is derived from PGA formed from RuDP carboxylation has been challenged in recent years on the basis of labeling studies (51, 133, 214), but it now seems clear that the extent to which this proposal can operate is influenced by the metabolic state of the plant

(177). The fundamental requirement that additional PEP be supplied from the Calvin cycle if the plant is to grow still holds, and it is conceivable that this PEP be supplied directly from PGA (32) or over a longer pathway involving glycolysis from starch (133) synthesized previously from intermediates of the Calvin cycle.

Purpose of the C₄ Pathway

An early proposed advantage of the C_4 pathway was that CO_2 could be concentrated in bundle-sheath cells so that the supposedly low affinity of RuDP carboxylase for CO_2 would be circumvented (97). However, recent measurements (14) indicating a high affinity of maize leaf RuDP carboxylase for CO_2, similar to the affinity of the enzyme from C_3 plants (13, 31), make it doubtful that concentrations of CO_2 greater than that in air are required to support appreciable photosynthesis in C_4 plants (14, 154). Nevertheless, the idea of concentrating CO_2 in the bundle sheath (29, 97) is not without merit since the limitation on photosynthesis by CO_2 supply (167) would be partially alleviated, permitting higher photosynthetic rates. Net photosynthesis could also be increased by provision of a mechanism to prevent escape of photorespired CO_2 to the atmosphere, and it is not inconceivable that in the leaves of C_4 plants a primary function of the C_4 pathway is to recapture CO_2 released during this apparently wasteful process (29, 230). By analogy to CAM plants, ideas that the C_4 pathway is associated with adaption to saline environments (143) and more efficient use of water (29) also have been advanced. Irregularities in CO_2 supply, as might occur during intermittent water stress, could be buffered by reservoirs of CO_2 concentrated in a latent form as 4C acids (63, 82, 141), in principle like malate accumulation by CAM plants but on a smaller scale. It is interesting that the life forms and habitats of C_4 plants have been shown recently to be varied and widespread (182); certainly the C_4 pathway can now be viewed as a versatile mechanism for ecological adaption permitting plants to continue fixing CO_2 even under somewhat adverse conditions. A realistic evaluation of the C_4 pathway is that of Gifford (89), who has concluded from a wide range of data that, at the level of crop growth rate, there is no apparent difference between the best examples of C_3 and C_4 plants growing in their own preferred natural environments; C_4 species have higher yields only because they choose a climate which allows them to grow for a longer time.

PHOTORESPIRATION

Synthesis of Glycolate

In addition to dark respiration, photosynthetic tissues also exhibit a light-dependent release of CO_2 believed to be closely associated with the metabolism of glycolate, a 2C acid. Zelitch (239) has shown that inhibition of glycolate synthesis in tobacco leaf discs is accompanied by a decrease in the amount of photorespired CO_2 and an increase in net CO_2 fixation. The mechanism of glycolate biosynthesis and the nature of the reactions by which it is metabolized with the associated release of CO_2 continue as subjects of contention; several proposals are included in Figure 3. Glycolate synthesis may involve oxidation of a glycolaldehyde-transketolase com-

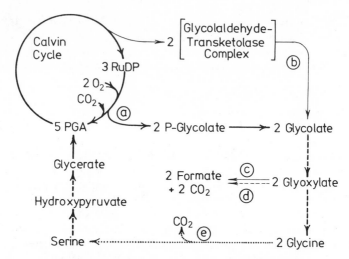

Figure 3 Proposed pathways of carbon movement during photorespiration in leaves. Two possible sources of glycolate and three possible sources of photorespiratory CO_2 are shown. Glycolate may be formed from (*a*) the oxygenase activity of RuDP carboxylase (30) or (*b*) oxidation of a glycolaldehyde/transketolase complex (see 86). Photorespiratory CO_2 may originate from decarboxylation of glyoxylate in (*c*) chloroplasts (237) or (*d*) peroxisomes (96) or (*e*) conversion of two glycines to one serine in mitochondria (see 222). The stoichiometry of carbon flow is shown for the hypothetical case where all carbon fixed is subsequently photorespired through the pathway (thicker lines) involving (*a*) RuDP oxidation and (*e*) decarboxylation during glycine-serine interconversion. Location of reactions: ____, chloroplast; _ _ _, peroxisome; . . . ., mitochondrion.

plex coupled to photosynthetic electron transport in the light (205) which would be consistent with reports that blue light inhibited glycolate synthesis in algae (165) and inactivated transketolase (52). However, other mechanisms for glycolate formation must exist since Chollet (44) has shown that glycolate is synthesized in isolated maize bundle-sheath strands in darkness. A currently popular alternative is based on the discovery by Bowes, Ogren & Hageman (30) that P-glycolate is produced in an oxygen-dependent reaction catalyzed by RuDP carboxylase. The appearance of [18]O in the carboxyl group of glycolate synthesized in plants exposed to [18]O_2 is further evidence for this reaction (158). The formation of glycolate from P-glycolate is feasible since chloroplasts contain a specific P-glycolate phosphatase (see 222) with an alkaline pH optimum (130) similar to the pH in the chloroplast stroma (108). The oxygen-dependent reaction (oxygenase activity) has since been observed with RuDP carboxylase from *Chromatium* (220) and *Rhodospirillum* (162, 196) which produce glycolate during photosynthesis in air (9, 53), *Chlorella* (156), soybean (144), and spinach (15). Reported pH optima for the oxygenase activity in chloroplast extracts are rather high (12, 15), and indeed in a recent study (136) the proportion of carbon fixed into glycolate by chloroplasts during photosynthesis was greater in more alkaline environments. Two reports (12, 144) have shown that the oxygenase activity is inhibited competitively by CO_2, the carboxylase activity is inhibited competitively by oxygen, and elevated temperature activates the oxygenase activity more than the carboxylase activity; these observations offer a possible explanation for the increased photorespiration seen with higher oxygen or decreased CO_2 levels or higher temperatures. The oxygenase activity, like the carboxylase activity, is influenced by FDP and 6-P-gluconate, suggesting regulation of glycolate formation by levels of metabolic intermediates (197). It is not unlikely that inactivation of RuDP carboxylase by the substrate RuDP may at times limit the oxygenase activity of the enzyme (49).

Other investigations give reason to doubt that oxidation of RuDP is the sole source of glycolate: isolated chloroplasts continued to produce glycolate even with saturating levels of CO_2 (194) and in leaves the levels of glycine and serine, two proposed photorespiratory intermediates presumably derived from glycolate, were unaffected by changes in temperature (201) or the concentration of CO_2 (209). It is possible that there are two or more pathways for glycolate biosynthesis. Eickenbusch, Scheibe & Beck (73) have shown that glycolate can be synthesized in a reconstituted chloroplast system from either fructose-6-P or RuDP, but only the synthesis from RuDP responded to changes in oxygen levels. The synthesis from fructose-6-P may have involved oxidation of a transketolase addition complex as proposed earlier (205). In other experiments, Bassham & Kirk (21) were unable to account for all glycolate in photosynthesizing *Chlorella* as having originated from P-glycolate. Other results consistent with more than one source of glycolate in *Chlorella* (77, 78) and higher plants (65, 238) are available.

The relationship between the oxygen inhibition of photosynthesis (Warburg effect) and glycolate biosynthesis has been studied with isolated chloroplasts, but since low concentrations of ribose-5-P or FDP which relieved the Warburg effect did not influence glycolate production it was concluded that glycolate formation was not a causal factor of the Warburg effect (194). This conclusion is strengthened by the observation that the temperature optima of photorespiration and the Warburg effect are different (62).

Metabolism of Glycolate

In the leaves of higher plants glycolate is oxidized to glyoxylate in specialized microbodies called peroxisomes; the formation of peroxisomes follows illumination and is believed to be independent of other types of microbodies (117). The oxidation of glycolate, catalyzed by the flavoprotein glycolate oxidase (81), is linked to H_2O_2 formation from oxygen. Glycolate oxidase, recently purified from pea leaves (131), also catalyzes the oxidation of glyoxylate to oxalate; considerable amounts of oxalate have been found in some leaves but the metabolism of this acid is far from understood. In algae glycolate oxidation is somewhat different from that in higher plants: some algae contain a glycolate dehydrogenase (81, 165) while there is evidence that in other algae glycolate is oxidized in mitochondria (55, 180, 210) in a reaction linked to oxygen uptake and possibly generation of ATP (55, 180).

Of the several pathways proposed for the further metabolism of glyoxylate (Figure 3), that involving conversion to glycine which is transferred to mitochondria where two molecules of this amino acid are converted to one molecule of serine and one of CO_2 (222) has received much attention. Bird et al (26) have correlated increased ATP synthesis with the latter reaction and made the interesting proposal that this could represent a light-dependent synthesis of ATP in mitochondria. The serine formed is returned to peroxisomes and converted to glycerate. Serine-glyoxylate aminotransferase (39, 222) and hydroxypyruvate reductase necessary for this conversion are contained in peroxisomes (222); serine was found to accumulate in leaves illuminated in CO_2-free air, possibly because the supply of α-keto acids for amino transfer was depleted in the absence of photosynthesis (228). Glycerate formed from serine is presumably transferred to chloroplasts and phosphorylated to PGA (222), but Heber et al (104) have questioned whether chloroplasts contain sufficient glycerate kinase to accommodate observed rates of photorespiration.

The involvement of glycine and serine in the glycolate pathway, as proposed by Tolbert (222), appears compatible with photorespiration since high levels of CO_2 which decrease carbon loss through photorespiration also reduce the proportion of carbon flowing through glycine and serine (151, 209). However, it cannot be assumed that a major portion of glycine and serine metabolized in leaves during photosynthesis passes through the glycolate pathway. Recent extensive investigations of the specific radioactivities of glycine, serine, alanine, and PGA in sunflower leaves after feeding [14]CO_2 at various oxygen and CO_2 levels (160, 161) indicated that intermediates of the glycolate pathway were not derived solely from the Calvin cycle, and the conclusion that at least some serine was produced from a precursor other than glycine (160) is reminiscent of the difficulties encountered by Kent et al (129) in explaining the biosynthesis of serine in photosynthesizing leaves. These results, and the apparent low activity of glycerate kinase in chloroplasts (104), raise doubts about the extent of the glycolate pathway and its contribution to photorespiration. Alternative proposals for the metabolism of glycolate in higher plants (Figure 3) are consequently worthy of attention. Zelitch (237) has proposed that glyoxylate, formed from glycolate oxidation in peroxisomes, could be returned to chloroplasts and then photooxidized (with H_2O_2 as the probable oxidant) to yield formate and CO_2. Halliwell & Butt (96) have suggested that a similar peroxidation of glyoxylate is feasible in peroxisomes; this location is attractive in that a minimum transfer of metabolites between cellular organelles would be involved.

The sequence of reactions constituting the glycolate pathway (222) does not seem to be universal: Lord & Merrett (157) demonstrated that in *Chlorella* glycerate is not returned to chloroplasts but rather metabolized to pyruvate, while Codd & Stewart (54) have proposed that the blue-green alga *Anabaena* produces glycerate from glyoxylate by a quite different pathway involving a condensative decarboxylation of two molecules of glyoxylate to tartronic semialdehyde which is then reduced.

Extent and Role of Photorespiration

A realistic appraisal of proposed photorespiratory pathways must account for the observation that 50% and more of the CO_2 fixed during photosynthesis subsequently can be evolved as photorespiratory CO_2 (236). If photorespiration involves oxidation of RuDP and decarboxylation of glycine, then in the hypothetical case where the number of RuDP molecules carboxylated is only half the number oxidized (as shown in Figure 3) all fixed CO_2 would be subsequently photorespired and the plant would cease to grow. However, the amount of RuDP carboxylated in air is believed to be at least four to five times that oxidized (15, 144) in which case less than 20%, rather than 50%, of the fixed CO_2 could be photorespired. In short, available experimental evidence does not explain the higher levels of photorespiration measured; alternative pathways of glycolate synthesis and metabolism (Figure 3) may hold the key to this problem.

Why the apparently wasteful process of photorespiration exists in plants at all continues as an enigma. The possibilities that it contributes to amino acid biosynthesis, disposal of excess reducing power and removal of H_2O_2 have already been considered (222); to these can be added the opportunity for light-dependent ATP synthesis in mitochondria (26). The fact that plants free of photorespiration have not been found suggests the process is essential; it is still puzzling why some plants have more than others (236).

FURTHER UTILIZATION OF FIXED CARBON

Starch Metabolism

Over 100 years ago Sachs (198) confirmed that starch observed in chloroplasts resulted directly from carbon fixation in the presence of light and chlorophyll. However, metabolic pathways for the synthesis and utilization of this starch are only now being identified. Starch is synthesized from Calvin cycle intermediates as shown in Figure 4; regulatory aspects of this synthesis have been reviewed previously (188). Preiss and co-workers (188) have evidence that an enzyme with a major role in regulating starch synthesis is ADP-glucose pyrophosphorylase; this enzyme is activated by PGA and fructose-6-P and inhibited by inorganic phosphate. Starch synthesis in chloroplasts could be favored by the pH rise in the stroma following illumination (108) since PGA activation of the pyrophosphorylase is greater at higher pH values (85), and the activity of chloroplast FDPase, which would influence the proportion of carbon flowing through fructose-6-P to starch, is enhanced by high pH (16). The pyrophosphorylase reaction is probably pulled towards ADP-glucose formation since the other product, pyrophosphate, would be efficiently hydrolyzed by chloroplast pyrophosphatase; this enzyme has a higher substrate affinity compared to the cytoplasmic pyrophosphatase (132). Other experiments have shown that in maize bundle sheath, starch phosphorylase may also play an active role in starch synthesis (66).

The subsequent metabolism of chloroplast starch has been unclear because conversion to triose phosphates for easy export from the chloroplast (107, Figure 4) seemed blocked by the absence of phosphofructokinase from chloroplasts (116, 147). However, a reasonable level of phosphofructokinase activity in chloroplasts has now been detected by Kelly & Latzko (125), and first indications of the regulatory properties of this enzyme, including strong inhibition by PEP, suggest ADP-glucose

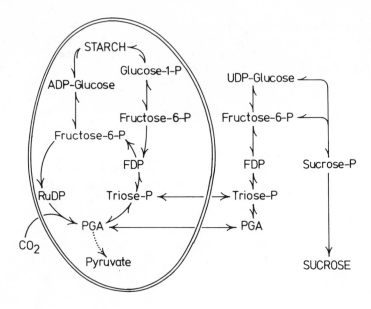

Figure 4   Synthesis and breakdown of starch in chloroplasts and synthesis of sucrose in the cytoplasm. Pyruvate formation (dotted line) represents the possibility of glycolysis in chloroplasts.

pyrophosphorylase and phosphofructokinase may complement each other in regulating starch metabolism (126). ATP required by phosphofructokinase could be obtained from the PGA kinase reaction if half of the triose phosphates formed from FDP were converted to PGA; this would provide a purpose for the well-documented ability of chloroplast G3P dehydrogenase to operate in the glycolytic direction with either NAD or NADP (see 188) and perhaps explain why chloroplasts contain NAD (105). Oxidation of triose phosphates to PGA in chloroplasts in darkness has been detected (148). The mechanism of NADH reoxidation would be open to speculation; a shuttle involving dicarboxylic acids (103) or intervention of ferredoxin which can be reoxidized by oxygen are two possibilities.

Chloroplast Glycolysis?

The degradation of starch to pyruvate by the glycolytic sequence in chloroplasts (Figure 4) has been considered unlikely, but of five glycolytic enzymes earlier reported absent from chloroplasts (147) there is now evidence that four of these are present: phosphofructokinase (125), phosphoglyceromutase and enolase (88, 202, 234), and pyruvate kinase (25, 202, 234). The likelihood of glycolysis in chloroplasts is thus less remote than previously believed (147) and, although such glycolysis could be valuable for the supply of biosynthetic intermediates (234), the intriguing question of how much ATP chloroplasts are able to produce in the dark is worthy of consideration.

Sucrose Synthesis

Sucrose is synthesized in the cytoplasm from triose phosphates exported from chloroplasts (Figure 4, see 103). UDP-glucose pyrophosphorylase, sucrose-P synthetase (27), and an FDPase with high affinity for FDP (149) are predominantly or exclusively located in the cytoplasm. The location of sucrose synthesis has been uncertain since sucrose has on occasions been synthesized by preparations of isolated chloroplasts (75) and enzymes of sucrose synthesis have been reported in isolated chloroplasts (28). The latter report has been attributed to an inherent error in the use of the technique of nonaqueous isolation of chloroplasts (25), but an explanation for the former observation is not clear; it is probable that the recently reported cytoplasm-like layer surrounding certain chloroplasts which could fix CO_2 into sucrose (145) is important in this respect.

3C compounds exported from chloroplasts may also be metabolized via glycolysis to pyruvate and then carbon skeletons for biosynthesis; studies with *Chlorella* (120) indicated that NH_4^+ facilitated this process by stimulating pyruvate kinase and inhibiting the hydrolysis of FDP and synthesis of sucrose-P. In bean leaves a high level of oxygen favored movement of carbon toward 4C compounds, but the mechanism of this effect was not clear (227).

Movement of Metabolites Across the Chloroplast Envelope

Good progress in understanding the mechanism and regulation of the flow of carbon during photosynthesis has followed the definitive experiments of Heldt & Rapley (107) showing that triose phosphates, PGA, and inorganic phosphate, but not hexose phosphates, are rapidly and specifically transported across the inner membrane of chloroplasts. A specific phosphate translocator is proposed whereby the transport of one component is counterbalanced by the movement of a second in the opposite direction (103, 107). This could explain the observed inhibition of chloroplast CO_2 fixation by higher concentrations of PGA (2, 17, 183) should too much of this substance move into chloroplasts in exchange for triose phosphates which would therefore become unavailable for regeneration of the CO_2 acceptor RuDP. Inhibition by relatively high levels of phosphate also appears related to excessive exchange for chloroplast triose phosphates (17). However, a certain level of phosphate is beneficial since this anion is probably the one normally exchanged for triose phosphates leaving the chloroplast during photosynthesis (103), and there is evidence that low levels of phosphate retard export of triose phosphates so that fixed carbon is instead directed into chloroplast starch (206). The availability of phosphate outside the chloroplast may be influenced by the activity of pyrophosphatase (153), which in turn requires Mg^{2+}. It appears important that all Mg^{2+} outside the chloroplast be sequestered since free Mg^{2+} ions strongly inhibit CO_2 fixation by isolated chloroplasts (11). Whatever the mechanism of this inhibition, it must occur outside the chloroplast since the permeability of the chloroplast envelope to Mg^{2+} is low (90). Stimulation of CO_2 fixation following chelation of Mg^{2+} by pyrophosphate has been observed (80, 153).

Although the chloroplast envelope is relatively impermeable to adenine and pyridine nucleotides (see 103), photosynthetically generated ATP and reducing power can be indirectly transferred to the cytoplasm via triose phosphate/PGA (212) and malate/oxaloacetate (103) shuttles. These shuttles have been concisely reviewed by Heber (103). By combining the two shuttles Heldt et al (106) have obtained CO_2 fixation by chloroplasts in the dark providing the pH of the stroma was maintained at about 8.0. Apparently an alkaline pH is more essential than light for CO_2 fixation and it is not unlikely that the response of chloroplast FDPase to pH (16) is critical in this respect. Reducing power transferred from chloroplasts can appear in the cytoplasm as either NADH (103, 212) or NADPH (124). In the latter case a triose phosphate/PGA shuttle utilizing nonreversible G3P dehydrogenase is involved; this enzyme is located in the cytoplasm and is specific for NADP (123). The shuttle using nonreversible G3P dehydrogenase can stimulate CO_2 fixation (17), and oxygen evolution (17, 124) by isolated chloroplasts and a "transport stimulation" mechanism whereby the enzyme acts through the shuttle to pull PGA toward triose phosphate formation in chloroplasts has been proposed by Bamberger et al (17). The elucidation of shuttle systems (103, 124, 212) implies a relatively free availability of photosynthetic energy in the cytoplasm. This must increase the flexibility of carbon flow in the cell, but at the same time necessitates additional regulatory mechanisms which still await discovery.

CONCLUSION

Opportunities for new insights into the regulation of carbon flow during photosynthesis are perhaps more numerous now than for a long time. Rapid advances can be expected from investigations utilizing the differential permeability of the chloroplast to metabolites, an approach which is only beginning to be used. Chloroplast starch, somewhat neglected in the past, will certainly receive new attention as a consequence. At the enzyme level, more detailed studies of kinetic and allosteric properties, particularly of RuDP carboxylase, are imminent, but the arrangement of the Calvin cycle enzymes in the chloroplast stroma can still only be contemplated with some degree of fascination. With respect to photorespiration, a clear understanding of the biochemistry of this phenomenon is at present burdened by contradictions; hopefully future research will clarify how and why fixed CO_2 is again released as CO_2. The C_4 plants may prove a useful tool here: now that initial concepts of the C_4 pathway have been superseded by an understanding that it is an auxiliary to the Calvin cycle, more attention to its contribution towards the adaptive and survival potentialities of plants can be expected.

ACKNOWLEDGMENTS

We wish to acknowledge the kind and dedicated assistance of Mrs. Rose Marie McHugh. Research in the authors' laboratories was supported by National Science Foundation Grant BMS 71-00978(0262), United States Energy and Research Administration Grant ET (11-1) 3231 Mod 1-2 (5848), and by generous grants from the Deutsche Forschungsgemeinschaft.

Literature Cited

1. Abdelal, A. T. H., Schlegel, H. G. 1974. *Biochem. J.* 139:481–89
2. Andersen, W. R., Gibbs, M. 1975. *Biochem. Biophys. Res. Commun.* 62: 953–56
3. Anderson, L. E. 1971. *Biochim. Biophys. Acta* 235:237–44
4. Ibid, 245–49
5. Ibid 1973. 321:484–88
6. Anderson, L. E. 1974. *Biochem. Biophys. Res. Commun.* 59:907–13
7. Anderson, L. E. 1974. *Proc. 3rd Int. Congr. Photosynth.,* ed. M. Avron, 1393-1405. Amsterdam: Elsevier
8. Anderson, L. E., Heinrikson, R. L., Noyes, C. 1975. *Arch. Biochem. Biophys.* 169:262–68
9. Asami, S., Akazawa, T. 1974. *Plant Cell Physiol.* 15:571–76
10. Avron, M., Gibbs, M. 1974. *Plant Physiol.* 53:136–39
11. Ibid, 140–43
12. Badger, M. R., Andrews, T. J. 1974. *Biochem. Biophys. Res. Commun.* 60: 204–10
13. Bahr, J. T., Jensen, R. G. 1974. *Plant Physiol.* 53:39–44
14. Bahr, J. T., Jensen, R. G. 1974. *Biochem. Biophys. Res. Commun.* 57: 1180–85
15. Bahr, J. T., Jensen, R. G. 1974. *Arch. Biochem. Biophys.* 164:408–13
16. Baier, D., Latzko, E. 1975. *Biochim. Biophys. Acta* 396:141–47
17. Bamberger, E. S., Ehrlich, B. A., Gibbs, M. 1975. *Plant Physiol.* 55:1023–30
18. Barber, J., Mills, J., Nicolson, J. 1974. *FEBS Lett.* 49:106–10
19. Bassham, J. A. 1964. *Ann. Rev. Plant Physiol.* 15:101–20
20. Bassham, J. A., Calvin, M. 1957. *The Path of Carbon in Photosynthesis.* Englewood Cliffs, NJ: Prentice Hall. 104 pp.
21. Bassham, J. A., Kirk, M. 1973. *Plant Physiol.* 52:407–11
22. Bassham, J. A., Levine, G., Forger, J. 1974. *Plant Sci. Lett.* 2:15–21
23. Bassham, J. A., Sharp, P., Morris, I. 1968. *Biochim. Biophys. Acta.* 153:898–900
24. Beuscher, N., Gottschalk, G. 1972. *Z. Naturforsch.* 27b:967–73
25. Bird, I. F., Cornelius, M. J., Dyer, T. A., Keys, A. J. 1973. *J. Exp. Bot.* 24:211–15
26. Bird, I. F., Cornelius, M. J., Keys, A. J., Whittingham, C. P. 1972. *Phytochemistry* 11:1587–94
27. Ibid 1974. 13:59–64
28. Bird, I. F., Porter, H. K., Stocking, C. R. 1965. *Biochim. Biophys. Acta* 100:366–75
29. Black, C. C. 1973. *Ann. Rev. Plant Physiol.* 24:253–86
30. Bowes, G., Ogren, W. L., Hageman, R. H. 1971. *Biochem. Biophys. Res. Commun.* 45:716–22
31. Bowes, G., Ogren, W. L., Hageman, R. H. 1975. *Plant Physiol.* 56:630–33
32. Bradbeer, J. W., Ranson, S. L., Stiller, M. 1958. *Plant Physiol.* 33:66–70
33. Brandon, P. C., van Boekel-Mol, T. N. 1973. *Eur. J. Biochem.* 35:62–69
34. Buchanan, B. B., Schürmann, P. 1973. *J. Biol. Chem.* 248:4956–64
35. Buchanan, B. B., Schürmann, P., Kalberer, P. P. 1971. *J. Biol. Chem.* 246: 5952–59
36. Buchanan, B. B., Schürmann, P., Shanmugam, K. T. 1972. *Biochim. Biophys. Acta* 283:136–45
37. Bucke, C., Long, S. P. 1971. *Planta* 99:199–210
38. Bucke, C., Oliver, I. R. 1975. *Planta* 122:45–52
39. Carpe, A. I., Smith, I. K. 1974. *Biochim. Biophys. Acta* 370:96–101
40. Cerff, R. 1974. *Z. Pflanzenphysiol.* 73:109–18
41. Cerff, R., Quail, P. H. 1974. *Plant Physiol.* 54:100–4
42. Chen, T. M., Dittrich, P., Campbell, W. H., Black, C. C. 1974. *Arch. Biochem. Biophys.* 163:246–62
43. Chollet, R. 1973. *Biochem. Biophys. Res. Commun.* 55:850–56
44. Chollet, R. 1974. *Arch. Biochem. Biophys.* 163:521–29
45. Chollet, R., Ogren, W. L. 1972. *Z. Pflanzenphysiol.* 68:45–54
46. Chu, D. K., Bassham, J. A. 1972. *Plant Physiol.* 50:224–27
47. Ibid 1973. 52:373–79
48. Ibid 1974. 54:556–59
49. Ibid 1975. 55:720–26
50. Cockburn, W. 1974. *J. Exp. Bot.* 25: 111–20
51. Cockburn, W., McAulay, A. 1975. *Plant Physiol.* 55:87–89
52. Codd, G. A. 1972. *Z. Naturforsch.* 27b:701–4
53. Codd, G. A., Smith, B. M. 1974. *FEBS Lett.* 48:105–8
54. Codd, G. A., Stewart, W. D. P. 1973. *Arch. Mikrobiol.* 94:11–28
55. Collins, N., Merrett, M. J. 1975. *Biochem. J.* 148:321–28

56. Coombs, J. 1971. *Proc. R. Soc. B* 179:221–35
57. Coombs, J., Baldry, C. W. 1975. *Planta* 124:153–58
58. Coombs, J., Baldry, C. W., Bucke, C. 1973. *Planta* 110:95–107
59. Coombs, J., Maw, S. L., Baldry, C. W. 1974. *Planta* 117:279–92
60. Coombs, J., Maw, S. L., Baldry, C. W. 1975. *Plant Sci. Lett.* 4:97–102
61. Cooper, T. G., Wood, H. G. 1971. *J. Biol. Chem.* 246:5488–90
62. Cornic, G. 1974. *Physiol. Vég.* 12:83–94
63. Créach, E., Michel, J. P., Thibault, P. 1974. *Planta* 118:91–100
64. Crews, C. E., Vines, H. M., Black, C. C. 1975. *Plant Physiol.* 55:652–57
65. D'Aoust, A. L., Canvin, D. T. 1974. *Physiol. Vég.* 12:545–60
66. de Fekete, M. A. R., Vieweg, G. H. 1974. *Planta* 117:83–91
67. Dittrich, P., Campbell, W. H., Black, C. C. 1973. *Plant Physiol.* 52:357–61
68. Dittrich, P., Salin, M. L., Black, C. C. 1973. *Biochem. Biophys. Res. Commun.* 55:104–10
69. Döhler, G. 1974. *Ber. Dtsch. Bot. Ges.* 87:229–38
70. Downton, W. J. S., Hawker, J. S. 1973. *Phytochemistry* 12:1551–56
71. Duffus, C. M., Rosie, R. 1973. *Planta* 114:219–26
72. Edwards, G. E., Gutierrez, M. 1972. *Plant Physiol.* 50:728–32
73. Eickenbusch, J. D., Scheibe, R., Beck, E. 1975. *Z. Pflanzenphysiol.* 75:375–80
74. El-Badry, A. M. 1974. *Biochim. Biophys. Acta* 333:366–77
75. Everson, R. G., Cockburn, W. , Gibbs, M. 1967. *Plant Physiol.* 42:840–44
76. Farineau, J. 1975. *Physiol. Plant.* 33:300–9
77. Fock, H., Bate, G. C., Egle, K. 1974. *Ber Dtsch. Bot. Ges.* 87:239–47
78. Fock, H., Bate, G. C., Egle, K. 1974. *Planta* 121:9–16
79. Forrester, M. L., Krotkov, G., Nelson, C. D. 1966. *Plant Physiol.* 41:422–27
80. Forti, G., Rosa, L. 1974. *Plant Sci. Lett.* 2:95–100
81. Frederick, S. E., Gruber, P. J., Tolbert, N. E. 1973. *Plant Physiol.* 52:318–23
82. Galmiche, J. M. 1973. *Plant Physiol.* 51:512–19
83. Garnier, R. V., Latzko, E. 1972. *Proc. 2nd Int. Congr. Photosynth. Res.,* ed. G. Forti, M. Avron, A. Melandri, 1839–45. The Hague: W. Junk
84. Garnier-Dardart, J., Queiroz, O. 1974. *Phytochemistry* 13:1695–1702

85. Ghosh, H. P., Preiss, J. 1966. *J. Biol. Chem.* 241:4491–4504
86. Gibbs, M., Ed. 1971. In *Structure and Function of Chloroplasts,* 169–214. Berlin-Heidelberg-New York: Springer-Verlag
87. Gibbs, M., Kandler, O. 1957. *Proc. Natl. Acad. Sci. USA* 43:446–51
88. Gibbs, M., Latzko, E., O'Neal, D., Hew, C.-S. 1970. *Biochem. Biophys. Res. Commun.* 40:1356–61
89. Gifford, R. M. 1974. *Aust. J. Plant Physiol.* 1:107–17
90. Gimmler, H., Schäfer, G., Heber, U. 1974. See Ref. 7, 1381–92
91. Goatly, M. B., Smith, H. 1974. *Planta* 117:67–73
92. Graham, D., Whittingham, C. P. 1968. *Z. Pflanzenphysiol.* 58:418–27
93. Gray, J. C., Kekwick, R. G. O. 1974. *Eur. J. Biochem.* 44:481–89
94. Ibid, 491–500
95. Grishina, G. S., Maleszewski, S., Frankiewicz, A., Voskresenskaya, N. P., Poskuta, J. 1974. *Z. Pflanzenphysiol.* 73:189–97
96. Halliwell, B., Butt, V. S. 1974. *Biochem. J.* 138:217–24
97. Hatch, M. D. 1971. In *Photosynthesis and Photorespiration,* ed. M. D. Hatch, C. B. Osmond, R. O. Slatyer, 139–52. New York: Wiley-Interscience
98. Hatch, M. D., Kagawa, T. 1974. *Arch. Biochem. Biophys.* 160:346–49
99. Hatch, M. D., Mau, S.-L. 1973. *Arch. Biochem. Biophys.* 156:195–206
100. Hatch, M. D., Slack, C. R. 1966. *Biochem. J.* 101:103–11
101. Hatch, M. D., Slack, C. R. 1970. *Ann. Rev. Plant Physiol.* 21:141–62
102. Heber, U. 1973. *Biochim. Biophys. Acta* 305:140–52
103. Heber, U. 1974. *Ann. Rev. Plant Physiol.* 25:393–421
104. Heber, U., Kirk, M. R., Gimmler, H., Schäfer, G. 1974. *Planta* 120:31–46
105. Heber, U. W., Santarius, K. A. 1965. *Biochim. Biophys. Acta* 109:390–408
106. Heldt, H. W., Fliege, R., Lehner, K., Milovancev, M., Werdan, K. 1974. See Ref. 7, 1369–79
107. Heldt, H. W., Rapley, L. 1970. *FEBS Lett.* 10:143–48
108. Heldt, H. W., Werdan, K., Milovancev, M., Geller, G. 1973. *Biochim. Biophys. Acta* 314:224–41
109. Hind, G., Nakatani, H. Y., Izawa, S. 1974. *Proc. Natl. Acad. Sci. USA* 71:1484–88
110. Höpner, T., Ruschig, U., Müller, U.

1973. *Hoppe-Seyler's Z. Physiol. Chem.* 354:216

111. Huber, S. C., Edwards, G. E. 1975. *Plant Physiol.* 55:835–44

112. Ihlenfeldt, M. J. A., Gibson, J. 1975. *Arch. Microbiol.* 102:13–21

113. Jacobson, B. S., Fong, F., Heath, R. L. 1975. *Plant Physiol.* 55:468–74

114. Jensen, R. G., Bassham, J. A. 1968. *Biochim. Biophys. Acta* 153:227–34

115. Johnson, H. S., Hatch, M. D. 1970. *Biochem. J.* 119:273–80

116. Kachru, R. B., Anderson, L. E. 1975. *Plant Physiol.* 55:199–202

117. Kagawa, T., Beevers, H. 1975. *Plant Physiol.* 55:258–64

118. Kagawa, T., Hatch, M. D. 1974. *Aust. J. Plant Physiol.* 1:51–64

119. Kagawa, T., Hatch, M. D. 1975. *Arch. Biochem. Biophys.* 167:687–96

120. Kanazawa, T., Kirk, M. R., Bassham, J. A. 1970. *Biochim. Biophys. Acta* 205:401–8

121. Karekar, M. D., Joshi, G. V. 1973. *Bot. Mar.* 16:216–20

122. Karpilov, Yu. S. 1960. *Kazakhstan Agric. Inst.* 4:21

123. Kelly, G. J., Gibbs, M. 1973. *Plant Physiol.* 52:111–18

124. Ibid, 674–76

125. Kelly, G. J., Latzko, E. 1975. *Nature* 256:429–30

126. Kelly, G. J., Turner, J. F. 1970. *Biochim. Biophys. Acta* 208:360–67

127. Kennedy, R. A., Laetsch, W. M. 1973. *Planta* 115:113–24

128. Kennedy, R. A., Laetsch, W. M. 1974. *Plant Physiol.* 54:608–11

129. Kent, S. S., Pinkerton, F. D., Strobel, G. A. 1974. *Plant Physiol.* 53:491–95

130. Kerr, M. W., Gear, C. F. 1974. *Biochem. Soc. Trans.* 2:338–40

131. Kerr, M. W., Groves, D. 1975. *Phytochemistry* 14:359–62

132. Klemme, B., Jacobi, G. 1974. *Planta* 120:147–53

133. Kluge, M., Kriebitzsch, C., von Willert, D. J. 1974. *Z. Pflanzenphysiol.* 72:460–65

134. Kluge, M., Osmond, C. B. 1972. *Z. Pflanzenphysiol.* 66:97–105

135. Kortschak, H. P., Hartt, C. E., Burr, G. O. 1965. *Plant Physiol.* 40:209–13

136. Krapf, G., Jacobi, G. 1975. *Plant Sci. Lett.* 5:67–71

137. Krause, G. H. 1974. *Biochim. Biophys. Acta* 333:301–13

138. Ku, S. B., Gutierrez, M., Edwards, G. E. 1974. *Planta* 119:267–78

139. Ku, S. B., Gutierrez, M., Kanai, R., Edwards, G. E. 1974. *Z. Pflanzenphysiol.* 72:320–37

140. Kwok, S. Y., Wildman, S. G. 1974. *Arch. Biochem. Biophys.* 161:354–59

141. Laber, L. J., Latzko, E., Gibbs, M. 1974. *J. Biol. Chem.* 249:3436–41

142. Laber, L. J., Latzko, E., Levi, C., Gibbs, M. 1972. See Ref. 83, 1737–44

143. Laetsch, W. M. 1974. *Ann. Rev. Plant Physiol.* 25:27–52

144. Laing, W. A., Ogren, W. L., Hageman, R. H. 1974. *Plant Physiol.* 54:678–85

145. Larsson, C., Albertsson, P.-A. 1974. *Biochim. Biophys. Acta* 357:412–19

146. Latzko, E., Garnier, R. V., Gibbs, M. 1970. *Biochem. Biophys. Res. Commun.* 39:1140–44

147. Latzko, E., Gibbs, M. 1968. *Z. Pflanzenphysiol.* 59:184–94

148. Latzko, E., Gibbs, M. 1969. *Plant Physiol.* 44:396–402

149. Latzko, E., Zimmermann, G., Feller, U. 1974. *Hoppe-Seyler's Z. Physiol. Chem.* 355:321–26

150. Lavergne, D., Bismuth, E., Champigny, M. L. 1974. *Plant Sci. Lett.* 3:391–97

151. Lee, R. B., Whittingham, C. P. 1974. *J. Exp. Bot.* 25:277–87

152. Lilley, R. McC., Holborow, K., Walker, D. A. 1974. *New Phytol.* 73:657–62

153. Lilley, R. McC., Schwenn, J. D., Walker, D. A. 1973. *Biochim. Biophys. Acta* 325:596–604

154. Lilley, R. McC., Walker, D. A. 1975. *Plant Physiol.* 55:1087–92

155. Lilley, R. McC., Walker, D. A., Holborow, K. 1974. *Biochim. Biophys. Acta* 368:269–78

156. Lord, J. M., Brown, R. H. 1975. *Plant Physiol.* 55:360–64

157. Lord, J. M., Merrett, M. J. 1973. *New Phytol.* 72:249–52

158. Lorimer, G. H., Andrews, T. J., Tolbert, N. E. 1973. *Biochemistry* 12:18–23

159. Lyttleton, J. W. 1975. *Plant Sci. Lett.* 4:385–89

160. Mahon, J. D., Fock, H., Canvin, D. T. 1974. *Planta* 120:125–34

161. Ibid, 245–54

162. McFadden, B. A. 1974. *Biochem. Biophys. Res. Commun.* 60:312–17

163. McFadden, B. A., Lord, J. M., Rowe, A., Dilks, S. 1975. *Eur. J. Biochem.* 54:195–206

164. McGowan, R. E., Gibbs, M. 1974. *Plant Physiol.* 54:312–19

165. Merrett, M. J., Lord, J. M. 1973. *New Phytol.* 72:751–67

166. Miginiac-Maslow, M., Champigny, M.-L. 1974. *Plant Physiol.* 53:856–62

167. Milthorpe, F. L., Moorby, J. 1974. *An Introduction to Crop Physiology.* London: Cambridge Univ. 202 pp.
168. Miziorko, H. M., Nowak, T., Mildvan, A. S. 1974. *Arch. Biochem. Biophys.* 163:378–89
169. Mukerji, S. K. 1974. *Plant Sci. Lett.* 2:243–48
170. Müller, B., Ziegler, I., Ziegler, H. 1969. *Eur. J. Biochem.* 9:101–6
171. Nagy, A. H., Gyurján, I., Székely, S., Doman, N. G. 1973. *Photosynthetica* 7:87–92
172. Nishimura, M., Akazawa, T. 1974. *Biochemistry* 13:2277–81
173. Nishimura, M., Takabe, T., Sugiyama, T., Akazawa. T. 1973. *J. Biochem.* 74:945–54
174. O'Brien, R. W. 1975. *Arch. Microbiol.* 103:71–76
175. O'Neal, D., Hew, C. S., Latzko, E., Gibbs, M. 1972. *Plant Physiol.* 49:607–14
176. Osmond, C. B. 1974. *Aust. J. Plant Physiol.* 1:41–50
177. Osmond, C. B., Allaway, W. G. 1974. *Aust. J. Plant Physiol.* 1:503–11
178. Pacold, I., Anderson, L. E. 1973. *Biochem. Biophys. Res. Commun.* 51:139–43
179. Pacold, I., Anderson, L. E. 1975. *Plant Physiol.* 55:168–71
180. Paul, J. S., Sullivan, C. W., Volcani, B. E. 1975. *Arch. Biochem. Biophys.* 169:152–59
181. Pawlizki, K., Latzko, E. 1974. *FEBS Lett.* 42:285–88
182. Pearcy, R. W., Troughton, J. 1975. *Plant Physiol.* 55:1054–56
183. Peavey, D. G., Gibbs, M. 1975. *Plant Physiol.* 55:799–802
184. Pocker, Y., Ng, J. S. Y. 1974. *Biochemistry* 13:5116–20
185. Poincelot, R. P. 1972. *Plant Physiol.* 50:336–40
186. Pon, N. G., Rabin, B. R., Calvin, M. 1963. *Biochem. Z.* 338:7–19
187. Preiss, J., Biggs, M. L., Greenberg, E. 1967. *J. Biol. Chem.* 242:2292–94
188. Preiss, J., Kosuge, T. 1970. *Ann. Rev. Plant Physiol.* 21:433–66
189. Pupillo, P. 1972. *Phytochemistry* 11:153–61
190. Pupillo, P., Piccari, G. G. 1973. *Arch. Biochem. Biophys.* 154:324–31
191. Pupillo, P., Piccari, G. G. 1975. *Eur. J. Biochem.* 51:475–82
192. Queiroz, O., Morel, C. 1974. *Plant Physiol.* 53:596–602
193. Rathnam, C. K. M., Das, V. S. R. 1975. *Z. Pflanzenphysiol.* 75:360–64
194. Robinson, J. M., Gibbs, M. 1974. *Plant Physiol.* 53:790–97
195. Robinson, J. M., Latzko, E., Gibbs, M. 1975. *Plant Physiol.* 55:12–14
196. Ryan, F. J., Jolly, S. O., Tolbert, N. E. 1974. *Biochem. Biophys. Res. Commun.* 59:1233–41
197. Ryan, F. J., Tolbert, N. E. 1975. *J. Biol. Chem.* 250:4234–38
198. Sachs, J. 1862. *Bot. Z.* 20:365–73
199. Salin, M. L., Black, C. C. 1974. *Plant Sci. Lett.* 2:303–8
200. Salin, M. L., Campbell, W. H., Black, C. C. 1973. *Proc. Natl. Acad. Sci. USA* 70:3730–34
201. Sawada, S., Miyachi, S. 1974. *Plant Cell Physiol.* 15:225–38
202. Scheibe, R., Beck, E. 1975. *Planta* 125:63–67
203. Schürmann, P., Buchanan, B. B. 1975. *Biochim. Biophys. Acta* 376:189–92
204. Segal, H. L., Boyer, P. D. 1953. *J. Biol. Chem.* 204:265–81
205. Shain, Y., Gibbs, M. 1971. *Plant Physiol.* 48:325–30
206. Sheu-Hwa, C.-S., Lewis, D. H., Walker, D. A. 1975. *New Phytol.* 74:383–92
207. Shomer-Ilan, A., Beer, S., Waisel, Y. 1975. *Plant Physiol.* 56:676–79
208. Sirevåg, R. 1974. *Arch. Microbiol.* 98:3–18
209. Snyder, F. W., Tolbert, N. E. 1974. *Plant Physiol.* 53:514–15
210. Stabenau, H. 1974. *Plant Physiol.* 54:921–24
211. Stamieszkin, I., Maleszewski, S., Poskuta, J. 1972. *Z. Pflanzenphysiol.* 67:180–82
212. Stocking, C. R., Larson, S. 1969. *Biochem. Biophys. Res. Commun.* 37:278–82
213. Sugiyama, T. 1973. *Biochemistry* 12:2862–68
214. Sutton, B. G., Osmond, C. B. 1972. *Plant Physiol.* 50:360–65
215. Tabita, F. R., McFadden, B. A. 1972. *Biochem. Biophys. Res. Commun.* 48:1153–59
216. Tabita, F. R., McFadden, B. A. 1974. *J. Biol. Chem.* 249:3453–58
217. Ibid, 3459–64
218. Tabita, F. R., McFadden, B. A., Pfennig, N. 1974. *Biochim. Biophys. Acta* 341:187–94
219. Tabita, F. R., Stevens, S. E., Quijano, R. 1974. *Biochem. Biophys. Res. Commun.* 61:45–52
220. Takabe, T., Akazawa, T. 1973. *Biochem. Biophys. Res. Commun.* 53:1173–79

221. Ting, I. P., Osmond, C. B. 1973. *Plant Physiol.* 51:448–53
222. Tolbert, N. E. 1971. *Ann. Rev. Plant Physiol.* 22:45–74
223. Turner, J. F., Black, C. C., Gibbs, M. 1962. *J. Biol. Chem.* 237:577–79
224. Usuda, H., Matsushima, H., Miyachi, S. 1974. *Plant Cell Physiol.* 15:517–26
225. Usuda, H., Samejima, M., Miyachi, S. 1973. *Plant Cell Physiol.* 14:423–26
226. Vacchi, C., Piccari, G. G., Pupillo, P. 1973. *Z. Pflanzenphysiol.* 69:351–58
227. Viil, J., Pärnik, T. 1974. *Photosynthetica* 8:208–15
228. Waidyanatha, U. P. deS., Keys, A. J., Whittingham, C. P. 1975. *J. Exp. Bot.* 26:15–26
229. Walker, D. A. 1973. *New Phytol.* 72:209–35
230. Walker, D. A. 1974. In *Plant Carbohydrate Biochemistry. Proceedings of the Tenth Symposium of the Phytochemical Society, Edinburgh, 1973,* ed. J. B. Prid-

ham, 7–26. London-New York: Academic
231. Walker, D. A., Lilley, R. McC. 1974. *Plant Physiol.* 54:950–52
232. Werdan, K., Heldt, H. W. 1972. *Biochim. Biophys. Acta* 283:430–41
233. Winter, K. 1974. *Planta* 121:147–53
234. Yamada, M., Nakamura, Y. 1975. *Plant Cell Physiol.* 16:151–62
235. Yonuschot, G. R., Ortwerth, B. J., Koeppe, O. J. 1970. *J. Biol. Chem.* 245:4193–98
236. Zelitch, I. 1971. *Photosynthesis, Photorespiration, and Plant Productivity.* New York: Academic. 347 pp.
237. Zelitch, I. 1972. *Arch. Biochem. Biophys.* 150:698–707
238. Zelitch, I. 1973. *Plant Physiol.* 51:299–305
239. Zelitch, I. 1974. *Arch. Biochem. Biophys.* 163:367–77
240. Ziegler, H., Ziegler, I. 1965. *Planta* 65:369–80

Ann. Rev. Plant Physiol. 1976. 27:207–28

THE DEVELOPMENT
OF FLESHY FRUITS[1]

❖7608

B. G. Coombe

Department of Plant Physiology, Waite Agricultural Research Institute,
The University of Adelaide, Glen Osmond, South Australia 5064

CONTENTS

[1]Growth substances are abbreviated as follows: ABA (abscisic acid); ethephon (2 chloro-ethyl phosphonic acid); IAA (indole-3-acetic acid); 2,4,5-T (2,4,5 trichlorophenoxyacetic acid).

INTRODUCTION

The numbers of research papers on basic questions concerning the growth and development of fruits are meager in comparison with those on other aspects of plant growth. The field is slow-moving and diffuse, and it is little wonder that during the 27 years of this journal the subject has been reviewed only twice, the first in 1953 by J. P. Nitsch (83) and the second, concerning the special aspects of growth regulators, by Crane in 1964 (26). Physiologists are naturally reluctant to work on a subject for which the material is the result of a long and complex growth process and often is extremely variable. On the other hand, manipulation of harvested fruit is comparatively simple, and considerably more research has been done on postharvest physiology; in fact, the subject has been reviewed four times in this journal alone (47, 90, 100, 118).

A milestone in the literature on fruit growth is the two-volume work on the biochemistry of fruits, edited by Hulme and published in 1970 and 1971 (53). Especially relevant are the two chapters on fruit physiology written by Bollard (8) and Nitsch (85). This publication removes any compulsion I might have had to cover the field broadly. Rather, I will avoid any emphasis of seed growth, abscission, and growth regulators, and instead will concentrate on flesh development in temperate and tropical fruits, leading to some comments about control mechanisms.

FRUIT FLESH

Definitions

A fruit is the product of determinate growth from an angiospermous flower or inflorescence. Brooks defined fruits as "matured carpels with or without accessory structures and/or seeds" (12). Nitsch recognized that the botanist's definition did not always meet the layman's concept of a fruit and emphasized that the unifying factor was physiological and, he suggested, was associated with the changes occurring in the ovules. He therefore defined fruits as "the tissues which support the ovules and whose development is dependent on the events occurring in these ovules" (82). This definition has many defects (118a). The word "fruit" derives from the Latin "fructus"—to enjoy, produce. The Oxford English Dictionary defines fruit as "the edible product of a plant or tree, consisting of the seed and its envelope, especially the latter when juicy and pulpy." If one interprets "envelope" in the broad sense, and does not confine it to the pericarp, the OED definition suits this review. The majority usage refers therefore to fleshy, edible fruits. With dry fruits such as nuts, grains, follicles, and achenes, it is the seed which is the important product. The major fruits of the world [grape, banana, tomato, citrus, cucurbits, pomes, stone fruits, mango (34)] are fleshy and justify an emphasis on the study of the physiology of fruit flesh.

Origins of Fruit Flesh

The astounding diversity of tissues which can become fleshy has been referred to by other authors (8, 83, 86). As Figure 1 illustrates, practically all parts of the total

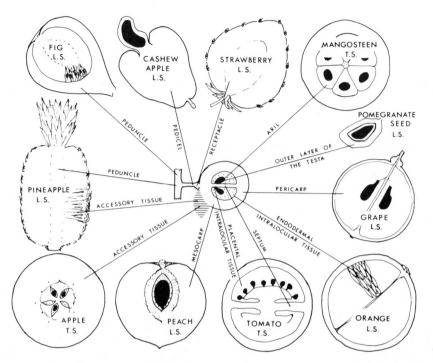

Figure 1   Outlines of sections of the fruits of 11 species showing the diversity of tissues which can develop into fruit flesh. [Some drawings copied from Ulrich (117).]

inflorescence structure are, in some species or other, developed into fruit flesh. It is not possible to ascribe any differences in developmental behavior or in the mature flesh to differences in morphological origin. The common factor is that these tissues accumulate water and many organic compounds, thus leading to their juiciness and attractiveness; they are bulky, parenchymatous tissues, frequently spherical or cylindrical, and are not subject to constraints by hard layers.

Fruits tend to fill their locules unless the cells lining the locules are so differentiated as to inhibit division or expansion. Intralocular tissue (pulpa) forms by intense meristematic activity after anthesis at one or more of the locular surfaces, e.g. placenta (tomato), septum (banana, grape), and endodermis (banana, orange). The tissue then fills the cavity by cell expansion and behaves in concert with the neighboring flesh (unless it is the only tissue to become fleshy, e.g. citrus).

"Functions" of Fruit Flesh

"But this (a fruit's) beauty serves merely as a guide to birds and beasts in order that the fruit may be devoured and the manured seeds disseminated" (28). Darwin is here explaining a selective advantage which is conferred on a species by having its seed covering conspicuous and attractive to animals, hence aiding dispersal (101, 118a).

On this interpretation, the prevalence of striking colors (reds, purples, and yellows) in fruit skin and of sweet and juicy flesh is not surprising. The fleshy tissue may also protect the seed and influence its environment (gas, water, chemicals), but it does not contribute to the nourishment of the germinating embryo as do the seed tissues. Fruits formed an important source of food for man when he was a hunter and gatherer, and it is understandable that fruit plants were domesticated and improved. The application of vegetative propagation aided this process.

DEVELOPMENTAL PATTERNS OF FLESHY FRUITS

Methods and Interpretations

The economic importance of fruits and the distinctiveness of their developmental processes have led to many growth studies. Unfortunately the majority of these studies are inadequate for an analysis of the components of growth. Size measurements alone are of limited use, and measures of concentrations of different compounds tell nothing about accumulation per fruit unless parallel data on fruit size (preferably fresh and dry weights) are provided. If these measures are obtained on the fleshy part and if the numbers of flesh cells are known, then one can interpret the data in terms of the rate and duration of the accumulation of both water and components of dry matter per cell.

The usual technique for gathering such data is to take samples of a number of fruits at intervals during growth. Sample size influences the accuracy of assessment of the population but does not permit assessment of the degree of asynchrony between individuals in their development. There are three methods which reduce or avoid this problem: (a) to select a population whose development is synchronous (a method that requires an objective, nondestructive measure of uniformity), (b) to seek indicators of development and to analyze data by reference to defined events (co-variance analysis is useful); (c) to use nondestructive methods of measurement of individual fruits in situ. With regard to c, simultaneous and nondestructive measurements can be made of size, gas exchange, skin color, deformability, and other characters. Volume can be estimated from linear dimensions or measured directly by fluid displacement; the use of liquids such as water presents difficulties, but the technique using an inert gas like helium, as has been used for the measurement of the volume of whole animals (109), warrants investigation. With knowledge of development gained by these types of measurements, the usefulness of sample averages can be greatly improved.

Aside from the problems of measurement, the problems of interpretation require comment. Some of them can be illustrated by reference to the double sigmoid curve of, say, volume against time so frequently shown by drupes and berries (Figure 2). It has been customary to designate the first and second rapid growth phases as Stages I and III and the intervening slow growth phase as Stage II (8, 20). Unfortunately the boundaries between these stages are determined arbitrarily; there is no indication of their precise position on the cumulative curve nor on the double-humped rate curve. A method for determining the position of bends in curves has

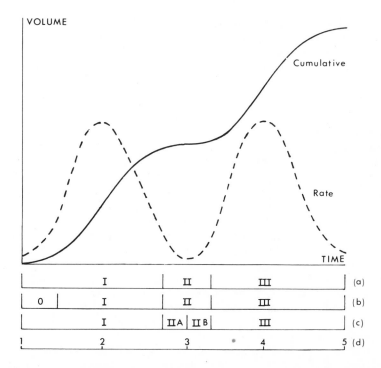

Figure 2   A double sigmoid growth curve of volume versus time expressed on cumulative and rate bases. Many methods have been used to describe this type of curve: (*a*) the classical method begun in 1914 by Connors (8, 20); (*b*) the designation of a preliminary phase (87); (*c*) the division of the lag phase into two parts (44); (*d*) the allocation of phases according to peaks and troughs in the growth rate (17).

been devised [the maximum likelihood method of Quandt (95)], but it has been used rarely, if ever, in the literature on fruit.

It is in some ways unfortunate that the three-stage system has been adopted because, apart from its arbitrary nature, it has logical difficulties. Some recognition of these has been made by designating additional stages such as Stage O and Stages IIA and IIB (see Figure 2). Basically, the two consecutive sigmoid curves each have an inception, a period of acceleration, a point of most rapid growth rate, a period of deceleration, and an end. These properties can be determined from rate curves (Figure 2) or from local maxima and local minima in the derivatives of the sigmoid curves. The slow growth phase (Stage II) consists of the final deceleration of the first cycle and the beginning acceleration of the second cycle with the inflexion marking its inception. Two methods could be used to quantify its length: if the cumulative curves are smooth, one could calculate the interval between local maxima in the second derivative, but if the curves have distinct bends, their timing can be determined using Quandt's method referred to above.

Another difficulty in interpretation is the actual relationship used. Quite different interpretations can emerge if data are calculated on different bases—per unit dry weight, fresh weight, protein, volume of water, per cell, etc—or if rates are made relative to a previous reference, e.g. relative growth rates (7) or the data transformed in other ways.

Developmental Patterns

The review by Bollard (8) provides a good account of the nature of fruit growth curves. Some of those having a single sigmoid curve are: apple, pear, date, pineapple, banana, avocado, strawberry, orange, tomato, and melon. Those having a double sigmoid are: all stone fruits, fig, blackcurrant, raspberry, blueberry, grape, and olive. The growth curve of *Actinidia chinensis* fruit is described as triple sigmoid (92a). For double sigmoid fruits interesting data have been compiled on the duration and rate of growth for the three stages in fruit of different species (8). Within a species, the fruit of cultivars which ripen early have a short slow-growth phase. From a comparison of three grape cultivars, all growth phases occupied 28 to 38 days except Stage II of an early-ripening cultivar which was only 5 days in length, and Stage III of a late-ripening cultivar which occupied 51 days (79). From comparisons of growth curves of the berries of cv. Muscat of Alexandria, the first growth cycle was found to be reasonably constant but the slow-growth phase varied from 8 to 48 days, depending on the environment and whether the inflorescence was primary or secondary (the author, unpublished).

Some interpretations of growth curves can be queried. The growth data (length and diameter) for the litchi are said to portray a single sigmoid curve (60), but if volumes are calculated and seed volume is subtracted, a double sigmoid curve is found. The curve of the classical single sigmoid fruit, the apple, shows a distinct aberration at an early stage according to one set of measurements (4). There is no reason why similar discrepancies should not occur commonly. For instance, by daily measurement of grape berries in situ, we have demonstrated that the second rapid growth phase begins with a significant, transient (one day's) spurt of growth (Coombe and Bishop, unpublished), thus confirming an earlier suggestion (23, 102). When measurements are precise, growth curves of organs are frequently erratic and are difficult to describe in simple mathematical forms.

Components of Growth

The interval from anthesis to ripeness of fruit varies for different species, from 3 weeks (strawberry) to 60 weeks (Valencia orange), but in many fruits it occupies about 15 weeks (8). During this interval fruits increase in volume and weight several thousand times. One of the larger increases is shown by avocado (300,000 times) and one of the smaller is that of dwarf squash (X 40) or Corinth grape (X 300) (23, 64, 107). The largest of fruits, pumpkin and watermelon, are known to attain volumes in excess of 30 liters per fruit, but do not have an unduly large expansion factor (in fact, no greater than most grapes: X 4000) because of their relatively large ovaries at anthesis (107).

The weight of the flesh of a ripe fruit is determined by cell number, cell volume, and cell density. The number and volume of cells at ripeness are influenced by the number and volume at anthesis and the rate and duration of cell division and cell expansion thereafter.

CELL NUMBER   During anthesis itself there is little cell division (83), but thereafter, when the fruit becomes an active importer of reserves or photosynthate, many of its tissues become meristematic and growth commences, that is, the fruit has set; those fruits in which these events are not initiated generally abscise (23, 45). Nitsch's reviews provide good accounts of the important events taking place in the flower and of the stimuli for development leading to the set fruit (82–86).

Active division in the flesh is usually limited to an initial period of a few weeks after anthesis (8). However, there are some notable exceptions: no divisions occur in the pericarp of Corinth grape after anthesis (23) nor in *Rubus* and certain *Ribes* (12); on the other hand, divisions continue in avocado throughout the life of the fruit (103). The most comprehensive analysis of the relative roles of cell division and cell enlargement in the growth and development of fruits is that of cucurbits by Sinnott (106, 107). He compared several races of *Cucurbita pepo* and showed that, compared with small-fruited gourds, the large-fruited pumpkins had a longer period of cell division, especially in the outer tissues of the fruit; then, after division had ceased, their cells expanded more.

There are two million cells in the flesh of an apple at anthesis and forty million at harvest (89). To achieve these numbers, 21 doublings are required before anthesis but only 4.5 doublings after. Similarly, in the grape there are 0.2 million cells in the ovary at anthesis and 0.6 million 40 days later (48). The number of doublings to achieve this are 17 before and 1.5 after anthesis (23). There would appear to be ample opportunity for variations in cell number to arise before anthesis. Indeed, Harris et al (48) showed that glasshouse-grown grape berries, cv. Sultana, had half as many cells as field-grown berries both at anthesis and 40 days later after division had stopped; this large difference was therefore due entirely to pre-anthesis divisions. Unfortunately there is little work of this type, and one suspects that differences in early cell division may commonly contribute much to fruit size variation. From correlations between fruit size, cell number, and cell volume of ripe apricot fruits from within individual trees, it was concluded that cell number was the most important factor contributing to variation in fruit size. (When the comparison was extended to between trees, then both components, cell number and cell size, contributed to variation.) Fruits from early flowers were large at ripeness due mainly to a larger number of cells. It was considered that these differences were due to variation in the number of cells at anthesis (56).

Not only the timing of divisions in different parts of the flesh, but also the direction of divisions (periclinal, anticlinal, random), and the interaction of both with the timing of cell expansion influence the final cell shape, cell size, and appearance and texture of the flesh. There are no periclinal divisions in the single layer of cells which develops into the flesh surrounding the pomegranate seed (128); its cell walls are thin and the tissue is transparent. Anticlinal divisions predominate in elderberry, periclinal in grape (12). Division appears to occur in many directions in intralocular tissue (78, 110). It should be emphasized that the cells of fruit tissues other than the flesh have their own distinctive timing and direction of division.

CELL VOLUME   While it is agreed that cell number is an important factor in fruit development and contributes to variation in fruit size, there is little doubt that for individual fruits of most species the increase in cell volume makes by far the greatest contribution to the total expansion of the fruit. The proportions of the total increase in size of a grape berry after anthesis that can be attributed to the three components of growth are as follows: cell number, 2-fold; cell density, 4-fold; cell volume, 300-fold or more. Some of the largest cells to be found in plants occur in the flesh of ripe fruits (8). Cell lengths between 150 and 700 μm are common and in some cases exceed 1 mm; those of the flesh surrounding pomegranate seeds often exceed 2 mm in length (128). Volumes range up to 10^8 μm^3 and figures of 10^6 to 10^7 μm^3 are usual. The fact that the cells of these tissues have a volume of only about 10^4 μm^3 at anthesis illustrates the huge amount of expansion achieved.

In mature fruits there is frequently a gradient in radial diameter of cells, decreasing from the center towards the outside, e.g. in *Cucurbita pepo* (106). The same gradient has been found in the mesocarp of apricot but there was no such trend in cell volume. It was argued that, since there was no gradient in cell volume, the gradient was one of cell shape and that this would be expected; at the completion of division cells are approximately isodiametric, and if they all expand to an equivalent volume within the confines of the skin, they would have to assume the shapes found (56).

The amount of expansion of cells in the flesh is influenced by cell wall behavior (19) (plasticizing, deposition of wall material, including the degree of secondary wall development), turgor (water flux and differences in osmotic pressure inside and outside of cells), and constraints imposed upon the flesh by the extensibility of the skin or other surrounding layers. Each of these components may be influenced separately by factors such as growth regulators and the environment.

Polysomaty (somatic polyploidy) has been found to occur in fruit flesh cells (10, 11, 108) and may well be common. Bradley has drawn attention to the direct relationship between nuclear volume and cell volume (10). The degree of ploidy is considerable and increases with age of flesh. Bradley & Crane were able to show in apricot that during Stage II flesh cells were on average 10-ploid, while one week before ripeness the average was 14-ploid; up to 64-ploid was measured (11). Treatment of apricots with the auxin 2,4,5-T at the end of Stage I increased ploidy during Stage II by 30 percent and at ripeness by 90 percent; fruit cells and fruits were commensurately larger (11). These authors suggested that the rate of increase in ploidy preceded the rate of increase in cell size and that hormone gradients may be involved in its control.

CELL DENSITY   Fruit flesh accumulates large amounts of various organic compounds and their concentrations increase with time. It is clear, however, that the increases in concentration cannot account for the large amount of dry matter accumulated per fruit; this is due more to the large increases which occur in cell volume (water) thereby providing the matrix in which solutes can accumulate. This thesis is discussed later.

Percentage dry weight, which parallels cell density, changes during the ontogeny of a fruit. In the pericarp of grape it is high at anthesis due to a high concentration of tartrate (62) and possibly also because the cells are highly protoplasmic. The percentage declines as the grapes develop, reaching a minimum at about the time of fastest growth in the first cycle. Thereafter the values increase, first due to an accumulation of malate and tartrate, then of glucose and fructose (62, 63). Many fruits display a similar trend, but Golden Queen peach is more complex because the bicyclic curves for fresh weight and dry weight are out of phase and water input precedes dry matter input in each growth cycle (17).

It has been claimed that on a per fruit basis the increase in dry weight with time shows a single sigmoid curve even in fruits which have double sigmoid volume curves (8), but this is disputed. The curves of dry weight per fruit for grape (62, 63) and peach (17) are distinctly bicyclic though the dimensions of the second cycle are much greater than those of the first.

In summary, cell division before anthesis and cell expansion after anthesis would appear to be the major determinants of the increase in fresh weight of fleshy fruits. Additional but smaller contributions result from cell division after anthesis and an increase in the concentration of solutes. The increase in dry weight per fruit is determined by the same factors.

Fruit Ripening

Apart from work on the effects of growth regulators, ripening is the most intensively studied aspect of fruit physiology. This has been due to the need to improve post harvest handling of fruit and a desire to gain an understanding of the mechanisms and control of respiration, for which fruits form an interesting experimental subject because of the phenomenon of the respiratory climacteric (1, 31, 92, 100). The work has only recently tended towards the aim of gaining an understanding of the developmental physiology of fruits.

Ripeness is the stage when the fruit is best for eating, and ripening is the complex of events culminating in ripeness. In the majority of fleshy fruits ripening includes softening, coloring, and sweetening, usually with an associated decline in acidity and astringency and an increase in aroma compounds. There are often other events which should be included such as an increase in the rate of respiration and ethylene production, loss of chlorophyll, and a continued expansion of cells. Terminology is a problem because of differences between species in the number and timing of these events. Though most would agree that this part of fruit development could be classed as senescence (100), some prefer to confine the use of this word to the over-ripeness stage (43). The word "maturation" is frequently applied to the events culminating in the mature (i.e. ripe) fruit. The difficulty here is that one can apply "maturation" to the latter parts of most growth cycles, including that of the fruit immediately preceding the ripening phase, whereas the word ripening is distinctive for fruits.

Rhodes has suggested that the definition of the word "climacteric" be widened to include the inception of all ripening changes (98). This is in keeping with Kidd and West's original usage to describe this critical phase in the ontogeny of a fruit. In this sense the suggestion has merit. Unfortunately the concept of "nonclimacteric" has developed, denoting fruits which do not display such features as the sharp rise in respiration rate. Rhodes argues that when so-called nonclimacteric fruits are examined more carefully they may be found to possess the characteristics of climacteric fruits, though on different time scales. It is possible that this opinion may be wrong and hence I prefer to use the expressions: "beginning of ripening," "ripening phase," and "ripeness" or "ripe."

The ripening phase of development does not start until the fruit has developed considerably from the tissues present at anthesis. It is difficult to stimulate fruits to develop ripening patterns before a certain state of readiness; some parts of the ripening process have been stimulated early, e.g. by ethylene or ethephon treatment, but the resulting product is not palatable (68). Ripening would seem to be a genetically programmed phase of development involving an array of enzyme activity different from that of the preceding phase. Its triggering is discussed later.

The ripening phase is said to be distinct in fruits which have a climacteric rise in respiration, e.g. apples, bananas, pears, melons, and avocados, and indistinct in nonclimacteric fruits such as citrus, grape, strawberry, and pineapple (74). The inception of ripening in the grape berry is, however, quite a distinct event; it is called veraison and marks the beginning of sugar accumulation, loss of acid, softening, skin coloring, and renewed cell expansion (23). It differs from the ripening of apples or peaches in commencing earlier in the fruit's development.

The timing of the processes leading to ripeness in the peach have been reexamined recently and with some interesting results (17, 59). During the period when dry matter accumulation is small, ethylene production by the fruit is low though the mesocarp tissue is responsive to exogenous ethylene. Then several processes commence together: the mesocarp cells begin to accumulate dry matter more rapidly, ethylene production increases, and the flesh starts to develop yellow color commencing in the tissue adjacent to the endocarp. The increased rate of water accumulation (cell expansion), which is usually regarded as coincident with dry matter increase, commences some weeks earlier in Golden Queen peach and is apparently under separate control.

It would be instructive to explore further the within-tissue origins of ripening because it should aid in the unraveling of mechanisms. It appears that, in contrast to the peach, the grape may ripen from the outside inwards, in that accumulatory processes are more intense in the skin than the flesh at the beginning of ripening (23). The ripening of dates, as indicated by sucrose levels, proceeds more rapidly at the distal end of the fruit (99). However, despite these differences in time and place of inception, most cells of the flesh undergo the same processes in an integrated manner, while cells of contiguous tissues, such as the pedicel, do not.

COMPOSITION OF FRUIT FLESH

The distinctive features of fruit flesh are that it expands and becomes juicy, sweet, and colored. Water contributes by far the greatest weight to the bulk of the flesh, but a large number of other compounds also accumulate, many of which are water soluble (53). The list includes sugars (especially glucose, fructose, sucrose), acids (malate, tartrate, oxalate, citrate, succinate), protons and other ions (especially K^+, Cl^-, $SO_4^=$, phosphate, Ca^{2+}, Mg^{2+}), alcohols (including inositol), esters, flavonoids and glycosides (including many pigments), phenolics, amino acids, amides, proteins, vitamins, alkaloids, terpenes, lipids, and many others. In certain cells are large bodies consisting of resins, tannins, or crystals (114). Carbohydrate polymers, e.g. starch, predominate in some fruits but are often hydrolyzed by the time the fruit is ripe.

The magnitude of the concentrations is illustrated by the following averages of the 11 most common compounds in grape juice, expressed on a molar basis: glucose 0.61 M, fructose 0.55 M, potassium 0.05 M, tartrate 0.03 M, malate 0.02 M, Mg^{2+} 0.007 M, phosphate 0.004 M, Ca^{2+}, inositol, proline, and arginine 0.003 M, with a total molarity of 1.3 (127). There is little doubt that water and sugars are the dominant compounds in most fruits. This fact is illustrated in Figure 3 showing the water content and sugar concentration, on a fresh weight basis, of the mature edible flesh of 55 different fruit species. The diagonal represents pure sugar solutions scaled on a percent water basis. The vertical distance from this line to any particular

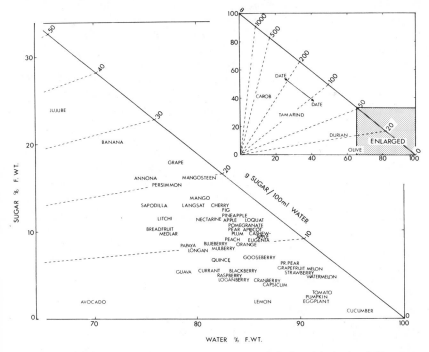

Figure 3   The sugar and water contents, expressed on a fresh weight basis, of the mature edible part of 55 fruit species. The range of these values is appreciable, but the value depicted is judged to be a reasonable average (from 3, 5, 29, 73, 105, 113, 124, 128).

fruit indicates its proportion of nonsugar solids. It can be seen that water and sugar predominate except in the so-called vegetable-fruits, and in accumulators of lipid (avocado, olive), acid (lemon) and starch (durian).

The major fruits of commerce (e.g. grape, banana, orange, apple) have from 9 to 20 percent sugar. Grapes can attain much higher concentrations. I have measured levels of more than 25 percent on a fresh weight basis (80% of dry weight) in the small beries of cv. Corinth, representing a hexose molarity of 1.6. The question arises whether these high sugar concentrations are attained by accumulation of the solute or by loss of the solvent, water. The data of Rygg for dates show that the individual fruits do indeed lose water (99). Nevertheless the fruits are at the same time accumulating sucrose on a per fruit basis and thus both accumulation and dehydration contribute to the final concentration. It is difficult to apportion the relative contribution made by these two processes, but before the final phase of "tree ripening," concentrations of 37 percent sugar are found (equivalent to 0.9 M sucrose and 0.4 M hexose); dehydration probably plays a large part in the final ripening, leading to concentrations of over 60 percent (2M). The high concentrations of solutes in ripe carob flesh (sugar 43 percent fr wt) and tamarind pulp (sugar 33 percent, tartrate 17 percent fr wt) are probably contributed to by dehydration as well as accumulation (29, 119). In general, when fruits are overripe and cells of the flesh are losing turgidity, it is commonly held that increases in concentration are solely due to dehydration. However, I have found that the weight of sugar per fruit, i.e. per cell, continues to increase in a grape berry during at least the first week of this phase.

Despite the above-mentioned exceptions, it seems certain that in most fruits the concentrations of solutes are increasing while the flesh cells are expanding. This means that both water and solutes are accumulating at the same time but the rate of solute accumulation is greater. The larger the volume of a fruit, the larger is its dry weight.

Accumulation of large molecular weight compounds such as starch and storage protein is not a prominent feature of the flesh of many fruit species. This contrasts with the situation in seeds. From an evolutionary viewpoint this probably reflects their relative role: the seed in nourishing the seedling and the flesh in aiding seed dispersal. From a broad morphogenetic viewpoint the difference probably reflects their relative morphology, the seed being soon constrained by rigid tissues, or otherwise inhibited, while the fruit flesh is often external and relatively uninhibited. In those fruits wherein the dry matter accumulated has little osmotic effect, e.g. oil droplets in olive and avocado, the mature flesh cells are small (61, 103).

The notion that physical restriction influences the development of these organs is in some respects analogous to the thesis of Williams that constraints within the shoot apex influence the growth rate and form of leaves (125).

ACCUMULATION OF WATER AND SOLUTES

Water and solutes accumulate mainly in the vacuoles of flesh cells. Though they accumulate together, there is little experimental work on the connection, if any, between the processes of cell expansion and solute accumulation. In 1960 (21) I postulated that the expansion of pericarp cells of grapes during the second growth cycle was due to an osmotic attraction of water following the accumulation of sugar in their vacuoles. There are two findings which negate this hypothesis. First, the rapid increase in growth rate at the beginning of this cycle is not matched by a similar increase in sugar accumulation (23). In this the grape resembles the peach (17). Secondly, when grape berries were fitted with plastic enclosures to prevent their expansion, they failed to accumulate sugar; upon removal of the enclosures both sugar concentration and fruit volume increased (23). This result suggests the reverse hypothesis, that solute accumulation depends on expansion. However, it is not essential that the two events be causally related; they simply may occur in these tissues at about the same time.

Supply of Solutes; Pathways

The main supply of the organic compounds which are stored in the flesh is undoubtedly from recent photosynthesis. It is possible that in large trees reserves could contribute. Reid & Bieleski (97) suggested this was likely with apricots because sorbitol, the chief carbohydrate translocated in phloem, was only metabolized with difficulty by ripening apricot flesh, and that the sucrose which accumulated in the fruit probably originated from reserves in the tree. This would seem unlikely to be the sole source when one calculates the relative quantities: according to their data apricot fruits accumulated 1 g sucrose per fruit during the 2 days before ripeness (97), and for a well-cropped tree this would represent an input into fruit of more than one kg sucrose per day. The reserves of an apricot tree are not described, but by analogy with the peach tree (16) they are such as to be unlikely to meet this sort of demand for more than 2 or 3 days. To extend this analogy, the rates of photosynthesis in peach leaves increase to high levels at the time when accumulation in the fruit is greatest (15). This is not to say that reserves cannot and do not contribute; grapevines which were defoliated before flowering succeeded in maturing a small crop (126).

During and shortly after anthesis the ovary has a poor ability to attract nutrients, that is, it is a weak sink (45). Because of this, the supply of nutrients to the ovary at the time of initial setting appears to depend on the overall status of nutrients in the plant. This phenomenon is illustrated by the setting of grape (22, 23) and of parthenocarpic apples (42). Once the fruit has commenced growth it develops an ability to attract nutrients, and different limitations to accumulation then operate (23, 45). The mobilizing ability of hormones synthesized by the seed and fruit has been referred to (27, 85).

Phloem is the most likely transport path into the fruit, and cell walls the path to flesh vacuoles. The possibility of large concentration gradients of sugar has been regarded as a problem for which mechanisms must account. But recent work suggesting that sugars may occur in the cell wall solution of storage tissue (40, 49, 65) could mean that sugar concentrations along the path from leaves to fruit vacuoles show smaller fluctuations than was thought. It has also been suggested that sugars move from the chloroplast to the phloem in the leaf veinlets via cell walls (37), though the symplastic route has some support (14).

Conceptually, only two barriers need be pictured in the pathway of sugars from leaves to fruit flesh: the first at the phloem in the leaves (or other source), and the second at the membranes surrounding the vacuoles of the flesh cells. Thus a normal pathway might be: photosynthesis in chloroplasts, diffusion of sugars to the phloem in the leaf, active "loading" into the phloem, movement along phloem down a concentration gradient to vascular bundles in the flesh, diffusion through outer space of flesh cells, and finally, active "loading" into flesh cell vacuoles.

Jenner's analysis of the transport into and accumulation of carbohydrates by wheat endosperm (57, 58) promises to provide a useful model for the similar process in fruit cells, bearing in mind that accumulation is not into starch grains but as simple sugars in the solution within expanding vacuoles. There are two other lines of research which impinge upon the problem of solute accumulation by fruit flesh vacuoles: studies of the properties of vacuoles and tonoplasts and the lysosome hypothesis, and mechanisms of sugar accumulation in sugarcane internode parenchyma.

Properties of Vacuoles

Reference to vacuoles is conspicuously lacking in the literature on the structure of plant cells. One recent book barely mentions them and the words "tonoplast" and "vacuole" are not listed in the index (46). This state of affairs is deplorable but understandable in view of their lack of internal structure and the difficulty of experimenting with them. Much of our understanding of their dynamic properties has arisen from studies of ion fluxes, especially in root cells.

It is stated that vacuoles provide a storage space for solutes. Further, because of the presence of solutes and water and the permeability properties of the plasmalemma and/or tonoplast, vacuoles are the source of a pressure acting against the cell wall leading to turgidity and tissue strength (114). The vacuolar contents include water, water-soluble ions and molecules, and various insoluble inclusions. The juice expressed from tissue with highly vacuolated cells is dominated by vacuolar solution.

The osmotic pressure of vacuolar sap varies from 3.5 to 150 bars and in the vacuoles of ripe fruit flesh ranges between 20 and 40 bars (114). The pH is always less than 7 and in fruit flesh it is often less than 4 because of the acidic compounds accumulated (114). The tonoplast is a unit membrane (71), and its permeability properties differ from those of the plasmalemma (25).

The inclusions in fruit flesh vacuoles are of many different types, both crystalline and amorphous. Though the crystals are of specific compounds, e.g. calcium oxalate and potassium bitartrate, they appear in numerous forms. The amorphous bodies are of aggregated or polymerized compounds such as tannins and resins (114). The cells containing these bodies are often scattered through the flesh. It has been demonstrated that in persimmon flesh the tannin cells increase not only in size as the fruit ripens but also in number (55). Presumably the cells containing vacuolar inclusions have a higher concentration of the particular compound than do neigh-boring cells, thus suggesting an uneven distribution of compounds between vacuoles. This phenomenon shows clearly in transverse sections of grape skin (48); at certain stages of development there is a mosaic appearance arising from differences in degree of pigmentation (anthocyanidins) between cells.

Vacuoles as Lysosomes

There is good evidence that lysosomes (i.e. membrane-bound organelles containing hydrolytic enzymes) occur in plant cells (38, 71) as they do in animal cells (30). Matile has proposed that vacuoles are a type of plant lysosome having a highly developed internal secretion capacity; as a consequence they expand vastly and become the structures so familiar to botanists (70). Methods have been devised for separating vacuoles from yeast cells and also from parts of higher plants, e.g. maize root tips; high specific activities of several acid hydrolases have been associated with them (70, 71). Necessarily these results have been obtained with small vacuoles, but now direct support has come from the finding of acid hydrolases in sap removed directly from the large vacuoles of *Nitella* cells (33). Matile prefers to use the word "lysosome" when referring to biochemical function and "vacuole" for the morpho-logical structure (71). He suggests that lysosomes may develop from rough endo-plasmic reticulum into organelles with associated ribosomes. Vesicles originated from Golgi bodies may be secreted into these organelles, thus adding further en-zymes and substrates. The development of the vacuole/lysosome is seen therefore as not only the containment of enzymes but also one of internal secretion (incre-tion!). In particular, Matile has emphasized the ability of vacuoles to sequester cytoplasmic material by vesiculation and phagocytosis. These processes provide one mechanism for achieving and controlling turnover, the phenomenon so well estab-lished from metabolic studies (71).

Senescence is thought to involve phagocytotic activity with the cell's cytoplasm declining in amount although the ability to synthesize proteins is maintained (71, 72). The ripening of fruit flesh is regarded as a form of senescence (see above), but it is difficult to imagine that the large and rapid input of solutes into flesh vacuoles is a phagocytotic process. Mechanisms involving carriers and enzymes on or in the tonoplast seem more likely. There is cytochemical evidence from intact vacuoles (91, 121) and analytical evidence from sedimented fractions (88) that acid hydrolases can be associated with tonoplasts. In the work with sedimented fractions enzymes were thought to be associated with the inner surface of the tonoplast. There is also evidence that yeast vacuoles, which are known to accumulate arginine to high concentrations, have a specific arginine transport system; properties of the system, such as its apparent energy of activation, its kinetics and specificity, have been determined (9). Presumably it operates at the tonoplast.

It remains to be seen how relevant the foregoing studies on vacuoles are to the behavior of vacuoles in the flesh of ripening fruits. The concepts are not incompati-ble with the ideas which have been put forward to explain sugar accumulation by sugarcane internode cells (see next section). It is also possible that the variation between cells in their vacuolar composition (mentioned at the end of the previous section) could be explained by differences in their enzyme complement due to vagaries in the development of each large central vacuole (69, 71).

Sugar Accumulation by Sugarcane Internodes

The presence, location, and variation in enzyme activities are one indication of metabolic capabilities of a tissue, though they do not prove that particular pathways operate. So far as ripening fruits are concerned, there have been many findings which indicate large changes in enzyme activity associated with the events of ripening. A good summary of information about 24 classes of enzymes in developing fruits has been given by Dilley (32). The usefulness of this information is limited by a lack of knowledge of the intracellular location of enzymes and by the many other uncertainties associated with the enzymology of fruit tissues (51). An important addition to this work is the description of sucrose phosphate synthetase and sucrose synthetase in the grape berry, along with other enzymes involved in the metabolism of carbohydrates (50). These enzymes are similar to those which occur in sugarcane when internode cells are accumulating sugars (41). This latter tissue lacks many of the problems associated with fruit flesh, and considerable progress has been made in understanding the mechanism of sugar storage (2, 41). The information warrants close attention since it can serve as a useful model for studies on the accumulation of sugar by fruit flesh.

While the sugarcane internode parenchyma cells are elongating the accumulating mechanism appears to be: sucrose in the cell wall solution is hydrolyzed by a soluble acid invertase; glucose and fructose traverse the plasmalemma by separate, energy-coupled mechanisms; in the metabolic compartment (cytoplasm) the hexoses are phosphorylated and sucrose phosphate is synthesized; the sucrose moiety of sucrose phosphate is transferred across the tonoplast by an energy-coupled mechanism. This can proceed against a concentration gradient. An invertase in the vacuole converts sucrose to glucose and fructose (41). When extension growth stops and the internode matures there is a large increase in the concentration of vacuolar sucrose. The accumulating mechanism now differs from the preceding in that the wall invertase is a bound enzyme and there is no invertase activity in the vacuole. At all stages there is a neutral invertase in the cytoplasm which inverts free sucrose occurring there (41).

In addition to the value of this work as a model there are two other findings of interest. One is that while internode cells are elongating and accumulating sugars, direct correlations exist between growth rate and total acid invertase activity (39). this is interpreted in terms of two components: (a) the cell wall invertase which controls the overall rate of entry of sucrose into the cell, and (b) the vacuolar invertase which occurs in greater amount and which redirects sucrose from storage to structural materials. The second finding which may be relevant to the ripening of fruits is that exogenous ABA greatly increases invertase synthesis; inhibitor studies suggested that ABA's stimulatory effects operated at some stage after the formation of invertase mRNA (36). Similarly, a relationship has been found between invertase activity and growth of excised tomato roots, and ABA affects both (18).

Wall Growth and Water Accumulation: Softening

There are two phenomena in fruit development whose expression depends, at least in part, on water accumulation and on the behavior of cell walls: fruit growth (cell expansion) and fruit softening (deformability). The timing of softening in relation to growth varies considerably between species. Some do not soften until after detachment (avocados grown commercially). A number soften just before or during the final ripening events, by which time the majority of expansion has been accomplished (banana, soft fruits). The grape berry softens at the beginning of the second growth cycle many weeks before ripeness. From daily measurements of diameter and deformability of single berries in situ we have found that softening precedes the renewed swelling in these berries by an average of 7 days (Coombe and Bishop, unpublished).

The following factors are required for cell extension: a sufficient turgor pressure to set wall tension above a certain critical value, permeability of cell membranes adequate to permit a required flux of water, and the initiation and maintenance of the making and breaking of bonds in the wall, i.e. a biochemically mediated, viscoelastic flow of material in the wall (93, 94, 96). For the latter, auxin is required. During the initial development of fruits, cell extension would seem to be controlled by these factors. But the picture becomes confused during ripening when the fruit cells expand and soften, or soften without expansion. In the latter case there must be a change in wall deformability induced without the stimulus of turgor pressure; this has been referred to for tomatoes (120). An association has been suggested between softening and cellulase activity in peach (52) and β-glycosidase activity in tomato (122).

To conclude this section, there is reason to suspect that the three important contributors to ripening—solute accumulation, expansion, and softening—each has its own timing and control. The control mechanisms may be interrelated but the events do not need to be strictly coincident.

CONTROL MECHANISMS

Fruits and seeds have been a happy-hunting-ground for hormone seekers because their concentrations are generally considerably greater than in vegetative tissue and extraction and purification problems are lessened. There is good support for the hypothesis that the initial growth of fruits is dependent on hormones produced by the developing seed (27, 85, 86). For those fruit tissues which are not dependent on associated seed growth (e.g. the parthenocarpic Washington navel orange, pineapple, banana, Corinth grape) the same types of hormones are thought to be involved in preventing abscission and promoting fruit growth, but they are perhaps synthesized by the fruit tissue itself (67, 82, 85). Auxins, gibberellins, cytokinins, abscisins, and ethylene have been found to be produced, often in large amounts, and often in a sequence typical for a species (27). Results from excision of parts and treatment with exogenous growth substances show that compounds are sometimes synergistic in promoting growth and sometimes can substitute for each other. The general picture is of control by the interaction and balance of hormones (27, 85). A particular case has been made for a balance between GA and ABA in the control of growth of the grape berry (23).

Crane has suggested that this control is effected by the ability of hormones to influence movement of organic substances into the fruit (27). This is a useful concept at this stage of our understanding, although final clarification is unlikely until we have a picture of the mechanism of action of each class of hormone. These aspects will not be developed here, not because they are unimportant, but because there are many excellent reviews available (26, 27, 85, 86). However, some comment can be made on the control of fruit ripening, especially its inception.

The Triggering of Ripening

Unlike the early growth of the fruit, the events involved in ripening apparently do not depend on the presence of the seed. As has been said before, ripening follows only after a certain minimum amount of prior development and involves a significant change in the types of enzyme activities. The control for this type of change could be one of a long list of possibilities ranging from activity at the gene level to inhibition of preformed enzymes or simply to changed permeability of membranes. [Sacher has referred to the evidence for the latter (100).] Each could be mediated by phytohormones. Three suggestions which have been made for the hormonal control of the inception of ripening will be mentioned: ethylene, ABA, and IAA oxidation products.

ETHYLENE   Ethylene has long been known to be involved in fruit ripening (6, 13) and has been regarded by many as the fruit ripening hormone (68, 74, 92). This may be true for some fruits but is unacceptable as a generalization for all fruits. The grape berry, for instance, has a constant but very low production of ethylene during the inception of ripening. Its tissues can be stimulated to produce large amounts of ethylene by many different treatments but there is no correlation between these levels and the timing of ripening (24). Doubt has now been raised about the primary role of ethylene in the ripening of tomato, a fruit which has hitherto been regarded as a typical example of the involvement of ethylene. Propylene, like ethylene, stimulated the respiratory climacteric in tomato fruits, but ethylene production did not increase until ripening commenced (75); similarly, the effects of reduced atmospheric pressure on the time of ripening of tomato fruits were not related to the amounts of ethylene present (112). In both papers it is agreed that ethylene production is an integral part of ripening but it does not act as a trigger. It has been suggested that the presence of a water-soluble substance, not involved in ethylene synthesis, is required in the pericarp of tomato for ripening to occur (104), though similar results obtained with slices of avocado are interpreted in terms of a restricted supply of oxygen (115).

Recent work on Golden Queen peach is useful in pointing to the possibility of separate controls for the expansion of cells on the one hand and for the accumulation of dry matter on the other. The rise in ethylene concentration has been found to coincide with the latter; water input accelerated 20 days earlier, and it is suggested that explanations other than ethylene should be sought for the triggering of the expansion in volume (17, 59). The effects of ethephon applied at different times on the promotion of ripening of peaches (111) are not at variance with this general picture. Ethylene treatment has also been found to stimulate dry matter input and size increase in the ovules of cut carnation flowers (80, 81).

ABA   This hormone has been proposed as a possible trigger of ripening in some fruits (24, 44, 66, 76, 77). The evidence for its role in the ripening of grapes is as follows: ABA concentration in berry flesh declined steadily as the first rapid growth cycle progressed, reaching a low value about 7 to 10 days before ripening processes became evident. Its level then began to increase, and this increase continued until ripening events were well established, whereafter it declined. Treatments which delayed or hastened ripening had parallel effects on this increase in ABA (24). The amount of increase was greatest (on a fresh weight basis) in the skin (23). While it was increasing there was a close correlation between the concentrations of ABA and hexose, there being $10^{5.5}$ moles of hexose per mole of ABA (Coombe, unpublished). Treatment of grapes with ABA hastened ripening when applied after endogenous ABA had reached low levels, whereas earlier treatment was ineffective (44).

It is proposed that the preliminary decline of ABA to a low concentration is an integral part of the control system and that low ABA permits a change in metabolism. Such a concept has support in, for instance, the suggested role for ABA in controlling dormancy of buds and seeds (123). Similarly, in maturing cotton embryos, germination and an associated increase in protease activity were correlated with a lowered concentration of ABA, achieved by washing; experiments on the inhibition of protease activity by ABA and its restimulation by actinomycin D led to the conclusion that mRNA for protease was being produced but that ABA was inhibiting its translation (54).

IAA OXIDATION PRODUCTS   The delay in the ripening of tomatoes caused by storage at low air pressure has been found to be due to the low pressure of oxygen and not to the low concentration of ethylene (112). Similarly, the delay in the ripening of avocado slices by washing was attributed to a restricted supply of oxygen (115). Frenkel found that the ripening of whole green pears was hastened by treatment with IAA oxidation products or by an atmosphere of oxygen. Though these treatments stimulated ethylene production, he concluded that the promotion of ripening could not be attributed to the production of ethylene. He suggests in fact that the IAA oxidation products stimulate ripening and ethylene synthesis (35). The conversion of one compound, IAA, from an inhibitor to a promotor of fruit ripening by a single positive action such as oxidation is an attractive mechanism and the hypothesis deserves further study. The dual effects of IAA, depending on the concentration applied, will need to be taken into account (116).

CONCLUSIONS

The development of fleshy fruits is seen from an evolutionary point of view as the acquisition of characteristics which attract birds and other animals, thus aiding seed dispersal.

The attractive tissues may originate from practically any part of the inflorescence provided there is no constraint from inflexible layers; the pericarp is often involved.

The tissues become fleshy by an integrated and phased development involving cell division and cell expansion, accumulation and coloring, and softening. During development there is a stage assessed subjectively as "ripeness."

Accumulation of water is an adjunct to the accumulation of dry matter.

Two processes are considered to be of fundamental importance: (a) cell wall extension, and (b) water and solute influx into the vacuole. The properties of the tonoplast and the triggering of these processes are of particular interest.

NOTE ADDED IN PROOF   The proceedings of the CNRS International Colloquium (No. 238, Paris, 1975) entitled "Facteurs et Regulation de la Maturation des Fruits" were unfortunately unknown to me when preparing this review. This publication provides an important addition to modern literature on post-harvest physiology and includes some mention of developmental physiology of fruits. It does not, however, alter the arguments developed in the review.

Literature Cited

1. Akamine, E. K., Goo, T. 1973. *J. Am. Soc. Hortic. Sci.* 98:381–83
2. Alexander, A. G. 1973. *Sugar Cane Physiology.* Amsterdam: Elsevier
3. Ashwawi, H., Aref, H., Hussein, A. E. A. 1956. *J. Sci. Food Agric.* 7:623–28
4. Bain, J., Robertson, R. N. 1951. *Aust. J. Sci. Res. B* 4:75–91
5. Biale, J. B. 1960. *Adv. Food Res.* 10:293–354
6. Biale, J. B. 1964. *Science* 146:880–88
7. Blackman, G. F. 1961. In *Growth in Living Systems,* ed. M. X. Zarrow, 525–56. New York: Basic Books
8. Bollard, E. G. 1970. See Ref. 53, 1: 387–425
9. Boller, T., Dürr, M., Wiemken, A. 1975. *Eur. J. Biochem.* 54:81–91
10. Bradley, M. V. 1954. *Am. J. Bot.* 41:398–402
11. Bradley, M. V., Crane, J. C. 1955. *Am. J. Bot.* 42:273–81
12. Brooks, R. M. 1957. *Fruit Morphology Course Notes.* Univ. Calif., Davis
13. Burg, S. P., Burg, E. A. 1965. *Science* 148:1190–96
14. Cataldo, D. A. 1974. *Plant Physiol.* 53:912–17
15. Chalmers, D. J., Canterford, R. L., Jerie, P. H., Jones, T. R., Ugalde, T. D. 1975. *Aust. J. Plant Physiol.* 2:635–45
16. Chalmers, D. J., van den Ende, B. 1975. *Ann. Bot.* 39:423–32
17. Chalmers, D. J., van den Ende, B. 1975. *Aust. J. Plant Physiol.* 2:623–34
18. Chin, C. K., Weston, G. D. 1975. *Plant Sci. Lett.* 4:25–30
19. Cleland, R. 1971. *Ann. Rev. Plant Physiol.* 22:197–222
20. Connors, C. H. 1919. *NJ Agric. Exp. Sta. Ann. Rep.* 40:82–88
21. Coombe, B. G. 1960. *Plant Physiol.* 35:241–50
22. Coombe, B. G. 1970. *J. Hortic. Sci.* 45:415–25
23. Coombe, B. G. 1973. *Acta Hortic.* 34:261–73
24. Coombe, B. G., Hale, C. R. 1973. *Plant Physiol.* 51:629–34
25. Cram, W. J., Laties, G. G. 1974. *J. Exp. Bot.* 25:11–27
26. Crane, J. C. 1964. *Ann. Rev. Plant Physiol.* 15:303–26
27. Crane, J. C. 1969. *HortScience* 4:8–11
28. Darwin, C. R. 1906. *The Origin of Species,* p. 151. London: Murray. 6th ed.
29. Davies, W. N. L., Orphanos, P. I., Papaconstantinou, J. 1971. *J. Sci. Food Agric.* 22:83–86
30. DeDuve, Ch. 1969. In *Lysosomes in Biology and Pathology,* ed. J. L. Dingle, H. B. Fell, 1:3–40. Amsterdam:North-Holland
31. Dilley, D. R. 1969. *HortScience* 4:111–14
32. Dilley, D. R. 1970. See Ref. 53, 1:179–207
33. Doi, E., Ohtsuru, C., Matoba, T. 1975. *Plant Sci. Lett.* 4:243–47
34. Food & Agricultural Organization of the United Nations 1972. *Production Yearbook,* Vol. 26. Rome: FAO
35. Frenkel, C. 1975. *Plant Physiol.* 55: 480–84

36. Gayler, K. R., Glasziou, K. T. 1969. *Planta* 84:185–94
37. Geiger, D. R., Sovonick, S. A., Shock, T. L., Fellows, R. J. 1974. *Plant Physiol.* 54:892–98
38. Gibson, R. A., Paleg, L. G. 1975. *Aust. J. Plant Physiol.* 2:41–49
39. Glasziou, K. T., Bull, T. A. 1967. *Proc. 12th Int. Soc. Sugar-Cane Technol.*, 575–81. Amsterdam: Elsevier
40. Glasziou, K. T., Gayler, K. R. 1972. *Plant Physiol.* 49:912–13
41. Glasziou, K. T., Gayler, K. R. 1972. *Bot. Rev.* 38:471–90
42. Goldwin, G. K., Schwabe, W. W. 1975. *J. Hortic. Sci.* 50:175–78
43. Gortner, W. A., Dull, G. G., Krauss, B. H. 1967. *HortScience* 2:141–44
44. Hale, C. R., Coombe, B. G. 1974. *R. Soc. N. Z. Bull.* 12:831–36
45. Hale, C. R., Weaver, R. J. 1962. *Hilgardia* 33:89–131
46. Hall, J. L., Flowers, T. J., Roberts, R. M. 1974. *Plant Cell Structure and Metabolism.* London:Longman
47. Hansen, E. 1966. *Ann. Rev. Plant Physiol.* 17:459–80
48. Harris, J. M., Kriedemann, P. E., Possingham, J. V. 1968. *Vitis* 7:106–19
49. Hawker, J. S. 1965. *Aust. J. Biol. Sci.* 18:959–69
50. Hawker, J. S. 1969. *Phytochemistry* 8:9–17
51. Hawker, J. S., Downton, W. J. S. 1974. *R. Soc. N. Z. Bull.* 12:819–22
52. Hinton, D. M., Pressey, R. 1974. *J. Food Sci.* 39:783–85
53. Hulme, A. C., Ed. 1970, 1971. *The Biochemistry of Fruits and their Products,* Vols. 1 and 2. London: Academic
54. Ihle, J. N., Dure, L. 1970. *Biochem. Biophys. Res. Commun.* 38:995–1001
55. Ito, S. 1971. See Ref. 53, 2:281–301
56. Jackson, D. I., Coombe, B. G. 1966. *Aust. J. Agric. Res.* 17:465–77
57. Jenner, C. F. 1973. *J. Exp. Bot.* 24:295–306
58. Jenner, C. F., Rathjen, A. J. 1975. *Aust. J. Plant Physiol.* 2:311–22
59. Jerie, P. H., Chalmers, D. J. 1976. *Aust. J. Plant Physiol.* In press
60. Kanwar, J. S., Nijjar, G. S., Rajput, M. S. 1972. *Punjab Hortic. J.* 12:146–51
61. King, J. R. 1938. *Hilgardia* 11:437–58
62. Kliewer, W. M. 1965. *Am. J. Enol. Vitic.* 16:92–100
63. Ibid, 101–10
64. Kopp, L. E. 1966. *Mem. NY Bot. Gard.* 14:1–120
65. Kriedemann, P. E. 1969. *Planta* 85:111–17

66. Looney, N. E., McGlasson, W. B., Coombe, B. G. 1974. *Aust. J. Plant Physiol.* 1:77–86
67. Luckwill, L. C. 1957. *Symp. Soc. Exp. Biol.* 11:63–85
68. Marei, N., Crane, J. C. 1971. *Plant Physiol.* 48:249–54
69. Matile, Ph. 1968. *Planta* 79:181–96
70. Matile, Ph. 1969. See Ref. 30, 1:406–30
71. Matile, Ph. 1974. In *Dynamic Aspects of Plant Ultrastructure,* ed. A. W. Robards, 178–218. London: McGraw Hill
72. Matile, Ph., Winkenbach, F. 1971. *J. Exp. Bot.* 22:759–71
73. McCance, R. A., Widdowson, E. M. 1960. *The Composition of Foods.* MRC Spec. Rep. Ser. 297. London: H.M.S.O.
74. McGlasson, W. B. 1970. See Ref. 53, 1:475–519
75. McGlasson, W. B., Dostal, H. C., Tigchelaar, E. C. 1975. *Plant Physiol.* 55:218–22
76. Milborrow, B. V. 1974. *Ann. Rev. Plant Physiol.* 25:259–307
77. Milborrow, B. V., Robinson, D. R. 1973. *J. Exp. Bot.* 24:537–48
78. Mohan Ram, H. Y. M., Ram, M., Steward, F. C. 1962. *Ann. Bot.* 26:657–72
79. Nakagawa, S., Nanjo, Y. 1966. *J. Jap. Soc. Hortic. Sci.* 35:29–38
80. Nicholls, R., Ho, L. C. 1975. *Ann. Bot.* 39:287–96
81. Ibid, 433–38
82. Nitsch, J. P. 1952. *Q. Rev. Biol.* 27:33–57
83. Nitsch, J. P. 1953. *Ann. Rev. Plant Physiol.* 4:199–236
84. Nitsch, J. P. 1965. *Encycl. Plant Physiol.* 15(1):1537–1647
85. Nitsch, J. P. 1970. See Ref. 53, 1:427–71
86. Nitsch, J. P. 1971. In *Plant Physiology,* ed. F. C. Steward, 6A:413–56. New York: Academic
87. Nitsch, J. P., Pratt, C., Nitsch, C., Shaulis, N. J. 1960. *Am. J. Bot.* 47:566–76
88. Parish, R. W. 1975. *Planta* 123:15–31
89. Pearson, J. A., Robertson, R. N. 1953. *Aust. J. Biol. Sci.* 6:1–20
90. Pentzer, W. T., Heinze, P. H. 1954. *Ann. Rev. Plant Physiol.* 5:205–24
91. Poux, N. 1963. *J. Microsc.* 2:485–89
92. Pratt, H. K., Goeschl, J. D. 1969. *Ann. Rev. Plant Physiol.* 20:541–84
92a. Pratt, H. K., Reid, M. S. 1974. *J. Sci. Food Agric.* 25:747–57
93. Preston, R. D. 1974. See Ref. 71, 256–309
94. Preston, R. D. 1974. *The Physical Biology of Plant Cell Walls.* London: Chapman & Hall

95. Quandt, R. E. 1958. *Am. Stat. Assoc. J.* 53:873–80
96. Ray, P. M., Green, P. B., Cleland, R. 1972. *Nature* 239:163–64
97. Reid, M. S., Bieleski, R. L. 1974. *R. Soc. N.Z. Bull.* 12:823–30
98. Rhodes, M. J. C. 1970. See Ref. 53, 1:521–33
99. Rygg, G. L. 1946. *U.S. Dep. Agric. Tech. Bull.* 910
100. Sacher, J. A. 1973. *Ann. Rev. Plant Physiol.* 24:197–224
101. Salisbury, E. J. 1974. *Proc. R. Soc. London B* 186:83–88
102. Saulnier-Blache, P., Bruzeau, F. 1967. *Ann. Physiol. Vég.* 9:179–96
103. Schroeder, C. A. 1953. *Proc. Am. Soc. Hortic. Sci.* 61:103–9
104. Simons, D. H., Bruinsma, J. 1973. *Plant Physiol.* 52:132–36
105. Singh, L. B., Singh, U. P. 1954. *The Litchi.* Lucknow:Supt. Printing & Stationery
106. Sinnott, E. W. 1939. *Am. J. Bot.* 26:179–89
107. Sinnott, E. W. 1960. *Plant Morphogenesis.* New York: McGraw Hill
108. Sinnott, E. W., Franklin, A. H. 1943. *Am. J. Bot.* 30:87–94
109. Siri, W. E. 1956. *Rev. Sci. Instrum.* 27:729–38
110. Smith, O. 1935. *Cornell Univ. Agric. Exp. Sta. Mem.* 184:3–16
111. Stembridge, G. E., Raff, J. W. 1973. *HortScience* 8:500–1
112. Stenvers, N., Bruinsma, J. 1975. *Nature* 253:532–33
113. Teaotia, S. S., Singh, R. D., Awasthi, R. K. 1972. *Punjab Hortic. J.* 12:152–57
114. Thomas, M., Ranson, S. L., Richardson, J. A. 1973. *Plant Physiology.* London: Longman. 5th ed.
115. Tingwa, P. O., Young, R. E. 1974. *Plant Physiol.* 54:907–10
116. Ibid. 55:937–40
117. Ulrich, R. 1952. *La Vie des Fruits.* Paris: Masson
118. Ulrich, R. 1958. *Ann. Rev. Plant Physiol.* 9:385–416
118a. van der Pijl, L. 1966. *Proc. Kon. Ned. Akad. Wettenschappen, Ser. C* 69:597–640
119. Verhaar, G. 1949. *Indonesian J. Nat. Sci.* 104:8–11
120. Vickery, R. S., Bruinsma, J. 1973. *J. Exp. Bot.* 24:1261–70
121. Villiers, T. A. 1971. *Nature New Biol.* 233:57–58
122. Wallner, S. J., Walker, J. E. 1975. *Plant Physiol.* 55:94–98
123. Wareing, P. F., Phillips, I. D. J. 1970. *Control of Growth and Differentiation in Plants.* Oxford: Pergamon
124. Whiting, G. C. 1970. See Ref. 53, 1:1–31
125. Williams, R. F. 1975. *The Shoot Apex and Leaf Growth.* Cambridge: Univ. Press
126. Winkler, A. J. 1929. *Hilgardia* 4:153–73
127. Winkler, A. J., Cook, J. A., Kliewer, W. M., Lider, L. A. 1974. *General Viticulture.* Berkeley: Univ. California Press, 2nd ed.
128. Winton, A. L., Winton, K. B. 1935. *The Structure and Composition of Foods.* New York: Wiley

Ann. Rev. Plant Physiol. 1976. 27:229–65

BIOCHEMICAL AND MOLECULAR-GENETIC ASPECTS OF CELLULAR SLIME MOLD DEVELOPMENT

❖7609

Maurice Sussman[1]

Section of Developmental and Molecular Biology, Hebrew University, Jerusalem, Israel

Robert Brackenbury

The Rockefeller University, New York, NY 10021

CONTENTS

---

[1]Present address: Department of Life Sciences, University of Pittsburgh, Pittsburgh, Pennsylvania 15213.

Cellular Slime Molds and the Genesis of Multicellular Organization

In the *Annual Review of Microbiology* for 1956, an article entitled "The Biology of the Cellular Slime Molds" (202) began on the following plaintive note:

"At present there are to my knowledge five laboratories throughout the world engaged in studying the cellular slime molds. In this circumstance, an annual review of the combined efforts of these investigations would be a very comfortable task but one that could carry little information to the reader."

In contrast, this review[2] begins on a note of nervous complacency. Figure 1 summarizes the publication kinetics for the order Acrasiales, family Dictyosteliaceae. In the intervening years, the increase is seen to have been consistently exponential and the slope formidable.

Why the increasingly sharp interest in this group of organisms? In retrospect, the spectacular progress of molecular biology and molecular genetics over the past 30 years was due in no small measure to the particular organisms chosen for study and the methodology behind these choices. Select an organism which embodies the problem at hand in its simplest, most paradigmal form. Choose one which grows rapidly and conveniently enough to permit an experiment a day; one in which mutant isolations and recombination and segregation analyses can be conducted so

---

[2]The reader may find useful the recent publications which review many different aspects of growth and morphogenesis in these organisms (5, 21, 79, 84, 85, 89, 96, 128, 134, 154).

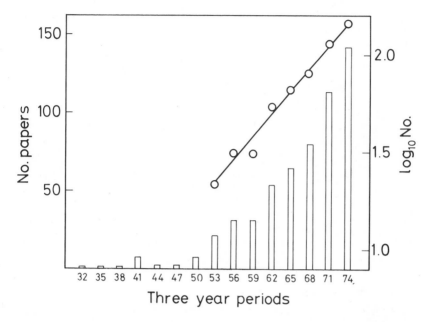

Figure 1 Growth kinetics of *Dictyostelium* papers in the literature, showing lag and exponential phases, with no indication of a stationary phase.

that biochemical and genetic investigations of the problem can go hand in hand. Define the conditions of growth and experimentation in order to guarantee a high degree of experimental reproducibility. In recent years attention has been turned to problems of cellular differentiation and morphogenesis as being suitable subjects for study at the level of molecular biology and molecular genetics. It is in the context of choosing appropriate experimental models that the sudden sharp interest in the cellular slime molds has emerged. In the following subsections the developmental cycle of *Dictyostelium discoideum,* the species most studied, is described and the currently used methods of growing and experimenting with these organisms are summarized.

DEVELOPMENTAL CYCLE OF *DICTYOSTELIUM DISCOIDEUM*   Figure 2 illustrates the developmental cycle schematically. The individual cells are uninucleate, amoeboid forms bounded by plastic plasma membranes which divide mitotically (32, 217, 241). After cessation of growth, they collect together into multicellular aggregates of varying size depending on the population density at the time of aggregation (215). Responding to several environmental parameters, each aggregate can either construct a fruiting body directly at the site of aggregation or transform into a migrating slug and move away (27, 160, 177). At any time thereafter, from hours to days, the slug can stop migrating and enter the program of fruiting body construction as shown. The fruiting body consists of an apical viscous mass of spores

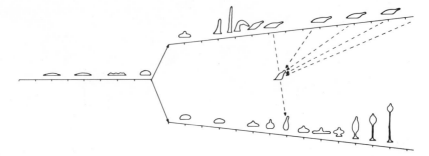

Figure 2   Developmental cycle of *Dictyostelium discoideum* (160). After removal of nutrients, the individual cells collect into aggregates. The alternatives are described in the text. Direct construction of fruiting bodies (bottom pathway) requires 24–25 hours.

surmounting a stalk composed of a tapered, cylindrical sheath of cellulose enclosing vacuolated stalk cells with rigid cellulose walls, packed together as in the parenchymatous tissue of a plant and resting upon a basal disc also composed of vacuolated rigid walled cells (178). Each spore, when dispersed and suitably activated, germinates into a vegetative amoeba.

GROWTH AND MAINTENANCE OF THE ORGANISMS   Growth occurs on agar plates (207) in association with bacteria. The mixture is spread over the surface, and 10^5–10^7 spores or ameobae grow into a smooth lawn of ca 10^9 amoebae virtually bacteria free in 1–2 days, depending on the inoculum size, and then construct about 10^4 fruiting bodies. If clones are wanted, the inoculum is limited to < 100 spores or amoebae. Plaques are formed as the amoebae of their progeny eat holes in the layer of bacteria. After 3–4 days fruiting bodies appear within the expanding plaques (207). The amoebae can also be cultivated in shaken liquid suspension, either in a nutrient broth with growing bacteria (203) or in buffer with washed bacteria (81). The stationary phase yield is 1–5×10^7 cells/ml or 0.8–4 g dry weight/l. In all of these conditions the doubling times are 3–4 hr, depending on the species. Two species have been successfully cultivated in axenic medium. *Polysphondylium pallidum* is grown in suspension with proteose peptone, phosphate buffer, and lecithin (204) or in a somewhat more complex medium containing embryo extract, albumin, and vitamins (112). In either case the doubling time is 3 hr and the yield about 2×10^7 cells/ml. *D. discoideum* was slowly adapted (223) to axenic medium (HL-5) containing yeast extract, peptone, and salts. The medium was initially fortified with embryo extract and liver extract, but these have since been eliminated (44, 193, 231). The doubling time is 10–12 hr. Axenically grown *D. discoideum* can be employed in experiments, particularly those involving isotopic labeling, which were formerly questionable because of the contaminating presence of the bacterial associate (167). The morphogenetic and metabolic properties of axenically grown *D. discoideum* have been described in detail (6, 9, 176). Three strains—AX-1, 2, 3 —exist (140, 223, 231). However, all were derived from the same parent strain and are probably identical. A recent parasexual analysis (239, 240) has shown that the capacity for axenic growth is due to two recessive mutant alleles located in linkage groups II and III. The original isolation of Ax-1 suggested that a very slow growing variant had been initially selected which was then superseded in subsequent passages by a faster growing derivative. Presumably this selected two successive mutations.

EXPERIMENTAL METHODS FOR THE STUDY OF CELL AGGREGATION, FRUIT-ING BODY CONSTRUCTION, AND SLUG MIGRATION   Biochemical and physio-logical investigations of fruiting body construction are now carried out in almost all laboratories using a single experimental system (207). Vegetative cells are harvested during or at the end of the exponential phase, washed by successive centrifugations, and aliquots containing 5×10^7–10^8 cells are dispersed on 2" millipore or Whatman filter circles resting on absorbent pads saturated with a buffer, salts, streptomycin solution (LPS) inside 60 mm Petri dishes. About 1000 aggregates of equal size (encompassing all the cells) are formed by 8 hr, and mature fruiting bodies appear by 24 hr. Morphogenetic synchrony is quite good so that a time spread of no more than 30–60 min is usually encountered between the least and most advanced struc-ture on a filter. Exogenous isotopes or inhibitors can be administered simply by shifting a filter to a new absorbent pad saturated with the appropriate solution. Cells can be quantitatively recovered at any time by vortexing the filter in a few milliliters of liquid. Entrance of the aggregates into the alternative program of slug migration (and their return to the fruiting program) can be induced by appropriate manipula-tion of pH, humidity, salt concentration, metabolite accumulation, and light (160). Slugs of equal size and age can also be obtained for special studies by light-directed migration on agar (57, 159, 171). Aggregation can also occur in a gently shaken suspension of stationary phase cells, although the aggregates develop no further. This system has been quantified in a very elegant way in order to study the acquisi-tion of aggregative competence (14–16, 29, 83).

MUTANT STRAINS   A wide variety of mutant strains is now available, particularly ones derived from *D. discoideum*. An appreciation of the potential reservoir of material for comparative studies can be gained from the collection described below:

1. cannot begin and/or complete aggregation (135, 180, 220, 249);
2. cannot develop beyond aggregation (135, 180, 220, 249);
3. produce nothing but migrating slugs or are biased heavily toward slug migration (135, 220, 249);
4. form bizarre fruiting bodies, e.g. "fruity, curly, glassy, forked, bushy" etc (220);
5. produce fruiting bodies with spores but little or no stalk cells (249);
6. are temporally deranged (139, 200);
7. are deficient or deviant in fruiting body pigmentation (222);
8. are drug resistant (92, 119, 120, 142, 240);
9. are temperature sensitive for growth and/or morphogenesis (136);
10. contain structural gene mutations (53);
11. produce spores which germinate defectively (58, 123);
12. are capable of growth in axenic medium (239, 240).

The search for such mutants and their genetic and biochemical analyses presently represent especially popular avenues of investigation.

Genetics: Parasexual Recombination and Segregation

HAPLOID, DIPLOID AND METASTABLE STRAINS   Stained metaphase figures have revealed the existence of haploid and diploid cells with 7 and 14 chromosomes respectively (186, 204) and occasional aneuploid cells bearing intermediate numbers (32). Ploidal composition of a population is a clonally inherited property. Three types of clonal isolates have been described (221); *Stable Haploid* isolates in which the great majority of cells are haploid and yield clones in which the incidence of diploids is less than 10^{-4}; *Stable diploid* isolates in which the great majority of cells are diploid and yield clones in which the incidence of haploids is less than 10^{-4}; *Meta stable clones* in which both haploid and diploid cells are present in significant proportions (10–90%) and each of these cells yields a clone with a similarly mixed population. Hence in the latter, ploidal composition appears to be a more unstable character. The metabolic basis of these differences in stability is unknown.

The three types of strains are interconvertible since each can be isolated from the others (205, 222). Despite the low incidence of haploid cells in stable diploid clones and vice versa, differences in growth rates (due to segregation of recessive alleles) and in morphogenetic competence can, by selection, lead to rapid changes in an uncloned population.

FORMATION AND SEGREGATION OF HETEROZYGOTES   The formation of diploid heterozygotic clones and the isolation of haploid segregants derived from them was first demonstrated (222) by growing a mixed culture of two haploid mutant strains bearing (recessive) fruiting body pigmentation markers and isolating diploid clones bearing the wild type pigmentation. On continued passage the diploid isolates yielded haploid segregant clones which included all four expected pigmentation classes, two parental and two recombinant. The segregations appeared to be randomly assorted. Both processes, however, were exceedingly infrequent, i.e. diploid heterozygotes were encountered at a frequency of about 10^{-4} and these yielded haploid segregants at a frequency of 10^{-3} to 10^{-4}.

SELECTION OF HETEROZYGOTES   Selective techniques have been devised which now permit relatively rapid and efficient use of this system for genetic mapping. Original attempts employed mixed growth of independent "min" mutants (strains which grew slowly and produced small plaques). From these, recombinants capable of forming large plaques were isolated (142, 195). The current system employs pairs of independently derived temperature-sensitive mutants which grow at 22°C but not at 27°C, and which bear outside markers including the two previously used recessive pigmentation markers (120). After mixed growth and/or mixed fruit construction, the cells are plated out with bacteria and incubated at 27°. Temperature-resistant clones whose fruits bear the wild type pigmentation and whose spores display a size distribution characteristic of stable diploid strains appear at a frequency of ca 10^{-4}. The isolation of temperature-sensitive haploid strains has been facilitated by selection after growth in BUdR (124).

SELECTION OF SEGREGANTS   Cycloheximide resistance in *D. discoideum* is a recessive character (120). Hence heterozygotic diploid strains are cycloheximide-sensitive. Growth on SM agar containing cycloheximide automatically selects the class of haploid segregants bearing the resistant allele and the distribution of other markers can then be studied. By these means seven markers were located on three linkage groups (120). The incidence of such segregants was ca 10^{-3} to 10^{-4}, confirming the previous estimate (222). Recently two acriflavin-resistant mutants (one of them also resistant to methanol) have been isolated which are also recessive. They are located in different linkage groups, separate as well from cycloheximide resistance, and this has greatly increased the efficiency of the segregation analysis. The present map representing the combined efforts of a number of laboratories (53, 120, 123, 140, 186, 221, 239) is summarized in Table 1.

MECHANISMS OF HETEROZYGOTE FORMATION AND SEGREGATION Though heterozygote formation must involve syngamy and karyogamy, the actual process has not been observed. Engulfment of amoebae one by another does occur (222), particularly at the end of the growth phase, and perhaps on occasion eating turns into mating. With respect to segregation, the most likely mechanism appears to be a piecemeal loss of chromosomes leading to the haplophase (7, 32, 192). In addition, genetic evidence (120) suggests that in some aneuploids a hemizygous chromosome can reduplicate and return the cell to the diplophase. Multiple fissions (216) and tripolar mitotic spindles (222) have been observed, and it is possible that this is an alternate means of segregation. Recombination via somatic crossover has now been definitely established (92, 119, 240).

FUTURE PROSPECTS   The way is now clear for the systematic mapping of genes which regulate all phases of aggregation, slug migration, and fruiting body construction, and the attendant processes of cytodifferentiation and morphogenesis. For example, a systematic complementation analysis of aggregateless mutants is now under way (P. C. Newell, private communication). Existence of regulatory genes, *cis* and *trans* dominance relationships, etc can be investigated.

Sexual Genetics: Macrocyst Formation and Germination

The occurrence of bizarre structures called macrocysts, thick-walled spores enclosing many cells in various states of development and degeneration, was originally

Table 1   Linkage groups in *Dictyostelium*[a]

Linkage group	I	II	III	IV	V	VI (or V)
	acrB	*acrA*	*acrC*	*bwnA*	*tsgC*	*tsgG*
	cycA	*axeA*	*axeB*	*tsgB*		
	devA	*devB*	*tsgA*			
	sprA	*tsgD*				
	tsgE	*tsgF*				
		whiA				

[a] (120, 191a, 240)

reported by Raper and colleagues (18, 227, 228). They were thought to be an alternative to fruiting body construction and perhaps might represent a sexual phase. Recent studies (40, 63, 64, 143, 162, 163) have confirmed this speculation. Macrocysts have now been observed in five species of Dictyosteliaceae. They are circular or ellipsoidal bodies enclosed by a three-layered wall, and they form shortly after aggregation. The choice between macrocyst formation and fruiting depends on light, temperature, moisture, pH, and the composition of the medium. A large cell (the zygote) appears at the center and ingests all the peripheral amoebae, eventually reaching giant size. Germination is accompanied by the reappearance of cells within the homogeneous mass. The wall ruptures and uninucleate haploid amoebae are released. Mating types exist although some strains are self-compatible. Cytological and genetic evidence of meiosis though sketchy is impressive.

Severe technical problems remain to be solved before the system can be employed for genetic analysis. Germination has been observed after 10 days, but it usually takes 6–10 weeks and even then is unsatisfactory. Unfortunately, *D. discoideum* macrocysts germinate very poorly if at all. Similarly, the conditions for macrocyst formation are still imperfectly defined.

Aggregation

On a solid substratum, vegetative amoebae form a smooth lawn of dispersed cells. Some hours after entering the stationary phase (the exact time depending on the species and the cell density), the cells aggregate. If the lawn is several cells thick (for example, after growth on SM agar with bacteria or after deposition of 10^8 cells on a 2 inch filter), a stippling of the surface is observed, then a condensation into loose mounds, and finally the appearance of separate tight hemispheres, each with an apical nipple (Figure 2). If the lawn is thin so that the cells are separated from one another, they elongate and move toward centers of aggregation generally condensing into radial streams branched at the distal ends. The completed aggregates, though smaller than those formed at higher cell densities, have the same morphology. These directed movements are the result of a chemotactic attraction of the outlying cells by the center and streams.

In a gently shaken suspension, stationary phase cells initially form loose clusters and, some hours later, tight, spherical, or ovoid aggregates which eventually acquire a cortex like the sheath of a migrating slug, but develop no further. Deposited on a solid substratum, the initial loose clusters rapidly disperse but the tight aggregates remain intact and immediately go on to complete fruiting body construction (84). The loose clustering is EDTA-sensitive. The subsequent formation of tight aggregates is EDTA-resistant (16, 84). Aggregative competence once acquired is not lost. Aggregates even at late stages of development can be dispersed to a single cell suspension by applying sufficient shear forces through repeated vigorous pipettings or intense shaking (157). If then gently shaken, the cells immediately readhere and within minutes form tight spherical aggregates. This too is EDTA-resistant (3, 16). In suspension, aggregation and reaggregation can be followed quantitatively by measuring the decrease in light scattering (14, 16), by the increase in particle size in a Coulter counter (182, 183), or by determining microscopically the proportion of cells still in groups of one to three (3, 31, 209, 232).

Three particular aspects of aggregation are currently under intensive investigation: the adhesive process itself; the chemotactic system; and patterning, i.e. how the aggregation of a population or solid substratum is regulated spatially, temporally, and quantitatively.

THE ADHESIVE PROCESS   Considerable progress has been made recently toward defining the molecular basis of cell adhesion in *D. discoideum*. Cell ghosts have been prepared consisting of largely intact plasma membranes with a few empty vesicles and exploded mitochondria but devoid of nuclei, ribosomes, RNA, soluble cytoplasm, and ATP. Suspensions of such ghosts prepared from pre-aggregative and post-aggregative cells retain the aggregative capacities of the cells from which they were derived whether in the presence or absence of EDTA. Thus both types of adhesion appear to result from simple interactions between the plasma membranes which are neither ATP dependent nor metabolically driven (209). The two types of adhesion appear to be associated with two classes of cell surface antigens called A and B (16). Homologous univalent antibody fragments (F_{ab}) inhibit each type of adhesion separately (15, 16). The A-sites are virtually absent in stationary phase cells and accumulate prior to and during aggregation. They presumably cause the end-to-end (EDTA-resistant) binding. Titrations with ^3H-F_{ab} indicate the presence of about 3×10^5 A-sites/cell. The B-sites are present in both stationary phase and developing cells at the level of ca 2.5×10^6 sites/cell and appear to be homogeneously dispersed over the cell surface. Presumably they cause side-to-side (EDTA-sensitive) binding (16, 17). Trypsin treatment can specifically inactivate EDTA-resistant adhesivity by aggregative-competent cells without affecting EDTA-sensitive binding (3). Trypsin-treated cells can be recovered during subsequent incubation either in suspension or on a solid substratum but not in the presence of cycloheximide. Experiments with cell ghosts derived from disaggregated, trypsinized, and recovered cells show that these changes are associated exclusively with the cell surface (3).

The cell membrane has been purified to a high state of homogeneity (99, 106, 197) and characterized in a variety of ways in order to correlate changes in composition and topography with the acquisition of aggregative competence. "Discoidin," a carbohydrate binding protein with specific hemagglutinin activity, has been isolated from aggregation-competent cells of *D. discoideum* and a corresponding protein with different binding specificity from *Polysphondylium violaceum* (182, 183). However, the evidence implicating discoidin in the adhesive process is not yet compelling. Intact pre- and post-aggregative cells have been labeled with ^{125}I by the lactoperoxidase procedure (197). Membranes from aggregation competent cells contained a labeled component absent in vegetative cells. However, aggregates formed in suspension also lacked the component and formed it only when they were dispersed on solid substratum and allowed to form apical nipples. Hence the protein may titillate the student of cell contact-induced gene expression (see a later section) but does not appear to be involved in the adhesive process. Changes in phospholipid composition of the membrane have also been reported (56, 238).

The adhesion of highly washed ghosts (both types of adhesion) requires the presence of a cofactor (209). Any of the cations Ca^{2+}, Mn^{2+}, Zn^{2+}, or Cu^{2+} (but not

Mg^{2+}, Co^{2+}, or Ni^{2+}) were active. In binding assays with $^{45}Ca^{2+}$ and $^{54}Mn^{2+}$, ghosts and sonicates thereof showed the presence of two classes of binding sites, one with affinity for Ca^{2+} only and a second with affinity for either Ca^{2+} or Mn^{2+}. The latter class increased fifteen to twenty fold prior to the onset of aggregation (210).

Fishing expeditions have been carried out with conconavalin-A as bait. Vegetative cells are agglutinated strongly; aggregation competent cells very weakly (232). The binding sites are dispersed over the cell surface but move freely to produce the usual capping phenomenon (90). An antigenically active glycoprotein which accumulates on the cell surface prior to aggregation reacts with Con-A (238) and hence may be the binding site. The presence of Con-A impeded the onset of aggregation and induced the accumulation of membrane bound 3',5'-cyclic AMP phosphodiesterase 10–12 hr prematurely (91). Structural changes in the unit membrane during acquisition of aggregative competence have been observed by freeze etching of fractured membranes (2) and by scanning electron microscopy (187).

CHEMOTAXIS, cAMP, cAMP SITES, AND THE MORPHOGENETIC FIELDS OF *D. DISCOIDEUM*   3',5'-cyclic AMP (cAMP) has been shown to be the chemotactic agent produced by the centers and streams during aggregation in *D. discoideum* (130). It also appears to be a primary means by which vegetative cells locate and move toward bacterial prey (131). The transition from vegetative to aggregation-competent cells is accompanied by a dramatic increase in their production of and sensitivity to cAMP (21). Of seven species and two genera examined, four were attracted to cAMP in chemotactic assays, but all were found to produce cAMP and to secrete an extracellular cAMP-specific phosphodiesterase (26).

Specificity   Extensive studies (127–129) of the relative chemotactic activities of cAMP analogs has revealed that for *D. discoideum* cells the purine ring is most important (cGMP is 10^{-3} and cIMP 10^{-4} less active than cAMP); any change in the 5' position of the ribose reduces the activity; the 3'5' cyclic phosphate ring is essential but replacements of O with NH_2 or CH_2 are permissible.

The cAMP site   Radioautographs suggest that little if any cAMP penetrates the cell and hence the cAMP receptor must lie in or on the plasma membrane (152). Freeze-etched, fractured membranes contain particulate structures which appear to swell when aggregation-competent cells are exposed to exogenous cAMP (98). The functional detection of the receptor site is made difficult by the presence of membrane bound and extracellular phosphodiesterase (see below) which destroy the added cAMP almost immediately. Fortunately, cGMP is an excellent substrate for the enzyme but is 3 orders of magnitude less effective as a chemotactic agent. Transient binding of ^3H-labeled cAMP to intact aggregation-competent cells was carried out in the presence of excess cGMP (85, 146, 147). cAMP was bound to the surface with an affinity constant of ca 10^{-7} (within the range of chemotactic effectiveness) and then decayed while 5'-AMP appeared simultaneously in the medium. Binding specificities of cAMP analogs corresponded to their relative chemotactic activities. The estimated number of binding sites per cell was 5×10^5.

cAMP-related enzymes in D. discoideum   The membrane bound and extracellular phosphodiesterase have been subjects of intensive study. The enzyme appears to be initially released as a protein of 135,000 molecular weight with relatively high substrate affinity (39) and undergoes slow conversion to a form of molecular weight 65,000 with low substrate affinity (39, 166). The conversion is prevented or reversed by dithiothreitol. The membrane bound and extracellular phosphodiesterases showed identical binding affinities and rates with a series of cAMP analogs (145), thereby raising the possibility that the former is the precursor of the latter. Cells incubated in the presence of anti-phosphodiesterase γ-globulin failed to aggregate and the inhibition was reversible (93). Mutants with defective phosphodiesterases show deranged aggregation patterns (180). The release by stationary phase cells of a heat stable macromolecule which combines with and inactivates the extracellular phosphodiesterase has been reported (87, 179, 180). Some aggregation-defective mutants either failed to release the inhibitory factor or released it late.

The presence of an adenylate cyclase activated by 5'-AMP and an ATP pyrophosphohydrolase (which converts ATP directly to 5'-AMP) and which is activated by cAMP, as well as a 5'-nucleotidase, have been reported (188, 189). These together with the phosphodiesterase might form a double feedback regulatory loop in vivo such that when a cell is exposed to a pulse of cAMP it would make an amplified pulse of cAMP. All these enzymes are associated with the cell membrane (E. F. Rossomando, unpublished results).

Oscillatory response to and production of cAMP   Pulses of cAMP delivered periodically to an agar surface through a micro electrode at a frequency of $\sim$4.5/min induced the formation of an aggregate at the electrode tip (181). Suspensions of aggregation-competent cells show periodic spikes or sinusoidal oscillations of light-scattering properties (reflecting changes of shape or volume) and correlated changes in the redox state of cytochrome *b* (86). The property is acquired about 3–4 hr after the start of the stationary phase, i.e. at the onset of aggregation. Addition of exogenous cAMP to preaggregative-competent cells induces a double response: a fast spike which shows ancillary characteristics of the chemotactic response and a slower spike resembling those formed spontaneously by aggregation-competent cells. Addition of cAMP to the latter can either change the phase or wipe out the oscillation altogether. It can readily be imagined that this oscillating behavior would be accompanied by and perhaps directed by the oscillatory production and release of cAMP. Work of Gerisch and collaborators (unpublished data) indicates very convincingly that this is the case. Using the feedback loop of cAMP associated enzymes previously described and the kinetic properties reported (189), Goldbeter (94) has shown by computer simulation that an oscillatory pattern of cAMP production can be generated spontaneously.

Other and later functions of cAMP   The migrating slug of *D. discoideum* constitutes a classical morphogenetic field in which the apical tip provides polarity and exerts physiological dominance (177). The apex of the developing fruiting body is thought to serve in a similar capacity during fruit construction (178). It is likely that cAMP mediates in these later morphogenetic events. Bioassays have shown that these apical regions continue to secrete the chemotactic agent differentially (19), and a recent immunohistochemical study (164) confirmed the presence of bound cAMP in these regions. Exposure of migrating slugs and developing fruits to high concentrations of cAMP in the substratum wipes out polarity and dominance and induces multiple and topographically bizarre fruiting structures (161). A theoretical model in which cAMP production is linked to the activation of "front" and "rear" cell surface contact-sensing molecules can simulate the observed distribution of cAMP within the aggregate under a variety of conditions (149). A cAMP binding protein with extremely high affinity ($K_a \sim 10^{-7}$M) has been found to accumulate at the later stages of *D. discoideum* development (148). Its function is not yet accounted for.

PATTERNS OF AGGREGATION   The patterns formed by aggregating cell populations have for many years been subjects of experimental (7, 25, 82, 194, 215) and theoretical analyses (45, 121). The aim has been to account for the initiation of the aggregative centers and to relate the numbers, sizes, and territorial extents of the aggregates to such parameters as population density, cell number, genetic constitution, etc. *D. discoideum* cells when aggregating at high cell density move toward the center by concerted periodic movements observed in time-lapse films as concentric waves (1, 89). At first glance it would appear to be related to the cAMP-associated pulsations exhibited by aggregation-competent cells in suspension, and it is being reexamined in great detail from this viewpoint (1).

The Migrating Slug

SLUG OR FRUIT   Slug migration is not an obligatory preamble to fruit construction in *D. discoideum*. A newly formed aggregate transforms into a slug in response to: pH (high); buffer capacity (low or absent); salt concentration (low); humidity (high). This pathway can also be induced by accumulation of a metabolite[3] secreted by the cells before and during aggregation (196, 238). An aggregate prior to the 17 hr stage of fruit construction, if shifted to conditions which favor slug migration, will abandon the fruiting program and transform into a slug. If shifted afterward, it remains committed to fruit construction. In the dark, the slug migrates randomly. In a horizontal light gradient it moves directly toward the light source, turning if necessary (27, 171). Any time (from less than an hour to many days) the slug is shifted to conditions which favor fruiting, it stops migrating immediately and constructs a fruiting body over a 7 hr period. Exposure to overhead light also induces the transition from slug to fruit, and this environmental signal appears to override all the others (160).

The slug-fruit transition is influenced in a highly specific manner by the inosine analog, Formycin B (30). Exposure to this drug under conditions which otherwise favor fruiting causes the aggregate at the 17 hr stage of fruit construction to deviate

[3]Recent unpublished work in our laboratory indicates that the material is of low molecular weight (around 250), volatile, and neither acidic nor basic to a significant degree. It has already been prepared in purified form and should be identified shortly.

and transform into a slug. Shortly thereafter it reverts to the fruiting mode and completes the formation of a normal fruit without further interference. The morphogenetic deviation always begins at the 17 hr stage regardless of when the Formycin B was added or of the concentration employed. A slug shifted to conditions which favor fruiting and simultaneously exposed to Formycin B enters the fruiting mode, but having reached the 17 hr stage reverts to slug migration a second time before completing the fruiting process! Recent work (208) indicates that this agent exerts its effect by interfering with guanosine metabolism. It acts as a competitive inhibitor of the enzyme purine ribonucleoside phosphorylase which converts guanosine to guanine and ribose-1-P. Externally supplied guanosine reverses the Formycin B-induced deviation, depending on the concentration of the two. The internal guanosine pool accumulates progressively after addition of Formycin B(thereby eventually overcoming the competitive inhibition), and the higher the concentration of Formycin B, the longer the duration of the slug stage. Four other competitive inhibitors of the nucleoside phosphorylase induce precisely the same morphogenetic duration. Considerable information about the pathways of guanosine metabolism has already been collected (208). Identification of the product required to trigger or maintain fruit construction when made should open the way to some exceedingly fruitful (sorry) investigations.

ORGANIZATION OF THE SLUG The slug is surrounded by a cortical sheath composed of protein; short, randomly oriented cellulose fibrils; and a polysaccharide containing N-acetyl glucosamine, fucose, and mannose (88, 111). The slug moves within this sheath, and it remains as a collapsed tube, marking the migratory path. Temperature-sensitive structural gene mutants for N-acetyl glucosaminidase (53), developing at the restrictive temperature, form slugs containing only about a tenth the normal number of cells and migrate at only a third of the normal rate (although this could be mainly a reflection of reduced size). Radioautography after short pulses of ^{14}C-GNAC suggest that cells throughout the length of the slug contribute to the formation of the sheath, so that it must be thinnest at the apex and thickest at the tail (141). This apparently is the cause of a differential permeability barrier which severely restricts inward diffusion along the posterior 80% of the slug and probably restricts outward diffusion as well (61). It has been suggested (5, 61, 141) that these differential aspects of sheath structure and function contribute to the determination of the developmental fates of the cells as a function of their position along the longitudinal axis. The role of the sheath in affecting the migratory function and in maintaining directional polarity has recently been demonstrated (141). Raper (177) had reported that after cutting the slug, the anterior segment continued to migrate with its original polarity while the posterior segment stopped. However, if the sheath is removed from the cut surface of the posterior segment, it develops a new tip and continues to migrate (141). If the sheath is removed from both ends of a median segment, in about half the cases it develops a new tip at the rear and reverses its migratory polarity.

Depending on their relative positions, the cells in the slug have already begun the developmental programs that lead to the appearance of spores and stalk cells. Thus

UDP-galactosyl polysaccharide transferase activity (involved in the synthesis of the mucopolysaccharide outer spore layer) is detected only in the prespore contingent (The posterior cells) and not in the prestalk cells (the anterior 20%), whereas another enzyme, UDP-glucose pyrophosporylase, is homogeneously distributed (155). Stalk specific and spore specific antigens (among them the spore mucopolysaccharide) and prespore vesicles are correspondingly distributed (96, 153, 224). As noted, cAMP accumulates only in the apex and apparently contributes to the maintenance of polarity and developmental dominance. In some strains the prespore and prestalk cells differ with respect to buoyant density (225) and cell size (28). Once the aggregate is established, reassortment of the cells is virtually nonexistent (62) despite earlier observations (20, 23) which are of doubtful significance because the staining techniques employed are now known to be ambiguous (62). However, considerable assortment may occur during the formation of the aggregate and the very early stages of its development, depending on physiological inhomogeneities that may have arisen during growth. Slugs have been formed from mixed populations of two mutants of strain AX-2 (132). These were grown separately under nutritional conditions which lead to significant differences in their physiological state (78). The cells assorted randomly if grown in identical media, preferentially if grown on different media. When segments were fused the cells reassorted in a manner consistent with their nutritional history. In these strains buoyant density differences did not affect assortment.

As noted previously (132), assortment within the slug, though influenced by nutritional history, does not commit cells unalterably to their developmental fates. First, segments of an aggregate can separately form normal fruits, and hence the cells must be able to reverse their development programs according to their altered relative positions. Second, the fruity mutant Fty-1 can form normal fruits with the usual proportions of spores, stalk and basal disc cells from aggregates composed of as few as 10–12 cells and perhaps even fewer (201). In this circumstance prior commitments to specific developmental fates would be expected to lead to wide statistical variations in the proportions, and these are not observed.

PHOTOTAXIS   The action spectrum for phototaxis by migrating slugs yields peaks at 430 and 560 nm respectively, the blue being the more sensitive (75, 170). The dissociated cells when irradiated show a difference spectrum with two peaks, a small fast decaying (half decay time $= 7$ sec) peak at 411 induced by light at 550–600 nm and a larger slower decaying peak at 430 which is induced by light at < 520 nm (170, 172).

This photo response could be duplicated in cell extracts and was found to be associated with the particulate fraction. The active material has been solubilized (by sonication) and purified (169, 170, 172). The 2000X purified photoreceptor appears to be a heme protein of 240,000 molecular weight and the light-induced changes resemble the photoreduction of a b-type cytochrome. It is suggested (169) that the photoactive complex consists of a receptor pigment, possibly a flavin absorbing at 465 nm and a photoresponder which is the cytochrome. Possibly the two prosthetic groups reside on the same protein carrier as in a b_2-type cytochrome. The authors conclude that this photoactive complex closely resembles others characterized previously in Phycomycetes, algae, and in higher plants and animals. The mechanism of phototaxis has recently been reexamined (171). In agreement with previous findings (24), the apical 5–10% of the slug was shown to be the photosensitive area. Slugs allowed to move in a liquid film whose refractive index exceeded that of the slugs became photophobic. Illumination of only one side of the apex, using a narrow vertical beam, induced the slug to turn away from the illuminated side. If irradiated from both sides by equally intense horizontal beams, the slug moved straight ahead but twice as rapidly as before. It is concluded that the convex apical surface acts as a lens, focusing the light distally. The cells on the photoexcited distal side of the apex are induced to move twice as fast as those on the proximal side, thereby causing the apex to turn in the direction of the horizontal beam. (In making the turn the peripheral side would by geometrical calculation need to move 60% in the same time period.)

Cytodifferentiation Within the Fruiting Body

In recent years a combination of biochemical studies and electron microscopic fine structure analyses have yielded a wealth of details concerning the development of spores, stalk cells, and basal disc cells; the construction of the stalk sheath and the stalk cell cortex; the morphology and physiology of spore germination.

STALK AND BASAL DISC CELL DEVELOPMENT   Recent work (80, 109, 111) has extended and refined earlier studies (22, 95, 178). Food vacuoles disappear before aggregation and are replaced after aggregation by autophagic vacuoles. Mitochondrial inclusions disappear and the mitochondria condense. Electron transparent vesicles disappear in the prestalk and prebasal disc cells concurrently with the appearance of prespore vacuoles in the prespore cells. The prestalk cells swell markedly (in contrast to the prespore cells which shrink) and display the first sign of nuclear degeneration. Ultimately their cytoplasmic content also degenerates and comprises a relatively thin layer surrounding an enlarged central vacuole. The entire cell is finally enclosed within a relatively thick cortical layer of cellulose.

Stalk sheath construction   (80) Having initially constructed the stalk sheath rudiment during a concerted downward movement at 16–18 hr, the cells begin their "inverted fountain" migration up the outside surface of the sheath, then turn at the apex inward and downward. At this time the leading prestalk cells, the intermediate prespore cells, and the rearguard prebasal disc cells form clearly separate cell groups but without visible signs of physical barriers. Some of the rearguard cells climb up the outside of the sheath, forming a layer between it and the concurrently rising prespore cells. The sheath increases in height via deposition of cellulose by the apical cells just before they turn inward and move downward. The sheath increases in thickness through deposition of cellulose by the stalk cells that have already moved downward and come to rest. The cellular cortices also form at this time.

Within the apex, particularly at the tip, the cells are flattened and elongated with their long axes horizontal, i.e. perpendicular to the direction of migration. Their contents are stratified into an inner zone filled with cellulose fibrils and with filopodial processes that touch the sheath and are surrounded by extracellular cellulose deposits, next a zone of mitochondria, a zone of autophagic vacuoles, the nucleus, and finally a heterogeneous cytoplasmic zone.

SPORE DEVELOPMENT   This process is marked by the degeneration of mitochondria, appearance of autophagic vacuoles, emergence of endoplasmic reticulum, and formation of two types of vesicles: the prespore vacuoles (97, 110, 111, 144) apparently lined with mucopolysaccharide, which ultimately link with the cell membrane and evaginate thereby producing the outer spore coat; spore vesicles (97) with a transparent interior and a peripheral double layer of structures resembling ribosomes. These vesicles are thought to sequester trehalose. The spore wall consists of an outer mucopolysaccharide layer, two fibrillar median layers composed of cellulose, one oriented and the other random, and an inner layer which can be disrupted only by the joint action of pronase and cellulase (47, 97, 107, 110). The spore interior contents include condensed mitochondria surrounded by ribosomes, protein crystals, spore vesicles, lipoidal deposits, and a compressed vacuole which probably gives rise to autophagic vacuoles during germination (47, 97, 144).

SPORE GERMINATION   This consists of three stages: activation, swelling of the coat, and emergence of the vegetative amoeba (47, 49–51). The variety of germination-defective mutants thus far isolated suggests that the actions of many proteins are involved (58, 123). Activation requires the prior removal of a spore germination inhibitor produced during fruit construction and presumably designed to prevent germination in situ. This self-inhibitor was recently identified as N,N-dimethyl guanosine (12), and reported to act by inhibiting protein synthesis without affecting RNA synthesis or respiration (11). This identification has been contested (225a). Activation can be accomplished by heat (49), dimethyl sulfoxide (48), or in a mixture of exogenous metabolites and bacterial metabolic products, since untreated spores germinate in a complex medium with bacteria with an efficiency of almost 100% (49). Morphological changes during swelling and emergence have been described in detail (50). The splitting of the spore coat is accomplished enzymatically and can be inhibited by cycloheximide (50). The energy sources for all these activities are initially free glucose (34) and later trehalose (47).

DNA Composition

CHROMOSOME ORGANIZATION   The genome size of haploid *Dictyostelium* is 36×10^{10} daltons (219), i.e. about 15 times that of *E. coli*. Of this total, ca 30% is mitochondrial (69, 219). When separated on CsCl gradients, three bands are evident. The origins and properties of these bands are detailed in Table 2 (69, 219).

　　When renaturation is monitored by optical methods, 70% of the nuclear DNA is found to consist of single-copy sequences characterized by a $Cot_{1/2}$ (pure) of 70. The 30% repetitive sequences are present in three classes which hybridize at $Cot_{1/2}$ (pure) values of 4×10^{-4}, 0.065, and 1.3 (69). The ribosomal RNA cistrons comprise 2.2% of nuclear DNA (ca 150 copies per haploid genome) and

Table 2 Characterization of *Dictyostelium* DNA

Nuclear	Density[a]	G + C (%)[a]	Fraction of total[a]
Mainband	1.676, 1.683	23, 23	~0.70, 0.60-0.65
Satellite	1.687 —	28 —	0.05-0.07, —
Mitochondrial	1.682, 1.688	33, 28	0.24-0.28, 0.35-0.40

[a]Comparative figures shown are from (69) and (219), respectively.

band at rho=1.682, in the same region as mitochondrial DNA. The composition of rRNA is 43% G+C (165).

Recent studies (73) on the organization of the genome have demonstrated that 60–70% of the nuclear DNA consists of single-copy sequences 1000–1500 nucleotides in length interspersed with short reiterated sequences of 250–450 nucleotides. (20–30% of the single-copy sequences are *not* associated with a repetitive sequence.) A second class of reiterated sequences (not associated with single copy sequences) is greater than 1000 base-pairs in length.

Dictyostelium DNA contains segments of oligo dT extending over 25 nucleotides (118). These segments comprise 0.3% of the nuclear DNA, enough to code for 15,000 copies. The copies are interspersed rather than clustered (73, 118).

These findings, together with studies of the structure of RNA transcripts, have served as the basis for a model of genome organization shown in Figure 3. (72–74, 134).

Dictyostelium DNA is associated with basic, histone-like proteins similar to those found in the true slime mold *Physarum polycephalum* and the ciliate protozoa *Tetrahymena pyriformis* (52).

RNA Composition and Metabolism

RIBOSOMAL RNA SYNTHESIS AND PROCESSING   *Dictyostelium* possesses typical eukaryotic 80S ribosomes, composed of 60S and 40S subunits (38, 115). The initial transcript of rRNA is apparently a 36S precursor which matures, via 30S and 28S intermediates, to 26S RNA, and via 19S to 17S RNA (114). The large ribosomal subunit (50S in high ionic strength gradients) is formed via 43S and 47S intermediates, both of which contain the precursor to 26S RNA. The small subunit (30S in high ionic strength gradients) matures from a 25S particle which contains 17S RNA (151). The newly formed 40S subunit reaches the cytoplasm before the 60S (36, 122, 150) in growing cells. The ribosomal subunits are stable during growth (35, 44) but are degraded during morphogenesis on a large scale so that by the end of the sequence more than 75% of the old ribosomes have been replaced with ribosomes containing newly synthesized rRNA (44, 218). The processing of the rRNA precursors is greatly slowed (122), and in contrast to the growth phase, the 40S subunits are retained in the nucleus for extended periods (122, 150). The reason why cells developing in starvation conditions degrade old ribosomes and replace them with new is not understood. Comparison by base composition, hybridization competition (218), and sequence analysis (A. Jacobson, private communication) of ribosomal

STRUCTURE AND TRANSCRIPTION OF DICTYOSTELIUM DNA

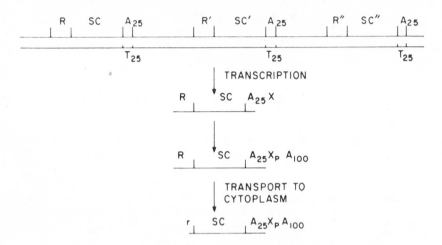

Figure 3   Model of genome structure and transcription in *Dictyostelium* (72–74, 133, 134). The primary transcription unit consists of a reiterated sequence (R), a single copy sequence (SC), and an oligo dA-dT sequence 25 bases long. After this unit is transcribed, a poly-A sequence of 100 bases (A_{100}) is added at the 3' end of the RNA molecule, and some portion of the reiterated sequences at the 5' is removed, leaving a small reiterated sequence (r).

RNAs extracted from growing and developing cells revealed no differences. However, specific differences in ribosomal proteins have been detected (J. M. Ashworth, private communication). The significance of the retention of 40S subunits in the nucleus is not known.

A mutant of *Dictyostelium*, which possessed nucleoli during growth but lost them during development, was isolated and subsequently lost (113). The aggregates stopped morphogenesis before culmination, failing to produce spores or stalk cells. If disaggregated and provided with food, the cells reconstructed nucleoli.

STRUCTURE, SYNTHESIS, AND PROCESSING OF MESSENGER RNA   Greater than 95% of cytoplasmic heterogeneous RNA (5S–16S; average size 400,000 daltons) is present on polysomes (74). At least 90% of these molecules possess a covalently linked sequence of poly-A, permitting purification on poly-U Sepharose (71). The latter is a 125-nucleotide sequence and is composed of two poly-A subsequences present in approximately equimolar amounts, one of ca 25 nucleotides and one of ca 100 nucleotides, separated by a small number of non-A residues. Since there are no sequences of oligo dT of length 100 in the DNA, the poly-A-100 sequence must be added post-transcriptionally (118). The poly-A_{25} is believed to be transcribed from the DNA since, as noted above, there are oligo-dT_{25} sequences in the nuclear DNA of sufficient number and distribution, and since its kinetics of appearance in the cytoplasm are similar to those of the structural part of the message

(73, 118). About 90% of messenger RNA purified by poly-U Sepharose chromatography renatured to single-copy DNA sequences (71).

The heterogeneous nuclear RNA (hnRNA) sediments in a broad peak whose average molecular weight is 500,000 daltons, 25% larger than mRNA, and no component larger than the ribosomal RNA precursor has been detected (74, 122). The hnRNA contains poly-A_{25} and poly-A_{100} in a molar ratio of 3–4:1. When purified by poly-U Sepharose chromatography, 25% of the sequences renature to reiterated sequences in the DNA (74). Thus some sequences (reiterated) are present in the nucleus but absent from the cytoplasm. This is also substantiated by experiments in which DNA copies of messenger RNA were made with reverse transcriptase (72, 230). These copies hybridize to over 90% of the mRNA, but to only ca 70% hnRNA, indicating that some sequences exist in the nucleus which do not appear in the cytoplasm. In pulse-chase experiments, 75% of the poly-A-containing hnRNA appeared in the cytoplasm. Thus a large amount of the hnRNA serves as a precursor to mRNA, and the material which is lost must be enriched in reiterated sequences. Two extreme alternatives may be proposed (74): (*a*) There are two classes of RNA molecules. One is greatly enriched in reiterated sequences and is degraded within the nucleus, while the other is fully conserved in transport to the cytoplasm. (*b*) There is only one class of molecules. All contain a reiterated sequence, some portion of which is removed and degraded in the nucleus, while the remaining sequence is fully conserved during passage to the cytoplasm.

The hnRNA has been fractionated into molecules which contain both classes of poly-A sequences and those which contain only the poly-A_{25}. The former renatures to DNA with the same kinetics as mRNA, while the latter is enriched in reiterated sequences (73). According to model *a* above, the latter molecules would represent molecules destined to be degraded within the nucleus. According to model *b*, these are primary transcript molecules to which the poly-A_{100} sequence has not been added, and from which the reiterated sequences have not been removed. Two experiments shed light on these alternatives. Although only 70% of the hnRNA *sequences* hybridized with cDNA made from mRNA, greater than 90% of the hnRNA *molecules* contained hybrid regions (72). In addition, in experiments in which the location of reiterated sequences in mRNA and hnRNA was examined, it was found that the 10% reiterated sequences in mRNA are equally distributed between the 5' and 3' halves of the molecule, while the reiterated sequences were concentrated in the 5' half of the hnRNA molecules (74). Both of these findings favor model *b* above. On the basis of these experiments and the structure of the genome described above, a model of transcription and processing of mRNA in *Dictyostelium* was proposed (72–74, 133, 134; see Figure 3) in which the primary unit of transcription consists of a reiterated sequence, followed by a single-copy structural gene, and terminated by a poly-A_{25} sequence. The poly-A_{100} sequence is added post-transcriptionally, at the same time that the reiterated sequences are being removed from the 5' end (73). A complication is the recent finding (133) that the 5' end of both mRNA and poly-A containing nuclear RNA contain methylated nucleotides similar to those found in mammalian systems. The validity of this model will be rigorously established only when the synthesis and processing of specific mRNAs is examined. Such studies are presently in progress in several laboratories.

The kinetics and logistics of mRNA processing and transport are quite different in cells engaged in fruit construction as compared with those growing exponentially (122). In the latter, nascent mRNA appears in the cytoplasm after a 6 min lag and is transported virtually quantitatively within an hour. In the former the lag is 20 min, and even after many hours a significant proportion remains sequestered in the nucleus.

CHANGES IN THE mRNA POPULATION DURING GROWTH AND MORPHO-GENESIS   Cytoplasmic mRNA samples from exponentially growing cells and from those at several different stages of fruit construction have been hybridized to single-copy DNA (65). Taken together they hybridized with 56% of the single-copy DNA (16,000 genes of 1000 nucleotide pairs). Competition studies revealed that as the cells move from exponential growth through the various stages of fruit construction, qualitative changes in the mRNA population occur. The increase in synthesis of actin during the first hours of development is paralleled by a corresponding increase in the amount of actin mRNA (133).

Changes in Protein Constitution During Growth and Morphogenesis

Protein degradation and synthesis are major activities during fruiting body construction (9, 76, 77, 100, 102, 229, 234, 243). Available turnover estimates (77, 100, 243) indicate that of the protein present in vegetative cells as little as 10% may survive in the cells comprising the mature fruit, i.e. as much as 90% may have been synthesized during aggregation, slug migration, and/or fruit construction. As will be seen, significant changes in protein constitution appear to take place as the result of altered differential rates of synthesis and disappearance of specific proteins. In these studies, particular proteins have been characterized by their activities as enzymes, antigens, binding proteins, or as cell membrane, spore coat, or slime sheath components, or identified as bands in SDS acrylamide gel electrophorograms.

ENZYME ACCUMULATION AND DISAPPEARANCE   At least 15 well-character-ized proteins have been shown to increase significantly in specific activity during particular stages of fruit construction. Subsequently some of them disappear partially or completely. They include:

alanine transaminase (70)
leucine aminopeptidase (70)
N-acetyl glucosaminidase (55, 59, 60, 135)
α-mannosidase (59, 138, 176)
trehalose-6-P synthetase (30, 104, 156, 191)
threonine deaminase (173, 174)
tyrosine transaminase (173)
uridine diphosphate glucose pyrophosphorylase (8, 55, 158, 176)
UDP-galactose-4-epimerase (226)
UDP-galactosyl: polysaccharide transferase (214)
glycogen phosphorylase (67, 68, 116)
alkaline phosphatase (137, 168)

β-glucosidase (46, 176)
trehalase (33, 191)
inorganic pyrophosphatase (J. M. Ashworth, private communication)

Isozymic forms exist in at least five of the above: threonine deaminase (175), alkaline phosphatase (137), β-glucosidase (46), N-acetyl glucosaminidase (54), UDP-glucose pyrophosphorylase (158). Four of these involve the replacement of one isozyme present uniquely or predominantly during vegetative growth by a second form which accumulates during fruit construction while the first remains constant or disappears.

The frequency of isozyme replacement thus far encountered suggests that the process may occur ubiquitously during fruit construction. Thus relatively slight variations in total activity may in fact involve wholesale changes in the population of molecules. In most of the examples cited above, the changes in enzyme activity have been shown to accurately reflect changes in the level of a protein either by measurements of serological activity in crude extracts or by actual physical separation.

The pattern of accumulation and disappearance of trehalose-6-P synthetase previously reported for bacterial grown *D. discoideum* (30, 104, 156, 191) has been seriously criticized on the grounds (*a*) that the enzyme is cold sensitive, thereby reducing the accuracy of the activity measurements, and (*b*) that the vegetative cells possess considerable activity which, however, is masked by association with another protein (125). The significance of these criticisms is open to question since a reexamination (4) showed that the enzyme is in fact not cold sensitive at all and is undetectable in bacterial grown cells when care is taken to sample them during exponential growth, nor could evidence of masked enzyme in stationary phase (or vegetative) cells be confirmed.

Similarly, criticisms by Wright & Dahlberg (246) of the regulatory pattern reported for UDP-glucose pyrophosphorylase was shown to be the result of instability of the enzyme in vitro due to their unfortunate choice of buffers (158) and to the contaminating presence of 6-phosphogluconate dehydrogenase activity whose effect was magnified by their choice of assay conditions (55). There now appears to be general agreement (100) about the developmental kinetics of this enzyme in cells grown both axenically and with bacteria, as well as agreement that the reported increase in activity reflects an equivalent increase in the quantity of enzyme protein per cell (76, 77, 100).

Modulation of enzyme levels also occurs during exponential growth in response to nutritional variations. The levels of a number of enzymes, including N-acetyl glucosaminidase, UDP-glucose pyrophosphorylase, α-mannosidase and β-glucosidase (6, 237), as well as trehalose-6-P synthetase (4, 104), have been shown to change significantly depending on whether the cells are grown axenically or in association with bacteria.

ACTIN   The reported presence of an actomyosin complex associated with the cell membrane (242) has been confirmed, and the actin and myosin have been isolated and characterized (41). SDS-acrylamide gel separations of extracts from cells labeled in short pulses with ^{35}S-methionine have shown that actin is synthesized at an enormous differential rate during the early stages of fruit construction (229). Thus in the first 2 hr after entrance into the stationary phase, actin synthesis represented 22% of the total rising from a level of 4% during vegetative growth. Subsequently the differential rate progressively decreased to the 4% level by the end of cell aggregation. No estimates are yet available concerning the absolute changes in the absolute level of actin brought about by these alterations in the differential rate of synthesis.

OTHER PROTEINS   Evidence ranging from delicately suggestive to strongly compelling indicate dramatic shifts in the levels of other proteins during slug migration and fruit construction. These include changes in cell membrane components, particularly those associated with the acquisition of aggregative competence (15, 182, 183, 197, 199, 238), the protein component of the sheath which covers the migrating slug and which is spun out behind as it moves over considerable distances (111), the synthesis of microtubules, ER lamellae and specific vesicles associated with spore differentiation (47, 97, 110, 144), proteins present in the spore coat layers (107), changes in levels of proteins capable of binding cAMP (147, 148), and of binding Ca^{2+} or Mn^{2+} (210).

DIFFERENTIAL PROTEIN SYNTHESIS   Cycloheximide is a reversible inhibitor of protein synthesis in D. discoideum (206). Cells exposed in situ to cycloheximide at any stage of fruiting body construction stop further development immediately (206). If disaggregated and redeposited on filters in the presence of cycloheximide, the cells immediately reaggregate and recapitulate previous morphogenesis within 2–3 hr, but when they have reached the stage at which they were dispersed they stop further development (157). Migrating slugs, switched to conditions which would normally induce them to stop migrating and to construct fruiting bodies, remain slugs if exposed to cycloheximide (159). Finally, spore germination is blocked in the presence of cycloheximide. All these effects are reversible after removal of the agent. Hence it must be concluded that some protein synthesis is required to accomplish every stage of D. discoideum development.

D. discoideum has been labeled with ^{35}S-methionine during consecutive 2 hr pulses throughout the period of aggregation and fruiting body construction (229). Crude cell extracts were separated on SDS-acrylamide gels and radioautographed. The results show that: (a) many bands are marked by dramatic increases and/or decreases in intensity at specific stages of fruit construction, denoting initiation or cessation of synthesis of one or more proteins within those bands; (b) gels obtained from labeled vegetative cells produce radioautographs with a huge number of intense bands and a continuous high background between, denoting the synthesis of a wide variety of proteins. This continues during the preaggregative period, but intensity changes do occur within a considerable number of bands. (The changes in the differential rate of actin synthesis have already been described.) After aggregation the background diminishes and most of the label is restricted to 30–40 well-defined bands. Since different bands emerge and disappear during this period, and since each band may consist of several polypeptides of identical molecular weight, the number of different proteins synthesized at the later stages may well be many times that number.

These results indicate that changes in the differential rates at which particular proteins are synthesized (i.e. the rate with respect to the synthesis of other or all other proteins) are manifold and dramatic throughout morphogenesis. They suggest further that the formation of cell aggregates is not only an important morphogenetic event but may also serve to signal the cells to stop synthesizing a wide variety of proteins as well as to initiate the synthesis of others. This is consistent with results described in a later section (Morphogenetic Feedback).

The synthesis of UDP-glucose pyrophosphorylase has also been examined from this viewpoint. This enzyme rises about tenfold after aggregation to a peak level near the end of fruit construction which comprises about 0.5% of the total cell protein. Cells were labeled during pulses covering all stages of development. The enzyme was quantitatively precipitated from cell extracts with anti-pyrophosphorylase γ-globulin, redissolved in SDS and the enzyme subunit peak separated by SDS-acrylamide gel electrophoresis in order to determine the associated radioactivity and to calculate the differential incorporation ratio, i.e. ratio of radioactivity incorporated into the enzyme protein as a percentage of the radioactivity incorporated into all proteins during the labeling period. For very short pulses where turnover could be minimized, this ratio was equivalent to the differential rate of synthesis. Before aggregation when the enzyme level held constant, the synthesis of the pyrophosphorylase was found to amount initially to no more than 0.04% of the total, rising to about 0.08% near the end of the preaggregative period. As the enzyme accumulated, the ratio increased to a peak value of 0.7% and then declined. Thus the accumulation could be accounted for in a simple manner by the increased differential rate of synthesis of this protein (76, 77). On the basis of similar experiments, Gustafson et al (100, 102) have concluded that the enzyme is synthesized at a constant rate throughout growth and development both temporally and differentially and that the accumulation after aggregation is due to a decreased rate of degradation. Their incorporation data were expressed as cpm-incorporated/μg enzyme protein and cpm incorporated/μg total cell protein. Since both of these quantities change during development with respect to time and to one another (total enzyme increases and total protein decreases), it is difficult to evaluate their results. However, when expressed in the form of differential incorporation ratios as described above, they turn out to be in qualitative agreement with the data of Franke et al (76, 77). Thus, during the preaggregative period the ratio was 0.075% and rose to 0.22% during the period of enzyme accumulation. Relatively long labeling periods were employed, and this may have contributed to the fact that the differential rate rose only threefold instead of nine to tenfold, but the fact is it did rise significantly, and hence the conclusion reached by Gustafson et al (100, 102) is untenable.

TRANSLATIONAL CONTROLS   The existence of translational controls has been invoked (229) to explain certain rapid changes in the differential rates of protein synthesis during the shift from exponential growth to the stationary phase and the start of the fruiting program, after disaggregation of and reaggregation of cells (156, 157) and during the switch from slug migration to fruit construction (57, 159).

In this connection the virtually complete replacement of ribosomes present in vegetative cells by those synthesized during aggregation and fruit construction (44) raises the possibility that ribosomal specificity plays a role in regulating mRNA ribosomal association and/or initiation of translation. No differences in the rRNA have been detected, but specific differences may exist in respect to the ribosomal proteins (J. M. Ashworth, private communication).

PRETRANSLATIONAL CONTROLS   As already described, the population of ribosome-associated mRNA molecules does change qualitatively and quantitatively during the course of growth and development. Hence pretranslational controls must operate to regulate transcription and/or processing, transport, and association of the transcript with ribosomes. Consistent with this are the findings that exposure to actinomycin D stops further morphogenesis (after a brief lag) at any stage of fruit construction (66, 211), stops the environmentally induced transition from migrating slug to fruit (159), prevents the appearance of specific organelles such as the prespore vacuoles (97), and inhibits spore germination (47). Depending on the time of addition, prior exposure to actinomycin D (8, 46, 59, 67, 70, 135, 137, 156, 173, 190, 216, 226) or to a mixture of actinomycin and daunomycin (66) completely prevents or decreases the extent of accumulation of each of the enzymes mentioned previously. A study of the hybridization of mRNA to single-copy DNA (65) has shown that extensive changes take place in the mRNA population as the cell moves from vegetative growth through the various stages of fruit construction.

These results have led to the conclusion (134, 213) that pretranslational controls predominate in the regulation of morphogenesis and cytodifferentiation. Certainly the evidence is encouraging enough to warrant further systematic investigations of the levels of control. Some information along these lines already exists. Multiple DNA-dependent RNA polymerases have been purified and characterized (175). They appear to be typical eukaryotic polymerases. No evidence was obtained to indicate a difference between the enzymes present in vegetative cells and in cells taking part in fruit construction. As already noted, kinetic studies of mRNA synthesis and transport (122) have indicated that whereas in vegetative cells entrance of newly made RNA into the cytoplasm is very rapid and complete within a short period, during fruit construction the entrance is delayed and not complete even after several hours. Hence it may be that mRNA processing or transport is not only slower but is preferentially regulated. One of the potentially most fruitful experimental approaches has recently been initiated by establishing optimal conditions for RNA synthesis and processing by isolated nuclei (117, 198).

ENZYME DISAPPEARANCE THROUGH PREFERENTIAL RELEASE   This phenomenon was first observed in the case of UDP-galactose polysaccharide transferase (212). During the period of its synthesis 100% of the activity was associated with the cells, but shortly after the peak level had been attained most of the activity was released into the extracellular space along with about 2% of the total cell protein. UDP-galactose-4-epimerase, which supplies the substrate for the transferase, was shown to be released concurrently (226). Sequestration of the two enzymes within vesicles responsible for mucopolysaccharide synthesis was postulated at that time (226). Structures of this type, called "prespore vacuoles," have been described and shown to contain the mucopolysaccharide (97, 110, 144).

Similarly, trehalase is released during aggregation, and it has been suggested that this plays a role in the accumulation of trehalose (33). Already described is the continuous release of cAMP phosphodiesterase. In addition, a number of enzymes are excreted via lysosomal release (10, 237), including N-acetyl glucosaminidase.

MORPHOGENETIC FEEDBACK AND THE REGULATION OF PROTEIN ACCU-MULATION AND DISAPPEARANCE   The patterns of enzyme accumulation and disappearance have been shown to be intimately tied to the morphogenetic sequence and to keep perfectly in step with it. A wide variety of morphogenetically deficient mutants described in a previous section have been examined in this respect (8, 55, 68, 70, 135, 139, 173, 174, 191, 200, 214, 226, 249). The mutants studied include those which: do not begin aggregation; stop during or at the end of aggregation; stop after aggregation but short of mature fruiting bodies; transform into migrating slugs but do not fruit; are temporally deranged. Some are temperature sensitive, developing normally at 22°C but defective at 27°C. The findings are consistent and are summarized below.

1. Enzyme accumulation and/or disappearance are disturbed in a manner consistent with the stage at which morphogenesis is blocked and the stage at which the enzyme in question normally accumulates or disappears. Thus mutants which show no overt signs of aggregation fail to accumulate any of the enzymes described previously. Others blocked after aggregation accumulate early enzymes like N-acetyl glucosaminidase at the normal rate and to the usual extent, but trehalose-6-P synthetase activity, though it accumulates normally, does not disappear, and later enzymes like UDP-glucose pyrophosphorylase do not accumulate at all. In a mutant blocked after the construction of the fruiting body but before the final transformation of prespore cells into spores, UDP-galactosyl polysaccharide transferase accumulates normally but is not released and does not disappear.

2. If in a given mutant the regulatory pattern of one enzyme is disturbed, then the patterns of all other enzymes associated with later morphogenetic events are also disturbed.

3. Two types of temporally deranged mutants have been isolated in which morphogenesis and cell differentiation (including the appearance of spores and stalk cells) occur either too rapidly or too slowly. The regulative patterns of *all* of the enzymes are consistently accelerated or decelerated in strict correspondence with the altered timing of the morphogenetic events.

Recent studies indicate that the cells within the developing aggregate receive three kinds of morphogenetic information and modulate the patterns of enzyme accumulation and disappearance accordingly.

Positional information   As noted previously, the developmental fate of a cell is determined by its axial position within the aggregate. Aggregates engaged in fruit construction and slug migration were sampled (apex vs base, inside vs outside, etc) to determine the specific activities of UDP-glucose pyrophosphorylase and UDP-galactosyl polysaccharide transferase at various developmental stages. The former accumulated homogeneously in all parts of the aggregates. The latter was uniquely associated with the prespore cells (155).

Morphogenetic status of the aggregate as a whole   The regulatory patterns of four functionally related enzymes have been examined in aggregates engaged in fruit construction, in migrating slugs, and in slugs that have been induced to stop migrating and switch to fruit construction (30, 57, 159, 208). The results for four of these are shown in Figures 4 and 5. In the slug two of these enzymes accumulate at the same rate as in the fruit, one much more slowly and the fourth not at all. Those that do accumulate reach the same peak activities as they do in the fruit but then disappear either very slowly or not at all. When a slug is induced to stop migrating and start fruiting, a belated though otherwise normal round of UDP-Galactose-4-epimerase accumulation and disappearance occurs perfectly in step with the usual stages of fruit construction. No additional trehalose-6-P synthetase accumulates, but the enzyme already present disappears at the same stage as it would have in an aggregate that had fruited directly. In the case of UDP-galactosyl polysaccharide transferase, the previously accumulated enzyme disappears dramatically (possibly by preferential release), and then a complete second round is accomplished once again in step with the appropriate stages of fruit construction. In the case of UDP-glucose pyrophosphorylase, depending on the time at which the slug is induced to fruit, it either rapidly completes the normal round of synthesis, or if that has already been completed, initiates a second complete round. These events, morphogenetic and enzymic, can be prevented by prior exposure to actinomycin D or actinomycin plus daunomycin and hence appear to be under pretranslational control.

When aggregates engaged in fruit construction are induced by exposure to Formycin B to temporarily transform into migrating slugs and subsequently to revert to the fruiting program, the regulatory patterns of the four enzymes are modulated in step with each morphogenetic change in a manner completely consistent with those described in Figures 4 and 5 (30). In contrast, the patterns of two other enzymes—N-acetyl glucosaminidase and alanine transaminase—which accumulate long before aggregation are unaffected by the specific morphogenetic pathway elected.

Cell contact-mediated regulation of enzyme expression   As described previously, aggregation appears to trigger a significant change in the pattern of protein synthesis revealed by SDS-acrylamide gels (229) and by the accumulation and disappearance of specific enzyme activities. Disaggregation terminates the synthesis of these enzymes and reaggregation triggers complete new rounds of synthesis from newly made transcripts (31, 79, 156, 157). However, enzymes which normally accumulate before aggregation, like N-acetylglucosaminidase, remain unaffected by disaggregation and subsequent reaggregation. Recently it was found (31) that mutant Fr-17, late in its development, loses the capacity for cell contact-mediated regulation. Cells from aggregates dispersed late in development when redeposited on filters do not reaggregate but remain as an uneven lawn of cells. However, they can go on to differentiate into normal appearing spores and stalk cells! The patterns of enzyme accumulation and disappearance also reflect loss of the ability to signal the fact of disaggregation and the failure to reaggregate.

In what molecular forms the cells receive all these varieties of morphogenetic information and how the programs of gene expression are modulated thereby would seem to be among the most fascinating biochemical problems to be faced in the near future.

QUANTAL CONTROL (213)   As outlined above, a given enzyme can accumulate rapidly or slowly, now or later, and by two or even three successive rounds of synthesis, depending upon shifts in the morphogenetic program or the establishment of cell contacts via aggregation or reaggregation. The data for a considerable number of such enzymes indicate that under all these conditions initiation of a synthetic round if allowed to progress undisturbed invariably results in the accumulation of a quantal level of activity characteristic of that particular enzyme (i.e. 300–350 units of UDP-glucose pyrophosphorylase, 16–18 units of UDP-galactose-4-epimerase, etc) regardless of the level previously accumulated. The same quantal response occurs during growth in response to nutritional conditions (5). This may reflect a basic quantal feature of the system of gene expression that follows from the way in which mRNA is synthesized, processed, or translated in this organism. As pointed out elsewhere (5), data for eight glycolytic enzymes in yeast suggest that their synthesis may also be quantally ordered (108) and may indicate a generality of mechanism.

Carbohydrate Metabolism During Growth and Morphogenesis

THE MAJOR SACCHARIDES ASSOCIATED WITH MORPHOGENESIS   The total hexose content of bacterial grown *D. discoideum* is about 500 μg glucose equivalent/10^8 cells and remains constant or increases slightly during fruit construction (234). However, extensive changes in carbohydrate content occur due to the synthesis of specialized products. The major ones are listed below:

Cellulose   It is present in the spore coat (47, 107, 110), in the outer cylindrical sheath of the fruiting body stalk in the thickened stalk cell walls (178), and as small fibrils in the sheath of the migrating slugs (111). Cellulose accumulates during fruiting by bacterial grown *D. discoideum* to about 100–150 μg/10^8 cells starting from an insignificant level (185, 236).

Mucopolysaccharide   This is composed of galactose, N-acetylgalactosamine, and galacturonic acid (235), is associated exclusively with the prespore cells and mature spores (235), and serves as the outer spore coat (107). It accumulates from an undetectable level to a peak of about 50 μg/10^8 cells.

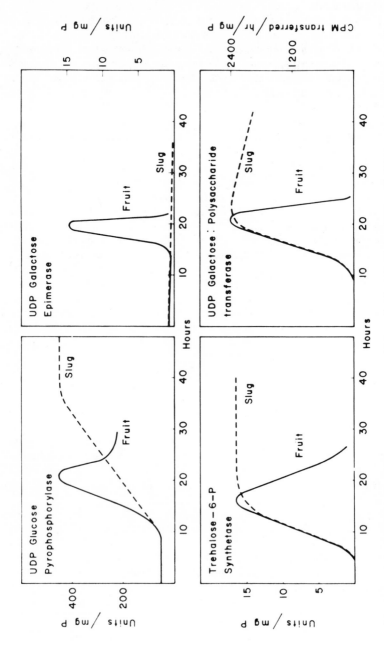

Figure 4   Comparisons of enzyme expression in aggregates which are fruiting directly, and those which have transformed into migrating slugs.

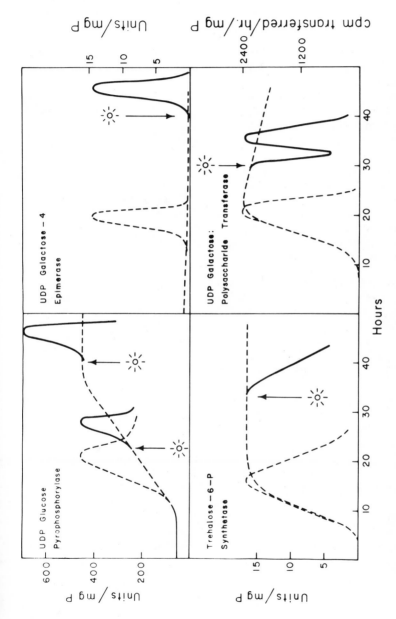

Figure 5 Changes in the expression of enzymes when migrating slugs are induced to fruit by exposure to light. Dotted lines: enzyme patterns in aggregates fruiting directly and aggregates which are following the migrating slug pathway (see Figure 4). Solid lines: enzyme patterns after migrating slugs have been induced to fruit.

Trehalose   This disaccharide is low or absent in vegetative cells, is present in the spores, and is hydrolyzed during germination (27). It normally accumulates during fruit construction to a level of about 150 $\mu g/10^8$ cells in *D. discoideum* (37, 103, 104), although a lower value (50 $\mu g/10^8$) was recently reported (185)[3].

Slug sheath polysaccharides   These are present as components of the sheath spun out behind the advancing slug. They are composed of N-acetyl glucosamine, mannose, and fucose (88).

In mutants which cannot begin or complete fruit construction, saccharides normally synthesized after the morphogenetic block do not appear, and in temporally deranged mutants the temporal patterns of the accumulations are correspondingly affected (235, 236). Hence these biosynthetic events must be developmentally regulated.

These saccharide syntheses are carried out against a background of glycogen formation and degradation. Although previously explored (103, 185, 234, 235), a recent series of papers (6, 55, 103–105, 176, 233) has provided a more definitive characterization of glycogen metabolism during growth and morphogenesis and its impingement upon the entire pattern of saccharide synthesis. It has also provided a very useful method of dissecting the regulatory features of this metabolic network and has already cleared away some previous misconceptions (245).

GLYCOGEN CONTENT DURING GROWTH AND FRUIT CONSTRUCTION
Strain Ax-2 was grown in axenic medium containing glucose in concentrations ranging between 0 and 86 mM. The glycogen contents of the resulting stationary phase cells ranged between 50 μg and 5.6 mg/10^8 cells. In the glucose containing media, transition from exponential to stationary phase was accompanied by preferential synthesis of glycogen which raised the level as much as threefold from the log phase level. At all times glycogen degradation was negligible. The levels appear to be set by the concentration of the synthetase (233). The glycogen content of *A. aerogenes* grown stationary phase Ax-2 cells is about 30 $\mu g/10^8$ cells (148), but the latter are half the volume and mass of the axenically grown individuals.

In populations containing more than 100 μg glycogen/10^8 cells, the level falls very sharply (in proportion to the initial content) over the first 5 hr of fruit construction and less sharply thereafter. All end up with the same low level regardless of initial content. In populations containing less than 100 μg glycogen/10^8, i.e. Ax-2 grown in media with little or no glucose or cells grown with *A. aerogenes,* the level also falls sharply during the first 5 hr. However, after the onset of aggregation it rises dramatically to a peak and approaches the levels retained at that time by the cells which started with higher glycogen contents, but eventually it falls to the same low level in the mature fruit. Rosness et al (185) have reported that glycogen content

---

[3]It should be noted that the temporal pattern of trehalose accumulation reported by Hames & Ashworth (103, 104) is very much different from that described by Wright and collaborators (185, 246). The former find that trehalose synthesis starts at a much earlier stage of fruit construction than reported by the latter and is biphasic, reaching an intermediate plateau between 13 and 21 hr stages.

in *E. coli*-grown cells remains constant at about 150 μg/10^8 cells and then falls near the end of fruit construction.

RATES OF GLYCOGEN SYNTHESIS AND DEGRADATION   The rate of glycogen synthesis increases dramatically at the onset of aggregation (5 hr) and then falls during the late stages of fruit construction. The rate of glycogen degradation remains high and relatively constant throughout the first 12 hr of fruit construction and then falls (105). In cells with initially high glycogen content, the synthetic component is overshadowed by the degradative and the net level decreases smoothly. In cells with initially low glycogen content the reverse is true, and this accounts for the initial fall and subsequent rise (105, 236). Most of the degraded glycogen is converted to nonhexose materials, and despite earlier conclusions (42), the hexose supply appears to be replenished by a significant rate of gluconeogenesis (43).

EFFECTS OF INITIAL GLYCOGEN CONTENT ON PATTERNS OF SACCHARIDE SYNTHESIS AND OTHER ASPECTS OF MORPHOGENESIS   A comparison was made between stationary phase populations that contained 5.6 and 0.3 mg glycogen/10^8 cells. During fruit constrution the former accumulated 25% more cellulose, 150% more mucopolysaccharide, 200% more free glucose, and 300% more trehalose (104). However, the temporal patterns were identical.

Stationary phase populations with glycogen content ranging between 50 μg and 5 mg/10^8 cells constructed fruiting bodies of identical appearance and over exactly the same time period. Patterns of accumulation and/or disappearance of a number of enzymes, including UDP-glucose pyrophosphorylase, trehalose-6-P synthetase, trehalose, and glycogen synthesase, were identical temporally and quantitatively although glycogen phosphorylase did accumulate to a somewhat higher peak level in the latter population. Finally the net losses and turnover rates of total cell protein and RNA were unaffected, suggesting to the authors (103, 104) that these processes are not needed merely to provide an energy source but must play a more intrinsic role, i.e. to facilitate qualitative changes in the protein and RNA populations. Taken together, these results suggest that rather drastic changes in the carbohydrate economy can be accomodated without feeding back upon and altering the overall pattern of morphogenesis or the temporal and quantitative aspects of cytodifferentiation (other than with respect to a carbohydrate content per se). Hence these changes can scarcely be viewed absolutely as "critical variables in differentiation" (245). Hames & Ashworth (103, 104) provide a particularly trenchant discussion in this respect. They are impressed by the fact that although the supply of carbon and energy can be enormously varied via the hundredfold change in the initial levels of glycogen the timing and quality of fruit construction remains largely unaltered. They feel that this rules out the simplistic view (244) of starvation (i.e. a diminished energy supply) as a trigger or a timing device for cell differentiation.

LEVELS OF REGULATION   Glycogen synthetase activity remains relatively constant during fruit construction (105). Hence the differential pattern of glycogen synthesis cannot be ascribed to changes in enzyme concentration. The synthetase was initially reported to be activated by G-6-P (246), but it now appears that the enzyme is inhibited by ATP and G-6-P acts by reversing this inhibition (233). Since intracellular G-6-P does rise significantly over the first 5 hr (103, 104), it may indeed play a regulatory role. A concurrent rise in UDP-glucose (103, 104) may also play a role via increased substrate availability. In this connection it should be noted that UDP-glucose pyrophosphorylase activity may be regulated in part by the level of intracellular pyrophosphate. The latter strongly inhibits the forward reaction by binding at a noncatalytic site (76). Inorganic pyrophosphatase activity has been found (J. M. Ashworth, unpublished data) to rise significantly during fruit construction and might conceivably be the controlling element in vivo.

Glycogen breakdown is quite complicated. Glycogen phosphorylase activity is detectable only after 10 hr and peaks at 20 hr (67, 68, 116). Hence it can only account for the last stages of glycogen disappearance and the earlier degradation must be hydrolytic. Some evidence supports the possibility that two separate through interconnected glycogen pools exist during fruit construction (103, 104). Activation of glycogen phosphorylase by cAMP has been reported and this too may play a role in vivo (184).

Bauman & Wright (13) have characterized phosphofructokinase and examined it as a potential site of gluconeogenic regulation in vivo. The enzyme is inhibited by ADP and pyrophosphate and this is competitively overcome by ATP. It is also inhibited by fructose-1,6-diphosphate, and this is competitively overcome by fructose-6-phosphate. The pattern is not one to be expected for a pathway primarily involved in energy generation. The authors suggest a primarily biosynthetic role, possibly for the production of triose and acetate building blocks to be used when glucose (and ATP) are in excess.

Enzyme excretion may play a role in controlling the synthesis of trehalose since the observed release of trehalase during aggregation (33, 34) coincides with the first phase of trehalose accumulation. However, the biphasic kinetics remain mysterious. Trehalose itself may be sequestered in specific spore vesicles (97), thus opening the way to some sort of topographical control. Compartmentalization also certainly plays a prominent role in the synthesis of the mucopolysaccharide which is associated with the prespore vacuoles.

In recent years an ambitious attempt (101, 126, 247) has been made to simulate the temporal and quantitative aspects of the saccharide metabolic network, using a computer to solve simultaneously a series of differential equations physically characterized in terms of in vivo substrate levels and reaction rates (measured by radioactive precursor incorporation and decay), K_m values where known, enzyme concentrations where known, and several gratuitous assumptions. The details of these computations and the conclusions reached have been described and discussed at length elsewhere (101, 126, 244) and will not be resummarized here. However, the recent data of Ashworth et al (6, 55, 103–105, 176, 233) indicate that both the assumptions and the equations should be revised. In particular the assumption of negligible gluconeogenesis during fruit construction must be discarded. The observed rate of glycogen degradation is said (233) to be contrary to the requirements of the kinetic model. The observed changes in the levels of UDP-glucose and glucose-6-P during fruiting, particularly as a function of initial glycogen content, are different from those predicted by computer simulation (6, 176). Finally, the suggestion (248) that trehalose, cellulose, and mucopolysaccharide accumulation are controlled in common by simple regulation of the UDP-glucose pool does not jibe with the observed disproportionate variations in these end products in cells with differing initial glycogen contents. The computational approach is also said (6, 176) to be seriously hampered by the assumption that the enzymes involved obey simple Michaelis-Menton kinetics in vivo and by the disregard of the compartmentalization now known to exist of enzymes, substrates, and products.

Literature Cited

1. Alcantara, F., Monk, M. 1974. *J. Gen. Microbiol.* 85: 321
2. Aldrich, H. C., Gregg, J. H. 1973. *Exp. Cell Res.* 81:407
3. Alexander, S., Brackenbury R., Sussman, M. 1975. *Nature* 754:698
4. Alexander, S., Sussman, M. 1975. *Dev. Biol.* 46:211
5. Ashworth, J. M. 1971. *Symp. Soc. Exp. Biol.* 25:27
6. Ashworth, J. M., Quance, J. 1972. *Biochem. J.* 126:601
7. Ashworth, J. M., Sackin, M. J. 1969. *Nature* 224:817
8. Ashworth, J. M., Sussman, M. 1967. *J. Biol. Chem.* 242:1696
9. Ashworth, J. M., Watts, D. J. 1970. *Biochem. J.* 119:175
10. Ashworth, J. M., Wiener, E. 1972. *Lysosomes in Biology and Pathology*, ed. J. T. Dingle, 3:36. Amsterdam: North-Holland
11. Bacon, C. W., Sussman, A. S. 1973. *J. Gen. Microbiol.* 76:331
12. Bacon, C. W., Sussman, A. S., Paul, A. G. 1973. *J. Bacteriol.* 113:1061
13. Baumann, P., Wright, B. E. 1968. *Biochemistry* 7:3653
14. Beug, H., Gerisch, G. 1972. *J. Immunol. Methods* 2:49
15. Beug, H., Gerisch, G., Kempff, S., Riedel, V., Cremer, G. 1970. *Exp. Cell Res.* 63:147
16. Beug, H., Katz, F. E. Gerisch, G. 1973. *J. Cell Biol.* 56:647
17. Beug, H., Katz, F. E., Stein, A., Gerisch, G. 1973. *Proc. Natl. Acad. Sci. USA* 70:3150
18. Blaskovics, J. C., Raper, K. B. 1957. *Biol. Bull.* 113:58
19. Bonner, J. T. 1949. *J. Exp. Zool.* 110:259
20. Bonner, J. T. 1959. *Proc. Natl. Acad. Sci. USA* 45:379
21. Bonner, J. T. 1971. *Ann. Rev. Microbiol.* 25:75–92

22. Bonner, J. T., Chiquoine, A. D., Kolderie, M. 1955. *J. Exp. Zool.* 130:133
23. Bonner, J. T., Clark, W., Neely, C., Slifkin, M. 1950. *J. Cell. Comp. Physiol.* 36:149
24. Ibid, 149
25. Bonner, J. T., Dodd, M. 1962. *Biol. Bull.* 122:13
26. Bonner, J. T., Hall, E. M., Noller, S., Oleson, F. B. Jr., Roberts, A. B. 1972. *Dev. Biol.* 29:402
27. Bonner, J. T., Shaw, M. J. 1957. *J. Cell. Comp. Physiol.* 50:145
28. Bonner, J. T., Sieja, T. W., Hall, E. M. 1971. *J. Embryol. Exp. Morphol.* 25:457
29. Born, G. V. R., Garrod, D. 1968. *Nature* 220:616
30. Brackenbury, R. W., Schindler, J., Alexander, S., Sussman, M. 1974. *J. Mol. Biol.* 90:529
31. Brackenbury, R. W., Sussman, M. 1975. *Cell* 4:347
32. Brody, T., Williams, K. L. 1974. *J. Gen. Microbiol.* 82:371
33. Ceccarini, C. 1966. *Science* 151:454
34. Ceccarini, C. 1967. *Biochim. Biophys. Acta* 148:114
35. Ceccarini, C., Campo, M. S., Andronico, F. 1970. *J. Cell Biol.* 46:428
36. Ceccarini, C., Campo, M. S., Andronico, F. 1970. *J. Mol. Biol.* 54:33
37. Ceccarini, C., Filosa, M. F. 1965. *J. Cell. Comp. Physiol.* 66:135
38. Ceccarini, C., Maggio, R. 1968. *Biochim. Biophys. Acta* 166:134
39. Chassy, B. M. 1972. *Science* 175:1016
40. Clark, M. A., Francis, D., Eisenberg, R. 1973. *Biochem. Biophys. Res. Commun.* 52:672
41. Clarke, M., Spudich, J. A. 1974. *J. Mol. Biol.* 80:209
42. Cleland, S. V., Coe, E. L. 1968. *Biochim. Biophys. Acta* 156:94
43. Ibid 1969. 192:446
44. Cocucci, S. M., Sussman, M. 1970. *J. Cell. Biol.* 45:399

45. Cohen, M. 1971. *Symp. Soc. Exp. Biol.* 25:455
46. Coston, M. B., Loomis, W. F. 1969. *J. Bacteriol.* 100:1208
47. Cotter, D. A., Miura-Santo, L. Y., Hohl, H. R. 1969. *J. Bacteriol.* 100:1020
48. Cotter, D. A., O'Connell, R. W. 1974. *Am. Soc. Microbiol. Abstr.*, p. 29
49. Cotter, D. A., Raper, K. B. 1966. *Proc. Natl. Acad. Sci. USA* 56:880
50. Cotter, D. A., Raper, K. B. 1968. *J. Bacteriol.* 96:86
51. Ibid, 1690
52. Coukell, M. B., Walker, J. O. 1973. *Cell Differ.* 2:87
53. Dimond, R., Brenner, M., Loomis, W. F. 1973. *Proc. Natl. Acad. Sci. USA* 70:3356
54. Dimond, R., Loomis, W. F. 1974. *J. Biol. Chem.* 249:5628
55. Edmundson, T. D., Ashworth, J. M. 1972. *Biochem. J.* 126:593
56. Ellingson, J. S. 1974. *Biochim. Biophys. Acta* 337:60
57. Ellingson, J. S., Telser, A., Sussman, M. 1971. *Biochim. Biophys. Acta* 244:388
58. Ennis, H. L., Sussman, M. 1975. *J. Bacteriol.* 124:62
59. Every, D., Ashworth, J. M. 1973. *Biochem. J.* 133:37
60. Ibid 1974. 143:785
61. Farnsworth, P. A., Loomis, W. F. 1974. *Dev. Biol.* 41:77
62. Farnsworth, P. A., Wolpert, L. 1971. *Nature* 231:329
63. Filosa, M. F., Chan, M. 1972. *J. Gen. Microbiol.* 71:413
64. Filosa, M. F., Dengler, R. E. 1972. *Dev. Biol.* 29:1
65. Firtel, R. A. 1972. *J. Mol. Biol.* 66:363
66. Firtel, R. A., Baxter, L., Lodish, H. F. 1973. *J. Mol. Biol.* 79:315
67. Firtel, R. A., Bonner, J. 1970. *Fed. Proc.* 29:669
68. Firtel, R. A., Bonner, J. 1972. *Dev. Biol.* 29:85
69. Firtel, R. A., Bonner, J. 1972. *J. Mol. Biol.* 66:339
70. Firtel, R. A., Brackenbury, R. W. 1972. *Dev. Biol.* 27:307
71. Firtel, R. A., Jacobson, A., Lodish, H. F. 1972. *Nature New Biol.* 239:225
72. Firtel, R. A., Jacobson, A., Tuchman, J., Lodish, H. F. 1974. *Genetics* 78:355
73. Firtel, R. A., Kindle, K., Huxley, M. P. 1976. *Fed. Proc.* 35:13
74. Firtel, R. A., Lodish, H. F. 1973. *J. Mol. Biol.* 79:295
75. Francis, D. 1964. *J. Cell. Comp. Physiol.* 64:131
76. Franke, J., Sussman, M. 1971. *J. Biol. Chem.* 246:6381
77. Franke, J., Sussman, M. 1973. *J. Mol. Biol.* 81:173
78. Garrod, D. R., Ashworth, J. M. 1972. *J. Embryol. Exp. Morphol.* 28:463
79. Garrod, D., Ashworth, J. M. 1973. *Symp. Soc. Gen. Microbiol.* 23:407
80. George, R. P., Hohl, H. R., Raper, K. B. 1972. *J. Gen. Microbiol.* 70:477
81. Gerisch, G. 1959. *Naturwissenschaften* 46:654
82. Gerisch, G. 1961. *Dev. Biol.* 3:685
83. Gerisch, G. 1962. *Naturwissenschaften* 48:436
84. Gerisch, G. 1968. *Curr. Top. Dev. Biol.* 5:157
85. Gerisch, G., Beug, H., Schwartz, H., Stein, A. 1974. *Miami Winter Symp.* 7:49
86. Gerisch, G., Hess, B. 1974. *Proc. Natl. Acad. Sci. USA* 71:2118
87. Gerisch, G., Malchow, D., Riedel, V., Müller, E., Every, M. 1972. *Nature New Biol.* 235:90
88. Gerisch, G., Malchow, D., Wilhelms, H., Lüderitz, O. 1969. *Eur. J. Biochem.* 9:229
89. Gerisch, G., Normann, I., Beug, H. 1966. *Z. Naturwiss.* 53:618
90. Gillette, M. U., Dengler, R. E., Filosa, M. F. 1974. *J. Exp. Zool.* 190:243
91. Gillette, M. U., Filosa, M. F. 1973. *Biochem. Biophys. Res. Commun.* 53:1159
92. Gingold, E. B., Ashworth, J. M. 1974. *J. Gen. Microbiol.* 84:70
93. Goidl, E. A., Chassy, B. M., Love, L. L., Krichevsky, M. I. 1972. *Proc. Natl. Acad. Sci. USA* 69:1128
94. Goldbeter, A. 1975. *Nature* 253:540
95. Gregg, J. H. 1965. *Dev. Biol.* 12:377
96. Gregg, J. H. 1966. *The Fungi*, ed. A. Sussman, 2:235. New York: Academic
97. Gregg, J. H., Badman, S. 1970. *Dev. Biol.* 22:96
98. Gregg, J. H., Nesom, M. G. 1973. *Proc. Natl. Acad. Sci. USA* 70:1630
99. Green, A. A., Newell, P. C. 1974. *Biochem. J.* 140:313
100. Gustafson, G. L., Kong, W. Y., Wright, B. E. 1973. *J. Biol. Chem.* 248:5188
101. Gustafson, G. L., Wright, B. E. 1972. *Crit. Rev. Microbiol.* 1:453
102. Gustafson, G. L., Wright, B. E. 1973. *Biochem. Biophys. Res. Commun.* 50:438
103. Hames, B. D., Ashworth, J. M. 1974. *Biochem. J.* 142:301
104. Ibid, 317
105. Hames, B. D., Weeks, G., Ashworth, J. M. 1972. *Biochem. J.* 126:627

106. Hammond, J. R. M. 1973. *Biochim. Biophys. Acta* 291:371
107. Hemmes, D. E., Kojima-Buddenhagen, E. S., Hohl, H. R. 1972. *J. Ultrastruct. Res.* 41:406
108. Hess, B., Boilenx, A., Kruger, J. 1969. *Adv. Enzyme Regul.* 7:149
109. Hohl, H. R., George R. P. 1966. *J. Cell. Biol. 31:* 47A
110. Hohl, H. R., Hamamoto, S. T. 1969. *J. Ultrastruct. Res.* 26:442
111. Hohl, H. R., Jehli, J. 1973. *Arch. Microbiol.* 92:179
112. Hohl, H. R., Raper, K. B. 1963. *J. Bacteriol.* 85:199
113. Ishida, S., Maeda, Y., Takeuchi, I. 1973. *J. Gen. Microbiol.* 81:491
114. Iwabuchi, M., Mizukami, Y., Sameshima, M. 1971. *Biochim. Biophys. Acta* 228:693
115. Iwabuchi, M., Ochiai, H. 1969. *Biochim. Biophys. Acta* 190:211
116. Jones, T. H. D., Wright, B. E. 1970. *J. Bacteriol.* 104:754
117. Jacobson, A., Firtel, R. A., Lodish, H. F. 1974. *J. Mol. Biol.* 82:213
118. Jacobson, A., Firtel, R. A., Lodish, H. F. 1974. *Proc. Natl. Acad. Sci. USA* 71:1607
119. Katz, E. R., Kao, V. 1974. *Proc. Natl. Acad. Sci. USA* 71:4025
120. Katz, E. R., Sussman, M. 1973. *Proc. Natl. Acad. Sci. USA* 69:495
121. Keller, E. F., Segal, L. A. 1970. *J. Theor. Biol.* 26:399
122. Kessin, R. H. 1973. *Dev. Biol.* 31:242
123. Kessin, R. H., Newell, P. C. 1974. *J. Bacteriol.* 117:379
124. Kessin, R. H., Williams, K. L., Newell, P. C. 1974. *J. Bacteriol.* 119:776
125. Killick, K. A., Wright, B. E. 1972. *J. Biol. Chem.* 247:2967
126. Killick, K. A., Wright, B. E. 1974. *Ann. Rev. Microbiol.* 28:139–66
127. Konijn, T. M. 1973. *FEBS Lett.* 34:263
128. Konijn, T. M. 1974. *Antibiot. Chemother.* 19:96
129. Konijn, T. M., Jastorff, B. 1973. *Biochim. Biophys. Acta* 304:774
130. Konijn, T. M., Van de Meene, J. G. C., Bonner, J. T., Barkley, D. S. 1967. *Proc. Natl. Acad. Sci. USA* 58:1152
131. Konijn, T. M., Van de Meene, J. G. C., Chang, Y. Y., Barkley, D. S., Bonner, J. T. 1969. *J. Bacteriol.* 99:510
132. Leach, C. K., Ashworth, J. M., Garrod, D. R. 1973. *J. Embryol. Exp. Morphol.* 29:647
133. Lodish, H. F., Alton, T., Dottin, R. P., Weiner, A. M., Margolskee, J. P. 1975. In *The Molecular Biology of Hormone Action,* 34th Symp. Soc. Dev. Biol. In press
134. Lodish, H. F., Jacobson, A., Firtel, R., Alton, T., Tuchman, J. 1974. *Proc. Natl. Acad. Sci. USA* 71:5103
135. Loomis, W. F. 1969. *J. Bacteriol.* 97:1149
136. Ibid. 99:65
137. Ibid. 100:417
138. Ibid 1970. 103:375
139. Loomis, W. F. 1970. *Exp. Cell Res.* 60:285
140. Ibid 1971. 64:484
141. Loomis, W. F. 1972. *Nature* 240:6
142. Loomis, W. F., Ashworth, J. M. 1969. *J. Gen. Microbiol.* 53:181
143. Macinnes, M. A., Francis, D. 1974. *Nature* 251:321
144. Maeda, Y., Takeuchi, I. 1969. *Dev., Growth & Differ.* 11:232
145. Malchow, D., Fuchila, J., Jastorff, B. 1973. *FEBS Lett.* 34:5
146. Malchow, D., Gerisch, G. 1973. *Biochem. Biophys. Res. Commun.* 55:200
147. Malchow, D., Gerisch, G. 1974. *Proc. Natl. Acad. Sci. USA* 71:2423
148. Malkinson, A. M., Kwasniak, J., Ashworth, J. M. 1973. *Biochem. J.* 133:601
149. McMahon, D. 1973. *Proc. Natl. Acad. Sci. USA* 70:2396
150. Mizukami, Y., Iwabuchi, M. 1970. *J. Biochem. (Tokyo)* 67:501
151. Mizukami, Y., Iwabuchi, M. 1972. *Biochim. Biophys. Acta* 272:81
152. Moens, P. B., Konijn, T. M. 1974. *FEBS Lett.* 45:44
153. Muller, U., Hohl, H. R. 1973. *Differentiation* 1:267
154. Newell, P. C. 1971. *Essays Biochem.* 7:87
155. Newell, P. C., Ellingson, J., Sussman, M. 1969. *Biochim. Biophys. Acta* 244:2990
156. Newell, P. C., Franke, J., Sussman, M. 1972. *J. Mol. Biol.* 63:373
157. Newell, P. C., Longlands, M., Sussman, M. 1971. *J. Mol. Biol.* 58:541
158. Newell, P. C., Sussman, M. 1969. *J. Biol. Chem.* 244:2990
159. Newell, P. C., Sussman, M. 1970. *J. Mol. Biol.* 49:627
160. Newell, P. C., Telser, A., Sussman, M. 1969. *J. Bacteriol.* 100:763
161. Nestle, M., Sussman, M. 1972. *Dev. Biol.* 28:545
162. Nickerson, A. W., Raper, K. B. 1973. *Am. J. Bot.* 60:190
163. Ibid, 247
164. Pan, P., Bonner, J. T., Wedner, H. J., Parker, C. W. 1974. *Proc. Natl. Acad. Sci. USA* 71:1623

165. Pannbacker, R. G. 1966. *Biochem. Biophys. Res. Commun.* 21:340
166. Pannbacker, R. G., Bravard, L. J. 1972. *Science* 175:1014
167. Pannbacker, R. G., Wright, B. E. 1966. *Biochem. Biophys. Res. Commun.* 24:334
168. Parish, R. W., Pelli, C. 1974. *FEBS Lett.* 48:293
169. Poff, K. L., Butler, W. L. 1974. *Nature* 248:799
170. Poff, K. L., Butler, W. L., Loomis, W. F. 1973. *Proc. Natl. Acad. Sci. USA* 70:813
171. Poff, K. L., Loomis, W. F. 1973. *Exp. Cell Res.* 82:236
172. Poff, K. L., Loomis, W. F., Butler, W. L. 1974. *J. Biol. Chem.* 249:2164
173. Pong, S. S., Loomis, W. F. 1971. *J. Biol. Chem.* 246:4412
174. Ibid 1973. 248:4867
175. Pong, S. S., Loomis, W. F. 1973. *J. Biol. Chem.* 248:3933
176. Quance, J., Ashworth, J. M. 1972. *Biochem. J.* 126:609
177. Raper, K. B. 1940. *Am. J. Bot.* 27:436
178. Raper, K. B., Fennell, D. I. 1952. *Bull. Torrey Bot. Club* 79:25
179. Riedel, V., Gerisch, G. 1971. *Biochem. Biophys. Res. Commun.* 42:119
180. Riedel, V., Gerisch, G., Müller, E., Beug, H. 1973. *J. Mol. Biol.* 74:573
181. Robertson, A., Drage, C., Cohen, M. 1972. *Science* 175:333
182. Rosen, S. D., Kafka, J. A., Simpson, D. L., Barondes, S. H. 1973. *Proc. Natl. Acad. Sci. USA* 70:2554
183. Rosen, S. D., Simpson, D. L., Rose, J. E., Barondes, S. H. 1974. *Nature* 252:128
184. Rosness, P. A., Gustafson, G., Wright, B. E. 1971. *J. Bacteriol.* 108:1329
185. Rosness, P. A., Wright, B. E. 1974. *Arch. Biochem. Biophys.* 164:60
186. Ross, I. K. 1960. *Am. J. Bot.* 47:54
187. Rossomando, E. F., Steffek, A. J., Mujwid, D. K., Takashimaya, I., Alexander, S. 1974. *Exp. Cell Res.* 85:73
188. Rossomando, E. F., Sussman, M. 1972. *Biochem. Biophys. Res. Commun.* 47:609
189. Rossomando, E. F., Sussman, M. 1973. *Proc. Natl. Acad. Sci. USA* 70:1254
190. Roth, R., Ashworth, J. M., Sussman, M. 1968. *Proc. Natl. Acad. Sci. USA* 59:1235
191. Roth, R., Sussman, M. 1968. *J. Biol. Chem.* 243:5081
191a. Rothman, F., Alexander, E. T. 1975. *Genetics* 80:715–31
192. Sackin, M. J., Ashworth, J. M. 1969. *J. Gen. Microbiol.* 59:275
193. Schwalb, M., Roth, R. 1970. *J. Gen. Microbiol.* 60:283
194. Shaffer, B. M. 1961. *J. Exp. Zool.* 38:833
195. Sinha, U., Ashworth, J. M. 1969. *Proc. R. Soc. B* 173:531
196. Slifkin, M. K., Bonner, J. T. 1952. *Biol. Bull.* 102:273
197. Smart, J. E., Hynes, R. O. 1974. *Nature* 251:319
198. Soll, D., Sussman, M. 1973. *Biochim. Biophys. Acta* 319:312
199. Sonneborn, D. R., Sussman, M., Levine, L. 1964. *J. Bacteriol.* 87:1321
200. Sonneborn, D. R., White, G. J., Sussman, M. 1963. *Dev. Biol.* 7:79
201. Sussman, M. 1955. *J. Gen. Microbiol.* 13:295
202. Sussman, M. 1956. *Ann. Rev. Microbiol.* 10:21–50
203. Sussman, M. 1961. *J. Gen. Microbiol.* 25:375
204. Sussman, M. 1963. *Science* 139:338
205. Sussman, M. 1964. *Nature* 201, 216
206. Sussman, M. 1965. *Biochem. Biophys. Res. Commun.* 18:763
207. Sussman, M. 1966. *Methods in Cell Physiology,* ed. D. Prescott, D. Mazia. New York: Academic
208. Sussman, M., Alexander, S., Boschwitz, Ch., Brackenbury, R. W., Cohen, A., Schindler, J. 1975. *ICN-UCLA Winter Conf. Dev. Biol.* In press
209. Sussman, M., Boschwitz, Ch. 1975. *Dev. Biol.* 44:362
210. Sussman, M., Boschwitz, Ch. 1975. *Exp. Cell Res.* 95:63
211. Sussman, M., Loomis, W. F., Ashworth, J. M., Sussman, R. 1967. *Biochem. Biophys. Res. Commun.* 26:353
212. Sussman, M., Lovgren, N. 1965. *Exp. Cell Res.* 38:97
213. Sussman, M., Newell, P. C. 1972. *Molecular Genetics and Developmental Biology,* ed. M. Sussman, p. 275. New York: Prentice-Hall
214. Sussman, M., Osborn, M. J. 1964. *Proc. Natl. Acad. Sci. USA* 52:81
215. Sussman, M., Sussman, R. R. 1961. *Exp. Cell Res.* Suppl. 8:91
216. Sussman, M., Sussman, R. R. 1965. *Biochim. Biophys. Acta* 108:463
217. Sussman, R. R. 1961. *Exp. Cell Res.* 24:154
218. Sussman, R. R. 1967. *Biochim. Biophys. Acta* 149:407
219. Sussman, R. R., Raynor, E. P. 1971. *Arch. Biochem. Biophys.* 144:127

220. Sussman, R. R., Sussman, M. 1953. *Trans. NY Acad. Sci.* 56:949
221. Sussman, R. R., Sussman, M. 1962. *J. Gen. Microbiol.* 28:417
222. Ibid 1963. 30:349
223. Sussman, R. R., Sussman, M. 1967. *Biochem. Biophys. Res. Commun.* 29:53
224. Takeuchi, I. 1963. *Dev. Biol.* 8:1
225. Takeuchi, I. 1969. *Nucleic Acid Metabolism, Cell Differentiation, and Cancer,* ed. E. V. Cowdry, S. Senso, p. 297. New York: Pergamon
225a. Tanaka, Y., Yanagisawa, K., Hashimoto, Y., Yamaguchi, M. 1974. *Agric. Biol. Chem.* 38:689
226. Telser, A., Sussman, M. 1971. *J. Biol. Chem.* 246:2252
227. Toama, M. A., Raper, K. B. 1967. *J. Bacteriol.* 94:1143
228. Ibid, 1150
229. Tuchman, J., Alton, T., Lodish, H. F. 1974. *Dev. Biol.* 40:116
230. Verma, I., Firtel, R. A., Lodish, H. F., Baltimore, D. 1974. *Biochemistry* 13:3917
231. Watts, D. J., Ashworth, J. M. 1970. *Biochem. J.* 119:171
232. Weeks, G. 1973. *Exp. Cell. Res.* 76:467
233. Weeks, G., Ashworth, J. M. 1972. *Biochem. J.* 126:617
234. White, G. J., Sussman, M. 1961. *Biochim. Biophys. Acta* 53:285
235. Ibid 1963. 74:173
236. Ibid, 179
237. Wiener, E., Ashworth, J. M. 1970. *Biochem. J.* 118:505
238. Wilhelms, O. H., Lüderitz, O., Westphal, O., Gerisch, G. 1974. *Eur. J. Biochem.* 48:89
239. Williams, K. L., Kessin, R. H., Newell, P. C. 1974. *Nature* 247:142
240. Williams, K. L., Kessin, R. H., Newell, P. C. 1974. *J. Gen. Microbiol.* 84:59
241. Wilson, C. M. 1953. *Am. J. Bot.* 40:714
242. Wooley, D. F. 1972. *Arch. Biochem. Biophys.* 150:519
243. Wright, B. E. 1966. *Science* 153:830
244. Wright, B. E. 1973. *Critical Variables in Differentiation.* New Jersey: Prentice-Hall
245. Wright, B. E., Dahlberg, D. 1967. *Biochemistry* 6:2074
246. Wright, B. E., Dahlberg, D. 1968. *J. Bacteriol.* 95:983
247. Wright, B. E., Gustafson, G. L. 1972. *J. Biol. Chem.* 247:7875
248. Wright, B. E., Simon, W., Walsh, B. T. 1968. *Proc. Natl. Acad. Sci. USA* 60:644
249. Yanagisawa, K., Loomis, W. F., Sussman, M. 1967. *Exp. Cell Res.* 46:328

Ann. Rev. Plant Physiol. 1976. 27:267–90

HORMONE BINDING
IN PLANTS[1]

❖7610

Hans Kende and Gary Gardner

MSU/ERDA Plant Research Laboratory, Michigan State University,
East Lansing, Michigan 48824

CONTENTS

[1]Dedicated to Prof. Dr. Kurt Mothes on the occasion of his 75th birthday.

INTRODUCTION

In the summer of 1973, we were asked to write a review on "Hormone Receptors in Plants," a topic which had been previously reviewed only once, in the form of a short commentary by Venis (111). In the hope that more published data on this subject would become available, we delayed the writing of our review article by one year. However, in 1975 we still find ourselves confronted with the fact that no single plant hormone receptor has been isolated. This is in marked contrast to the rapid progress of research on animal hormone receptors. In the case of steroid hormones, for example, a number of specific proteinaceous receptor molecules has been characterized, and the fate of several hormone-receptor complexes has been determined (44, 82). Quite obviously, our review precedes substantial breakthroughs in the elucidation of the site of action of plant hormones. However, by summarizing the cases where hormone binding to plant cell constituents has been demonstrated and by discussing possible approaches to the problem of hormone-receptor interactions in plants, we hope to contribute to experimental advances in this field.

THE HORMONE-RECEPTOR CONCEPT

As the most trivial basis for studies on the mechanism of plant hormone action, it has to be assumed that hormones interact with some cellular component, most likely a macromolecule, in order to exert their effects. The biological activity of plant hormones and their analogs is determined by structural and often stereospecific properties of the compounds in question. For example, the 2-*trans* isomer of abscisic acid (ABA) shows very low, if any, biological activity (71), and the (–)-enantiomer of ABA is less potent in some systems than the (+)-enantiomer (19). Similar examples are known for other plant hormones. Since it is generally felt that only proteins are able to recognize subtle structural differences between small molecules, it is assumed that plant hormones, like animal hormones, react with some protein in order to initiate the biochemical events leading to the physiological responses. In animal endocrinology, such proteins are defined as "hormone receptors." Hormone receptors must, therefore, possess specific binding sites for hormones, and the hormone-receptor complex must represent an activated structure capable of inducing the primary hormonal reaction.

Methods of Assessing Hormone-Receptor Interactions

The interaction between a hormone and a receptor was first investigated indirectly in the case of estrogen by injecting rats with radioactive hormone and by measuring the distribution of radioactivity among different organs of the animal. It was shown that tissues which exhibit a physiological response to the hormone (target tissues) accumulate it, whereas tissues which are hormone insensitive do not (45). In vivo binding of estrogen in target tissues occurred only with biologically active analogs of the hormone. The hypothesis that in vivo binding was due to the presence of specific hormone receptors in target tissues was proved to be correct by subsequent isolation of receptor proteins.

In all known cases, binding of hormones to their receptors is noncovalent and reversible. There are a number of assays designed to measure the binding of radioactively labeled hormone to protein. In cases where the rate constant of dissociation (K_D) is very low, the hormone receptor complex can be isolated intact by centrifugation or gel filtration. When significant dissociation of the hormone and the receptor occurs during the assay, binding can only be demonstrated under conditions where equilibrium between bound and free hormone is maintained. The best known binding assay designed to fulfill this requirement is equilibrium dialysis (57). Solutions of the protein and the ligand are placed into two compartments which are separated by a dialysis membrane, and dialysis is allowed to proceed until equilibrium is reached. At that point, the concentration of *free* ligand is equal on both sides of the dialysis membrane. The difference between the total ligand concentration in the compartment with the protein and the compartment with the ligand equals the concentration of *bound* ligand. Since equilibrium dialysis is fairly time consuming, a number of faster techniques have been developed to measure binding of a ligand to a macromolecule under equilibrium conditions. Such methods include ultrafiltration (62) or chromatography of the ligand-protein complex on a small gel filtration column which is equilibrated and eluted with a buffer containing the ligand at low concentration (42). In instances where the receptor is associated with subcellular particles, isolation of the respective organelle by centrifugation from a solution containing the ligand can serve the same purpose (61).

Kinetic Analysis of Hormone Binding

Whichever modification of an equilibrium-binding assay is used, it must permit easy calculation of the concentrations of bound and free hormone. The most widely used method to calculate the dissociation constant (K_D) of the hormone-receptor complex and the number of available binding sites is that developed by Scatchard (92). In the so-called Scatchard plot, one graphs the ratio of the concentrations of bound to free hormone (ordinate) as a function of the concentration of bound hormone (abscissa). If the points thus obtained fall on a straight line, one is dealing with a single type of binding site, the concentration of which is given by the intercept at the abscissa. The slope of the line equals $-1/K_D$. The binding or affinity constant (K_A) is the reciprocal of the K_D. If the points on a Scatchard plot fall on a concave curve, the existence of multiple types of binding sites is indicated. High affinity binding, which rapidly becomes saturated, is represented by the steep part of the curve. Binding sites with low affinity are evident at higher hormone concentrations where the slope of the curve is less steep. A composite curve representing binding of a hormone to a high- and a low-affinity site can be "peeled" to yield two linear slopes which define the K_D's and the concentration of both binding sites (20).

Criteria for Physiologically Meaningful Binding

In microbial systems, studies on binding of inducers to repressor molecules have been greatly helped by the availability of appropriate mutants which either lack the binding protein or possess one with altered characteristics. In some animal systems, in vitro binding of a hormone leads to the same biochemical response, e.g. activation of adenyl cyclase, as is observed in vivo following application of the same hormone (12). In plants there are no known receptor mutants, and the primary responses to hormones have not yet been elucidated. For this reason, indirect approaches must be used to assess the relevance of hormone binding.

STRUCTURAL SPECIFICITY   Each plant hormone possesses a number of analogs with a wide range of biological activities. Ideally, such differences in biological potency should be reflected in the affinity constants of the respective compounds. An inactive analog is not expected to bind to the receptor, and a compound of intermediate biological activity should have a lower affinity than a highly potent analog. However, divergence from expected results is likely to occur. It is possible that two compounds effecting one and the same physiological response do not function through the same mechanism. For example, indoleacetic acid (IAA) and the fungal toxin fusicoccin both promote cell elongation but may not act at the same site (25). On the other hand, some biologically inactive hormone analog may turn out to be a competitive inhibitor of an active hormone, in which case both would bind to the same site.

KINETIC PARAMETERS   Ideally, the kinetic parameters of the biological response should show some correspondence to the kinetics of hormone binding. For example, there should be agreement between the K_D of the hormone as measured by a binding assay and the half saturation of the biological response. However, deviations from such correlations can occur. First, the affinity of the receptor to the hormone may change during extraction. Second, since it is not known whether the biological response is limited by the availability of binding sites or by other limiting parameters, the half saturation of the biological response may only be a lower estimate of the in vivo K_D. Third, in deriving dose response curves, one assumes that the external hormone concentration is equivalent to the hormone concentration of the milieu surrounding the active site. This assumption may be correct, but it has never been verified.

TISSUE SPECIFICITY   By analogy with the situation in animals, one may expect that hormone receptors in plants are restricted to their respective target tissues. However, plants, unlike animals, do not have a large number of hormones each of which controls a clearly defined set of physiological processes. Instead, plants use the same hormone to regulate many diverse functions. The nature of the response is determined by the tissue to which the hormone is applied or in which it occurs endogenously. Auxin, for example, stimulates cell extension in the elongating zone of the stem, cell division in the cambium, formation of adventitious roots on stem cuttings, etc. These are but three processes affected by auxin along the stem of a plant. It is very likely that auxin plays some physiological role in most plant tissues, hence auxin receptors would be expected to occur in most, if not all, tissues. The same considerations hold for the other plant hormones as well.

In conclusion, one has to be aware of the fact that no single indirect method will answer the question of whether or not any in vitro binding of a hormone represents binding to the receptor. It is necessary to apply as many criteria as possible to determine the relevance of hormone binding. Of those mentioned above, establishment of structure specificity and of kinetic parameters is absolutely essential. Any divergence from results predicted on the basis of the biological properties of the respective hormone must be further explored experimentally. The ultimate confirmation of the significance of hormone binding will probably only be obtained by work with receptor mutants and by elucidating in vitro and in vivo the primary hormonal response.

Binding of Hormones to Cellular Components Other than Receptors

All plant hormones are known to be metabolized, some of them quite vigorously. For this reason, there certainly exist enzymes in the plant which have an affinity to hormones. Since hormones occur in cells at low concentration, the affinity constants of such enzymes may be quite high and may mimic specific hormone binding to a receptor.

It is known that animal hormones bind to inert, nonbiological materials with surprisingly high affinity (18). Such binding may even exhibit structure and stereo specificity. A similar situation was found with radioactive benzyladenine (BA) which binds to glass and to talcum powder (Gardner, Sussman and Kende, unpublished data). Small amounts of the radioactive cytokinin could be displaced competitively by unlabeled hormone. The existence of nonspecific binding sites in cell extracts is a very real possibility. If such sites exhibit high affinity to the hormone and are present in large excess, the detection of a limited number of specific binding sites may pose great difficulties. Again, kinetic data are indispensable to differentiate between different types of binding sites.

AUXINS

Since auxins have been the most widely studied group of plant hormones for the longest period of time, it is not surprising that there is a tremendous number of reports concerned with the mode of action of this hormone. However, few of these reports provide data which imply hormone binding to a specific subcellular entity, and despite the widespread commercial availability of radioactively labeled auxins, fewer still actually demonstrate direct auxin binding. Auxin has been a very congenial hormone for plant physiologists; it has been purported to bind to whatever biochemical constituent of the cell was fashionable at that particular time. This review will attempt to be comprehensive only about direct evidence of binding, although some studies which imply binding will also be considered.

Autoradiographic Studies

There have been quite a few attempts to localize auxin by autoradiography. Most of these were only concerned with localization at the tissue level [see (14) for references], and the few which provide information on subcellular localization do not agree in their conclusions. Liao & Hamilton (63) examined root tip squashes of *Allium cernuum* and *Vicia faba* which had been treated with ^{14}C-indoleacetic acid (IAA) or ^{14}C-2,4-dichlorophenoxyacetic acid (2,4-D). They found that the label in the cytoplasm decreased with the time after incubation and was not observed in cells fixed 120 hr after removal from the radioactive hormone. Nuclear (and chromosomal) labeling was found at all time intervals. Unfortunately, the authors did not determine whether the radioactivity in these preparations was still associated · ith undegraded hormone. Similar results were obtained by Merkys et al (70). In sections of *Coleus* explants Veen (106) found that label from 4×10^{-4} M ^{14}C-α -naphthylacetic acid (NAA) was located in the cytoplasm next to the cell wall 24 hr after hormone treatment. Sabnis et al (89) applied 5×10^{-7} M ^{3}H-IAA to *Coleus* internode segments, prepared thin sections, and found label after 3 hr only over secondary cell walls of the youngest tracheary elements. A similar pattern was observed after 24 hr, but after 48 hr there was also prominent labeling of plastids within parenchymatous cells. None of these workers took precautions to avoid solubilization and redistribution of the label. No autoradiographic studies at the electron microscopic level have yet been reported, and the question of the morphological subcellular entity to which auxin binds remains unresolved.

Auxin and DNA

The work of Fellenberg suggested that auxin might be active via a direct interaction with the genome. IAA, NAA, and 2,4-D all lowered the melting point of nucleoprotein extracted from pea epicotyls (27, 28). IAA also had the same effect on DNA isolated from this tissue (28). This effect was not specific for auxin-responsive tissue, since salmon-sperm DNA responded in the same way to added IAA or α-NAA (29). This basic phenomenon was confirmed by Bamberger (5). IAA, 2,4-D, and 2,4,5-trichlorophenoxyacetic acid (2,4,5-T) all caused a concentration-dependent downward shift in the melting point (T_m) of pea and calf thymus DNA. Penner & Early (84) explicitly repeated the experiments of Bamberger and found that all auxin-induced changes in T_m values were associated with changes in the pH of the solution. When the pH was maintained at 7.0, none of these compounds significantly altered the T_m.

Auxin binding to pea histone fractions has been measured by equilibrium dialysis (108). The affinities observed were generally too low to be physiologically meaningful.

Interaction of Auxin with RNA

As was the case for cytokinins, it was suggested in the 1960s that auxins exerted their action via an association with tRNA. Kefford et al (50) observed that RNA isolated from peas could complex in vitro with an oxidation product of IAA, as measured by the Salkowski color reaction. Complex formation only occurred at pH values lower than 4.8. Later work (32) showed that this association could not be observed if the RNA was precipitated with 70% ethanol instead of perchloric acid. A similar phenomenon was observed if binding was measured by incorporation of label from either ^{14}C-IAA or ^{14}C-2,4-D. The accumulation of counts was concentration-dependent and did not appear to saturate. No other information was presented as to specificity or reversibility of the interaction.

Bendaña et al (7) supplied light-grown pea stem sections with carboxyl-labeled ^{14}C-IAA and found radioactivity associated with a fraction similar to RNA. Incorporation of counts was both time- and concentration-dependent. Ten times more radioactivity was incorporated when the sections were treated with IAA rather than with 2,4-D and 2–3 times more when the ^{14}C was in the carboxyl position rather than in the methylene position. The authors acknowledged the possibility that ^{14}C in the carboxyl group might have been recycled. However, hydrolysis of the RNA followed by ether extraction and chromatography indicated that at least some of the label was probably still in IAA. The RNA was prepared by phenol extraction and ethanol precipitation, and the only reported attempt at fractionation was by sucrose density gradient centrifugation. In this system, some of the radioactivity co-sedimented with the 4S RNA peak. Key & Ingle (56) found that radioactivity from ^{14}C-IAA and ^{14}C-2,4-D was incorporated into all fractions of RNA. They felt that their results could be attributed largely to the utilization of products of auxin catabolism rather than from direct attachment of the auxin molecule to RNA.

Subsequent work (24) negated the conclusions of Bendaña et al (7). While the earlier experiments could be repeated, salt fractionation and gel filtration on Sephadex G-100 separated the label, originally supplied in IAA, from the tRNA; further chromatography on Sepharose 4B separated the radioactivity from most of the material with absorbancy at 254 nm. Many of the radioactive fractions did not contain indole and gave a strongly positive anthrone reaction, indicating the presence of carbohydrate. However, a few high molecular weight fractions did contain a small quantity of indoles, probably IAA and indole aldehyde. It was pointed out that phenol extraction could also be used for the isolation of polysaccharides and that the earlier observation of Bendaña et al (7) could be attributed to label in polysaccharide with a similar sedimentation coefficient as 4S RNA. Since the IAA-macromolecular conjugates were formed in vivo and not during the extraction, it was suggested that they might be of importance in the metabolism of auxin (24).

More recently, Kobayashi & Yamaki (58, 59, 124) reported that mung bean hypocotyls which had been floated on IAA-2-^{14}C contained radioactivity associated with sRNA. The RNA was characterized by column chromatography on methylated albumin-kieselguhr (MAK) and two subsequent ion exchange columns. A careful examination of the data (Figure 2 in ref. 59) indicates that a peak of radioactivity overlaps but does not coincide with the peak of optical density corresponding to sRNA on the MAK column. Davies (23) carried out similar experiments with pea stems and, using MAK column chromatography, found no peak of radioactivity associated with RNA. In addition, extraction of polyribosomes followed by sucrose density centrifugation showed no correlation between radioactivity and absorbancy at 254 nm (23).

Auxin and Nuclei

Since auxin effects on nucleic acid metabolism imply involvement of the nucleus, several attempts have been made to demonstrate auxin binding to isolated nuclei. Roychoudhury & Sen (88) reported that coconut milk nuclei took up radioactivity after 3 hr incubation with 10^{-3} M NAA-1-^{14}C. No specificity was shown for this accumulation, and the bound label was not identified. Spelsberg & Sarkissian (98) incubated intact bean hypocotyl segments with 10^{-5} M ^{14}C-IAA for 6 hr and found the highest amount of radioactivity in a fraction containing nuclei. Further subfractionation indicated that most of the label was associated with alkali-extractable proteins from chromatin. In vitro incubation of nuclei with ^{14}C-IAA did not yield the same results, and in neither case was there an attempt to determine the specificity of the labeling or the nature of the bound radioactivity.

The most extensive study on auxin binding to nuclei was that of Tautvydas & Galston (101). Pea nuclei were incubated with several concentrations of ^{14}C-IAA for varying times at 20°, and then "the binding was stopped" by extensive washing with a cold solution containing 0.1 M nonradioactive IAA. Incorporation of radioactivity into the nuclei was quite rapid, reaching a maximal level in 60 sec, and the binding appeared to saturate at 3×10^{-5} M IAA. When a correction was made for nonspecific adsorption (probably equivalent to trapped water volume in the pellet), saturation occurred at 4×10^{-6} M IAA. The amount of binding was reduced, but not eliminated, by pretreatment with 3 mM iodoacetamide. Several problems exist in the interpretation of these data. First, as the authors pointed out, they did not demonstrate that the bound radioactivity was still associated with IAA. Second, if the interaction of a hormone with its site of action is noncovalent, one would, a priori, expect binding and exchange to occur in the cold. It is probable that washing with 0.1 M IAA would eliminate any noncovalent binding. Third, there was no attempt to demonstrate physiological relevance of this binding.

Auxin and RNA Synthesis

Although Tautvydas & Galston (101) were not able to demonstrate promotion of RNA synthesis by IAA, many authors have reported effects on RNA synthesis and RNA polymerase activity. While there is good evidence that in vivo auxin treatment does cause a marked increase in RNA polymerase activity (36), the mechanism of this effect and the existence of a similar effect in vitro are still not clarified. O'Brien et al (81), working with soybean, could not detect an in vitro auxin effect on RNA synthesis in chromatin preparations, but hypocotyls treated for at least 4 hr with 2,4-D showed a concentration-dependent increase in RNA synthesis using isolated chromatin. Hardin et al (39) isolated a factor from soybean cotyledons which enhanced RNA synthesis in chromatin from control plants but not in chromatin from auxin-treated plants. The stimulation was relatively small, and no indication was given as to the variability of the data. The factor also stimulated the activity of E. coli RNA polymerase added to the soybean chromatin system. Characterization of this factor was the subject of a subsequent report from these workers (38). Various membrane fractions from etiolated soybean hypocotyls were characterized on the basis of morphology and marker enzymes. These fractions were assayed directly for their ability to stimulate RNA polymerase, and it was stated that such stimulation was "in proportion to the plasma membrane content of the fraction." However, an analysis of these data by Student's t test indicates that none of these fractions promoted RNA synthesis significantly at the $p = .05$ level. When the plasma membrane-rich fractions were incubated with auxin, and subsequently centrifuged, the resultant supernatant promoted RNA synthesis in isolated chromatin. IAA and 2,4-D were effective, but the biologically inactive compound 3,5-dichlorophenoxyacetic acid was not. Most of the increased activity was sensitive to the fungal toxin α-amanitin, an inhibitor of RNA polymerase II in animal systems. In all these experiments, the effect on RNA synthesis was relatively small, and except for the data mentioned above, there was no indication of the variability of the data. No direct attempt was made to detect binding of auxin to any subcellular fraction.

Venis (109, 110) attempted to isolate auxin-reactive proteins by affinity chromatography using Sepharose linked to the ϵ-lysyl derivatives of IAA and 2,4-D, and the N-(6-aminocaproyl)- derivative of the auxin-type herbicide Amiben (2,5-dichloro-3-aminobenzoic acid). These columns retained material from extracts of pea or corn, and some of this material could be eluted successively with 1 M NaCl, water, and then 2 mM KOH. Early experiments (110) indicated that a fraction from corn isolated on the Amiben-caproic column stimulated RNA synthesis in an incubation mixture containing corn chromatin and $E.$ $coli$ polymerase. This effect was only observable if the chromatin was used within 90 min of its isolation. Further experiments were, therefore, carried out using purified DNA. Fractions eluted from the 2,4-D-lysyl column by 2 mM KOH promoted RNA synthesis with purified DNA as template (109). This activity from peas was not dialyzable and was completely destroyed by freezing or brief heating. Increasing amounts of the factor stimulated RNA synthesis up to a maximum of 200% of control, and the effect of the factor could be blocked with rifampicin. It was suggested that the active material was a high-molecular weight protein. The factor from pea or corn was active on DNA from both pea and corn; however, a fraction prepared in a similar manner from mouse liver was not active on pea or corn DNA. Addition of auxin was not necessary for activity, and attempts to detect auxin binding to these fractions by equilibrium dialysis were not successful. These observations point to one of the difficulties in the use of affinity chromatography for the isolation of plant hormone receptors. Unless one has a specific assay (either binding or physiological) with which to test the column fractions, one cannot distinguish between chromatographic separation on the basis of specific affinity or on the basis of ion-exchange, partitioning, or adsorption.

Matthysse & Phillips (67) found that nuclei of cultured tobacco cells showed an increase in RNA synthesis if they were isolated in the presence of 2,4-D. If the nuclei were resuspended in buffer without auxin and collected by centrifugation, they no longer showed this stimulation. However, addition of the supernatant fraction from the centrifugation caused the nuclei to become auxin-responsive. This factor, called hormone-reactive substance or hormone-reactive protein, could also be isolated from pea buds. The factor from both pea buds and tobacco nuclei stimulated RNA synthesis in a preparation of pea bud chromatin if 2,4-D was added. IAA and 2,3,6-trichlorobenzoic acid also promoted RNA synthesis in the presence of the factor, but the anti-auxin 2,3,6-trichlorophenoxyacetic acid was inactive. No effect was observed if pure DNA was used as a template. Subsequently (65), the factor was also isolated from pea roots, and it was reported that the factor from either pea roots or pea buds showed organ specificity, i.e. showed maximal stimulation only with the chromatin of the same organ. This seems inconsistent with the earlier observation (67) that the factor from tobacco nuclei caused a greater stimulation of RNA synthesis with pea bud chromatin as template than did the factor from pea buds. As in the case with many of the above studies, there was no direct evidence presented to indicate that the auxin actually bound to the factor or to the chromatin.

Characterization of a similar system was reported by Mondal et al (72). [A subsequent publication from the same laboratory (73) contains no additional data than those already presented in (72).] A factor isolated from disrupted coconut nuclei was found to stimulate RNA synthesis when IAA was added to an incubation mixture containing purified components. This material was chromatographed on carboxymethylcellulose. It was stated that the activity was in the protein eluted with 0.5 M KCl, although no RNA polymerase assays of the column fractions were presented. It was also stated that this peak "was found to be homogeneous by polyacrylamide gel electrophoresis"; however, a cursory examination of the photograph of the gel which was presented indicates at least three bands. Binding of ^{14}C-IAA to this fraction was measured by equilibrium dialysis, but no competition experiments were done to test whether bound IAA could be displaced with high concentrations of nonradioactive hormone or to demonstrate specificity of binding in any manner whatsoever. The authors also state that "hormone acceptor protein complex . . . can interact with DNA." Unfortunately, the experiment referred to only measured retention of ^{3}H-DNA by Millipore filters. The control with the factor but without IAA was not given, and, since labeled IAA was not used, it cannot even be assumed that IAA was being retained on the filters with the DNA. Analysis of the products of RNA synthesis on polyacrylamide gels indicated that two new bands appeared in the presence of IAA, and a DNA-RNA hybridization experiment indicated that new classes of RNA were being synthesized in the presence of the hormone. Recently, workers from the same laboratory (13) have reported that IAA can promote RNA synthesis in suspensions of isolated cells and nuclei. They reported that binding of ^{14}C-IAA to the "acceptor protein" was observable on polyacrylamide gels. However, experimental details given were insufficient to allow evaluation of the data.

In spite of the multitude of reports on the effects of auxin on RNA synthesis, the magnitude of any in vitro effect is generally small and the variability of the assay, if given at all, is generally high. Although terms like "auxin-reactive protein" and "acceptor protein" are used, the evidence that these factors, which stimulate RNA synthesis, are actually auxin receptors is, at best, circumstantial.

Auxin and Protein

The view that auxins are associated with proteins in vivo is one of the oldest concepts in auxinology. A variety of treatments could indeed release auxin activity from preparations of plant protein (35, 97, 117). However, a putative IAA-protein complex formed in vivo (95) was regarded as an artifact of the trichloroacetic acid precipitation procedure (3). The first attempts to find auxin binding with ^{14}C-IAA (33) were unsuccessful. In other studies the nature of the immobilized or "bound" auxin remaining in *Avena* coleoptiles following transport of ^{14}C-IAA was examined (118). It was found that the radioactivity could be removed from the tissue by 10% urea, trypsin, or chymotrypsin, but not by extraction with water, buffer, or ribonuclease.

There are a great many reports in the literature of in vitro auxin effects on enzymes, but most of these studies made no attempt to measure direct binding of auxin to the enzyme. Sarkissian (91) has found an in vitro effect of IAA on citrate synthase and has reported (90) that ultrafiltration membranes retain radioactivity from a mixture of ^{14}C-IAA and this enzyme. However, no indication of specificity was given, and binding could not be detected by gel filtration. Two recent publications report auxin effects on membrane-bound enzymes. VanDerWoude et al (105) found in vivo and in vitro stimulation by 2,4-D of glucan synthetase activity in particulate fractions from onion stems. The hormone effect was greatest on the synthesis of hot-water-soluble polysaccharides, and maximal stimulation occurred when hormone was supplied both to the tissue and to the synthetase assay. The effects were small, the variability of the assays was high, and no further characterization of this response has been reported. Kasamo & Yamaki (47) reported that IAA stimulated particulate ATPase activity from mung bean hypocotyls. Only Mg-dependent ATPase was affected and the in vitro response was negligible unless the tissue sections were treated with 10^{-5} M IAA prior to extraction. Fractionation of these membranes on discontinuous sucrose density gradients yielded discrete bands of enzyme activity; however, the auxin effect on these fractions was extremely small (48). Auxin binding, assayed in the manner of Hertel et al (41), was found in the active fractions, but the small numbers and the absence of raw data make it difficult to ascertain whether this binding is significant.

Auxin-Lipid Interactions in Model Systems

There have been several reports that auxins can interact in vitro with lipid constituents of cellular membranes. Weigl (114–116) found that ^{14}C-IAA or ^{14}C-2,4-D would partition into CCl_4 if the apolar solvent contained lecithin. The effect seemed relatively specific in that urea, glucose, malate, valeric acid, tryptophan, and glycerin did not partition in that manner. Moreover, the lipid used also seemed to be specific; cephalin and phosphatidylserine also caused partitioning of auxin into CCl_4, although not as effectively as lecithin, but a wide variety of other lipids did not show this effect. The partitioning had characteristics similar to saturation; if the concentration of IAA was increased, the percentage of IAA in the lecithin phase decreased. Specific competition was also observed since nonradioactive IAA or indolebutyric acid reduced the amount of ^{14}C-IAA in the lecithin phase, but benzoic acid, phenoxyacetic acid, and phenylacetic acid did not. However, nonradioactive IAA did not reduce the amount of ^{14}C-2,4-D in the lecithin phase. If lecithin lamellae were swollen in the presence of ^{14}C-IAA or ^{14}C-2,4-D, radioactivity was retained by the lamellae during subsequent dialysis. Such lecithin preparations in dialysis bags also accumulated ^{14}C-IAA from a 10^{-8} M external solution. Veen (107) examined whether this effect observed by Weigl could be correlated to the biological activity of the respective compounds. ^{14}C-IAA and ^{14}C-α-NAA partitioned into lecithin-CCl$_4$, but so did the inactive compound α-decalylacetic acid (α-DAA). Whereas IAA interacted with lecithin at a molar ratio of 0.8 to 1.0, 80% of the α-NAA was associated with the lecithin independent of the lecithin concentration. Because α-DAA is less soluble in petroleum ether than in CCl$_4$, partitioning between water and lecithin-petroleum ether was also studied. IAA and α-NAA were still associated with the lecithin phase under these conditions, but so were α-DAA and the inactive analog β-NAA. It was concluded that the observed interaction of IAA with lecithin was not related to the biological activity of auxins.

Kennedy (54) prepared model membranes consisting of a Millipore filter impregnated with egg yolk lecithin, n-octanol, and n-tetradecane and found that 10^{-3} M 2,4-D at pH 3.0 would cause a marked drop in conductivity across this membrane. The effect did not occur at pH 5.5, and IAA had no effect on membrane conductivity. Kennedy & Harvey (55) measured binding of growth-regulating compounds to vesicles prepared from lecithin or lecithin-cholesterol. They found that the non-ionized forms of IAA, 2,4-D, 2,4,5-T, and 2,6-dichlorophenoxyacetic acid bound more strongly to the lecithin vesicles than did the ionized forms. Only the nonionized form of these compounds had any significant effect on Cl$^-$ flux across these vesicles, and the effects were only observed with high levels (0.015 to 1.5 mM) of these substances. Paleg et al (83) found that IAA caused a concentration-dependent shift in the location of the trimethylamino resonance of the NMR spectrum of phosphatidylcholine in deuterochloroform. Effects of other auxins were not reported.

While it is clear from the above that several auxins can interact with naturally occurring lipids, no evidence has been presented that such interactions are related to (or correlated with) biological activity of the hormone. The observation that 2,4-D and 2,4,5-T can bind to bovine serum albumin (64) emphasizes the need for such physiological correlations.

Binding to Particulate Sub-Cellular Fractions

NAPHTHYLPHTHALAMIC ACID   From indirect evidence, Hertel and co-workers postulated that the plasma membrane might be the site of auxin transport and that this organelle might therefore contain specific sites for auxin binding. Initial attempts with IAA were inconclusive; however, specific binding of N-1-naphthylphthalamic acid (NPA), a rapid inhibitor of auxin transport, to a membrane fraction could be demonstrated (61). A centrifugation assay was used to detect specific binding of ^{3}H-NPA to particulate fractions. These were suspended in a medium containing ^{3}H-NPA at 1 to 6×10^{-9} M and collected by centrifugation. A second tube containing the same components plus unlabeled NPA at saturating concentration (e.g. 10^{-5} M) was treated identically. The radioactivity associated with both pellets was determined, and specific binding was taken as the difference between the label found in the first pellet minus the label in the second one. Membrane preparations from corn coleoptiles were fractionated on discontinuous sucrose density gradients, and the binding of ^{3}H-NPA was directly correlated with the plasma membrane content of the fractions. Plasma membranes were identified by electron microscopy using the phosphotungstic acid-chromic acid stain adapted for use with plant tissue by Roland et al (87). The binding of ^{3}H-NPA occurred at very low concentrations, was concentration-dependent, and saturated at 10^{-6} M NPA. IAA did not inhibit the binding. Further characterization (102) indicated a K_D of 1.3×10^{-8} M. The specificity of the binding site for NPA was tested with a wide variety of compounds: IAA, gibberellic acid (GA$_3$), ABA, α-NAA, 2,4-D, 2,3,5-triiodobenzoic acid (TIBA), and lycoricidinol did not compete with ^{3}H-NPA for binding. If the bound material was sedimented through a sucrose cushion without ^{3}H-NPA, the amount of binding was drastically reduced, indicating reversibility and hence probably noncovalent interaction. Extraction and chromatographic separation of the bound material in two thin-layer systems indicated that it was still NPA. Boiling destroyed the binding activity of the membrane fraction. The correlation between binding properties and the physiological action of NPA was strengthened in three ways: (a) NPA inhibited basipetal exit of IAA from coleoptile sections within one minute; (b) the NPA effect on auxin efflux was reversible; (c) the inhibition of auxin efflux was half-saturated at ca. 10^{-7} M. It was also firmly established that the NPA binding site was distinct from the auxin site; NPA did not affect ^{14}C-NAA binding and α-NAA did not affect ^{3}H-NPA binding.

Given that a wide variety of compounds did not affect NPA binding, a subsequent study (104) tested several phthalamic acid derivatives for competition. A relatively good correlation was found between activity in the binding assay and inhibition of auxin transport. Of greater interest was the finding that morphactins (fluorenol derivatives), which are effective inhibitors of auxin transport at high concentrations, also competed very well with ^{3}H-NPA in the binding test. The methyl esters of the morphactins did not compete in the binding assay (except to the extent that they became hydrolzyed to the free acids), but they were extremely potent transport inhibitors. This apparent discrepancy has not been clarified, although it is likely that the methyl esters are taken up to a greater extent than the free acids and then are hydrolyzed in the tissue. The binding of the morphactin ^{14}C-2-chloro-9-hydroxyfluorene-9-carboxylic acid (Cl-HFC) was inhibited by NPA as well as nonradioactive Cl-HFC, and a double reciprocal plot of the data indicated that Cl-HFC is a competitive inhibitor of NPA binding. The K_D for Cl-HFC was calculated to be approximately 2.9×10^{-7} M. This is the only known example in higher plants of two classes of growth regulators which interact competitively in vitro at the same binding site. If this site is involved in auxin transport but not in the binding of auxin, a major question is what compounds bind to the NPA site in nature, since both NPA and morphactins are synthetic products?

AUXIN Application of the above techniques led to the discovery of specific auxin binding sites in particulate fractions from corn coleoptiles (41). Binding of ^{14}C-α-NAA was measured; nonradioactive α-NAA competed for binding sites which became saturated at about 2×10^{-5} M. IAA also competed with ^{14}C-α-NAA, but no saturation of binding was reached at the concentrations used. β-NAA and indolepropionic acid competed poorly with ^{14}C-α-NAA. The binding occurred at an optimal pH of 6.0, was reversible, and reached equilibrium within 15 min (the minimum time necessary for the binding test). After correction for nonspecific binding, a Scatchard plot of the data indicated a K_D of $1-2 \times 10^{-6}$ M. Similar experiments with ^{3}H-IAA indicated a K_D of $3-4 \times 10^{-6}$ M, although the variability of the data was high. These values agree roughly with estimates of saturation kinetics from transport and growth studies. The following information has been provided about the specificity of the binding: NAA bound 2–3 times more strongly than IAA; ^{14}C-2,4,-D bound very weakly; and ^{14}C-benzoic acid did not bind specifically at all. Benzoic acid, GA_3, ABA, and NPA did not compete for the binding of ^{14}C-α-NAA. 2,4-D competed relatively well; the d-isomer of dichlorophenoxyisopropionic acid competed slightly, but the l-isomer not at all, which is in agreement with the biological activities of these two substances. The antiauxin p-chlorophenoxyisobutyric acid (PCIB) competed at high concentrations, as did TIBA, an inhibitor of auxin transport. It will be recalled (102, 103) that TIBA did not compete for NPA binding. Thus these two inhibitors of auxin transport interact with two different binding sites. No kinetic data were given to indicate whether inhibition of auxin binding by TIBA was competitive or not. This first report on auxin binding contained some characterization of the binding site. Activity was abolished by heat or detergent treatment. Differential centrifugation separated the auxin-binding activity from 95% of the cytochrome c oxidase activity (a mitochondrial marker) and from more than 90% of the DNA.

Subsequently, it was reported (40) that dithioerythritol inhibited the binding, suggesting the involvement of -SH groups. It was noted that the binding was improved by washing the particulate fractions prior to the assay, indicating the existence of a supernatant factor with effect on the binding. It was also mentioned that distribution of auxin-binding activity in isopycnic sucrose gradients suggested localization of binding sites on the endoplasmic reticulum with a minor component on the plasmalemma. These last two topics have been the objects of intensive recent study (25; P. M. Ray & R. Hertel, unpublished observations). These workers found that the supernatant factor affected the affinity of the auxin binding sites without altering the number of sites. The factor may be important in controlling the specificity of auxin binding; the affinities of different compounds are affected differently by the factor. Without the factor, the K_D for α-NAA was 3.8×10^{-7} M. With the factor, the affinity for α-NAA was decreased threefold. The affinity for β-NAA was decreased twentyfold, and the affinity for 2,4-D was increased twofold. The factor has not been chemically characterized beyond the fact that it is soluble, heat-stable, and dialyzable. In isopycnic sucrose density gradients NAA-binding activity showed a sharp peak at 25% (w/w) sucrose, with a shoulder at 30–35% sucrose. This main peak coincided with a peak in NADH: cytochrome c reductase activity, a marker enzyme for endoplasmic reticulum (ER). At higher Mg^{2+} concentration, the peak of auxin binding and the reductase peak shifted to a much higher density, at about 35% sucrose, a property characteristic of rough ER. In low Mg^{2+} auxin binding was separated from NPA binding, which was located in a broad peak at 35–38% sucrose. Glucan synthetase II, a putative plasma membrane marker which requires high UDPG levels, also peaked at 35–38% sucrose. The Golgi marker glucan synthetase

I, active at low UDPG levels, peaked at 31% sucrose. While it is clear that the major peak of auxin binding coincides with the ER, the identity of the cell constituents sedimenting as a shoulder is still unknown. The auxin-binding sites in these two regions of the gradient appear to have different properties with regard to specificity (α-NAA vs β-NAA), affinity for auxin analogs, inhibition by dithioerythritol, and sensitivity to the supernatant factor. The relationship, either biochemical or physiological, between these two types of binding sites has yet to be determined.

The basic findings of Hertel and his colleagues have been confirmed in two other laboratories. Jablanovic & Noodén (43) used the centrifugation assay to detect NAA-competible binding of ^{3}H-IAA in homogenates of pea buds. They compared buds of different physiological stages and found that terminal buds and inhibited buds had more binding activity than dormant or released buds. These properties were correlated with the physiological response to auxin. It was also found that α-NAA and benzyladenine (BA) competed for ^{3}H-IAA binding to the same extent. Unfortunately, no concentration series or binding kinetics for the effect of BA on auxin binding were presented. Because the authors incubated the reaction mixtures at 25° for 30 min before centrifugation and did not provide evidence that the auxin remained undegraded, interpretation of these results might be difficult. Venis & Batt (112) also used the centrifugation assay to study particulate binding of ^{14}C-NAA in corn homogenates. Scatchard plots were biphasic, indicating two sites, the first with a K_D of 1.5×10^{-7} M and the second with a K_D of 1.6×10^{-6} M. Double-reciprocal plots indicated that IAA, 2,4,5-T, benzoic acid, and 2,6-D were competitive inhibitors at the first site, whereas only the two active auxins competed at the second site. Thus, surprisingly, it appeared as if the lower affinity site was the more relevant one in physiological terms. It was also stated that the two sites could be separated on sucrose density gradients, but data pertaining to this point were not given in this preliminary report. It is possible that these properties of auxin binding could be explained by the supernatant factor discussed above, but such an explanation is premature until both laboratories have published more extensive data.

It is clear from the above discussion that efforts to find the auxin receptor have concentrated in recent years on two major areas: effects of auxin on RNA synthesis and binding of labeled auxins to particulate subcellular fractions. In vitro effects of auxin on RNA synthesis are generally small and variable, and the only reports of actual auxin binding (13, 72) give no evidence concerning specificity. On the other hand, the characterization of particulate binding sites of auxin has established specificity of binding which correlates well with the physiological properties of auxin. If this binding activity can be solubilized and is shown to be a protein which retains its specificity in solution, the case that this is the auxin receptor will be significantly strengthened.

GIBBERELLINS

Synthesis of Radioactive Gibberellins

The detection of a small number of hormonal binding sites per cell requires the use of radioactive gibberellin (GA) with high specific activity. Such labeled GAs can be prepared by introducing tritium into known, stable positions of the GA molecule through catalytic reduction of an unsaturated precursor with tritium gas. This method was first employed by Kende (51) to prepare dihydrogibberellic acid-1,2-^{3}H (^{3}H-GA$_1$) from gibberellic acid (GA$_3$). The conditions of reduction and the purification of ^{3}H-GA$_1$ were subsequently improved by Pitel & Vining (85) and by Nadeau & Rappaport (80). The latter invesitgators also found that a surprisingly large amount of ^{3}H-GA$_3$ was formed during the catalytic reduction, probably through exchange of tritium with alkane hydrogen atoms of the GA molecule. ^{3}H-GA$_1$ served as precursor for the preparation of ^{3}H-GA$_5$, another naturally occurring plant gibberellin (79). ^{3}H-GA$_4$ was obtained by selective reduction of GA$_7$ with tritium (26) and ^{3}H-GA$_{20}$ by reduction of GA$_5$ methyl ester-16,17-epoxide (76).

In Vivo Binding Studies

Musgrave et al (77) investigated the distribution of applied ^{3}H-GA$_1$ and ^{3}H-GA$_5$ in dwarf pea shoots. Both hormones were found to accumulate in the growing, GA-sensitive region of dark-grown pea stems. Illumination with red light, which decreases the responsiveness of dwarf peas to GA$_1$ and GA$_5$, greatly reduced the capacity of pea shoots to accumulate these GAs. Similarly, GA derivatives of low or no biological activity were accumulated in the apical region of the stem only to a slight extent if at all. Thus the growing portion of the pea axis exhibited the properties expected from a hormonal target tissue. However, there was a significant difference from animal target tissues; the accumulation of the hormone was not saturable up to 10^{-4}M GA$_1$ or GA$_5$. At this concentration, GA started to affect the permeability of the tissue and, as an apparent consequence, there was a marked increase in the uptake of GA into the basal, nonelongating portion of the stem.

Working with seedlings of *Pharbitis nil,* Barendse (6) found an accumulation of radioactive GA$_3$ in the hormone-sensitive region of the stem. This accumulation was saturable, and a biologically inactive derivative, GA$_3$ methyl ester, did not show the same distribution pattern as the free acid. In contrast to these two cases, where a positive correlation of GA accumulation and biological effectiveness of the hormone was found, uptake of GA into barley aleurone layers was directly related to the subsequent metabolism rather than to the physiological potency of GA (78). Greatest accumulation was found with the biologically inactive methyl ester of GA$_5$, which was rapidly converted to a number of polar compounds.

Attempts to determine the intracellular fate of ^{3}H-GA by microautoradiography using nonaqueous procedures were inconclusive (34); the radioactivity appeared to be randomly distributed in the cells.

In Vitro Binding Studies

Early efforts to detect in vitro binding of ^{3}H-GA$_1$ and ^{3}H-GA$_5$ to cellular components from dwarf peas were unsuccessful (34, 51, 79). When pea shoots were treated with ^{3}H-GA$_1$ or ^{3}H-GA$_5$ and extracted 24 to 48 hr later, the radioactivity was found to be associated with unchanged GA or with GA metabolites of low molecular weight (51, 79). No detectable radioactivity was bound to macromolecular cell constituents as shown by Sephadex chromatography. When tissue treated with radioactive GA was homogenized and fractionated by differential centrifugation, less than 1% of the radioactivity was sedimentable, and 99% of the label remained in the postribosomal supernatant fraction (34, 79). The amount of radioactivity in the particulate fraction was not reduced by addition of unlabeled GA. In subsequent investigations, GA binding to soluble protein and organelle fractions of peas and aleurone layers was investigated using equilibrium dialysis, chromatography on Sephadex columns equilibrated with ^{3}H-GA$_1$ or ^{3}H-GA$_5$, and affinity labeling (Kende, Ginzburg, Johnson, Gardner, unpublished results). While GA binding to soluble protein was found with the above techniques, it could not be correlated to the physiological action of the hormone using criteria such as specificity and comparisons of binding kinetics to dose response curves in biological tests. Most importantly, no in vitro binding of GA could be demonstrated that would have accounted for the in vivo accumulation of the hormone in the growing region of the pea stems.

Stoddart et al applied ^{3}H-GA$_1$ of very high specific activity to dwarf pea shoots which were extracted 12 hr later for analysis on Sephadex G-200 columns (99). ^{3}H-GA$_1$ was found to be associated with a high and an intermediate molecular-weight fraction. At present, the physiological significance of the observed binding is not clear. Although it is assumed that the GA-binding entity was a protein, no data were presented to show its susceptibility to proteolytic enzymes or heat treatment. Binding of ^{3}H-GA$_1$ was also demonstrated by equilibrium dialysis, but no kinetic data were given to indicate the K_D and saturability of the binding or the number and diversity of the binding sites. The specificity of binding also needs further clarification; of the two biologically inactive GA$_1$ analogs used, one was not bound while the other exhibited similar binding properties as ^{3}H-GA$_1$.

Model Systems

In a series of investigations, Paleg and co-workers explored the effect of GA on the permeability of artificial membranes (119–122). Liposomes of varying lipid composition were preloaded with glucose, sucrose, or chromate, and the efflux of sugar or the ion was measured in the presence and absence of GA$_3$. In general, GA increased leakage from liposomes, apparently by shifting the transition point of the membrane to a lower temperature. Interaction of GA with purified phosphatidyl choline was inferred from NMR spectroscopy (83, 123). The significance of this GA effect in artificial membrane systems with regard to the physiological action of the hormone is not clear. For one, enhancement of leakage from artificial membranes is not specific for GA. The same effect has also been observed with GA$_8$, which has no biological activity, with IAA, and with diethylstilbestrol (119, 120). Furthermore, it is not known whether lipids, even in complex biological membranes, possess the capacity to differentiate active and inactive stereoisomers of plant hormones.

CYTOKININS

Synthesis of Radioactive Cytokinins

Carbon-labeled cytokinins are commercially available or can be synthesized by condensation of 6-chloropurine and the ^{14}C-containing amine of the appropriate side chain (e.g. as in ref. 53). However, the specific radioactivities obtained in this way are 2–3 orders of magnitude too low to detect binding sites similar to those of animal hormones such as the estrogen receptor. Sussman & Firn (100) devised a simple method to prepare and purify ^{3}H-benzyladenine (BA) of high specific activity. Para-bromobenzyladenine was dehalogenated catalytically using carrier-free tritium gas; the reaction yielded BA-p-benzyl-^{3}H of 10 Ci/mmole specific activity which could be purified in one chromatographic step.

In Vivo Binding of Cytokinins

Treatment of moss protonemata with cytokinin results in the development of gametophyte buds on specific cells of the filaments. Brandes & Kende (15) investigated the distribution of radioactivity in ^{14}C-BA-treated protonemata of *Funaria hygrometrica* using nonaqueous techniques of autoradiography. An accumulation of label was found in the newly formed buds and in those caulonema cells from which they arose. A short washing period removed this accumulated radioactivity and caused subsequent de-differentiation of buds to chloronema filaments. This fact suggests that the observed concentration of label in the target cells may somehow be related to the action of the cytokinin. However, the specificity and the kinetics of this "binding" have not been investigated.

In Vitro Binding of Cytokinins

The relationship between cytokinins covalently bound in certain tRNA species and free cytokinins exerting hormonal control in plants has been the subject of intense debate (for a review see ref. 52). The reasons as to why it is unlikely that cytokinins exert their hormonal effect through their presence in tRNA have been outlined in detail (52). Since then, Skoog and co-workers have supplied additional evidence further supporting the notion that the hormonal activity of free cytokinins is independent of cytokinins in tRNA. 1. Tobacco tissue culture which requires addition of free cytokinin for continuous growth is perfectly capable of synthesizing the usual complement of cytokinins in tRNA (17). 2. Double-labeling experiments showed that benzyladenine was incorporated as the intact molecule into tRNA, but the level of BA recovered from tRNA hydrolysates was far below that of naturally occurring cytokinin ribosides (113). The possibility of free cytokinins acting as side chain donors in the formation of tRNA-bound cytokinins was thus excluded. 3. Radioactive benzyladenine was incorporated to a larger extent into rRNA than into tRNA (4). 4. Certain 7-substituted pyrazolo[4,3-d]pyrimidine analogs of cytokinins exhibit hormonal activity but, because of their structural features, are most unlikely to be incorporated into tRNA (96). The weight of the combined evidence justifies shifting the search for the site of action of cytokinins from tRNA to a hormonal receptor with which the hormone is expected to interact noncovalently.

Because of reports that cytokinins stimulate in vitro protein synthesis (e.g. see ref. 22), Berridge et al (8, 9) investigated the interaction of cytokinins with ribosomes isolated from Chinese cabbage leaves. They detected reversible binding of cytokinins to 83S ribosomes as shown by equilibrium dialysis, chromatography on Sephadex G-200 columns equilibrated with radioactive cytokinins, and by sucrose gradient centrifugation with labeled cytokinins present throughout the gradient. There was a fairly good correlation between the affinity of cytokinins to Chinese cabbage leaf ribosomes and the biological activity of the respective compounds. However, binding was not saturated at concentrations approaching the solubility limit of cytokinins, and no data on binding kinetics were obtained. Attempts to demonstrate an effect on cytokinins on in vitro protein synthesis using amino acid-incorporating systems from Chinese cabbage leaves and etiolated peas were unsuccessful (8, 9).

Recently, Fox & Erion (30), using a centrifugation assay and equilibrium dialysis, confirmed the results of Berridge et al (8, 9) by showing that benzyladenine bound to ribosomes of wheat germ and tobacco callus. Much less binding was observed with ribosomes isolated from rat liver or *E. coli.* Scatchard plots pointed to a low and a high affinity site with binding constants (K_A) of 9 $\times$ 10^{3}M^{-1} and 1.6 $\times$ 10^{6}M^{-1}, respectively. The high-affinity binding site, which was susceptible to trypsin and boiling, could be solubilized by washing the ribosomes with 0.5M KCl and retained its binding capacity. The specificity of the binding for biologically active cytokinins has not been documented as yet. It also has to be pointed out that the K_D of the high-affinity binding site ($1/K_A = 6.25 \times 10^{-7}$M) is approximately at, or even above, the concentration at which many physiological responses to cytokinins are saturated.

Investigating the effect of plant hormones on in vitro RNA synthesis, Matthysse & Abrams (66) observed a stimulatory effect of kinetin, provided that a "cytokinin-reactive" protein was added back to the purified chromatin preparation. From these experiments, it has been inferred that "the protein and hormone must in some way recognize some aspect of the DNA," but no direct evidence has been presented to show cytokinin binding to the putative protein factor.

LéJohn (60) described binding of cytokinins, tryptophan, IAA, and Ca^{2+} to a glycoprotein isolated from the water mold *Achlya* sp. No specificity or kinetics of binding were given, and the significance of these data with regard to hormone action in higher plants is not clear.

OTHER HORMONES

Abscisic Acid

^{14}C-labeled abscisic acid (ABA) can be obtained commercially, and a method for labeling ABA with tritium has recently been published (86). However, ^{3}H-ABA obtained in this fashion was of relatively low specific radioactivity and the compound was not stable above pH 8. No binding studies using radioactive ABA have yet been reported.

Ethylene

Early work on the metabolism of ^{14}C- and ^{3}H-labeled ethylene and its incorporation into cellular components gave conflicting results (for a review see 1). These experiments were open to criticism since the purity of the radioactive ethylene was not verified and since no precautions were taken to exclude microbial contamination. More recently, Beyer (11) investigated the fate of highly purified ^{14}C-ethylene applied to aseptically grown etiolated pea seedlings. A significant, but very small portion of the ^{14}C-ethylene was recovered in the tissue homogenate and in CO_2 trapped during the experiment. The significance of these findings with regard to ethylene action is not clear. Information on the mode of ethylene action was also sought by investigating the possible exchange of deuterium in deuterated ethylene with hydrogen in pea tissue (2, 10). This approach is only valid, of course, if ethylene binds reversibly to its site of action. Within experimental error, no deuterium-hydrogen exchange between ethylene and the tissue was observed, and C_2D_4 proved to be biologically just as effective as C_2H_4. The lack of an isotope effect in the biological response indicates that breaking of C-H bonds does not occur during complexing of ethylene and its active site, since such reactions would discriminate against the compound of higher mass.

Based on analogies of olefin binding to silver and based on the biological effectiveness of CO as an ethylene analog, Burg & Burg (16) suggested that the site of action of ethylene may contain a metal. No direct evidence is available to substantiate this hypothesis, however.

The effect of ethylene on the properties of model membranes has been investigated by Mehard et al (69). Thin films of lipids, proteins, and mixtures of both showed changes in surface tension when treated with ethylene and other aliphatic gases. However, this effect was related to the molecular size of the gas, and ethylene did not exhibit any specific properties in this test system.

DOSE-RESPONSE CURVES OF PLANT HORMONES AND THEIR POSSIBLE SIGNIFICANCE REGARDING HORMONE-RECEPTOR INTERACTIONS

In most cases, the concentration range over which plant hormones elicit an increasing response covers 3 to 4 orders of magnitude and, in some instances, even 5 to 6 orders of magnitude (for examples see references 31, 46, 52). Within a certain concentration range, the response is linearly related to the logarithm of the hormone concentration, meaning that low hormone doses are relatively much more effective than high ones. In barley aleurone layers, for example, there is a nearly linear relationship between the logarithm of the GA_3 concentration from 5×10^{-5} to 5×10^{-1} μg/ml (1.4×10^{-10} to 1.4×10^{-6}M) and the level of the hormonally induced α-amylase (46). In contrast, induction of the synthesis of a specific uterine protein by estrogen exhibits a saturation curve which covers only two decades, from 10^{-10} to 10^{-8} M (49). In that case, there is a very close correspondence between the dose response curve and the saturation curve of hormone binding to the uterine estrogen receptor. In earlier work, Hamilton (37) also demonstrated a steep saturation curve for the induction of protein synthesis by estrogen in rat uteri. It appears then that biological responses to estrogen and the binding of estrogen to its receptor both fit Michaelis-Menten-type saturation kinetics. Since the dose response curves of plant hormones diverge, in most cases, from Michaelis-Menten-type saturation curves, the question arises whether the interaction between plant hormones and their receptors also deviates from Michaelis-Menten kinetics. The answer to this question must await unequivocal identification of plant hormone receptors. However, whether binding of plant hormones follows Michaelis-Menten kinetics or not, one will have to explain the extended concentration range over which plant hormones elicit increasing responses.

The effective concentration range of plant hormones resembles that of sensory stimulants. For example, in odor perception, an animal can distinguish differences in the concentration of olfactory agents over a concentration range of several decades (93). In sensory physiology, the extended dose-response curve has usually been interpreted in terms of an adaptation phenomenon. In the broadest sense, adaptation describes the ability of an organism to decrease its sensitivity towards a stimulant as the concentration of this stimulant is raised. The molecular mechanisms underlying adaptation are not known. It is possible that an olfactant, for example, reacts with a specific proteinaceous receptor, and that this interaction may show in vitro Michaelis-Menten kinetics. It is also conceivable that such binding may exhibit negative cooperativity, i.e. the affinity of the ligand to the protein would decrease with increasing ligand concentration, thus accounting for the progressively decreasing sensitivity to the odorant molecule. Less conventional theories of olfactory perception regard partitioning of olfactants into epithelial membranes rather than binding to a receptor as the mode of interaction with the sensory tissue (21, 74, 75). According to one of these hypotheses, stimulation occurs when one or several adsorbed odorant molecules desorb from the cell membrane, leaving a sharp hole through which ions may flow to initiate nervous impulses (21). The surface viscosity of membranes and the structural properties of the olfactant may confer specificity to this response. Plant hormones may perhaps act in a similar fashion as ionophores. Again the viscous properties of the membranes and the structure of the hormones may determine the specificity of interaction. In this case, the action of the hormone would not depend on binding to a specific proteinaceous receptor with a limited number of binding sites. Some analogy may be drawn to the action of the Ca^{2+}-ionophore A-23187 which is able to simulate the action of epinephrin in rat parotid tissue by causing massive release of K^+ (94). One is tempted to ask whether ABA may act in some similar fashion in effecting rapid closure of stomates through redistribution of K^+ between guard and subsidiary cells.

Initiation of hormonal responses through specific partitioning of plant hormones into membranes may explain some apparent paradoxes. The low threshold concentration required for hormonal responses in plants would indicate a high affinity between the hormone and its receptor. The fact that saturation of hormonal responses is usually reached at relatively high hormone concentrations points to the existence of many binding sites. Why has it not been possible to isolate hormone-receptor complexes from plants? In most cases where a biological process is regulated through specific interaction between a small molecule and a protein one has been able to find analogs of the respective low-molecular weight compound which act as competitive inhibitors. With the possible exception of CO_2 and PCIB which may act as competitive inhibitors of ethylene (16) and of auxin (68), respectively, there are no known competitive inhibitors of plant hormones. This seems odd considering the large-scale screening tests performed by chemical companies and research laboratories in search of substances with agricultural applicability. If plant hormones do not act by binding to a limited number of specific sites, we would, of course, not be able to find competitive inhibitors.

On the preceding pages we have discussed experiments that were directed toward identification of the site of action of plant hormones. In the quest to discover the mode of action of these compounds, it will be necessary, of course, to find out where they act. However, one is faced with the fact that no single receptor protein for any of the plant hormones has yet been isolated, despite many efforts in a number of laboratories. The experiments of auxin binding to cell membranes (25, 41) may, we hope, lead to the isolation of a specific receptor for this hormone. In assessing the situation with the other hormones, one must carefully consider the potential difficulties that may have prevented success. It would be difficult, for example, to isolate a receptor which has a relatively low affinity to the hormone and which occurs at low concentrations in the cell. The task would be made even more difficult if large numbers of unspecific binding sites were present as well. It is also quite possible that one is not dealing with a conventional interaction between a small molecule and a regulatory protein. In that case, only new avenues of approach may lead to the localization of the site of action of plant hormones.

ACKNOWLEDGMENTS

We thank Michael R. Sussman for many stimulating discussions and valuable criticism. We gratefully acknowledge support from the US Energy Research and Development Administration under Contract E(11-1)-1338 and from the National Science Foundation under Grant No. BMS74-23471.

Literature Cited

1. Abeles, F. B. 1973. *Ethylene in Plant Biology.* New York: Academic. 302 pp.
2. Abeles, F. B., Ruth, J. M., Forrence, L. E., Leather, G. R. 1972. *Plant Physiol.* 49:669–71
3. Andreae, W., Van Ysselstein, M. W. 1960. *Plant Physiol.* 35:225–32
4. Armstrong, D. J., Murai, N., Taller, B. J., Skoog, F. 1976. *Plant Physiol.* 57:15–22
5. Bamberger, E. S. 1971. *Phytochemistry* 10:957–66
6. Barendse, G. W. M. 1974. In *Plant Growth Substances 1973,* 332–41. Tokyo: Hirokawa
7. Bendaña, F. E., Galston, A. W., Kaur-Sawhney, R., Penny, P. J. 1965. *Plant Physiol.* 40:977–83
8. Berridge, M. V., Ralph, R. K., Letham, D. S. 1970. *Biochem. J.* 119:75–84
9. Berridge, M. V., Ralph, R. K., Letham, D. S. 1972. In *Plant Growth Substances 1970,* ed. D. J. Carr, 248–55. Berlin: Springer
10. Beyer, E. M. Jr. 1972. *Plant Physiol.* 49:672–75
11. Beyer, E. M. Jr. 1975. *Nature* 255: 144–46
12. Birnbaumer, L. 1973. *Biochim. Biophys. Acta* 300:129–58
13. Biswas, B. B., Mondal, H., Ganguly, A., Das, A., Mandal, R. K. 1974. In *Control of Transcription,* ed. B. B. Biswas, R. K. Mandal, A. Stevens, W. E. Cohn, 279–92. New York: Plenum
14. Bowen, M. R., Wilkins, M. B., Cane, A. R., McCorquodale, I. 1972. *Planta* 105:273–92
15. Brandes, H., Kende, H. 1968. *Plant Physiol.* 43:827–37
16. Burg, S. P., Burg, E. A. 1967. *Plant Physiol.* 42:144–52
17. Burrows, W. J., Skoog, F., Leonard, N. J. 1971. *Biochemistry* 10:2189–93
18. Cuatrecasas, P., Hollenberg, M. D. 1975. *Biochem. Biophys. Res. Commun.* 62:31–41
19. Cummins, W. R., Sondheimer, E. 1973. *Planta* 111:365–69
20. Davies, I. J. 1973. In *Molecular Techniques and Approaches in Developmen-*

tal Biology, ed. M. J. Chrispeels, 39–54. New York: Wiley
21. Davies, J. T. 1965. *J. Theor. Biol.* 8:1–7
22. Davies, J. W., Cocking, E. C. 1967. *Biochem. J.* 104:23–33
23. Davies, P. J. 1971. *Plant Cell Physiol.* 12:785–89
24. Davies, P. J., Galston, A. W. 1971. *Plant Physiol.* 47:435–41
25. Dohrmann, U. 1975. *Charakterisierung der In-vitro-Bindung des Pflanzenhormons Auxin bei Koleoptilen von Zea mays L.* Inaugural-Dissertation Albert-Ludwigs-Universität, Freiburg i. Br. 85pp.
26. Durley, R. C., Pharis, R. P. 1973. *Planta* 109:357–61
27. Fellenberg, G. 1969. *Planta* 84:195–98
28. Ibid, 324–38
29. Fellenberg, G. 1971. *Z. Naturforsch.* 26b:607–12
30. Fox, J. E., Erion, J. L. 1975. *Biochem. Biophys. Res. Commun.* 64:694–700
31. Galston, A. W., Baker, R. S. 1951. *Plant Physiol.* 26:311–17
32. Galston, A. W., Jackson, P., Kaur-Sawhney, R., Kefford, N. P., Meudt, W. J. 1964. In *Régulateurs Naturels de la Croissance Végétale,* 251–64. Paris: Éditions du Centre National de la Recherche Scientifique
33. Galston, A. W., Kaur, R. 1961. In *Plant Growth Regulation,* 355–62. Ames: Iowa State Univ. Press
34. Ginzburg, C., Kende, H. 1968. In *Biochemistry and Physiology of Plant Growth Substances,* ed. F. Wightman, G. Setterfield, 333–40. Ottawa: Runge
35. Gordon, S. A. 1946. *Am. J. Bot.* 33:160–69
36. Guilfoyle, T. J., Lin, C. Y., Chen, Y. M., Nagao, R. T., Key, J. L. 1975. *Proc. Natl. Acad. Sci. USA* 72:69–72
37. Hamilton, T. H. 1963. *Proc. Natl. Acad. Sci. USA* 49:373–79
38. Hardin, J. W., Cherry, J. H., Morré, D. J., Lembi, C. A. 1972. *Proc. Natl. Acad. Sci. USA* 69:3146–50
39. Hardin, J. W., O'Brien, T. J., Cherry, J. H. 1970. *Biochim. Biophys. Acta* 224:667–70
40. Hertel, R. 1974. In *Membrane Transport in Plants,* ed. U. Zimmerman, J. Dainty, 457–61. Berlin: Springer
41. Hertel, R., Thompson, K.-St., Russo, V. E. A. 1972. *Planta* 107:325–40
42. Hummel, J. P., Dreyer, W. J. 1962. *Biochim. Biophys. Acta* 63:530–32
43. Jablanović, M., Noodén, L. D. 1974. *Plant Cell Physiol.* 15:687–92
44. Jensen, E. V., DeSombre, E. R. 1972. *Ann. Rev. Biochem.* 41:203–30
45. Jensen, E. V., Jacobson, H. I. 1962. *Recent Progr. Horm. Res.* 18:387–414
46. Jones, R. L., Varner, J. E. 1967. *Planta* 72:155–61
47. Kasamo, K., Yamaki, T. 1974. *Plant Cell Physiol.* 15:965–70
48. Kasamo, K., Yamaki, T. 1974. See Ref. 6, 699–707
49. Katzenellenbogen, B. S., Gorski, J. 1972. *J. Biol. Chem.* 247:1299–1305
50. Kefford, N. P., Kaur-Sawhney, R., Galston, A. W. 1963. *Acta Chem. Scand.* 17:S313–18
51. Kende, H. 1967. *Plant Physiol.* 42: 1612–18
52. Kende, H. 1971. *Int. Rev. Cytol.* 31: 301–37
53. Kende, H., Tavares, J. E. 1968. *Plant Physiol.* 43:1244–48
54. Kennedy, C. D. 1971. *Pestic. Sci.* 2:69–74
55. Kennedy, C. D., Harvey, J. M. 1972. *Pestic. Sci.* 3:715–27
56. Key, J. L., Ingle, J. 1968. See Ref. 34, 711–22
57. Klotz, I. M., Walker, F. M., Pivan, R. B. 1946. *J. Am. Chem. Soc.* 68:1486–90
58. Kobayashi, K. 1974. See Ref. 6, 573–81
59. Kobayashi, K., Yamaki, T. 1972. *Plant Cell Physiol.* 13:49–65
60. LéJohn, H. B. 1975. *Can. J. Biochem.* 53:768–78
61. Lembi, C. A., Morré, D. J., Thompson, K.-St., Hertel, R. 1971. *Planta* 99: 37–45
62. Lever, J. E. 1972. *Anal. Biochem.* 50:73–83
63. Liao, S., Hamilton, R. H. 1966. *Science* 151:822–24
64. Matlib, M. A., Kirkwood, R. C., Patterson, J. D. E. 1971. *Weed Res.* 11: 190–92
65. Matthysse, A. G. 1970. *Biochim. Biophys. Acta* 199:519–21
66. Matthysse, A. G., Abrams, M. 1970. *Biochim. Biophys. Acta* 199:511–18
67. Matthysse, A. G., Phillips, C. 1969. *Proc. Natl. Acad. Sci. USA* 63:897–903
68. McRae, D. H., Bonner, J. 1953. *Physiol. Plant.* 6:485–510
69. Mehard, C. W., Lyons, J. M., Kumamoto, J. 1970. *J. Membr. Biol.* 3:173–79
70. Merkys, A. I., Putrimas, A. D., Marciukaitis, A. S. 1971. *Sov. Plant Physiol.* 18:61–66
71. Milborrow, B. V. 1974. *Ann. Rev. Plant Physiol.* 25:259–307

72. Mondal, H., Mandal, R. K., Biswas, B. B. 1972. *Nature New Biol.* 240:111–13
73. Mondal, H., Mandal, R. K., Biswas, B. B. 1972. *Biochem. Biophys. Res. Commun.* 49:306–11
74. Mozell, M. M. 1970. *J. Gen. Physiol.* 56:46–63
75. Mozell, M. M., Jagodowicz, M. 1973. *Science* 181:1247–48
76. Murofushi, N., Durley, R. C., Pharis, R. P. 1974. *Agric. Biol. Chem.* 38:475–76
77. Musgrave, A., Kays, S. E., Kende, H. 1969. *Planta* 89:165–77
78. Ibid 1972. 102:1–10
79. Musgrave, A., Kende, H. 1970. *Plant Physiol.* 45:56–61
80. Nadeau, R., Rappaport, L. 1974. *Phytochemistry* 13:1537–45
81. O'Brien, T. J., Jarvis, B. C., Cherry, J. H., Hanson, J. B. 1968. *Biochim. Biophys. Acta* 169:35–43
82. O'Malley, B. W., Means, A. R. 1974. *Science* 183:610–20
83. Paleg, L. G., Wood, A., Spotswood, T. M. 1974. See Ref. 6, 732–36
84. Penner, D., Early, R. W. 1972. *Phytochemistry* 11:3135–38
85. Pitel, D. W., Vining, L. C. 1970. *Can. J. Biochem.* 48:259–63
86. Ring, S. G., Milborrow, B. V., Isherwood, F. A. 1975. *Anal. Biochem.* 65:543–45
87. Roland, J.-C., Lembi, C. A., Morré, D. J. 1972. *Stain Technol.* 47:195–200
88. Roychoudhury, R., Sen, S. P. 1964. *Physiol. Plant.* 17:352–62
89. Sabnis, D. D., Hirshberg, G., Jacobs, W. P. 1969. *Plant Physiol.* 44:27–36
90. Sarkissian, I. V. 1970. *Biochem. Biophys. Res. Commun.* 40:1385–90
91. Sarkissian, I. V. 1972. See Ref. 9, 265–71
92. Scatchard, G. 1949. *Ann. NY Acad. Sci.* 51:660–72
93. Schneider, D. 1966. *Symp. Soc. Exp. Biol.* 20:273–97
94. Selinger, Z., Eimerl, S., Schramm, M. 1974. *Proc. Natl. Acad. Sci. USA* 71:128–31
95. Siegel, S. M., Galston, A. W. 1953. *Proc. Natl. Acad. Sci. USA* 39:1111–18
96. Skoog, F., Schmitz, R. Y., Bock, R. M., Hecht, S. M. 1973. *Phytochemistry* 12:25–37
97. Skoog, F., Thimann, K. V. 1940. *Science* 92:64
98. Spelsberg, T. C., Sarkissian, I. V. 1970. *Phytochemistry* 9:1203–9
99. Stoddart, J., Breidenbach, R. W., Nadeau, R., Rappaport, L. 1974. *Proc. Natl. Acad. Sci. USA* 71:3255–59
100. Sussman, M. R., Firn, R. 1976. *Phytochemistry.* 15:153–55
101. Tautvydas, K. J., Galston, A. W. 1972. See Ref. 9, 254–64
102. Thompson, K.-S. 1972. In *Hormonal Regulation in Plant Growth and Development. Proc. Adv. Study Inst. Izmir 1971*, ed. H. Kaldeway, Y. Vardar, 83–88. Weinheim: Verlag Chemie
103. Thompson, K.-S., Hertel, R., Müller, S., Tavares, J. E. 1973. *Planta* 109:337–52
104. Thompson, K.-S., Leopold, A. C. 1974. *Planta* 115:259–70
105. Vanderwoude, W. J., Lembi, C. A., Morré, D. J. 1972. *Biochem. Biophys. Res. Commun.* 46:245–53
106. Veen, H. 1966. *Acta Bot. Neerl.* 15:419–33
107. Veen, H. 1974. *Z. Naturforsch.* 29c:39–41
108. Venis, M. A. 1968. See Ref. 34, 761–75
109. Venis, M. A. 1971. *Proc. Natl. Acad. Sci. USA* 68:1824–27
110. Venis, M. A. 1972. See Ref. 9, 240–47
111. Venis, M. A. 1973. *Curr. Adv. Plant Sci.* 2:21–28
112. Venis, M. A., Batt, S. 1975. *Biochem. Soc. Trans.* 3:1148–51
113. Walker, G. C., Leonard, N. J., Armstrong, D. J., Murai, N., Skoog, F. 1974. *Plant Physiol.* 54:737–43
114. Weigl, J. 1969. *Z. Naturforsch. B* 24:365–66
115. Ibid, 367–68
116. Ibid 1046–52
117. Wildman, S. G., Gordon, S. A. 1942. *Proc. Natl. Acad. Sci. USA* 28:217–28
118. Winter, A., Thimann, K. V. 1966. *Plant Physiol.* 41:335–42
119. Wood, A., Paleg, L. G. 1972. *Plant Physiol.* 50:103–8
120. Wood, A., Paleg, L. G. 1974. *Aust. J. Plant Physiol.* 1:31–40
121. Wood, A., Paleg, L. G., Raison, J. K. 1974. See Ref. 6, 725–31
122. Wood, A., Paleg, L. G., Sawhney, R. 1972. See Ref. 9, 37–43
123. Wood, A., Paleg, L. G., Spotswood, T. M. 1974. *Aust. J. Plant Physiol.* 1:167–69
124. Yamaki, T., Kobayashi, K. 1972. See Ref. 9, 196–206

Ann. Rev. Plant Physiol. 1976. 27:291–319

PHYTOHEMAGGLUTININS (PHYTOLECTINS)[1]

◆7611

Irvin E. Liener

Department of Biochemistry, College of Biological Sciences, University of Minnesota, St. Paul, Minnesota 55108

CONTENTS

[1]The survey of literature pertaining to this review was concluded in August 1975.

INTRODUCTION

The task of writing this review has been made much less painful as a result of several recent reviews on the subject (146, 243) and the publication of the proceedings of a conference on agglutinins sponsored by the New York Academy of Sciences in 1973 (45). The interested reader may consult these references for information on the historical background of the phytohemagglutinins as well as for a review of much of the literature available up to about 1972. In the interim however, the literature on this subject has continued to proliferate, and an assessment of the current status of our knowledge on this subject seems appropriate at this time.

The interest manifested in the phytohemagglutinins is due in large part to the many and varied effects which they produce in biological systems as a consequence of their unique property of being able to bind saccharides and saccharide-containing proteins in a highly specific fashion. By virtue of this property, the phytohemagglutinins have provided investigators with an extremely useful tool, not only for isolating and characterizing polysaccharides and glycoproteins, but also for probing the molecular architecture of cell surfaces and the changes induced therein by transformation. Fascinating and important as these facets of the subject may be, the limitation of space precludes a coverage of these topics; more specific reviews dealing with the interaction of phytohemagglutinins with animal cell surface may be found elsewhere (177, 242). A survey of 2663 plant species revealed that over 800 of them displayed hemagglutinating activity (6), and in the family Leguminosae alone, over 600 species and varieties have been shown to contain phytoagglutinins (264). This review will be concerned only with those phytohemagglutinins which have been isolated in pure form and characterized with respect to their physicochemical and biological properties. In addition, some consideration will be given to the physiological function which these substances may have in the plant itself and, because many of these plants are consumed by man and animals, to their possible influence on the nutritional value of such plants.

The growing realization that proteins capable of specific interaction with carbohydrate-containing substances are found not only in plants but also in invertebrates (45, 238), fish (128), fungi (46, 70, 239), bacteria (75), lichen (104), and even in mammalian tissue (228, 255) has posed a vexing question with respect to terminology. The term "lectin" was originally proposed by Boyd & Sharpleigh (29) to denote those substances of plant origin which agglutinate red blood cells, frequently showing a high degree of specificity towards human erythrocytes of specific blood groups as well as towards the blood of different species of animals. Although the term "lectin" is commonly used as a synonym for phytohemagglutinin, it is clear that we need to broaden its original definition in order to include those substances which may not be of plant origin. Furthermore, it is now evident that some of these substances, although capable of interacting with sugars or sugar derivatives, do not necessarily produce visible agglutination of cells or precipitation of complex polysaccharides or glycoproteins. It is proposed, therefore, that the term "lectin" be used as a generic term to denote all sugar-specific proteins, with perhaps a further designation as "phytolectins," "zoolectins,"[2] or "mycolectins," depending on whether they are of plant, animal, or fungal origin respectively. Those lectins which do not agglutinate cells but which exhibit some other describable property such as mitogenicity or toxicity could be simply referred to as mitogenic or toxic lectins.

METHODOLOGY

Purification Techniques

The technique of affinity chromatography, which is based on the ability of lectins to bind a carbohydrate ligand covalently bound to an insoluble matrix, has proved to be a convenient means for purifying many phytolectins. Compilations of lectins which have been purified by this technique may be found elsewhere (129, 143, 146, 242); only those lectins whose purification by affinity chromatography has not been included in these reviews will be considered in connection with the specific lectins to be discussed later.

Sepharose activated with cyanogen bromide continues to provide the most direct and convenient means of immobilizing a wide variety of sugar ligands. In a method described by Bloch & Burger (24), the p-nitrophenylglycoside derivative of a sugar is reduced and coupled to the activated Sepharose. Alternatively, the N-alkylglycoside can be synthesized by reaction of sugars with β-(p-aminophenyl)-ethylamine and, after reduction to a secondary amine, is coupled to activated Sepharose (114).

Several procedures involving affinity chromatography on synthetic gels have been recently described which also appear to have general applicability to the isolation of lectins of known specificity. Hǒrejší & Kocourek (96, 99) describe the preparation of acrylamide gels which have been copolymerized with various alkenyl-O-glycosides, and in this way were able to isolate lectins from *Ulex europeus, Bandeiraea simplicifolia,* and *Pisum sativum.* Such gels could also be used for the electrophoretic separation of lectins from complex mistures (98, 100). In this technique, referred to as "affinity electrophoresis," lectins having combining sites for a particular sugar residue interact with the affinity gel and remain adsorbed to it, while all of the other proteins of the mixture separate in the usual fashion. This method provides a rapid means for detecting the presence of lectins of a given specifity and permits a quick decision as to which type of sugar ligand would be most suitable for preparative affinity chromatography.

In a technique developed by Hayes & Goldstein (93), the sugar ligand (in the form of a di- or oligosaccharide possessing the desired nonreducing terminal sugar and glycosidic linkage) is oxidized to the corresponding aldonic acid and condensed to aminoethyl-Bio-Gel P-300. A somewhat similar approach has been reported by Gray (81), involving the direct coupling of reducing carbohydrates to aminoethyl gels by reductive amination. Schnaar & Lee (237) describe still another method for incorporation of sugars into gels. Active esters of acrylic acid (N-succinimidyl- or

---

[2]This term would presumably include the "protectins," a term proposed by Prokop et al (217) for agglutinating proteins present in albumin of snails and the eggs of fish and amphibia.

N-phthalimidyl acrylate) are copolymerized with acrylamide and N,N'-methy-lenebisacrylamide. Various sugar derivatives containing aliphatic amino groups are used to displace the active ester in the gel to form stable amide bonds between the ligands and the gel.

Although not strictly in the category of affinity chromatography, mention should be made of the use of formalinized erythrocytes for the isolation of lectins from crude extracts of plant material (226). Formalinized erythrocytes of a specific human blood group or of a particular animal species were used in a batchwise step to absorb lectins from the jack bean, wheat germ, the seeds of *Ulex europeus,* and lima beans, followed by elution with an appropriate sugar specific for the lectin being isolated.

Assays for Biological Activity

Most workers in this field still seem to be content to measure agglutinating activity towards various kinds of cells by a serial dilution technique with visual estimate of the end-point. Some of these techniques have been critically evaluated by Burger (36). Attempts have been made to improve the precision of such assays by spectro-photometric techniques which measure the decrease in the turbidity of a suspension of cells induced by their agglutination by lectins (107, 119, 145) or by the direct measurement of the rate of formation of aggregated cells (157). More sophisticated modifications have been proposed which involve the use of specialized instrumenta-tion to measure agglutination by light scattering (20, 25) or by means of an elec-tronic particle counter (196). An assay has been described for cell agglutination in which a suspension of single, labeled cells are exposed to a confluent cell layer, and the attachment of the single cells to the cell layer is determined as a function of the time of incubation (232). The possibility that some commercial preparations of sugars may be contaminated with material having hemagglutinating activity, and thus interfere in inhibition studies, has been recently pointed out (162).

The mitogenic activity of lectins is frequently measured by their ability to stimu-late the in vitro synthesis of DNA by peripheral lymphocytes, an activity which can be quantitated by measuring the uptake of labeled thymidine. Rapid micromethods for conducting such an assay have been recently introduced (202, 203).

Noonan & Burger (181) have described a technique involving the use of tritiated concanavalin A for determining the number of binding sites on a variety of normal and transformed cells.

PROPERTIES OF PURIFIED LECTINS

Concanavalin A

Studies on concanavalin A (Con A), the lectin of the jack bean (*Canavalia ensifor-mis*), continue to dominate the scene. More is now known about the structure of this lectin than any other, and concerted attempts are well under way to relate the many interesting biological properties of Con A to its structure.

The general features of the molecular structure of Con A had been previously reported independently about 3 years ago by Edelman's group at the Rockefeller University (57) and by Hardman & Ainsworth at the Argonne National Laboratory (88). These results have now been further documented and expanded in a series of four papers from the Rockefeller group (14, 47, 222, 282). Despite some initial uncertainty, it is now generally accepted that Con A in solution at neutral pH is a tetramer composed of four identical subunits, each of which has a molecular weight of 26,000. Each subunit is a single polypeptide chain comprised of 237 amino acid residues whose sequence has been established[3] (47). Each subunit contains one Mn^{2+} and one Ca^{2+} binding site as well as a single sugar binding site. X-ray studies, carried out at 2Å resolution on the tetrameric form of the protein with both metal sites occupied, have provided an insight into the finer structural details of Con A (14, 220). The overall shape of the monomer is best described as a flat-based dome (42 × 40 × 39 Å) whose structure is dominated by two large, entirely antiparallel sheets. The two metal binding sites are located in a surface cavity near the apex of the dome, only 4.6 Å apart. A more detailed picture of the environment of the metals, and the manner in which they are coordinated is shown in Figure 1. Not shown here, however, but located about 20 Å from the metal positions, is a deep cavity between the two large β-sheets wherein resides the saccharide binding site. The latter appears to be composed of two distinct subsites, one of which is hydrophobic and the other hydrophilic. Conflicting chemical and physical evidence (7, 18, 32, 89, 277), however, does not permit an unequivocal identification of the saccharide-binding site.

The question relating to the precise role that metal ions play in the activity of Con A has been the object of considerable study. The fact that the ability of Con A to bind to Sephadex depends on the presence of metal ions (120) is certainly an indication of the importance of metal ions for its interaction with saccharides. Furthermore, occupation of the Mn^{2+}-binding or transition metal-binding site (S_1) is necessary before the second metal-binding site (S_2) can bind Ca^{2+}, and the occupation of both sites is necessary before saccharide-binding can occur (117). More recent evidence, based on studies involving electron spin resonance (31, 279), circular dichroism (165), spin-lattice relaxation (13), and spectral changes (55), supports the view that the bonding of Ca^{2+} to the S_2 site causes an alteration in the environment of the S_1 site, which, in turn, is important for the creation of the saccharide-binding site. Other studies (118, 244–246) have revealed that a variety of metals, including rare earth metals, may substitute for Mn^{2+} on the S_1 transition site, including cadmium (Cd^{2+}), cobalt (Co^{2+}), nickel (Ni^{2+}), zinc (Zn^{2+}), lead (Pb^{2+}), godalinium (Gd^{3+}), terbium (Tb^{3+}), and lanthanum (La^{3+}). This would indicate that the size of the metal located at the S_1 site is of little importance. On the other hand, the metal requirement for the S_2 is more rigid, and only those divalent

---

[3]Hague (86) found that Con A isolated from *C. maritima* had only one methionine residue compared to Con A isolated from *C. ensiformis* or *C. gladiata,* which contains two methionine residues. The methionine residue at position 129 appears to be absent from the Con A prepared from *C. maritima.*

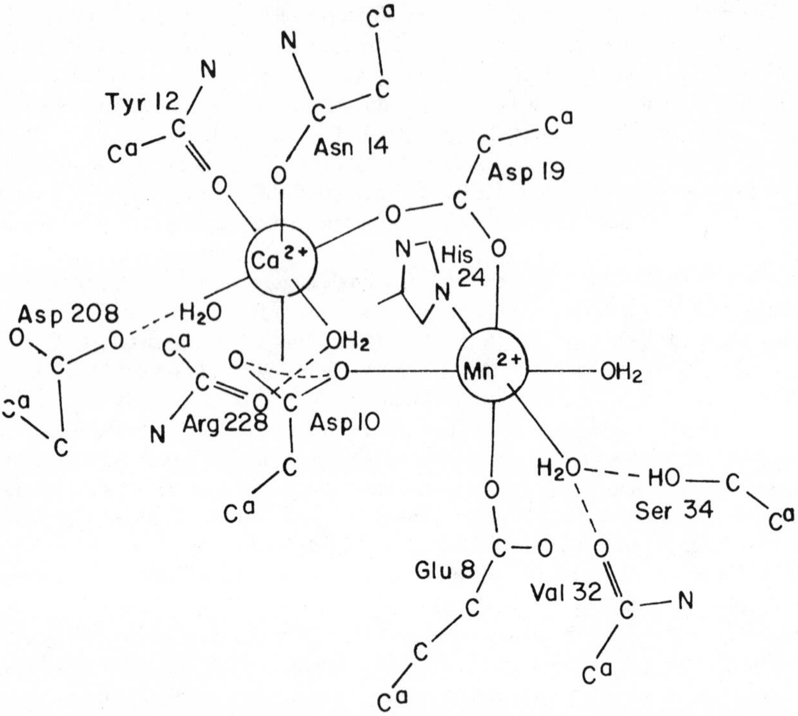

Figure 1 Schematic drawing of the metal coordination in Con A. Both metals are octahedrally coordinated by four protein ligands and two water molecules. Asp-10 and Asp-19 are ligands of both metals. The two carboxylic oxygens of Asp-10 form one vertex of the Ca^{2+} coordination shell. One of the waters on the Mn^{2+} and both waters on the Ca^{2+} are hydrogen-bonded to the protein; this is indicated by dashed lines. The entire binuclear complex is 20 Å from the saccharide-binding site. Figure taken from Ref. 221.

metal ions with radii near 1 Å, such as Ca^{2+} and Cd^{2+} can be accomodated at this site (246).

The activity of Con A is markedly influenced by pH (249, 250), temperature (80, 106, 249, 278), and chemical modification (84, 244, 296). It is significant to note that under those conditions where agglutinating activity towards cells or precipitability towards oligosaccharides or glycoproteins has been lost (i.e. low pH, low temperatures, and acylation of amino groups), Con A has been shown to exist largely in the form of a dimer rather than a tetramer. In contrast to succinylation which produces a dimer of Con A (84), acetylation does not alter its subunit structure although the acetylated protein induces blast transformation with diminished efficiency (224). It would appear, therefore, that the tetrameric form of Con A is necessary for those reactions involving agglutination or precipitation; the dimer, because of its reduced valence, can no longer provide the degree of cross-linkage necessary for aggregation.

The dimer, however, is still capable of binding low molecular weight sugar derivatives and yeast mannan (92) or binding to the surface of transformed cells (105). The dimer in the form of succinyl-Con A is also equally effective as a mitogen as native Con A (219) and, in contrast to an earlier report (269), is capable of inhibiting the growth of normal and transformed cells by an effect manifested during the early G_1 phase of the cell cycle (159). Agglutination or precipitation may therefore represent a two-step process: the first step involving a simple monovalent or possibly divalent binding process which is apparently sufficient to trigger mitogenesis or to inhibit cell growth, and a second step involving a multivalent process in which the cross-linking of macromolecules, or of cell surface receptor sites, results in the precipitation of macromolecules or in the agglutination of cells respectively.

Although Con A interacts specifically with α-D-mannopyranosyl, α-D-glucopyranosyl, and α-D-N-acetylglucosamine residues located at the terminal, nonreducing ends of polysaccharide chains, it is now evident that Con A is also capable of binding mannose residues located in the interior of the molecule (40, 77, 115, 125). This probably explains why a number of glycoproteins and glycopeptides are strong inhibitors of Con A despite the fact that their terminal position is blocked with sialic acid (40, 57, 176, 213). This ability to combine with internal sugar residues enables Con A to interact with a wide variety of glycoproteins of biological interest. The covalent attachment of Con A to an insoluble matrix such as Sepharose, followed by elution with a sugar such as methyl-α-D-gluco- (or manno-)pyranoside, has provided an extremely useful tool for isolating a host of biological components from complex mixtures (see Table 1).

Castor Bean Lectins

The earlier confusion regarding the identity of the toxic and hemagglutinating components in extracts of the castor bean, *Ricinus communis,* now seems to be well resolved. Funatsu and his group (71) were the first to separate a nonagglutinating toxic component from a nontoxic agglutinin. Since both components have an affinity for galactose-like residues but differ in molecular weight, other investigators have since succeeded in separating the toxin and the agglutinin by a combination of affinity chromatography on agarose[4] or ovomucoid-sepharose followed by separation by gel filtration (85, 127, 178, 263). Wei (285) has recently succeeded in crystallizing ricin as part of an effort to elucidate the three-dimensional structure of this molecule by X-ray crystallography. Although the toxin and the agglutinin both show specificity towards galactose, ricin is also inhibited by N-acetylgalactosamine whereas the agglutinin is not inhibited by this sugar (179). Advantage was taken of this difference in specificity to elute ricin from agarose with N-acetylgalactosamine and the agglutinin with galactose (63, 179). The toxic, nonagglutinating lectin is the smaller of the two lectins having a molecular weight of 60,000. Although it has been referred to in the past by a variety of different names, it is almost certain that previous workers were all dealing with the same molecule which shall be

---

[4]On the contrary, Lugnier & Dirheimer (154) claim that ricin is not retained on sepharose, but the reason for this difference in behavior is not clear.

Table 1 Biological substances which have been purified by affinity chromatography on immobilized-Con A

Class of substance	Specific component purified	Reference
Enzymes	Brain lysosomal arylsulfatase	2, 22
	Rat kidney α-glutamyltransferase	257
	Dopamine β-hydrolase	236
	Glycogen synthetase	251
	Venom exonuclease	256
	Placental acid hydrolase	21
	Human liver acid β-galactosidase	182
	Bull sperm hyaluronidase	294
Hormones	Human chorionic gonadotrophin	56
	Human lutenizing hormone	56
	Follicle stimulating hormone	56
Other lectins	Wax bean	16
	Soybean	16
	Bandieraea simplicifolia	16
Antigens	Carcinoembryonic antigen	26, 30, 43, 158, 229
	Herpes simplex virus-induced antigen	209
Serum proteins	α₁-antitrypsin	135
	Immunoglobulins	61
Cell surface	Mouse L-cells	106
receptor sites	Rat hepatoma cells	52, 248
	Chicken lymphoid cells	42
	Normal and transformed fibroblasts	247
	Human erythrocytes	68
	Human platelets	173
	Synaptic plasma membrane	299
	Liver microsomal membrane	290
	Plasma membrane of eukaryotic cells	298
Other	Interferon	15, 28, 50
	Soybean globulin 11 S	124
	Teichoic acid from *B. subtilis*	54
	Mycobacterial polysaccharides	49
	Achilles tendon glycoproteins	8

referred to here by its classical name *ricin.* The nontoxic agglutinin has a molecular weight of 120,000 and will be referred to as the *Ricinus* agglutinin. There is one report (154) that there may in fact be two agglutinins which apparently differ in charge.

Olsnes and co-workers (189, 190, 192, 194, 223) have made a detailed study of the structure of ricin and the mechanism whereby it exerts its toxicity. Ricin was found to be composed of two polypeptide chains having molecular weights of 32,000 and 34,000, and held together by disulfide bonds (see Figure 2). When these two chains were separated by reduction with mercaptoethanol, the smaller of the two

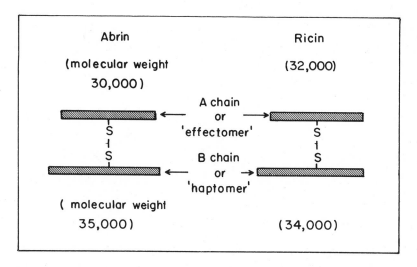

Figure 2 Schematic structure of abrin and ricin. Figure taken from Ref. 192.

chains, chain A or the "effectomer," was found to inhibit protein synthesis in a cell-free system of rabbit reticulocytes. Chain B, the "haptomer," on the other hand, had no effect on protein synthesis but, unlike chain A, it was capable of binding to sepharose. It thus appears that the B chain functions as a carrier moiety which serves to anchor the toxin to the cell surface, a binding which probably involves galactose-containing receptor sites. The binding of the toxin produces an increase in membrane fluidity (123), and the A chain (or possibly the whole toxin) is transported into the cytoplasm, where it exerts its toxic effect.

That the toxic effect of ricin is the result of an inhibition of protein synthesis is well substantiated (127, 136, 137, 140, 180, 188–192), an effect which accounts for the growth-inhibiting effect which ricin has on tumors (136, 137, 142, 270) and virus-transformed cells (180). Lugnier et al (155) reported that tryptic fragments of ricin with a molecular weight of about 12,500 retained the ability to inhibit protein synthesis. The specific target of ricin is the 60S subunit of the ribosome (37, 82, 172, 252) where it somehow interferes with the process of peptide chain elongation (37, 171, 187). It has been suggested that the action of ricin may be enzymatic in nature (172, 189, 192) and that its specific site of reaction may be guanosine triphosphatase (253). Whether or not this suggested enzymatic activity is in any way related to the proteolytic activity reported to be associated with ricin (72) remains to be explored.

Studies on the structure of ricin in relation to that of the agglutinin have revealed some interesting similarities. The native agglutinin, which has a molecular weight of 120,000, is a tetramer comprised of two different subunits, one with a molecular weight of 33,000–37,000 and the other, 27,500–31,000 (85, 179, 194). Chemical (179, 194) and immunochemical (193, 199) evidence indicates that the heavier of these two chains is probably identical to the B chain of ricin, whereas the lighter chain is homologous but not identical to the A chain of ricin (see Figure 3). Since

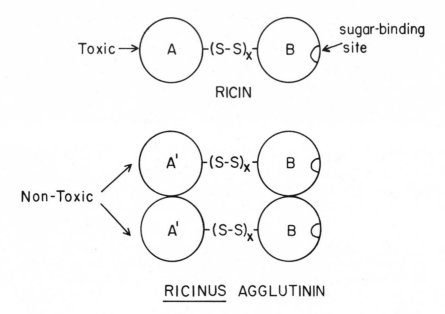

Figure 3   Schematic structure of ricin and the *Ricinus* agglutinin. The A and B chains shown here are equivalent to those shown in Figure 2 for ricin. The B chain carries a sugar binding site. The A chain is toxic and differs somewhat from the nontoxic A' chain of the agglutinin. The number of disulfide bonds connecting chain A or A' with chain B is not known.

the B chain of ricin is known to contain the sugar-binding site, one would predict that the agglutinin should have two binding sites. This has been experimentally verified (192, 274). Whatever difference exists between the A chain of ricin and the lighter chain of the agglutinin must be responsible for the extreme toxicity of ricin. A more detailed study of the structure of these two chains is required to reveal what the nature of this difference might be.

Abrus precatorius Lectins

Despite its remote taxonomic relationship to the castor bean, the seed of *A. precatorius* likewise contains a toxin, *abrin,* and agglutinins which bear a marked resemblance to those found in the castor bean. Using somewhat different techniques, both Lin et al (139, 141) and Olsnes & Pihl (191) have isolated a toxic protein having a molecular weight of 65,000. Like ricin, it is comprised of two polypeptide chains, one of which is responsible for its toxicity and the other functions as a carrier moiety for binding the toxic chain to the surface of the cell (191, 273). Abrin also owes its toxicity to the fact that it can inhibit protein synthesis (136–138, 191), presumably by inhibiting the elongation of peptide chains (187, 192). In spite of this similarity in mode of action, there are minor differences in molecular weight between the corresponding A and B chains of ricin and abrin (see Figure 2), and they do not cross-react to the same antisera (200). It is possible, however, to recombine the isolated A and B chains of ricin and abrin to produce toxic hybrid molecules consisting of abrin A chain/ricin B chain and ricin A chain/abrin B chain (200).

Wei et al (287) have reported the isolation of two toxic proteins from *A. precatorius* which differed somewhat in electrophoretic behavior, molecular weight, subunit structure, and toxicity. They concluded that one of those two forms of abrin (abrin A) corresponded to the abrin isolated by Lin et al (139) and that the other form (abrin C) most closely resembled the abrin described by Olsnes & Pihl (191). They felt that the difference between these two forms of ricin probably lies in the nature of the subunits of which they are composed. Preliminary crystallographic data on abrin A have appeared (285, 286).

Olsnes et al (194) have purified two nontoxic, galactose-binding agglutinins from *A. precatorius,* both of which had a molecular weight of approximately 134,000 but differed in subunit structure. One agglutinin was a tetramer of two heavy and two light subunits with molecular weights of 36,000 and 33,000 respectively; the other was likewise a tetramer with two heavy chains with a molecular weight of 35,000 and two light chains which were identical to the one found in the other agglutinin. The relationship between the subunit structure of these agglutinins to that of abrin is probably similar to that of the castor bean lectins (199). Wei et al (288) succeeded in crystallizing an *Abrus* agglutinin which was similar in properties to one of those described by Olsnes et al (194). Yet another "abrin" has been described (166) which has a molecular weight of 260,000 and appears to be either a dimer of the agglutinin or a tetramer of the toxin. Although toxic when freshly prepared, upon storage at 4° for several months the toxicity is lost, and the molecule then behaves as a potent mitogen (121).

Phaseolus Lectins

Over 200 species of *Phaseolus* have been found to exhibit hemagglutinating activity (185). Two principal groups can be distinguished according to their specificity of hemagglutination. One large group, represented by *P. vulgaris,* reacts nonspecifically with human erythrocytes of all blood groups, and the other, represented by *P. lunatus,* is specific for A blood group cells. There is also a third group which shows no hemagglutinating activity at all (33, 110). In addition to hemagglutinating activity, some of these seeds possess lectins capable of specifically agglutinating leucocytes and stimulating the mitosis of lymphocytes. Although most of the lectins isolated from *Phaseolus* are similar in molecular weight and subunit structure, differences in carbohydrate content, physicochemical parameters, and biological activities have been reported. To what extent these differences may be due to genetic factors, different methods of isolation, improper identification of species or varieties, or to inadequate criteria of homogeneity is difficult to assess.

RED KIDNEY BEAN (*P. VULGARIS*)   As pointed out in a recent review (146), attempts to separate the various components responsible for the erythroagglutinating, leucoagglutinating, and mitogenic activities of extracts of the red kidney bean have been "often contradictory and to some extent confusing." The air appears to

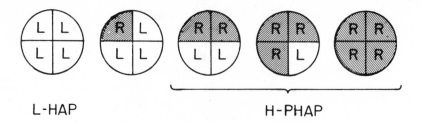

L-HAP   H-PHAP

Figure 4 Schematic representation of the tetrameric structure of the five lectins in the red kidney bean, where L and R are the subunits responsible for leucoagglutinating and hemagglutinating activities respectively. Figure taken from Ref. 168.

have been cleared somewhat by the recent work of Yachnin and co-workers (168, 169, 293). They found that all of the diverse biological activities of the kidney bean could be accounted for by a family of five heterogeneous proteins. Each of these consists of isomeric, noncovalently bound tetramers which are made up of two different subunits, designated as L and R (Figure 4). Each of these subunits has approximately the same molecular weight, 34,000, but differs in isoelectric points, and, although there is extensive hemology between the subunits, they also differ to some extent in their amino acid sequence, particularly in the N-terminal region. More importantly, however, is the fact that the L subunit has strong mitogenic activity and a high affinity for receptors of lymphocyte membranes, but little or no affinity for those of erythrocytes. Conversely, the R subunit has a high affinity for erythrocyte membrane receptors, but little for those of lymphocytes. As a consequence of this difference in specificity, the tetramer with 4 L subunits (L-PHAP) is a potent leucoagglutinin with low hemagglutinating activity. Those hybrid tetramers with two or more R subunits (2R-2L, 3R-1L, and 4R) exhibit potent hemagglutinating activity but modest leucoagglutinating activity and are referred to collectively as H-PHAP. The hybrid molecules (3R-1L, 2R-2L, and 1R-3L) have been found to be mitogenic, indicating that both L and R subunits are required for this kind of activity. The hybrid 1R-3L is devoid of hemagglutinating activity, presumably because it is monovalent with respect to its interaction with erythrocytes. Yachnin's model would seem to provide the most rational explanation for the differences in the activity of various lectin preparations reported by workers in the past (146) and may also account for the differences in activities observed in different cultivars of *P. vulgaris* (111).

Räsänen et al (220) have reported the crystallization of a leucoagglutinin from red kidney beans which had a molecular weight of 126,000, but which they concluded was composed of 4 identical subunits, molecular weight = 31,000. According to Yachnin's model this would correspond to a tetramer composed of 4 L subunits.

Harms-Ringdahl and co-workers (90, 91) isolated a mitogenic factor from red kidney beans which, unlike the mitogens previously described from this bean, had no effect on RNA synthesis by chicken spleen lymphocytes. It did, however, stimulate the synthesis of RNA by a bacterial system of plasmolyzed bacterial cells. The most unusual feature of this mitogen was its low molecular weight, about 10,000, and its unusually high content of cystine. In the latter respect, it most closely resembles the pokeweed mitogen which the authors state also stimulates RNA synthesis in their bacterial system (91).

An insoluble derivative of an agglutinin from the red kidney bean has been used to isolate asialointerferon, and it could be displaced from the lectin by a glycoprotein isolated from human erythrocytes (53).

WAX BEAN (*P. VULGARIS*) Sela et al (240) have reported the isolation of two agglutinins from the wax bean, both of which are tetramers comprised of four identical subunits with a molecular weight of 30,000. Both agglutinins agglutinated transformed cells at a concentration about 100 times lower than that required to agglutinate normal cells, and both fractions activated mouse spleen lymphocytes. Takahashi et al (258), on the other hand, isolated an agglutinin of similar size from the wax bean which had two different subunits with molecular weights of 20,000 and 25,000. This discrepancy is disconcerting but not surprising when one considers the possibility of genetic variations among species of *Phaseolus* (111).

NAVY BEAN (*P. VULGARIS*) Andrews (9) has isolated a lectin from the navy bean which has both strong erythroagglutinating as well as leucoagglutinating activities. It has been characterized as a tetramer with four identical subunits having a molecular weight of 32,000. Although it bears a strong resemblance in size, amino acid composition, and carbohydrate content to the lectins of the red kidney bean, the fact that it displays both kinds of activities would appear to be inconsistent with a tetrameric structure composed of identical subunits according to Yachnin's model. An alternative explanation is that the same subunit in this instance is endowed with the ability to combine with the receptor sites of either erythrocytes or leucocytes. Applying the technique of isoelectric focusing, Pusztai & Watt (219) demonstrated the presence of a whole family of closely related isolectins which were composed of two different subunits with molecular weights of 30,000 and 35,000 and a ratio of 3:1 respectively. These isolectins were highly active as hemagglutinins but poorly active as mitogens, suggesting that these lectins would correspond most nearly to the hybrid 3R-1L postulated by Yachnin, with minor differences in charge among the individual subunits.

LIMA BEAN (*P. LUNATUS*) Two lectins have been described which have molecular weights of 124,000 and 247,000; both are composed of identical subunits with a molecular weight of 31,000 linked by interchain disulfide bonds to form larger subunits of 62,000 (73). The two native lectins are therefore a dimer and tetramer of these larger subunits with two and four binding sites respectively (17). The tetramer has four times the agglutinating activity of the dimer (74) and is severalfold more potent than the dimer as a mitogen for normal leukemic lymphocytes (235). This enhanced activity of the tetramer is no doubt a reflection of its greater valence, which affords the opportunity for more extensive cross-linking of cell receptor sites.

Goldstein et al (76) have offered a tentative structure for the carbohydrate moiety of the lima bean lectins. The occurrence of two terminal α-D-mannopyranosyl units and an internal 2-0-linked mannopyranosyl residue would account for their strong interaction with Con A (16).

SCARLET RUNNER BEAN (*P. COCCINEUS*) Two lectins have been isolated from the scarlet runner bean by ammonium sulfate fractionation and ion-exchange chromatography (185). Both of these had a molecular weight of 120,000 with identical 34,000 subunits, and both displayed agglutinating activity towards all ABO erythrocytes. Only one of these, however, stimulated the mitosis of lymphocytes. The precise reason for this difference in mitogenic activity is not known. Erythroagglutination by both lectins was inhibited by N-acetylgalactosamine and by a glycopeptide isolated from human erythrocytes (131). In the former respect it resembles the specificity of the red kidney bean (243).

Wheat Germ Lectins

The purification of an agglutinin (WGA) from wheat germ (*Triticum vulgare*) has been accomplished by a variety of techniques involving affinity chromatography in which the ligand is N-acetylglucosamine or some macromolecule containing this sugar. These include Sepharose-ovomucoid (160), N-acetylgucosamine linked, via a spacer chain, to Sepharose (144, 148, 244). Glucosamine coupled to Sepharose through a caproylamido linkage in the C2 position (4), the incorporation of 6-aminohexyl-glucosamine into gel (237), and direct chromatography on powdered chitin (23). Most of these methods have yielded essentially one component, although Ewart (66), using the more conventional method of ion-exchange chromatography, was able to isolate three active components.

Earlier estimates placed the molecular weight of WGA at a value of about 20,000 (160), but more recent studies indicate its value to be closer to 36,000 (174, 175, 227). There seems to be rather general agreement that in the presence of denaturants the molecule dissociates into a single subunit which has a molecular weight of 17,000 to 18,000 (24, 66, 175, 227, 241). WGA would thus appear to be a dimer with two identical subunits. Considerable uncertainty exists regarding the exact number of binding sites on the agglutinin molecule, which can probably be attributed to different values assumed for its molecular weight. For example, Levine et al (133) reported that WGA had *one* binding site per molecule, assuming a molecular weight of 23,000, whereas Privat et al (215, 216), assuming the same molecular weight, concluded that there were *two* binding sites per molecule. Nagata & Burger (175) reported that there were *four* binding sites for N-acetylglucosamine per molecule, based on their data which showed WGA to be a dimer comprised of two subunits with a molecular weight of 17,000. The fact that the binding constant between WGA and sugars increases as the size of the oligomers of N-acetylglucosamine increases (5, 151, 214) has led to the suggestion that its binding site may actually consist of several subsites. Some of the confusion regarding the exact number of binding sites may be due to the fact that, depending on the saccharide being used, subsites are being measured as separate binding sites.

Two recent reports (291, 292) would indicate that X-ray crystallographic studies on WGA are well under way. The results of such studies with this agglutinin will be of particular interest because of the high degree of cross-linking imposed by the high content of cystine residues known to be present in this molecule; 28 out of its 165 amino acid residues are half-cystine residues (175).

Glycoprotein receptor sites for WGA have been isolated from the surface of mouse leukemia cells (112) and human erythrocytes (1). Although the N-acetyl-glucosamine residues of these glycoproteins represent the primary site of binding, one cannot dismiss the possibility that an interaction may occur with the sialic acid residues (83). Lotan et al (152) found that a peptidoglycan from *Micrococcus luteus* and teichoic acid from *Staphylococcus aureus* H were several times more inhibitory towards WGA than N-acetylglucosamine itself, suggesting that secondary, non-specific interactions (subsites ?) likewise contribute to the binding process.

Oikawa et al (186) have made the interesting observation that WGA can block the fertilization of hamster eggs by combining with sites in the outer region of the zona pellucida. This effect was believed to be due to the formation of cross-linkage of these sites so as to prevent the dissolution of the zona pellucida by capacitated spermatazoa.

Lentil Lectins

Two agglutinins may be isolated from the lentil bean, *Lens culinaris* or *esculenta*, by chromatography on DEAE-cellulose alone (103) or in conjunction with specific adsorption on Sephadex (69, 94, 261). Both lectins have very similar properties and the same molecular weight of about 52,000, and, according to Fliegerova et al (69), appear to be composed of two types of subunits with molecular weights of 18,000 and 8,000. This would suggest that both lectins are tetramers comprised of two of each of these subunits and that the difference between the two lectins must reside in some subtle difference in charge in one or both of the subunits. It had been previously reported by Howard et al (103) that the lentil lectins could be dissociated into identical subunits of 24,500 molecular weight. It is possible that the two different subunits obtained by Fliegerova et al were actually fragments of a single subunit having the molecular weight reported by Howard et al. The presence of fragments of a subunit in lectin preparations has a precedent in the case of Con A (281).

A somewhat different lectin has been isolated from a small seed variety of lentil, *Lens esculenta* Moensch., subsp. *microsperma* (67). Unlike the previously described lectins from the large seed lentil, this particular lectin was not adsorbed to Sephadex, and, while the large seed lectins show no specificity towards ABO human erythrocytes, this lectin showed a preference for the A type blood group. Despite these differences in specificity, the small seed lentil had the same molecular weight and subunit structure as the large seed lentils.

Although the lentil lectin is generally regarded as being specific for simple α-glycosides (101, 254), a greater degree of inhibition is observed with complex glyco-peptides isolated from human erythrocytes (35, 126, 131), transferrin (297), and IgM immunoglobulin (297). The substitution of the O-2 position of mannose with

N-acetylglucosamine causes a marked increase in inhibitory activity (115). The presence of such linkages in the aforementioned glycopeptides would explain their potent inhibition of the lentil agglutinin and points to the importance of an extended binding site in defining the specificity of this lectin. Advantage has been taken of the rather broad specificity of the lentil lectin to isolate lymphocyte plasma membrane glycoproteins (94), envelope glycoproteins of a variety of viruses (95), and for the electron microscopic detection of glycoproteins containing D-mannose, D-glucose, and N-acetylglucosamine located on the surface of various kinds of cells (231).

Soybean Lectins

Because of its affinity for galactose and N-acetylgalactosamine, the lectin of the soybean *Glycine max* may be purified by affinity chromatography by linking N-ϵ-aminocaproyl-β-galactopyranosylamine to Sepharose (78, 79), by coupling galactosamine directly to CH-Sepharose[5] (4), or by coupling p-aminophenyl-β-D-galactoside to AH-Sepharose[5], whose spacer arm had been further extended with a succinyl group.[6] The soybean lectin has a molecular weight of 122,000 and is composed of four identical subunits[7] which have a molecular weight of 30,000 (153). Equilibrium dialysis experiments indicate two binding sites per tetramer for N-acetylgalactosamine. The soybean lectin would appear to be an example of one of the few lectins in which the number of binding sites is not equal to the number of subunits.

Because of its reduced valence in comparison with other lectins it is perhaps not surprising that the agglutinating activity of the soybean lectin towards erythrocytes and lymphocytes would be enhanced by introducing additional cross-linkages by treatment of the lectin with glutaraldehyde (149). An increase in agglutinating activity may also be induced spontaneously as a result of aggregation which occurs when the lectin is stored in a lyophilized condition (150).

Periodate oxidation of the carbohydrate moiety of the soybean lectin, followed by reduction with [³H]-borohydride, yields a labeled product which retains full activity (147). Aside from its potential use as a general method for preparing radioactive glycoprotein lectins, these results show that the integrity of the carbohydrate chain of the soybean lectin is not essential for its biological activity.

Based on a detailed examination of its interaction with a wide variety of blood group substances, it has been established that the soybean lectin is specific for *terminal* α-linked N-acetylgalactosamine or to α- or β-D-galactopyranosyl residues (48, 208). Substances which have subterminal D-galactose or N-acetylgalactosamine residues act as very weak hapten inhibitors. This behavior is quite different from that of Con A which, as pointed out earlier, interacts quite readily with internal sugar

---

[5]CH- and AH-Sepharose are Sepharose 4B derivatives to which 6-aminohexanoic acid or 1,6-diaminohexane, respectively, have been incorporated as spacer arms. Both products are available from Pharmacia Fine Chemicals Inc, Piscataway, NJ.

[6]R. H. Turner and I. E. Liener, unpublished results.

[7]Lotan et al (146a) have more recently reported that they were able to detect two types of subunits which appear to differ in ratio of charge to frictional coefficient.

residues. That the soybean lectin prefers terminal galactosyl residues is further indicated by the fact that the enzymatic removal of terminal sialic acid residues from the surface of mouse lymphocytes, so as to expose galactosyl residues, renders such cells more responsive to stimulation by the soybean lectin (183, 184).

Pea Lectins

Kocourek and his group (59, 161) have been actively engaged in a study of the lectins of the pea *Pisum sativum*. They had previously reported that there were two main peak isolectins with isolectric points of 5.9 and 7.0 and that each was comprised of two heavy (H) chains, 18,000, and two light (L) chains, 10,500. A third pea lectin was subsequently detected by isoelectric focusing which had a pI of 6.35 (58) and which seemed to be the result of a hybridization of the other two principle lectins. It was postulated that there must be a charge difference either between the two H or between the two L chains of these two lectins in one of the two chains. If the difference were to reside in the L chain, as the authors seem to believe, then the two main lectins could be represented as HHLL and HHL'L' and the hybrid as HHLL'.

The activity of the pea lectins has a requirement for Ca^{2+} and Mn^{2+} (201), and a tryptophan residue seems to play an essential role in the expression of this activity (34). Circular dichroism revealed that, although activity was lost when a tryptophan residue had been destroyed by photooxidation, no conformational change had been induced. A virtual absence of α-helical structure was also noted, being similar in this respect to Con A.

Trowbridge (267, 268) has reported the isolation of two mitogenic lectins from the pea whose properties seemed to be very similar to the lectins described by Kocourek's group. Despite the fact that they are probably tetramers, the pea lectins have only two binding sites for mannose and methyl-α-D-glucoside (268), similar to what has been reported for the soybean (133) and lentil (254) lectins. Unlike Con A, the pea lectin retains its tetrameric structure after succinylation (267), although some reduction in mitogenic activity was noted as a result of this chemical modification. A protein which precipitates thyroglobulin has been isolated from the pea (156) which, on the basis of its physicochemical properties, seems to be identical to the pea lectin described by others.

The specificity of the pea lectin resembles that of Con A in that it may be isolated by adsorption to Sephadex (59) and displays an affinity for mannose and glucose, particularly the *p*-substituted phenyl glycosides (273, 275). The pea lectin, however, agglutinates erythrocytes of different origin (35) and tumor cells (276) much more readily than Con A. The 2-OH group of mannose seems to be essential for interaction with the pea lectin (115, 195), which likewise distinguishes it from Con A which reacts with 0–2 substituted mannose residues quite readily (115). Pospisilova et al (212) isolated a glycopeptide from rabbit erythrocytes whose interaction with the pea lectin was attributed to a nonreducing terminal galactose residue, although galactose itself was noninhibitory. This would indicate that the binding of a lectin to a cell surface receptor site does not necessarily indicate the presence of saccharides corresponding to the specificity of that lectin as revealed by inhibition studies with simple sugars.

Horse Gram Lectins

The seeds of the horse gram *Dolichos biflorus* contain a lectin which, unlike most lectins which are relatively nonspecific towards human erythrocytes of various blood groups, shows specificity towards type A erythrocytes and blood group A substance (62). Advantage was taken of this specificity by Etzler (62) to isolate this lectin by using insoluble polyleucyl hog blood group A + H substance as an affinity column followed by elution with N-acetylgalactosamine. The preparation so obtained could be further resolved into two components differing in carbohydrate content by chromatography on Sepharose-Con A using a gradient of increasing concentrations of methyl-α-D-glucoside for elution (39). These two components, designated as A and B, differed somewhat in molecular weight, 113,000 and 109,000 respectively, but were otherwise similar in amino acid composition, N- and C-terminal groups, and specificity. Both lectins were judged to be tetramers comprised of subunits with a molecular weight of 26,500 for lectin A and 26,000 for lectin B. A closer examination of the subunits of lectin A revealed that they could be further resolved by ion-exchange chromatography in 8M urea into two different polypeptide chains with molecular weights of 27,700 and 27,300 (38). It was suggested that lectin A probably consists of a pair of each of these two subunits, although other arrangements are possible as already pointed out in the case of the lectins from the red kidney bean.

Using the more conventional techniques of isolation involving gel filtration and ion-exchange chromatography, Pere et al (205) isolated a single lectin from *D. biflorus* which had a molecular weight of 120,000 and was composed of subunits with a molecular weight of 30,000. It is quite likely that these workers were dealing with at least one of the lectins described by Etzler, but because of the close similarities in the molecular weights and composition of the subunits, they were unable to detect more than one subunit. Pere et al (204) found that N-acetylgalactosamine induced a significant change in the near ultraviolet spectrum of the *D. biflorus* lectin, suggestive of the involvement of tyrosine and/or tryptophan in its interaction with this sugar. As in the case of Con A and the pea lectin, circular dichroism revealed a significant content of the β-pleated sheet conformation with little α-helical structure.

The *D. biflorus* lectin labeled with ferritin has proved to be useful for detecting the distribution of A sites in A_1 and A_2 erythrocytes (289). This lectin has also been used to study changes in cell growth and the incorporation of thymidine in embryo fibroblasts at various stages of differentiation (11, 230).

Other Lectins

The past several years has witnessed the isolation of lectins from a wide variety of plants. Some of these are still only incompletely characterized and much remains to be learned about their structure and properties. Since, in most cases, these lectins have attracted interest because of their unique specificity, they will be considered on the basis of common specificity towards saccharides and blood group substances.

MANNOSE AND GLUCOSE SPECIFIC   A lectin with a specificy for mannose and glucose residues (132) has been isolated in crystalline form from the fava bean (*Vicia faba*) by a procedure which included absorption to Sephadex (280). It has a molecular weight of 50,000 and appears to be a tetramer made of two subunits of 18,000 and two subunits of 9,000. Studies are now under way to determine its amino acid sequence and three-dimensional structure (280). A comparison of the structural features of this lectin with that of the chemically distinct but functionally similar lectin Con A should be useful in identifying the common features of these molecules which underlie their similar biological activities.

GALACTOSE SPECIFIC   A lectin displaying specificity towards N-acetylgalactosamine, and to a lesser extent to galactose, has been isolated from *Sophora japonica* seeds of the Japanese pagoda tree, by adsorption with insoluble polyleucyl hog gastric mucin (210, 211) or by affinity chromatography on agarose (260). This lectin is comprised of four identical subunits which have a molecular weight of 33,000. This lectin shows a preference for β-anomers of galactosides (211), with the phenyl and nitrophenyl derivatives being particularly inhibitory (19). It also shows a high degree of specificity towards A and B human erythrocytes, especially those with an I determinant (12, 41).

Agarose has also been used to isolate a N-acetylgalactosamine-specific lectin from *Bauhinia purpurea alba* (108). Although it is relatively nonspecific with respect to its ability to agglutinate various types of human erythrocytes, its activity towards human erythrocytes was enhanced when the latter were treated with neuraminidase in order to expose galactose-like residues adjacent to the terminal sialic acid units. Although it has been reported to have a molecular weight of 195,000 and a carbohydrate content of about 11%, this lectin does not appear to have been further characterized.

The Osage orange (*Maclura pomifera*) contains a lectin which can be isolated by affinity chromatography on galactosamine-Sepharose, followed by elution with D-melibiose (272). This lectin is inhibited by sugars with a D-galactose configuration as well as by antifreeze glycoproteins from an Antarctic fish (44). No data concerning the physicochemical properties of the purified lectin have been reported.

An antigalactose lectin has been isolated from crude extracts of the seeds of the sunn hemp *Crotalaria juncea* by affinity chromatography on a galactan gel modified by mild acid hydrolysis of agarose (60). This treatment serves to increase the number of terminal galactose residues available for binding the lectin without degrading the interlocking network of the gel. Although the homogeneity of this lectin was not indicated, it was reported to have a molecular weight of 120,000 and to contain 5% carbohydrate. This lectin was immobilized by coupling to CNBr-activated Sepharose and used for the selective fractionation of serum glycoproteins (61).

BLOOD GROUP SPECIFIC   A lectin which exhibits specificity for the H determinant of O group human erythrocytes and is strongly inhibited by L-fucose may be isolated from *Lotus tetragonolobus* (asparagus pea) by affinity chromatography on a Sepharose-fucose column (295) or by using insoluble polyleucyl hog blood group A + H substance (206, 207). After elution with L-fucose, three active components,

A, B, and C, may be obtained by chromatography on DEAE-cellulose (116, 295) or by preparative isoelectric focusing (206). Lectins A, B, and C have molecular weights of 120,000, 58,000, and 117,000 respectively, and all are comprised of subunits with a molecular weight of 27,000 (116). The oligomeric structure of these lectins has not been reported, but since lectins A and C have four binding sites and lectin B only two, it may be reasonable to assume that the former are tetramers and the latter a dimer. These lectins show a distinct specificity for blood group substances containing fucosyl residues on the C2 position of β-D-galactose $(1\longrightarrow 4)$-D-N-acetylgalactosamine; a second fucose residue in the C3 position of the N-acetylgalactosamine moiety serves to enhance the reactivity of this oligosaccharide (207).

Extracts from *Ulex europeus,* gorse or Furze seed, also display anti-H activity, and two such lectins have been isolated by Osawa & Matsumoto (197). Although they are of equivalent molecular weight, 170,000, they differ in that one is inhibited by L-fucose, while the other is not inhibited by this sugar but is inhibited by di-N-acetylchitobiose. A fucose-reactive lectin was isolated from *U. europeus* by Hŏrejší & Kocourek (97), using a fucose-containing acrylamide gel. The molecular weight of their preparation was about 43,000, and no dissociation into subunits could be effected by sodium dodecylsulfate. The difference in molecular weights observed by these two groups may be due to the fact that Osawa & Matsumoto may have isolated a tetramer whereas monomeric subunits had been isolated by Hŏrejší & Kocourek.

An anti-H lectin which is not inhibited by fucose has also been purified from *Cystisus sessilifolius* by affinity chromatography on a starch matrix cross-linked to tri-N-acetylchitobiose with epichlorhydrin (163, 164). Although this lectin is inhibited by oligosaccharides with terminal β-N-acetylglucosaminyl residues, the actual structure on the human erythrocyte surface which is recognized by the lectin is postulated to be O-α-L-fucopyranosyl-$(1\longrightarrow 2)$-O-β-D-galactopyranosyl-$(1\longrightarrow 3$ or 4)-β-D-N-acetylglucosamine (164).

The ability to agglutinate specifically type B human erythrocytes is a unique property displayed by few lectins. One which does have this property has been recently purified by Hayes & Goldstein (93) from *Bandieraea simplicifolia.* Melibiose, which had been oxidized to an aldonic acid and condensed with aminoethyl-Bio-Gel, served as a specific adsorbent for this purpose, and the lectin could be subsequently eluted with galactose. The purified lectin is a glycoprotein with a molecular weight of 114,000, and is composed of four apparently identical subunits. Its specificity is directed to terminal, nonreducing α-D-galactosyl residues in oligosaccharides or glycoproteins. Hŏrejší & Kocourek (96) have also reported the isolation of a lectin from *B. simplicifolia,* using as an adsorbent an acrylamide gel copolymerized with allyl-α-D-galactose, but the properties of their lectin were not described.

A lectin purified from *Vicia cracca* and coupled to activated Sepharose has been used to isolate fractions of blood group A substance from cyst fluid (130).

MITOGENIC LECTINS   One of the most potent plant mitogens is found in the pokeweed *Phytolacca americana.* Waxdal (283) isolated from crude extracts of this plant five different mitogenic proteins, each of which had distinct physicochemical properties and biological activities. One of these, designated as Pa-1, was the most potent hemagglutinin and mitogen and appeared to be a polymer of 22,000 molecular weight subunits. The other four mitogens were monomers with molecular weights ranging from 19,000 to 31,000, and, unlike Pa-1, were very rich in cystine (18% of the residues were half-cystine). One of these, Pa-2, corresponded most closely in properties to the pokeweed mitogen previously described (225). Like most of the other plant mitogens, the Pa-2 mitogen was active only on the T (thymus dependent) class of lymphocytes, whereas the polymeric Pa-1 mitogen was capable of stimulating B (thymus independent) lymphocytes as well as T-cells (284).

Two mitogenic proteins have also been isolated from a Japanese species of pokeweed called shoriku, *P. esculenta* (262). Their molecular weights—18,000 and 32,000—and their high content of cystine indicate their similarity to the monomeric mitogens described by Waxdal.

Toyoshima et al (265, 266) have described the purification of a potent mitogen from *Wistaria floribunda*. Unlike the monomeric pokeweed mitogens, this mitogen was judged to be a dimer consisting of two 32,000 subunits and had a relatively low cystine content. It seems to bear a closer resemblance to the Pa-1 polymeric mitogen isolated from the pokeweed by Waxdal. The *W. floribunda* mitogen caused an increase in the membrane fluidity of human peripheral lymphocytes, an effect which could represent a key biochemical event in the earliest stage of lymphocyte transformation. A hemagglutinin which appeared to be a tetramer of four identical subunits with a molecular weight of 35,000 has also been isolated from *W. floribunda* seeds (266), but this lectin was devoid of mitogenic activity. It did, however, exert a weak but definite mitogenic effect against neuraminidase-treated lymphocytes.

A strongly mitogenic lectin (MAM) was isolated from the seeds of *Maakia amurensis* by affinity chromatography on a column of Sepharose-bound glycopeptides, which had been isolated from porcine thyroglobulin, followed by ion-exchange chromatography and gel filtration (122). MAM was a dimer of disulfide-containing subunits with an approximate molecular weight of 75,000. Another lectin (MAH) which had strong hemagglutinating as well as moderate mitogenic activity was also isolated during the course of the purification of MAM. MAH was found to be a tetramer of subunits with a molecular weight of 33,000. Inhibition assays using various sugars and glycoproteins as hapten inhibitors revealed that MAM and MAH differ from each other in their specificities for sugars.

LECTINS FROM NONLEGUMINOUS PLANTS Relatively few lectins have been purified from plants other than legumes. In addition to the wheat germ agglutinin, which has already been considered, two other such lectins have been recently isolated and partially characterized, one from the potato (*Solanum tuberosum*) and the other from the rice seed (*Oryza sativa*).

An agglutinin isolated from potatoes by Allen & Neuberger (3), by means of ion-exchange chromatography, had some rather unusual properties. It had a molecular weight of 46,000, presumably a dimer of two identical subunits, contained almost 50% carbohydrate, and 16% of its amino acids were hydroxyproline and 11.5%, half-cystine. In the latter respect it resembles the wheat germ agglutinin and the pokeweed mitogen which also have a very high cystine content. The potato lectin displays a specificity towards oligosaccharides containing terminal N-acetylglucosamine residues, but not towards the monosaccharide unless it is attached to an aromatic aglycone. Based on this specificity, Delmotte et al (51) were able to purify the potato lectin in a relatively easy fashion by means of affinity chromatography on sepharose which had been substituted with p-aminobenzyl-1-thio-N-acetyl-β-glucosaminide.

The lectin isolated from rice seed (259) is a low molecular weight glycoprotein, about 10,000, containing 26.8% carbohydrate. In addition to being a hemagglutinin, it displayed mitogenic activity towards human lymphocytes. In view of its extremely small size, it would be of interest to know the number of binding sites in order to account for its ability to act as an agglutinin and mitogen.

DISTRIBUTION AND PHYSIOLOGICAL FUNCTION IN THE PLANT

Although in most species of plants the highest concentration of lectins are located in the seed, they may also be present to a lesser extent in the leaves, roots, and stems (264). The lectins appear to be localized in the cytoplasm of the cotyledon and embryonic cells (167). Since the proportion of lectin in mature leaves rapidly decreases as its concentration in the cotyledons increases (167), lectins are probably synthesized in the leaves and immediately transferred to the developing seed where they appear during the time of early development and differentiation of the embryo (102). As the seed germinates there is a progressive decrease in lectin content at a rate which parallels the loss of reserve protein (233, 234).

The fact that the lectins make up from 2% to 10% of the total protein in most leguminous seeds would suggest that the lectins must be playing some important physiological role in the plant. Speculations as to what this function might be have been many and varied and have been expressed in earlier reviews (243, 264). These include the following: (a) act as antibodies to counteract soil bacteria; (b) serve to protect plants against fungal attack by inhibiting fungal polysaccharases; (c) serve to transport or store sugars; (d) attach glycoprotein enzymes in organized multienzyme systems; and (e) play a key role in the development and differentiation of embryonic cells.

To the above list should be added several other possible functions for which evidence has recently been reported. There is some indication that the lectins may play a role in the symbiotic relationship between leguminous plants and bacteria. Hamblin & Kent (87) found that lectins were present in the roots of *Phaseolus vulgaris* and that a strain of *Rhizobium phaseoli* which had been treated with these lectins was capable of agglutinating erythrocytes. Although this evidence is indirect, it does suggest that lectins can serve to bind bacteria to the root nodules of the plant. The specificity of this relationship was further explored by Bohlool & Schmidt (27), who found that the soybean lectin was bound to only those bacteria which are known to nodulate the soybean. The lectins could therefore account for the specific interaction of legumes with certain bacteria in the nitrogen-fixing process. Based on their observation that the wheat germ agglutinin bound to the hyphal tips of the fungus *Trichoderma viride,* and inhibited its growth and spore germination, Mirelman et al (170) have suggested this agglutinin may serve to protect the wheat against certain phytopathogens during germination and early seedling growth.

If the lectins do in fact play an important role in the vital processes of the plant or in its relationship to bacteria or fungi, it is difficult to account for the fact that many strains of *P. vulgaris,* for example, are known to exist and flourish in which no lectins have been detected (33, 198).

NUTRITIONAL SIGNIFICANCE

The fact that lectins are found in those legumes, such as beans and peas, which constitute an important source of dietary protein for many segments of the world's population, raises the question as to their possible nutritional significance. The literature on this particular subject has been recently reviewed (134), so that consideration will be given here only to those papers which have appeared since that review was completed.

That the toxicity and growth-inhibiting effect produced by feeding animals raw beans, particularly *P. vulgaris,* is due, at least in part, to the effects of lectins is well documented (134). This conclusion has been further corroborated by Evans et al (65), who isolated a protein fraction from *P. vulgaris* (navy beans) which inhibited the growth of rats. On the basis of its hemagglutinating and mitogen activities and its physicochemical properties, it was judged to be similar, if not identical, to the lectins previously described for *P. vulgaris.* In a subsequent paper from the same laboratory (218), it was reported that the growth depression and toxicity of the albumin fraction of navy beans was due to the family of isolectins which this fraction contained. Andrews & Jayne-Williams (10) likewise reported that a lectin which had been previously purified from the navy bean (9) was toxic and inhibited the growth of Japanese quail.

It should be emphasized that not all lectins are necessarily toxic or even growth inhibitory when fed to animals. For example, Turner & Liener (271) fed rats a crude soybean extract from which the lectins had been removed by adsorption to Con A (16) and were unable to detect any significant improvement in growth performance compared to an extract from which the lectin had not been removed.

Jaffé (109) had proposed many years ago that the toxic effect of lectins when ingested orally may be due to their ability to bind to specific receptor sites on the surface of the intestinal epithelial cells. Support for this hypothesis comes from the studies of Etzler & Branstrator (64), who found that a number of different lectins react with the crypts and/or villi of the intestine, but at different regions of the intestine depending on the specificity of the lectin. Since surface-bound lectins are known to produce profound physiological effects on the cells with which they interact, one of these effects could be a serious impairment in the ability of these cells to absorb nutrients from the gastrointestinal tract, thus causing a serious inhibition of growth and, in extreme cases, even death.

An alternative effect on the intestinal cells is suggested by the studies of Jayne-Williams & Burgess (113), who observed that germ-free Japanese quail were much better able to tolerate the toxic effects of raw navy beans than conventional birds.

It was theorized that the binding of lectins to the cells lining the intestine may interfere with the normal defense mechanism of these cells whereby normally innocuous intestinal bacteria are prevented from passing from the lumen of the gut into the lymph, blood, and other tissues of the animal body.

Literature Cited

1. Adair, W. L., Kornfeld, S. 1974. *J. Biol. Chem.* 249:4696–4704
2. Ahmad, A., Bishayee, S., Bachhawat, B. K. 1973. *Biochem. Biophys. Res. Commun.* 53:730–36
3. Allen, A. K., Neuberger, A. 1975. *FEBS Lett.* 50:362–64
4. Allen, A. K., Neuberger, A. 1973. *Biochem. J.* 135:307–14
5. Allen, A. K., Neuberger, A., Sharon, N. 1973. *Biochem. J.* 131:155–62
6. Allen, N. K., Brilliantine, L. 1969. *J. Immunol.* 102:1295–99
7. Alter, G. M., Magnuson, J. A. 1974. *Biochemistry* 13:4038–45
8. Anderson, J. C. 1975. *Biochim. Biophys. Acta* 379:444–45
9. Andrews, A. T. 1974. *Biochem. J.* 139:421–29
10. Andrews, A. T., Jayne-Williams, D. J. 1974. *Br. J. Nutr.* 32:181–89
11. Aubery, M., Bourrillon, R. 1975. *Cell Differ.* 4:67–77
12. Balding, P., Gold, E. R. 1973. *Z. Immunitaetsforsch. Exp. Klin. Immunol.* 145:156–65
13. Barber, G. H., Carver, J. P. 1973. *J. Biol. Chem.* 248:3353–55
14. Becker, J. W., Reeke, G. N., Wang, J. L., Cunningham, B. A., Edelman, G. M. 1975. *J. Biol. Chem.* 250:1513–24
15. Bescanon, F., Bourgeade, M.-F. 1974. *J. Immunol.* 113:1061–63
16. Bessler, W., Goldstein, I. J. 1973. *FEBS Lett.* 34:58–62
17. Bessler, W., Goldstein, I. J. 1974. *Arch. Biochem. Biophys.* 165:444–45
18. Bessler, W., Shafer, J. A., Goldstein, I. J. 1974. *J. Biol. Chem.* 249:2819–22
19. Betail, G., Coulet, M. 1974. *C. R. Seances Soc. Biol.* 168:295–99
20. Beug, H., Gerisch, G. 1973. *J. Immunol. Methods* 2:49–57
21. Beutler, E., Guinto, E., Kuhl, W. 1975. *J. Lab. Clin. Med.* 65:672–77
22. Bishayee, S., Farooqui, A. A., Bachhawat, B. K. 1973. *Indian J. Biochem. Biophys.* 10:1–2
23. Bloch, R., Burger, M. M. 1974. *Biochem. Biophys. Res. Commun.* 58:13–19
24. Bloch, R., Burger, M. M. 1974. *FEBS Lett.* 44:286–89
25. Blume, P., Hanson, M., Mathys, J., Polesky, H. F. 1974. *Clin. Chem.* 20:1023–27
26. Boenish, T., Norgaard-Pederson, B. 1975. *Clin. Chim. Acta* 60:51–57
27. Bohlool, B. B., Schmidt, E. L. 1974. *Science* 185:269–71
28. Bourgeade, M.-F., Bescanon, F., 1973. *C. R. Acad. Sci. Ser. D* 277:2833–35
29. Boyd, W. C., Sharpleigh, E. 1954. *Science* 119:419
30. Brattain, M. G., Jones, C. M., Pittman, J. M., Pretlow, T. G. II. 1975. *Biochem. Biophys. Res. Commun.* 65:63–67
31. Brewer, C. F., Marcus, D., Grollman, A. P., Sternlicht, H. 1974. *Ann. NY Acad. Sci.* 222:978–86
32. Brewer, C. F., Sternlicht, H., Marcus, D. M., Grollman, A. P. 1973. *Biochemistry* 12:4448–57
33. Brücher, O., Wecksler, M., Levy, A., Palozzo, A., Jaffé, W. G. 1969. *Phytochemistry* 8:1739–43
34. Bures, L., Entlicher, G., Kocourek, J. 1972. *Biochim. Biophys. Acta* 285:235–42
35. Bures, L., Entlicher, G., Tichá, M., Kocourek, J. 1973. *Experientia* 29:1546–47
36. Burger, M. M. 1974. *Methods Enzymol.* 32:615–21
37. Carrasco, L., Fernandez-Puentes, C., Vazquez, D. 1975. *Eur. J. Biochem.* 54:499–503
38. Carter, W. G., Etzler, M. E. 1975. *J. Biol. Chem.* 250:2756–62
39. Carter, W. G., Etzler, M. E. 1975. *Biochemistry* 14:2685–89
40. Chase, P. S., Miller, F. 1973. *Cell Immunol.* 6:132–39
41. Chien, S.-M., Lemanski, T., Poretz, R. D. 1974. *Immunochemistry* 11:501–6
42. Choi, Y. S., Janson, J. C. 1974. *J. Exp. Med.* 140:597–602
43. Chu, T. M., Holyoke, E. D., Murphy, G. P. 1974. *Cancer Res.* 34:212–14
44. Chuba, J. V. et al 1973. *Nature* 242:342–43
45. Cohen, E., Ed. 1974. *Ann. NY Acad. Sci.* 234: 412 pp.

46. Coulet, M., Mustier, J., Guillot, J. 1970. *Rev. Mycol.* 35:71–89
47. Cunningham, B. A., Wang, J. L., Waxdal, M. J., Edelman, G. M. 1975. *J. Biol. Chem.* 250:1503–12
48. Dahr, W., Uhlenbruck, G. 1971. *Blut* 22:128–32
49. Daniel, T. M. 1975. *Am. Rev. Respir. Dis.* 111:787–93
50. Davey, M. W., Huang, J. W., Sulkowski, E., Carter, W. A. 1974. *J. Biol. Chem.* 249:6354–55
51. Delmotte, F., Kieda, C., Monsigny, M. 1975. *FEBS Lett.* 53:324–30
52. Dievard, J. C., Bourrillon, R. 1974. *Biochim. Biophys. Acta* 345:198–212
53. Dorner, F., Scriba, M., Weil, R. 1973. *Proc. Natl. Acad. Sci. USA* 70:1981–85
54. Doyle, R. J., Birdsell, D. C., Young, F. E. 1973. *Prep. Biochem.* 3:13–18
55. Doyle, R. J., Thomasson, D. L., Gray, R. D., Glew, R. H. 1975. *FEBS Lett.* 52:185–87
56. Dufau, M. L., Tsuruhara, T., Catt, K. J. 1972. *Biochim. Biophys. Acta* 278:281–82
57. Edelman, G. M. et al 1972. *Proc. Natl. Acad. Sci. USA* 69:2580–84
58. Entlicher, G., Kocourek, J. 1975. *Biochim. Biophys. Acta* 393:165–69
59. Entlicher, G., Kostír, J. V., Kocourek, J. 1970. *Biochim. Biophys. Acta* 221:272–81
60. Ersson, B., Aspberg, K., Porath, J. 1973. *Biochim. Biophys. Acta* 310:446–52
61. Ersson, B., Porath, J. 1974. *FEBS Lett.* 48:126–29
62. Etzler, M. 1972. *Methods Enzymol.* 28:340–44
63. Etzler, M. 1974. *Ann. NY Acad. Sci.* 234:260–74
64. Etzler, M., Branstrator, M. L. 1974. *J. Cell Biol.* 62:329–43
65. Evans, R. J., Pusztai, A., Watt, W. B., Bauer, D. A. 1973. *Biochim. Biophys. Acta* 303:175–84
66. Ewart, J. A. D. 1975. *J. Sci. Food Agric.* 26:5–22
67. Firlova, D., Tichá, M., Kocourek, J. 1975. *Biochim. Biophys. Acta* 393:170–81
68. Findlay, J. B. C. 1974. *J. Biol. Chem.* 249:4398–4403
69. Fliegerova, O., Salvetova, A., Tichá, M., Kocourek, J. 1974. *Biochim. Biophys. Acta* 351:416–26
70. Fujita, Y., Oishi, K., Aida, C. 1974. *J. Biochem. Tokyo* 76:1347–49
71. Funatsu, M. 1972. *Proteins: Structure and Function,* ed. M. Funatsu, K.

Hiromi, K. Imahori, T. Murachi, K. Narita, 2:103–40. New York:Wiley. 270 pp.
72. Funatsu, M., Hara, K., Ishiguro, M., Funatsu, G., Kishigawa, R. 1973. *Proc. Jpn. Acad.* 49:829–34
73. Galbraith, W., Goldstein, I. J. 1972. *Methods Enzymol.* 28:318–23
74. Galbraith, W., Goldstein, I. J. 1972. *Biochemistry* 11:3976–84
75. Gilboa-Garber, N. 1972. *Biochim. Biophys. Acta* 273:165–73
76. Goldstein, I. J., Reichert, C. M., Misaki, A. 1974. *Ann. NY Acad. Sci.* 234:283–95
77. Goldstein, I. J., Reichert, C. M., Misaki, A., Gorin, P. A. J. 1973. *Biochim. Biophys. Acta* 317:500–4
78. Gordon, J. A., Blumberg, S., Lis, H., Sharon, N. 1972. *Methods Enzymol.* 28:365–68
79. Gordon, J. A., Blumberg, S., Lis, H., Sharon, N. 1973. *FEBS Lett.* 21:193–96
80. Gordon, J. A., Marquardt, M. D. 1974. *Biochim. Biophys. Acta* 332:136–44
81. Gray, G. R. 1974. *Arch. Biochem. Biophys.* 163:426–28
82. Greco, M. et al 1974. *Biochem. J.* 142:695–97
83. Greenaway, P. J., Levine, D. 1973. *Nature New Biol.* 241:191–92
84. Gunther, G. R., Wang, J. L., Yahara, I., Cunningham, B. A., Edelman, G. M. 1973. *Proc. Natl. Acad. Sci. USA* 70:1012–16
85. Gürtler, L. G., Horstmann, H. J. 1973. *Biochim. Biophys. Acta* 295:582–94
86. Hague, D. R. 1975. *Plant Physiol.* 55:636–42
87. Hamblin, J., Kent, S. P. 1973. *Nature New Biol.* 245:28–30
88. Hardman, K. D., Ainsworth, C. F. 1972. *Biochemistry* 11:4910–19
89. Ibid 1973. 12:4442–47
90. Harms-Ringdahl, M., Fedorcsak, I., Ehrenberg, L. 1973. *Proc. Natl. Acad. Sci. USA* 70:569–73
91. Harms-Ringdahl, M., Jörnvall, H. 1974. *Eur. J. Biochem.* 48:541–47
92. Hassing, G. S., Goldstein, I. J. 1970. *Eur. J. Biochem.* 16:549–56
93. Hayes, C. E., Goldstein, I. J. 1974. *J. Biol. Chem.* 249:1904–14
94. Hayman, M. J., Crumpton, M. J. 1972. *Biochem. Biophys. Res. Commun.* 47:923–30
95. Hayman, M. J., Skehel, J. J., Crumpton, M. J. 1973. *FEBS Lett.* 29:185–88
96. Horejsí, V., Kocourek, J. 1973. *Biochim. Biophys. Acta* 297:346–51
97. Ibid 1974. 336:329–37

316   LIENER

98. Ibid, 338–43
99. Hořejší, V., Kocourek, J. 1974. *Methods Enzymol.* 34:361–67
100. Ibid, 178–81
101. Howard, I. K., Sage, H. J. 1969. *Biochemistry* 8:2436–41
102. Howard, I. K., Sage, H. J., Horton, C. B. 1972. *Arch. Biochem. Biophys.* 149:323–26
103. Howard, I. K. et al 1971. *J. Biol. Chem.* 246:1590–95
104. Howe, M. L., Barrett, J. T. 1970. *Biochim. Biophys. Acta* 215:97–104
105. Huet, C., Lonchampt, M., Hult, M., Bernadoc, A. 1974. *Biochim. Biophys. Acta* 365:28–39
106. Hunt, R. C., Bullis, C. M., Brown, J. C. 1975. *Biochemistry* 14:109–15
107. Hwang, K. M., Murphee, S. A., Sartorelli, A. C. 1974. *Cancer Res.* 34:3396–3402
108. Irimura, T., Osawa, T. 1972. *Arch. Biochem. Biophys.* 151:475–82
109. Jaffé, W. G. 1960. *Arneim. Forsch.* 12:1012–16
110. Jaffé, W. G., Brücher, O., Palozzo, A. 1972. *Z. Immun.-Forsch.* 142:439–47
111. Jaffé, W. G., Levy, A., Gonzalez, D. I. 1974. *Phytochemistry* 13:2685–93
112. Janson, V. K., Burger, M. M. 1973. *Biochim. Biophys. Acta* 291:127–35
113. Jayne-Williams, D. J., Burgess, C. D. 1974. *J. Appl. Bacteriol.* 37:149–69
114. Jeffrey, A. M., Zopf, D. A., Ginsburg, V. 1975. *Biochem. Biophys. Res. Commun.* 62:608–13
115. Kaifu, R., Osawa, T., Jeanloz, R. W. 1975. *Carbohydr. Res.* 40:111–17
116. Kalb, A. J. 1969. *Biochim. Biophys. Acta* 168:532–36
117. Kalb, A. J., Levitzki, A. 1968. *Biochem. J.* 109:669–72
118. Kalb, A. J., Pecht, I. 1973. *Biochim. Biophys. Acta* 303:264–68
119. Kaneko, I., Hayatsu, H., Ukita, T. 1975. *Biochim. Biophys. Acta* 392:131, 140
120. Karlstam, B. 1973. *Biochim. Biophys. Acta* 329:295–304
121. Kaufman, S. J., McPherson, A. 1975. *Cell* 4:263–68
122. Kawaguchi, T., Matsumoto, I., Osawa, T. 1974. *J. Biol. Chem.* 249:2786–92
123. Kishiye, T., Toyoshima, S., Osawa, T. 1974. *Biochem. Biophys. Res. Commun.* 60:681–86
124. Kitamura, K., Okubo, K., Shihasaki, K. 1974. *Agric. Biol. Chem.* 38:1083–85
125. Kornfeld, R., Ferris, C. 1975. *J. Biol. Chem.* 250:2614–19

126. Kornfeld, R., Kornfeld, S. 1974. *Ann. NY Acad. Sci. USA* 234:276–82
127. Kornfeld, S., Eider, W., Gregory, W. 1974. *Cold Spring Harbor Conf. Cell Proliferation* 1:435–45
128. Kothbauer, H., Schenkel-Brunner, H. 1975. *Comp. Biochem. Physiol. A* 50:27–29
129. Kristiansen, T. 1974. *Methods Enzymol.* 34:331–41
130. Kristiansen, T. 1974. *Biochim. Biophys. Acta* 338:246–53
131. Kubánec, J., Entlicher, G., Kocourek, J. 1973. *Biochim. Biophys. Acta* 304:93–102
132. Lee, J. K. N., Pachtman, E. A., Frumin, A. M. 1974. *Ann. NY Acad. Sci.* 234:162–68
133. Levine, D., Kaplan, M. J., Greenaway, P. J. 1972. *Biochem. J.* 129:847–56
134. Liener, I. E. 1974. *J. Agric. Food Chem.* 22:17–22
135. Liener, I. E., Garrison, O. R., Pravda, Z. 1973. *Biochem. Biophys. Res. Commun.* 51:436–43
136. Lin, J.-Y., Chang, Y.-C., Huang, Z.-Y., Tung, T.-C. 1973. *Toxicon* 11:379–81
137. Lin, J.-Y., Jai, S.-T., Wu, H.-L., Tung, T.-C. 1973. *Cancer Res.* 33:2688–91
138. Lin, J.-Y., Kao, W.-Y., Tserng, K.-Y., Chen, C.-C., Tung, T.-C. 1970. *Cancer Res.* 30:2431–33
139. Lin, J.-Y., Lei, L.-L., Tung, T.-C. 1969. *J. Formosan Med. Assoc.* 68:518–21
140. Lin, J.-Y., Liu, K., Chen, C.-C., Tung, T.-C. 1971. *Cancer Res.* 31:921–24
141. Lin, J.-Y., Shaw, Y.-S., Tung, T.-C. 1971. *Toxicon* 9:97–101
142. Lin, J.-Y., Tserng, K.-Y., Chen, C.-C., Lin, L.-T., Tung, T.-C. 1970. *Nature* 227:292–93
143. Lis, H., Lotan, R., Sharon, N. 1974. *Ann. NY Acad. Sci.* 274:232–38
144. Lis, H., Lotan, R., Sharon, N. 1974. *Methods Enzymol.* 34:341–46
145. Lis, H., Sharon, N. 1972. *Methods Enzymol.* 28:360–68
146. Lis, H., Sharon, N. 1973. *Ann. Rev. Biochem.* 42:541–74
146a. Lotan, R., Cacan, R., Cacan, M., Debray, H., Carter, W. G., Sharon, N. 1975. *FEBS Lett.* 57:100–3
147. Lotan, R., Debray, H., Cacan, M., Cacan, R., Sharon, N. 1975. *J. Biol. Chem.* 250:1955–57
148. Lotan, R., Gussin, A. E. S., Lis, H., Sharon, N. 1973. *Biochem. Biophys. Res. Commun.* 52:656–62
149. Lotan, R., Lis, H., Rosenwasser, A., Novogrodsky, A., Sharon, N. 1973. *Bio-*

chem. Biophys. Res. Commun. 55: 1347–55
150. Lotan, R., Lis, H., Sharon, N. 1975. *Biochem. Biophys. Res. Commun.* 62: 144–50
151. Lotan, R., Sharon, N. 1973. *Biochem. Biophys. Res. Commun.* 55:1340–46
152. Lotan, R., Sharon, N., Mirelman, D. 1975. *Eur. J. Biochem.* 55:257–62
153. Lotan, R., Siegelman, H. W., Lis, H., Sharon, N. 1974. *J. Biol. Chem.* 249:1219–24
154. Lugnier, A., Dirheimer, G. 1973. *FEBS Lett.* 35:117–20
155. Lugnier, A., LeMuir, M. A., Gerbinger, P., Dirheimer, G. 1974. *Biochemie* 56:1287–89
156. Lutsik, M. D. 1974. *Biokhimiya* 39: 811–15
157. Maca, R. D., Hoak, J. C. 1974. *J. Natl. Cancer Inst.* 52:365–67
158. MacSween, J. M., Fox, R. A. 1975. *Br. J. Cancer* 31:288–92
159. Mannino, R. J., Burger, M. M. 1975. *Nature* 256:19–22
160. Marchesi, V. T. 1972. *Methods Enzymol.* 28:354–56
161. Marik, T., Entlicher, G., Kocourek, J. 1974. *Biochim. Biophys. Acta* 336:53–61
162. Marquardt, M. D., Gordon, J. A. 1974. *Nature* 252:175–76
163. Matsumoto, I., Osawa, T. 1972. *Biochem. Biophys. Res. Commun.* 46: 1810–15
164. Matsumoto, I., Osawa, T. 1974. *Biochemistry* 13:582–88
165. McCubbin, W. D., Oikawa, K., Kay, C. M. 1971. *Biochem. Biophys. Res. Commun.* 43:666–74
166. McPherson, A. Jr., Rich, A. 1973. *FEBS Lett.* 35:257–61
167. Mialonier, G., Privat, J.-P., Monsigny, M., Kahlen, G., Durand, R. 1973. *Physiol. Veg.* 11:519–37
168. Miller, J. B., Hsu, R., Heinrikson, R., Yachnin, S. 1975. *Proc. Natl. Acad. Sci. USA* 72:1388–91
169. Miller, J. B., Noyes, C., Heinrikson, R., Kingdon, H. S., Yachnin, S. 1973. *J. Exp. Med.* 138:939–51
170. Mirelman, D., Galun, E., Sharon, N., Lotan, R. 1975. *Nature* 256:414–16
171. Montanaro, L., Sperti, S., Mattioli, A., Testoni, G., Stirpe, F. 1975. *Biochem. J.* 146:127–31
172. Montanaro, L., Sperti, S., Stirpe, F. 1973. *Biochem. J.* 136:677–83
173. Nachman, R. L., Hubbard, A., Ferris, B. 1973. *J. Biol. Chem.* 248:2928–36
174. Nagata, Y., Burger, M. M. 1972. *J. Biol. Chem.* 247:2248–50

175. Ibid 1974. 249:3116–22
176. Neri, G., Smith, D. F., Gilliam, E. B., Walborg, E. F. Jr. 1974. *Arch. Biochem. Biophys.* 165:323–30
177. Nicolson, G. L. 1974. *Int. Rev. Cytol.* 39:89–190
178. Nicolson, G. L., Blaustein, J. 1972. *Biochim. Biophys. Acta* 266:543–47
179. Nicolson, G. L., Blaustein, J., Etzler, M. 1974. *Biochemistry* 13:196–204
180. Nicolson, G. L., Lacorbiere, M., Hunter, T. R. 1975. *Cancer Res.* 35:144–55
181. Noonan, K. D., Burger, M. M. 1974. *Methods Enzymol.* 32:621–25
182. Norden, A. G. W., O'Brien, J. S. 1974. *Biochem. Biophys. Res. Commun.* 56: 193–98
183. Novogrodsky, A. 1974. *Eur. J. Immunol.* 4:646–48
184. Novogrodsky, A., Katchalski, E. 1973. *Proc. Natl. Acad. Sci. USA* 70:2515–18
185. Nowakova, N., Kocourek, J. 1974. *Biochim. Biophys. Acta* 359:320–33
186. Oikawa, T., Yanagimachi, R., Nicolson, G. L. 1973. *Nature* 241:256–59
187. Olsnes, S., Pihl, A. 1972. *Nature* 238:459–61
188. Olsnes, S., Pihl, A. 1972. *FEBS Lett.* 20:327–29
189. Ibid 1972. 28:48–50
190. Olsnes, S., Pihl, A. 1973. *Biochemistry* 12:3121–26
191. Olsnes, S., Pihl, A. 1973. *Eur. J. Biochem.* 35:179–85
192. Olsnes, S., Refsnes, K., Pihl, A. 1974. *Nature* 249:627–31
193. Olsnes, S., Saltvedt, E. 1975. *J. Immunol.* 114:1743–48
194. Olsnes, S., Saltvedt, E., Pihl, A. 1974. *J. Biol. Chem.* 249:803–10
195. Onodera, K., Shinohara, T. 1973. *J. Agric. Biol. Chem.* 37:1661–66
196. Oppenheimer, S. B., Odencrantz, J. 1972. *Exp. Cell Res.* 73:475–80
197. Osawa, T., Matsumoto, I. 1972. *Methods Enzymol.* 28:323–27
198. Palozzo, A., Jaffé, W. G. 1969. *Phytochemistry* 8:1255–58
199. Pappenheimer, A. M. Jr., Olsnes, S., Harper, A. A. 1974. *J. Immunol.* 113:835–41
200. Pappenheimer, A. M. Jr., Olsnes, S., Meren, R. 1974. *J. Immunol.* 113: 842–47
201. Paulova, M., Entlicher, G., Tichá, M., Kostír, J. V., Kocourek, J. 1971. *Biochim. Biophys. Acta* 237:513–18
202. Pellegrino, M. A., Furone, S., Pellegrino, A., Reisfeld, R. A. 1973. *Clin. Immunol. Immunopathol.* 2:67–73

203. Penhale, W. J., Farmer, A., Maccuish, A. C., Irvine, W. J. 1974. *Clin. Exp. Immunol.* 18:155–67
204. Pere, M., Bourrillon, R., Jirgensons, B. 1975. *Biochim. Biophys. Acta* 393:31–36
205. Pere, M., Font, J., Bourrillon, R. 1974. *Biochim. Biophys. Acta* 365:40–46
206. Pereira, M. E. A., Kabat, E. A. 1974. *Biochemistry* 13:3184–92
207. Pereira, M. E. A., Kabat, E. A. 1974. *Ann. NY Acad. Sci.* 234:301–9
208. Pereira, M. E. A., Kabat, E. A., Sharon, N. 1974. *Carbohydr. Res.* 37:89–102
209. Ponce de Leon, M., Hessle, H., Cohen, G. H. 1973. *J. Virol.* 12:766–74
210. Poretz, R. D. 1972. *Methods Enzymol.* 28:349–54
211. Poretz, R. D., Riss, H., Timberlake, J. W., Chien, S.-M. 1974. *Biochemistry* 13:250–56
212. Pospisilova, J., Entlicher, G., Kocourek, J. 1974. *Biochim. Biophys. Acta* 362:593–97
213. Pospisilova, J., Haskovic, C., Entlicher, G., Kocourek, J. 1974. *Biochim. Biophys. Acta* 373:444–52
214. Privat, J.-P., Delmotte, F., Mialonier, G., Bouchard, P., Monsigny, M. 1974. *Eur. J. Biochem.* 47:5–14
215. Privat, J.-P., Delmotte, F., Mosigny, M. 1974. *FEBS Lett.* 46:224–27
216. Ibid, 229–32
217. Prokop, O., Uhlenbruck, G., Kohler, W. 1968. *Dtsch. Gesundheitswes.* 23:318–20
218. Pusztai, A., Grant, G., Palmer, R. 1975. *J. Sci. Food Agric.* 26:149–56
219. Pusztai, A., Watt, W. B. 1974. *Biochim. Biophys. Acta* 365:57–71
220. Räsänen, V., Weber, T. H., Grasbeck, R. 1973. *Eur. J. Biochem.* 38:193–200
221. Reeke, G. N. Jr. et al 1974. *Ann. NY Acad. Sci.* 234:369–82
222. Reeke, G. N. Jr., Becker, J. W., Edelman, G. M. 1975. *J. Biol. Chem.* 250:1525–47
223. Refsnes, K., Olsnes, S., Pihl, A. 1974. *J. Biol. Chem.* 249:3557–62
224. Reichert, C. F., Pan, P. M., Mathews, K. P., Goldstein, I. J. 1973. *Nature New Biol.* 242:146–48
225. Reisfeld, R. A., Borjeson, J., Chessin, L. N., Small, P. A. Jr. 1967. *Proc. Natl. Acad. Sci. USA* 58:2020–27
226. Reitherman, R. W., Rosen, S. D., Barondes, S. H. 1974. *Nature* 248:599–600
227. Rice, R. H., Etzler, M. E. 1974. *Biochem. Biophys. Res. Commun.* 59:414–19
228. Roberts, T. K., Boursnell, J. C. 1974. *J. Reprod. Fertil.* 41:489–92
229. Rogers, G. T., Searle, F., Bagshawe, K. D. 1974. *Nature* 251:519–21
230. Roguet, R., Bourrillon, R. 1975. *Biochim. Biophys. Acta* 309:380–88
231. Roth, J., Thoss, K., Wagner, M., Mayer, H. W. 1975. *Histochemistry* 43:275–82
232. Rottmann, W. L., Walther, B. T., Hellerqvist, C. G., Umbreit, J., Roseman, S. 1974. *J. Biol. Chem.* 249:373–80
233. Rougé, P. 1974. *C. R. Acad. Sci. D* 278:449–52
234. Ibid, 3083–87
235. Ruddon, R. W., Weisenthal, L. M., Lundeen, D. E., Bessler, W., Goldstein, I. J. 1974. *Proc. Natl. Acad. Sci. USA* 71:1848–51
236. Rush, R. A., Thomas, P. E., Kindler, S. H., Udenfriend, S. 1974. *Biochem. Biophys. Res. Commun.* 57:1301–5
237. Schnaar, R. L., Lee, Y. C. 1975. *Biochemistry* 14:1535–41
238. Scott, M. T. 1972. *J. Invest. Pathol.* 19:66–71
239. Seeger, R., Weidmann, R. 1972. *Arch. Toxikol.* 29:189–217
240. Sela, B.-A., Lis, H., Sharon, N., Sachs, L. 1973. *Biochim. Biophys. Acta* 310:273–77
241. Shaper, J. H., Barker, R., Hill, R. L. 1973. *Anal. Biochem.* 53:564–70
242. Sharon, N. 1975. *Extracellular Matrix Influences on Gene Expression,* ed. H. C. Slavkin, R. C. Gruelich, 479–512. New York: Academic
243. Sharon, N., Lis, H., 1972. *Science* 949–59
244. Sherry, A. D., Cottam, G. L. 1973. *Arch. Biochem. Biophys.* 156:665–72
245. Sherry, A. D., Newman, A. D., Gutz, C. G. 1975. *Biochemistry* 14:2191–96
246. Shoham, M., Kalb, A. J., Pecht, I. 1973. *Biochemistry* 12:1914–17
247. Smart, J. E., Pearlstein, E., Waterfield, M. D. 1974. *Biochem. Soc. Trans.* 2:1316–17
248. Smith, D. F., Weri, G., Walborg, E. F. Jr. 1973. *Biochemistry* 12:2111–18
249. So, L. L., Goldstein, I. J. 1967. *J. Biol. Chem.* 242:1617–22
250. Ibid 1968. 243:2003–7
251. Solling, H., Wang, P. 1973. *Biochem. Biophys. Res. Commun.* 53:1234–39
252. Sperti, S., Montanaro, L., Mattioli, A., Stirpe, F. 1973. *Biochem. J.* 136:813–15
253. Sperti, S., Montanaro, L., Mattioli, A., Testoni, G. 1975. *Biochem. J.* 148:447–51
254. Stein, M. D., Howard, I. K., Sage, H. J. 1971. *Arch. Biochem. Biophys.* 146:353–55

255. Stockert, R. J., Morell, A. G., Schein-
berg, I. H. 1974. *Science* 186:365–66
256. Sulkowski, E., Laskowski, M. Sr. 1974.
Biochem. Biophys. Res. Commun.
57:463–68
257. Takahashi, S., Pollack, J., Seifter, S.
1974. *Biochim. Biophys. Acta* 371:71–75
258. Takahashi, T., Yagi, T., Oda, T.,
Liener, I. E. 1974. *Agric. Biol. Chem.*
38:865–67
259. Takahashi, T., Yamada, N., Iwamoto,
K., Shimabayashi, Y., Izutsu, K. 1973.
Agric. Biol. Chem. 37:29–36
260. Terao, T., Osawa, T. 1973. *J. Biochem.
Tokyo* 74:199–201
261. Tichá, M., Entlicher, G., Kostír, J. V.,
Kocourek, J. 1970. *Biochim. Biophys.
Acta* 221:282–89
262. Tokuyama, H. 1973. *Biochim. Biophys.
Acta* 317:338–50
263. Tomita, M. et al 1972. *Experientia*
28:84–85
264. Toms, G. C. 1971. *Chemotaxonomy of
Legumes,* ed. J. B. Harborne, D.
Boulter, B. L. Turner, 367–462. New
York: Academic. 612 pp.
265. Toyoshima, S., Akiyama, Y., Nakano,
K., Tonomura, A., Osawa, T. 1971. *Biochemistry* 10:4457–63
266. Toyoshima, S., Osawa, T. 1975. *J. Biol.
Chem.* 250:1655–60
267. Trowbridge, I. S. 1973. *Proc. Natl.
Acad. Sci. USA* 70:3650–54
268. Trowbridge, I. S. 1974. *J. Biol. Chem.*
249:6004–12
269. Trowbridge, I. S., Hilborn, D. A. 1974.
Nature 250:304–7
270. Tung, T.-C., Hsu, C.-T., Lin, J.-Y.
1971. *J. Formosan Med. Assoc.* 70:
569–78
271. Turner, R. H., Liener, I. E. 1975. *J.
Agric. Food Chem.* 23:484–87
272. Ulevitch, R. J., Jones, J. M., Feldman,
J. D. 1974. *Prep. Biochem.* 4:273–81
273. Van Wauwe, J.-P., Loontiens, F. G.,
Carchon, H. A., De Bruyne, C. K.
1973. *Carbohydr. Res.* 30:249–56
274. Van Wauwe, J.-P., Loontiens, F. G., De
Bruyne, C. K. 1973. *Biochim. Biophys.
Acta* 313:99–105
275. Ibid 1975. 379:456–61
276. Veseley, P., Entlicher, G., Kocourek, J.
1972. *Experientia* 28:1085–86
277. Villafranca, J. J., Viola, R. E. 1974.
Arch. Biochem. Biophys. 160:465–68
278. Vlodavsky, I., Inbar, M., Sachs, L.
1973. *Proc. Natl. Acad. Sci. USA* 70:
1780–84
279. Von Goldhammer, E., Zorn, H. 1974.
Eur. J. Biochem. 44:195–99
280. Wang, J. L., Becker, J. W., Reeke,
G. N. Jr., Edelman, G. M. 1974. *J. Mol.
Biol.* 88:259–62
281. Wang, J. L., Cunningham, B. A., Edelman, G. M. 1971. *Proc. Natl. Acad. Sci.
USA* 68:1130–34
282. Wang, J. L., Cunningham, B. A., Waxdal, M. J., Edelman, G. M. 1975. *J.
Biol. Chem.* 250:1490–1502
283. Waxdal, M. 1974. *Biochemistry* 13:
3671–76
284. Waxdal, M., Basham, T. Y. 1974. *Nature* 251:163–64
285. Wei, C. H. 1973. *J. Biol. Chem.* 248:
3745–47
286. Wei, C. H., Einstein, J. R. 1974. *J. Biol.
Chem.* 249:2985–86
287. Wei, C. H., Hartman, F. C., Pfuderer,
P., Yang, W. K. 1974. *J. Biol. Chem.*
249:3061–67
288. Wei, C. H., Koh, C., Pfuderer, P.,
Einstein, J. R. 1975. *J. Biol. Chem.*
250:4790–95
289. Williams, M. A., Voak, D. 1972. *Br. J.
Haematol.* 23:427–41
290. Winqvist, L., Eriksson, L. C., Dallner,
G. 1974. *FEBS Lett.* 42:27–31
291. Wright, C. S. 1974. *J. Mol. Biol.*
87:835–41
292. Wright, C. S., Keith, C., Nagata, Y.,
Burger, M. M., Langridge, R. 1974. *J.
Mol. Biol.* 87:843–46
293. Yachnin, S., Svenson, R. H. 1972. *Im-
munology* 22:871–83
294. Yang, C.-H., Srivastava, P. N. 1975.
Biochim. Biophys. Acta 391:382–87
295. Yariv, J., Kalb, A. J., Blumberg, S.
1972. *Methods Enzymol.* 28:356–60
296. Young, N. M. 1974. *Biochim. Biophys.
Acta* 336:46–52
297. Young, N. M., Leon, M. A. 1974. *Biochim. Biophys. Acta* 365:418–24
298. Zachowski, A., Paraf, A. 1974. *Biochem. Biophys. Res. Commun.* 57:
787–92
299. Zanetta, J. P., Morgan, I. C., Gombos,
G. 1975. *Brain Res.* 83:337–48

Ann. Rev. Plant Physiol. 1976. 27:321-48

PHYSIOLOGY OF
FLOWER FORMATION[1]

❖7612

Jan A. D. Zeevaart

MSU/ERDA Plant Research Laboratory, Michigan State University, East Lansing, Michigan 48824

CONTENTS

[1]ABA (abscisic acid); d (donor); DCMU [3-(3,4'-dichlorophenyl)-1,1-dimethylurea]; DNP (dayneutral plant); FR (far-red light); GA (gibberellin); IAA (indole-3yl-acetic acid); LD (long day); LDP (long-day plant); LSDP (long-short-day plant); r (receptor); R (red light); SD (short day); SDP (short-day plant); SLDP (short-long-day plant).

INTRODUCTION

Beginning with Lang's comprehensive review (178), this is the ninth article in this series dealing with physiology of flowering, or certain aspects thereof. Since the last review (88) several general articles and books dealing with flower formation have appeared. A chapter on plant reproduction (235) in a *Treatise of Plant Physiology* gives extensive coverage of the older literature on both vernalization and photoperiodism. The topic of vernalization has also been covered in a book on *Temperature and Life* (208). Reviews on phytochrome and flowering (269, 271), hormones and flowering (9), the shoot apex in seed plants (101), and a survey of early changes in evoked apices (16) all contain material pertinent to the present review. Several articles summarizing work in Chailakhyan's laboratory have appeared (43–46). Flowering in two of the world's major crops, rice (268) and sugarcane (7), have also been summarized. Further, a review on flower initiation in woody plants has appeared (129), and one on the role of GA in strobilus formation in conifers (217). Recently two books on flowering have been published: one (270) that gives a comprehensive coverage of all photoperiodic responses in plants with emphasis on flowering, and a paperback edition (90) that provides the beginning student with an excellent introduction to the field.

This abundance of reviews and books should not be taken as a reflection of progress in the field. On the contrary, no major advances have been made in recent years, and few laboratories are engaged in fundamental research on flowering today. This is not because the major problems have been solved, but because they turned out to be exceedingly complex. In retrospect, this should not come as a surprise since the overall flowering process involves many steps, usually starting with perception of an environmental factor and terminating with the differentiation of three-dimensional structures, the flower primordia. Since a certain degree of organization is required for flower formation to proceed, individual reactions cannot be studied in a test tube. Much is known about the various steps in a descriptive sense, but direct biochemical approaches to uncover the underlying mechanism have invariably turned into blind alleys.

The current review deals mainly with photoperiodic control of flower formation and is by no means a complete survey of the literature that has appeared since Evans's review (88). To the extent possible, recent developments and trends are evaluated in the framework of the mass of older literature that exists on the subject.

GENERAL PHENOMENOLOGY

In this section, work has been summarized that illustrates the enormous variety in flowering responses that plants display. While some of this work is essentially descriptive, it may provide useful material for future studies on mechanisms.

Adaptation to Photoperiod

Studies of the photoperiodic responses of many different populations of *Xanthium* have demonstrated considerable diversity in: (*a*) the critical dark period (7.5 to 11 hr); (*b*) the age at which seedlings are ripe-to-flower; and (*c*) the effect of temperature on photoinduction. A combination of these factors appears to be the basis for the successful adaptation of *Xanthium* in many different parts of the world (186, 188, 189).

Virtually all wild populations of rice exhibited a strong SD response, but only 27.5% of the cultivated varieties were photoperiodically sensitive (148), thus confirming that the trend has been to select nonsensitive varieties (268). Spring wheat cultivars from temperate regions were qualitative LDP with respect to ear emergence, whereas varieties adapted to lower latitudes exhibited only a quantitative LD response (275).

Sharp critical photoperiods close to 12 hr have been observed in certain varieties of rice (149) and sugarcane (141). It is obvious that when such plants are grown at low latitudes, they are able to perceive small changes in the daylength and exhibit seasonal flowering. Although sugarcane required an intermediate photoperiod around 12 1/2 hr for floral initiation, further development and elongation of the inflorescence proceeded under shorter photoperiods (140).

An attempt has been made to correlate the photoperiodic requirement for flowering with the C_3 and C_4 pathway of photosynthesis. Within the Gramineae and three other genera, most C_3 plants had a LD requirement for flower formation whereas species with the C_4 pathway were SDP or DNP (227). However, Evans (89) has supplied examples of several species in which C_4 metabolism was combined with a LD requirement for flowering. It must be concluded therefore that the SD photoperiodic response is not a constant feature of the C_4 pathway.

Interactions of External Factors

There is an ever-increasing list of plants, originally considered to be strictly photoperiodic, that can also be made to produce flower buds by a variety of other factors besides daylength. As a rule, however, flowering in response to these alternate factors is relatively weak. For example, the minimal duration for floral induction in the SDP *Perilla ocymoides* was 6 days at 22°C, but 45 days under continuous light at 5°C (77). The immediate effect of the low temperature took place in the leaves as shown by leaf grafts (78). Further, in the SDP *Pharbitis* flower formation under LD was induced by low temperature (28, 246), by high intensity light, by treatment with ABA or a growth retardant (245, 246), by removal of roots, and by a low nutrient level (273, 274). Vegetative growth was strongly reduced in all cases, but this was presumably not a prerequisite for flower formation since treatment with

GA_3 under high-intensity light promoted stem growth without preventing flower formation (246). Results obtained with the LDP *Silene armeria* (279), two *Blitum* species (LDP) (137), and a cold-requiring *Festuca* strain (26, 27) show that successive treatments with two inducing factors, each at a subthreshold level, resulted in flowering. In other words, the effects of two subthreshold treatments were additive which indicates that different factors acted through some common mechanism.

In many LDP the night temperature is an important factor that determines the flowering response. For example, *Calamintha officinalis* remained vegetative indefinitely under 9-hr photoperiods at 22°C, but flowered with a 15-hr dark period at 2°C (5). This species (4) as well as *Samolus parviflorus* (283), *Silene armeria* (264–267), and other LDP investigated earlier (see 264) flowered under SD with a night temperature above 30°C. A 4-hr treatment with the high temperature during the middle of the night was sufficient in *Silene* to cause flowering (264).

In earlier work with the LSDP *Bryophyllum daigremontianum* it had been shown that transfer from LD to SD resulted in flowering only when the temperature during the 16-hr dark period was 15°C or lower (299). Van de Pol (262) has defined this temperature requirement more precisely: *Bryophyllum* transferred from LD to an 8-hr photoperiod flowered with any combination of day and night temperatures, provided the sum of the products of temperature and hours in the 24-hr cycle was 472 or less.

An interesting modification of the photoperiodic response by mineral nutrition has been observed in *Nicotiana glutinosa*. At a high level of nutrition this plant flowered earliest under LD, at a low nutritional level it responded as a quantitative SDP, and with an intermediate level of nutrition it was indifferent to the photoperiod (81).

Reversion to Vegetative Growth

Reversion from the flowering to the vegetative condition was caused by weak light in *Nicotiana glutinosa* (79), by SD and low light intensity in *Sinapis alba* (10), and by high temperature in *Bryophyllum daigremontianum* (262). In the cold-requiring plant *Cheiranthus cheiri* flower initiation and anthesis took place at 5°C. Upon transfer to 22°C reversion to vegetative growth took place rapidly (80). Zonation of the shoot apex remained evident throughout the entire development of *Cheiranthus*. Depending on the prevailing temperature, either leaf or flower primordia were initiated on the flanks of the apical meristem (82).

Genetics of Flower Formation

The following strains of the LDP *Silene armeria* have been selected which vary in their response to applied GA: (*a*) a dwarf mutant in which neither stem growth nor flower formation was affected by applied GA_3 (282). Tall stem was dominant over dwarf (gene S); (*b*) the GA^+ strains in which application of GA_3 under SD conditions induced both stem elongation and flowering; (*c*) the GA^- strains where GA_3 caused only stem growth (280, 285, 286). Flowering in SD with GA_3 was inherited as a monogenic trait (gene F). Thus stem growth and flower formation are basically different processes, but since the genes S and F are linked (Wellensiek, personal communication), they usually occur at the same time.

A single-gene recessive mutant obtained by treatment of seedlings of *Lunaria annua* (dayneutral biennial) with a chemical mutagen, flowered in LD without cold treatment (284).

Hybridization of dayneutral *Xanthium* with plants that had a dark requirement of less than 10 hr, produced dayneutral hybrids. In crossings involving a dayneutral strain and a parent requiring nights of 10 hr or longer, the F_1 hybrids showed a dark requirement of 7.5 to 9 hr (187, 190). Photoperiodic responses were inherited independently of ripeness-to-flower responses (190).

PHYTOCHROME

Considerable progress has been made in recent years in formulating a unified hypothesis for the role of phytochrome in photoperiodic induction of both SDP and LDP (90, 270, 271). However, no advances have been made in detecting and measuring phytochrome in green plant material (162, 201), so that conclusions on the status of phytochrome in leaves of photoperiodic plants are based solely on indirect evidence from physiological experiments.

Role in SDP

The kinetics of Pfr disappearance in vivo during an inductive dark period have been investigated in physiological experiments with the null response technique. Plants were irradiated briefly during an inductive dark period with various mixtures of R and FR, and a null response was obtained with the mixture that had no effect on flower formation. Application of this procedure to *Chenopodium* (162) and *Pharbitis* (92) has shown that a high level of Pfr was maintained in the two plants during the first 3 and 6 hr of the dark period, respectively, after which rapid conversion to Pr took place. Pfr appeared to increase during darkness (inverse reversion) following a brief end-of-day irradiation with FR, and then disappeared again as in treatments starting with high Pfr. These results, as well as earlier work (see 88, 269), led to the conclusion that SDP have a requirement for a diurnal variation in the Pfr level. Presence of a large proportion of phytochrome as Pfr during the short photoperiod and early part of the night has a flower-promoting effect, while for the remainder of the dark period Pfr must be at a very low level or entirely absent. There is, however, an interaction between the light quality of the photoperiod and the phytochrome response during the subsequent dark period (e.g. 118, 128) which appears to be related to photoperiodic time measurement (160, 162).

Role in LDP

Applying the null response technique to *Lolium temulentum,* Evans (91) found that Pfr had disappeared after 5 hr in darkness, and, unlike in SDP, there was no indication that an increase in Pfr took place after an initial exposure to FR. Action spectra for flower promotion determined during the first and second half of the long night were different: the peak of maximal effectiveness was in the 720–740 nm region for the first half of the night compared with a peak at 670 nm later in the night (91). Thus optimal flowering in *Lolium* was obtained with most of the phytochrome present as Pr early in the night and as Pfr during the second half of the night (91,

124). A similar shift in sensitivity from FR to R during the long night was also found in *Hyoscyamus* (86) and in *Lemna gibba* (127), but not in *Fuchsia* (271). Both the high and low Pfr processes could proceed with a constant photostationary state, provided the proportion of the pigment present as Pfr was kept low (29, 126, 139, 272).

In conclusion, when comparing the requirements for high and low Pfr levels in SDP and LDP, the major difference appears to be the sequence in which the high and low Pfr processes must succeed each other during the long night (90, 270, 271). This diurnal fluctuation in sensitivity to the Pfr level is probably related to an endogenous rhythm involved in time measurement. For a further discussion of photoperiodic timing, the article by Hillman (119) in this volume should be consulted.

LEAF METABOLISM ASSOCIATED WITH INDUCTION

Numerous attempts have been made over the years to detect differences in metabolism or in chemical composition between induced and noninduced plants. Unfortunately, such results are difficult to interpret since a change in photoperiod or temperature usually causes many changes that are not related to floral induction. A case in point is photoperiodic induction of crassulacean acid metabolism in *Kalanchoë* which exhibits all the features of floral induction (36), yet the two processes are not causally related. Despite a voluminous literature on this topic, the biochemical approach has not yielded any clues as to the nature of the processes that are essential for floral induction. At present no compounds or biochemical reactions are known that occur exclusively in plants induced to flower.

Photosynthesis

Earlier work (88) has shown that photoinduction of LDP is more dependent on photosynthesis than is induction of SDP. This has been confirmed in *Anagallis* by inhibition of flowering with DCMU (125), and in *Sinapis* by exclusion of CO_2 from the air (157). However, an albino mutant of *Arabidopsis* produced floral primordia rapidly in LD while seedlings under SD remained vegetative (34). Continuous application of CO_2 at a high level induced flowering in *Silene* under SD, presumably as a result of enhanced photosynthesis (228). A night interruption could induce flowering in the LDP *Brassica crenata* only if CO_2 was present (205).

With respect to SDP, it appears from recent work that photosynthesis is not essential for photoinduction. Etiolated seedlings of *Pharbitis* became photoperiodically sensitive before they could carry out photosynthesis (98). DCMU did not affect induction in *Chenopodium* seedlings, although it did inhibit development of floral primordia (233, 234). Elevated CO_2 levels during photoinduction of *Pharbitis* and *Xanthium* (228) and *Lemna perpusilla* (219) reduced the flowering response.

The evidence concerning the need for CO_2 during a night interruption is conflicting. In *Perilla* a light break was equally effective with or without CO_2 (205). In contrast, in *Xanthium* an interruption of the dark period with red light inhibited flowering only in the presence of CO_2 (12). The role of CO_2 during the light break is not clear, but one possibility is that it functions as an antagonist of ethylene (1).

Nucleic Acids and Proteins

Cold treatment increased the total RNA content of a cold-requiring strain of *Arabidopsis* as compared to untreated control plants, while devernalization reduced the RNA content by almost 40%. Similar changes did not take place in an annual variety (31). Changes in the total nucleic acids and proteins were followed during induction of *Sinapis* and *Chenopodium* (6, 156). However, such gross analyses cannot be expected to yield meaningful data on flowering.

Application of cycloheximide to the leaves of *Hyoscyamus* resulted in flower formation under noninductive conditions (164). The presence of untreated leaves did not affect cycloheximide-mediated floral initiation, so that it is unlikely that the chemical acted by blocking synthesis of an inhibitor of flowering. Both cycloheximide and 2-thiouracil (85) inhibited protein synthesis in the leaves of *Hyoscyamus* (165). In the SDP *Impatiens* cycloheximide alone did not affect flowering, but it did enhance the response caused by GA_3 under noninductive conditions (207).

A dual-labeling technique provided no evidence for differences in the types of proteins synthesized in leaves of induced and vegetative *Xanthium* plants (244). On the other hand, the proteins extracted from GA-treated (vegetative) and control buds (with floral initiation) of *Citrus* exhibited different patterns when analyzed by gel electrophoresis (204).

No differences could be detected in histones extracted from vernalized and vegetative wheat plants (248). In *Silene* the histones from induced and noninduced leaves exhibited minor differences in the pattern of the lysine-rich fraction (67).

Sugars and Amino Acids

In the SDP *Lemna perpusilla* the flower-inhibiting effect of sucrose added to dilute medium became evident only in the presence of NH_4^+ (120). The inhibition was partially overcome by respiratory intermediates, certain amino acids, ATP, CO_2-free atmosphere (219), DCMU (220), or adenine derivatives (221). The interpretation was that sugar inhibited flowering by altering the levels of amino acids (219), or of adenine derivatives (221), although it was not made clear how these two groups of substances would specifically control flowering. Sugar inhibition of flowering in the LDP *Lemna gibba* could be reversed by cyclic AMP (213) or by catecholamines (214).

Serine and threonine promoted flowering in the SDP *L. perpusilla* under SD but not under LD (154, 191). It was suggested that serine functioned as a precursor of a flower-inducing substance (153). However, the results do not warrant the conclusion that serine plays such a determinative role in flowering.

Sterols

Suppression of flower formation by the hypocholesteremic drug tris(2-diethylaminoethyl)phosphate trihydrochloride (SK&F 7997-A_3) in *Xanthium* and *Pharbitis* was accompanied by inhibition of sterol biosynthesis as measured by incorporation of ^{14}C-mevalonic acid into the sterol fraction. However, with other chemicals it was possible to inhibit sterol biosynthesis without affecting floral induction. Moreover, inhibition due to SK&F 7997 could not be reversed by application of various sterols

(155). This suggests that sterol biosynthesis is not an essential part of floral induction. The possibility remains, however, that SK&F 7997 inhibited the formation of a specific sterol fraction that was related to flowering, but could not be detected with the techniques employed. Alternatively, the inhibitor might have affected pathways in addition to the one leading to sterols (32). Various steroids tested on plants under inductive or noninductive photoperiods had no effect on flower formation (66, 72, 76, 131).

THE FLORAL STIMULUS

Since efforts to identify the floral stimulus have met with failure thus far, movement of the stimulus from an induced plant part (donor) to a receptor bud remains the main physiological evidence for its existence. Carr (38) suggested that the primary photoperiodic stimulus emanating from a photoinduced leaf may be different from the secondary stimulus transmissible via a graft union from flowering donor plants to vegetative receptors. Elaborating Carr's ideas further, Evans (87, 88) concluded on the basis of differences in translocation velocities in the SDP *Pharbitis* and in the LDP *Lolium* that the primary stimuli are different in different response types, while the secondary stimulus would be common to all plants. Although this hypothesis cannot be ruled out at present, there is no conclusive evidence to support it either (292). I will, therefore, use the term floral stimulus in this review to indicate the photoperiodic stimulus generated in a photoinduced leaf as well as the agent(s) moving across a graft union from donor to receptor.

Generation and Movement

Export of the floral stimulus from the cotyledons of *Chenopodium* (SDP) seedlings (159) or from leaves of adult plants (161) was complete within 35 and 22.5 hr, respectively, from the beginning of darkness. In the LDP *Sinapis alba* and *Anagallis arvensis* the situation was complicated by the need for leaves both as a source of floral stimulus and of energy. Partial defoliation of *Anagallis* at various times indicated that the stimulus was exported gradually between 24 and 72 hr after the beginning of the LD (96). In *Sinapis* most of the stimulus moved out of the leaves between 16 and 24 hr after the start of the inductive treatment (158). A mitotic stimulus, under certain conditions distinct in its translocation characteristics from the floral stimulus, was also generated in induced *Sinapis* leaves and exported to the apex where it caused a rise in mitotic activity (17).

In *Perilla* movement of the floral stimulus and translocation of ^{14}C-assimilates from a grafted donor leaf in basipetal direction were closely correlated, which is consistent with the idea that long distance transport of the stimulus takes place in the phloem (163). However, in graft combinations between species of different families, no functional vascular connections were formed (281). Yet after a prolonged period of contact, receptor scions were induced to flower (see below). This indicates that in the absence of a phloem connection a slow transfer of the stimulus from cell to cell can take place.

When inhibitory leaves in *Perilla* grafts were removed, ^{14}C-assimilates from the donor leaf arrived in the receptor shoots within half an hour, whereas unobstructed contact between donor and receptor had to be maintained for 24 hr to obtain a 50% flowering response. This suggests that a threshold level of stimulus had to accumulate in the apex before flower formation could take place (163). Results of experiments performed with three different strains of *Xanthium* grafted on the same donor indicate that the threshold concentration of stimulus necessary for flowering of the receptors was higher the more SD were required for photoinduction. Consequently, differences in photoperiodic sensitivity were attributed to differences in sensitivity of the shoot apices to the floral stimulus (262). However, earlier experiments also showed that leaves of different *Xanthium* strains differed in the amount of stimulus produced (37). So varietal differences in photoperiodic sensitivity result from differences in both the leaves and the apices.

In addition to photoinduction, other conditions causing flower formation also resulted in the generation of a graft-transmissible stimulus. For example, *Silene* plants induced to flower by LD, by SD at 5°C or at 32°C, or by application of GA under SD conditions, all were effective donors in grafting experiments (262, 278). The same was found with *Perilla* leaf grafts induced either under SD at 22°C or by 5°C under 24-hr photoperiods (78).

Transfer between Different Response Types

Since the compilation of successful transfers between different response types by Lang (180), several new cases have been reported (Table 1). Of particular significance are those grafts that show transmission of the floral stimulus between species of different families. In the incompatible graft combinations of *Xanthium* (d) or *Perilla* (d) with *Silene* (r), the graft partners were left in contact for 5 weeks, after which the *Silene* scions were regrafted onto vegetative *Silene* stocks to observe expression of the flowering response. Unfortunately, in neither case was an adequate number of noninduced control grafts included (262, 281). When the same technique was used with the graft combinations *Silene* (d)/*Xanthium* (r), *Xanthium* (r)/*Bryophyllum* (d), *Xanthium* (d)/*Bryophyllum* (r), and *Silene* (r)/*Bryophyllum* (d) none of the receptors showed any flowering response (262).

As shown in Table 1, *Bryophyllum* was an effective donor for *Kalanchoë* and *Chenopodium* for *Blitum*. But in the reciprocal combinations a weak flowering response was obtained, suggesting that a lower level of floral stimulus was needed for flower formation in *Kalanchoë* and *Blitum* as compared with *Bryophyllum* and *Chenopodium*, respectively. An early flowering strain of *Kalanchoë* (r) required grafting contact of shorter duration with *Bryophyllum* (d) than a late strain, which suggests that the late strain needed more floral stimulus for flowering than the early strain (262).

Although transmission of the flowering condition between grafting partners of different response types favors the idea of a ubiquitous floral stimulus, caution is warranted in view of many negative results. For example, of 10 different species of Caryophyllaceae studied, the floral stimulus was transmitted in only two intraspecific grafts and in one interspecific combination (262). Furthermore, a graft-transmissible stimulus could be demonstrated in *Blitum capitatum* but not in *B. virgatum* (138). The reason for the negative result in the latter species is probably that it promptly reverted to vegetative growth in the absence of inductive treatment

Table 1 Successful transmission of the floral stimulus in grafts between different photoperiodic response types

	Donor				Receptor			
Species	Family	Response type	Conditions	Species	Family	Response type	Conditions	Source
Xanthium strumarium	Compositae	SDP	SD	Silene armeria	Caryophyllaceae	LDP	SD	(281)
Helianthus annuus	Compositae	DNP	LD	Xanthium strumarium	Compositae	SDP	LD	(261)
Calendula officinalis	Compositae	DNP	LD	Xanthium strumarium	Compositae	SDP	LD	(261)
Bryophyllum daigremontianum	Crassulaceae	LSDP	LD→SD→LD	Kalanchoë blossfeldiana	Crassulaceae	SDP	LD	(262)
Kalanchoë blossfeldiana	Crassulaceae	SDP	SD→LD	Bryophyllum daigremontianum[a]	Crassulaceae	LSDP	LD	(262)
Perilla crispa	Labiatae	SDP	SD	Silene armeria[a]	Caryophyllaceae	LDP	SD	(262)
Chenopodium polyspermum, C. rubrum	Chenopodiaceae	SDP	SD	Blitum capitatum, B. virgatum	Chenopodiaceae	LDP	SD	(138)
Blitum capitatum, B. virgatum	Chenopodiaceae	LDP	LD	Chenopodium rubrum[a]	Chenopodiaceae	SDP	LD	(138)

[a] Weak flowering response.

(136). This is further supported by the observation that in two-branched plants flowering could be induced in the receptor branch if the other branch was induced continuously (138). Thus failure to demonstrate transfer of flower induction in grafting experiments does not necessarily rule out the involvement of a floral stimulus in floral initiation. Differences among species in rate of production and persistence of the stimulus, as well as different sensitivities of the shoot apices to the stimulus, may give rise to negative results.

Complementary Stimuli?

The possibility that SDP and LDP produce two independent complementary stimuli was first considered by Lang (178), but was rejected on the basis of evidence then available. More recently, this question has been raised again (87, 90), particularly in connection with the dual daylength requirement of LSDP and SLDP (43–45). Results of interspecific grafting experiments indicate that the floral stimuli of the different photoperiodic groups are very similar or identical. However, only in a few cases have the necessary control grafts between noninduced partners been made, since they are technically difficult to maintain under different daylengths. In four different combinations between SDP and LDP, it was established unequivocally that flower formation in the receptors occurred only when the donors were photoinduced (180). There are, however, two cases in which a vegetative "donor" caused flower formation in the receptor. When *Nicotiana sylvestris* (r) was grafted on noninduced Maryland Mammoth (M.M.) tobacco (d), part of the receptors produced flower buds (178, 290), but this effect may have been nonspecific due to removal of inhibitory leaves. Alternatively, GA produced by M.M. tobacco was perhaps responsible for floral initiation in *N. sylvestris*. In the other case, both induced and noninduced M.M. tobacco caused flower formation in non-thermoinduced plants of the biennial strain of *Hyoscyamus niger* under LD (42, 192). This result is the basis for the vernalin hypothesis which states that vernalin is present in all annual plants but is produced only during or after thermoinduction in cold-requiring plants (180). In Chailakhyan's view (42) stem growth and flower formation in *H. niger* were due to GA supplied by the tobacco leaves. If correct, this explanation would obviate the vernalin hypothesis.

Chailakhyan's original concept of florigen as a single substance formed only in the leaves of induced plants has been replaced by a two-substance hypothesis: anthesin and GA (42–45). Anthesin would be the limiting factor for flower formation in SDP, and GAs would be limiting flowering in LDP. On the basis of this hypothesis one would predict that graft combinations of noninduced LDP and SDP would result in flowering, since each partner would supply the limiting factor to the other. However, most of these grafts have yielded negative results with the exception of flower formation in *Nicotiana sylvestris* (r) under the influence of vegetative M.M. tobacco (see above). Additional results have been obtained with the LSDP *Bryophyllum daigremontianum*. Grafts were made in such a way that one part of the graft combination was continuously (before and after grafting) in LD and the other in SD (54, 55). Receptor shoots were positioned between the LD and SD part. In certain combinations the terminal shoots of the scions also served as receptor.

Flower buds appeared after 3 months as compared to less than one month with induced donors (299). Similar grafts set up by van de Pol (262) were vegetative after 90 days. Chailakhyan (43–45) interpreted flower formation in grafts between two vegetative partners as being due to the influx into the receptor shoots of two groups of substances, GA from the LD and anthesin from the SD part. Thus by differential daylength treatment the two stimuli would be produced simultaneously, but separated in space rather than in time when induced by the sequence LD ⟶ SD. I propose an alternative interpretation of Chailakhyan's results with *Bryophyllum:* GAs are produced in relatively high amounts in the leaves of LD stocks (295) and move upwards into the SD scion where an increase in the GA level results in florigen production and subsequent flower formation in the receptor shoots. This interpretation is supported by the observation that in the combination SD scion/LD stock the middle and upper shoots flowered simultaneously (55), although the latter were much further away from the LD leaves than the former. Also, in the reverse combination, LD scion/SD stock, no flower formation took place (54), presumably because GA moved more readily in the acropetal than in the basipetal direction (52, 53). Other evidence supporting the view that LD and SD induction must be perceived by one and the same *Bryophyllum* leaf, as established unequivocally in the LSDP *Cestrum* (230), has been discussed previously (291). Contrary to the flower-inducing effect of GA in *Bryophyllum,* applied GA inhibited flower formation in *Cestrum* (230). In one SLDP, *Coreopsis grandiflora,* GA substituted for LD (151), while in two others, *Scabiosa succisa* and *Campanula medium,* GA was most effective under LD conditions (59). Thus in the latter two species GA replaced the SD rather than the LD requirement. Clearly, the anthesin-GA hypothesis is not generally applicable to explain flowering in the different response types. Moreover, all available evidence indicates that GA itself is not a flower-inducing substance, but acts indirectly through production of the floral stimulus (262, 278, 298, 299). Thus in essence Chailakhyan's anthesin is identical with the original florigen.

Perpetuation of the Flowering Condition

Three species, namely the SDP *Xanthium strumarium* (179, 180, 184, 262), the LDP *Silene armeria* (278), and the LSDP *Bryophyllum daigremontianum* (262, 291) exhibit the phenomenon of indirect induction. This means that receptor shoots brought into flowering by grafting can themselves function as donors in the next grafting experiment. Since the induced state can be transferred through several successive graftings, the floral stimulus of these three species is apparently self-perpetuating. This does not necessarily imply that the stimulus reproduces autocatalytically in the sense of virus replication (184), but it may induce a condition which causes the synthesis of more stimulus (positive feedback) in young leaves and buds. Likewise, the plant hormone ethylene can stimulate its own synthesis (150). The term nonlocalized synthesis of floral stimulus is perhaps more appropriate to describe the situation, which is in contrast to localized synthesis in *Perilla* (262). Several pertinent experiments to determine the physiological basis for the different properties of the stimulus in these two types of plants have been performed by van de Pol (262). For example, *Bryophyllum* was an excellent donor for *Kalanchoë* receptors, but it did not bring about nonlocalized synthesis of the floral stimulus in the latter. Thus different mechanisms to preserve the flowering condition in these two plants were not due to different stimuli, but were presumably the result of different internal conditions.

Silene receptors were indirectly induced by *Xanthium* (281), but not by *Perilla* donors (262). Dayneutral *Helianthus* caused nonlocalized synthesis of the floral stimulus in *Xanthium,* while *Calendula* and *Rudbeckia,* both of which caused only limited flowering in *Xanthium* receptors (261, 262), did not.

Extraction of Flower-Initiating Factors

It is obvious that in the search for the floral stimulus a convenient and reliable bioassay is essential, but none is available at present. The situation is like a vicious circle: floral stimulus activity cannot be tested for lack of an assay, and selection of suitable assay plants requires an active preparation. Thus one must resort to a strictly empirical approach. General guidelines for testing flower-promoting and flower-inhibiting substances have been proposed (70–72, 76). Excised stem tips of *Chenopodium* (71, 76), intact *Xanthium* plants (121, 122, 183), *Lemna gibba* G3 (62), and *L. perpusilla* 6746 (121, 122) all have been used as test plants. Although the latter gives a rapid response, a drawback is that a variety of chemicals (e.g. 142–144, 256) can cause flowering under noninductive conditions. The most promising results so far have been obtained with *Xanthium.* Lincoln et al (183) first reported that a methanol extract from lyophilized shoot tips of flowering *Xanthium* could induce flower formation in ca 50% of vegetative *Xanthium* plants. The active material had acidic properties and was, therefore, called florigenic acid (182). Hodson & Hamner (121, 122) extracted frozen material with acetone and found that crude extracts from flowering plants caused flower formation in *Lemna.* When tested on *Xanthium,* extracts were active only when supplemented with GA₃. Extracts from vegetative *Xanthium,* with or without GA₃, and GA₃ alone, lacked flower-inducing activity. The most active preparations were obtained from young expanding leaves and buds without mature leaves. The culture filtrate of a particular *Calonectria* strain, originally isolated from a flowering gall of cocoa, was also active in the *Xanthium* (181) and *Lemna* assays (121). Further progress towards purification and identification of the promotive principle(s) has been slow, because positive results cannot be obtained consistently (K. C. Hamner, R. G. Lincoln, personal communication). The work with *Xanthium* extracts has been confirmed in at least two laboratories (38, 99), but not in others (C. F. Cleland, personal communication; I. Mukherjee and J. A. D. Zeevaart, unpublished results). Although Gibby's initial experiments were successful, he was unable to duplicate them later on. Possible reasons for this lack of reproducibility have been discussed (99).

Extracts of phloem sap collected from aphids feeding on *Xanthium* caused flowering in the LDP *Lemna gibba* G3 (62). The active substance was identified as salicylic acid (64). Benzoic acid and several closely related compounds were also active in the *Lemna* assay (61). However, salicylic acid did not induce flowering in *Xanthium* when applied alone or in combination with GA₃ and/or kinetin. Furthermore, salicylic acid was present in honeydew from both vegetative and flowering plants, so that a role for this compound in the flowering process of *Xanthium* appears unlikely (64).

In the LDP *Hyoscyamus niger* and *Salvia splendens* (172), and in the SDP *Perilla ocymoides* and *Chenopodium rubrum* (173), estrogen-like substances were absent during vegetative growth, but appeared during photoinduction and reached their highest concentration during flower bud formation and flowering. The estrogen-like fraction isolated from *Salvia* caused 50% flowering in noninduced plants (174). Estradiol induced 36% flowering in *Salvia* and 85% flowering in cold-requiring *Cichorium* (171). These interesting observations await duplication in other laboratories.

The flowering response of the SDP *Lemna perpusilla* 6746 was reduced by daily transfer to water for short periods during the long night (83, 108). Flower-promoting activity was detected in water that had been incubated with fronds under dark but not under light conditions. The activity was destroyed by autoclaving (109). The relationship of the active material to the floral stimulus, if any, is unknown.

INHIBITION

Inhibitory Effects of Non-Induced Leaves

A scheme for control of flower initiation in SDP and LDP has been proposed (238) in which an inhibitor of flower formation blocked the reaction yielding the floral stimulus. The model could account for many responses in both SDP and LDP when tested by computer simulation.

In *Xanthium* Gibby & Salisbury (100) confirmed that to be inhibitory, LD tissue must be located between the SD tissue and the receptor bud. Tissue prevented from floral stimulus production (by low light intensity, by photoperiods exceeding the critical daylength, or by interruption of a long night) actively inhibited the flowering response. These results were interpreted as evidence for localized LD inhibition which could intercept the stimulus on its way to the apex. This interpretation may hold true in case the basal half of a leaf is in LD and the apical part in SD, but it is difficult to see how it could apply when an LD leaf was positioned between the SD leaf and the receptor bud (100). Instead, the rapidly expanding LD leaf might act as a sink for the assimilates and floral stimulus generated in the SD leaf. In earlier work with *Xanthium* a transmissible LD inhibitor was implied (239).

No evidence was obtained for a transmissible LD inhibitor in *Perilla.* In agreement with previous findings (48), inhibition by LD leaves interposed between a donor leaf and receptor bud, could be fully explained in terms of interference with translocation of the stimulus (163). Noninduced leaves below LD leaves reduced the flowering response in the LDP *Sinapis,* but the nature of the inhibition was not determined (158).

Another as yet unexplained inhibitory effect was observed in rhythmic induction of flowering in *Chenopodium.* An apparent paradox exists in that a 13.5 hr dark period given to a single leaf resulted in flowering, whereas 30 hr of darkness did not.

Since the stimulus had arrived at the apex after 22.5 hr, it was postulated that an inhibitory effect arising in the leaf after 24 to 30 hr of darkness was transmitted to the apex, but no experimental evidence to support this could be obtained (161).

Extraction of Flower-Inhibiting Substances

As is the case with assays for flower-promoting substances, reliable bioassays for flower-inhibiting substances are lacking. Moreover, interpretation of positive results in assays for flower inhibitors is complicated by the possibility that the inhibitory effect is nonspecific.

Sap extracted from *Kalanchoë* leaves in LD and injected into induced *Kalanchoë* plants (236), or applied to partially induced *Viscaria* apices (25, 223) reduced the flowering response as compared to sap from induced leaves. The active substance was identified as gallic acid (223). Its concentration in aqueous extracts was higher from plants under LD than under SD, but identical when extracted with organic solvents. This difference was due to the presence of gallic acid in a bound form in flowering plants. Gallic acid (500 μg/ml) applied to induced *Kalanchoë* caused 50% flower inhibition (223). However, Schwabe & Wimble (238) reported that 2000 μg/ml of gallic acid did not cause inhibitory effects. Thus this compound cannot be considered as the LD inhibitor of flowering in *Kalanchoë.*

HORMONES AND FLOWER FORMATION

Among the many growth and developmental phenomena that can be influenced or induced by hormones is flower initiation. Some of the effects of hormones on flowering are undoubtedly pharmacological, but the question as to what extent known hormones control flower formation endogenously still remains to be answered. To that end a detailed analysis of the dynamics of hormones in the shoot apex with respect to environmental conditions is necessary.

Correlative Influences and Hormones

Reproductive development of axillary buds of the quantitative LDP *Scrofularia arguta* (193–195) and of the quantitative SDP *Chenopodium polyspermum* (247) was controlled by the roots and by the shoot tip. The inhibitory effect of roots on flower formation in these plants could be simulated by applied cytokinin (194–196, 247), and the flower-promoting effect of the terminal apex could be replaced by IAA or ABA (196). Thus vegetative growth or flowering of axillary buds in situ was regulated by interactions between various organs which in vitro could be replaced by hormones (195). Correlative inhibition of flowering has also been observed in a dayneutral orchid: decapitation resulted in flowering from the higher axillary buds and IAA could substitute for the inhibitory effect of the shoot tip (102, 103). The juvenile condition in *Ribes* shoots with less than 20 nodes was due to proximity of the roots which generated a GA-like factor that was inhibitory to flower initiation (237). Removal of roots from *Silene* resulted in flowering under SD in 30% of the plants (262). Absence of the root system had no effect on flowering in the LSDP

Bryophyllum (56) and in dayneutral plants (50). The LDP *Rudbeckia* without roots was capable of perceiving LD, but floral expression was delayed, since stem growth was dependent on the presence of roots (51).

Hormonal Effects

ETHYLENE   This gaseous hormone induced rapid flower formation in all brome-liads tested (1, 21, 39, 69), suggesting that it may play a role as endogenous regulator of flowering in this family. Ethylene also stimulated flower initiation in apple (288) and mango trees (40, 41), and enhanced ear emergence of vernalized winter wheat (60). In the majority of other plants studied, however, ethylene exerted an inhibitory effect on flower formation. A detailed study of *Pharbitis* indicates that ethylene acted in the cotyledons during the second half of a 16-hr inductive dark period (251, 252).

CYTOKININS   Promotion of flower formation by applied cytokinins has been observed in several plants (15, 113, 216, 259). In one variety of *Chrysanthemum* benzyladenine had little effect on flower formation, but a combination of GA_5 and benzyladenine induced formation of inflorescences (216). In another *Chrysanthemum* variety, benzyladenine could substitute for the latter part of photoinduction (15). Inflorescence development of induced *Bougainvillea* was promoted by cytokinin applied to the terminal buds. This was probably due to increased accumulation of assimilates in the shoot tip (259).

Aphid honeydew from flowering *Xanthium* plants had a higher cytokinin content than that from vegetative plants (218), but extractions yielded the opposite result, namely a large reduction in the cytokinin content with increasing photoinduction (263). This decline in activity in extracts from buds and leaf blades and in root exudate could already be detected following one inductive dark period (116). The relationship between cytokinin level and floral induction in *Xanthium,* if any, remains to be determined.

GIBBERELLINS   Rapid termination of the juvenile phase with applied GA_3 was first accomplished in two families of the Coniferae, namely, the Cupressaceae and Taxodiaceae, and more recently with less polar GAs (GA_4, GA_5, GA_7, GA_9) in the Pinaceae (217, 229a). While in these conifers the GA level is too low during the juvenile phase, it appears to be too high in *Ribes nigrum* (237). In fact, applied GA_3 inhibits flower bud formation in most dicotyledonous woody plants (104, 129, 231).

Application of GA failed to induce flower formation in the following LDP under SD conditions: *Scrofularia marilandica* (66, 106), three species of *Hieracium* (215), and two species of *Melandrium* (262). In the SDP rice (250) and *Cosmos* (202) applied GA promoted reproductive development. Surprisingly, in *Hieracium floribundum* under LD conditions GA_3 completely suppressed flower formation and stem growth (215).

The inhibitory effect of autoclaved GA_3 and GA_7 solutions on flower formation in *Lemna perpusilla* (123) was caused by decomposition products that were identified as allogibberic and 13-deoxyallogibberic acid, respectively (224, 225). The related compound hexahydrofluorene-9-carboxylic acid had an effect on flowering of *L. perpusilla* similar to that observed with allogibberic acid (226).

The relationship between flower formation and stem elongation in rosette plants has occupied physiologists for a long time. Conclusive evidence has been obtained now that the two phenomena depend on separate processes. First of all, selection of different strains of *Silene armeria* and genetic analysis have demonstrated that GA-induced stem elongation and flower formation are determined by two separate genes (285). Secondly, growth retardants partly (167) or fully (65, 215) suppressed stem growth while flower formation took place normally. Suppression of stem growth in *Silene* with a growth retardant was associated with reduction in the GA level below the limits of detection (65). Thus, at least in this plant, flower formation could proceed in the absence of GA.

Extractions of GA have more often than not failed to establish a correlation between floral induction and GA content (31, 65, 97, 210, 293). This is not surprising, since endogenous GAs are in a dynamic state. Their concentration present at the time of killing the tissue is the outcome of GA biosynthesis and accumulation on the one hand and metabolism on the other. Additional information about GA biosynthesis and breakdown in relation to photoperiod has been obtained with diffusion experiments (65), metabolic studies with labeled GA (84, 260), and time course studies with growth retardants (293). As a whole, these experiments have shown that the transfer of LDP from SD to LD causes an increase in the rate of both GA biosynthesis and metabolism (297).

ABSCISIC ACID   Earlier expectations concerning the role of ABA in flowering (2) have not been fulfilled. It is clear now that applied ($\pm$)-ABA cannot induce flower formation in SDP under strictly noninductive conditions, but it can enhance the flowering response of slightly induced plants of *Pharbitis* (113, 206) and *Chenopodium* (175, 177). A combination of ($\pm$)-ABA and a growth retardant gave a weak flowering response in *Lemna* under LD (146). In the SDP *Kalanchoë* ($\pm$)-ABA as well as xanthoxin inhibited flower formation (236). Applied ($\pm$)-ABA was not inhibitory to flower formation in the LDP *Rudbeckia* (166).

With regard to endogenous ABA, the levels were higher under LD than under SD conditions (243, 294, 296), or the level remained virtually unchanged after transferring LDP from SD to LD (111, 166). These observations are not in agreement with the postulated role of ABA as an inhibitor of flower formation in LDP held under SD conditions (2).

EVENTS IN THE APEX

Plastochron and Photoperiodic Sensitivity

Jacobs (130) proposed that the minimal number of inductive cycles required for floral induction equals the number of days in a plastochron. There is, however, more evidence against this proposal than for it. In *Anagallis* there are 5 days in a plastochron, yet exposure to 1 LD induced flowering (94, 95). A whole plastochron was not necessary for complete induction of *Silene coeli-rosa* (199). The number of SD required for floral induction of different *Xanthium* strains varied considerably (262). It is unlikely that there is a comparable range in plastochron within the same species. Furthermore, induction of detached *Perilla* leaves took place independently of the events in the apex (290). Thus the correlation found in *Perilla* and *Xanthium* between plastochron and number of cycles necessary for floral induction (130) was probably coincidental.

Early Changes after Induction

During transition of the shoot apex from the vegetative to the flowering state an increase in mitotic activity throughout the meristem has been observed in a number of species (16, 101), but this does not necessarily reflect the true rate of cell division (159). Conclusive evidence on this point has been obtained only recently with the LDP *Sinapis* by measuring the accumulation of metaphases following colchicine application (30). The results show that after exposure to one LD the rate of cell division increased eightfold in the central zone and sixfold in the peripheral zone.

In the vegetative apex of *Sinapis* approximately half of the cells were in the G_2 phase, i.e. had 4C nuclei (133). In response to arrival of the floral stimulus (158) these cells entered mitosis, resulting in a peak in mitotic activity 26 to 30 hr after the beginning of the single LD. The function of this first mitotic wave in flower initiation is obscure since it could be induced by a daylength slightly shorter than the critical one for flower formation. However, all attempts to induce flowering in *Sinapis* without inducing the early increase in mitosis failed (19). Following cell division and synchronization of the cell population in the apex, a peak in DNA synthesis was observed 34 to 38 hr after the start of the LD, followed by a second maximum in the mitotic activity at 62 hr. The latter was associated with initiation of the first flower buds. Histone reached a minimum after 34 hr and then increased more rapidly than DNA; total protein paralleled the histone level (134).

Ultrastructural changes observed in evoked meristems of *Sinapis* included an increase in the size of the nucleus, more dispersed chromatin, and a late rise in the nucleolar size associated with ribosome synthesis (114). An early increase in the number of mitochondria was probably related to an increased energy demand in the evoked meristem (115).

With slight variations, similar cytological and histochemical changes have also been observed in evoked meristems of other species that require only one inductive cycle for flower formation. In *Anagallis* the mitotic index peaked 30 and 55 hr after the beginning of the inductive LD, and DNA synthesis reached a maximum at 38 hr (253, 255). Application of 5-fluoro-deoxyuridine to the shoot tips of *Anagallis* suppressed flower formation most strongly 10 to 14 hr after the start of the LD, and also inhibited the peak of DNA synthesis at 38 hr (254). King (159) observed increased mitotic activity in *Chenopodium* apices 6 hr after arrival of the floral stimulus. The course of events in evoked *Xanthium* apices was delayed considerably as compared to *Sinapis* (20). For instance, the lag period between arrival of the floral stimulus and beginning of the rise in mitotic activity was 20 hr in *Xanthium* (135), but only 4 hr in *Sinapis*. The mitotic index showed two peaks 52 and 72 hr after the beginning of the inductive dark period (135).

A general stimulation of RNA synthesis (as measured by incorporation of ^{3}H-uridine and autoradiography) in apical meristems of *Sinapis* was observed 16 to 18 hr after the start of the LD (33) and continued to increase (134). Likewise, maximum incorporation of ^{3}H-uridine in *Pharbitis* plumules occurred 14 and 17 hr after the beginning of the inductive night (105), especially in the peripheral zone and in the leaf primordia (8). Assuming that these increases in RNA labeling were neither due to changes in the precursor pool (300), nor to differences in penetration of the precursor, the earliest increase in RNA synthesis preceded or coincided with the arrival of the floral stimulus in the apex. This raises the possibility that an amount of floral stimulus below the threshold level for floral initiation, or a rapidly translocated component of the stimulus, was responsible for the early increase in RNA synthesis. Alternatively, the apical meristem with surrounding leaf primordia may have perceived the photoperiodic treatment directly as was also suggested for *Arabidopsis* (34) and *Chenopodium* (73).

There are, however, other species in which induction did not result in early changes in the apex. In *Chenopodium,* for example, activation of RNA synthesis was associated with actual floral differentiation rather than with evocation (240, 241). In the LDP *Silene coeli-rosa* which requires at least 5 LD for flowering, the rate of cell division in meristems of induced plants did not change until differentiation of the terminal flower bud had begun (197, 198). Exposure to 3 LD, or GA application under SD, produced an increase in RNA without flower formation. Conversely, LD treatment at 13°C caused flowering without concomitant increase of RNA in the apex (199). Thus in this *Silene* species flower formation could take place without an increase in RNA in the shoot apex, and vice versa. Additional studies with other rosette plants requiring several inductive cycles are needed to determine if *Silene coeli-rosa* is unique in this respect.

An important but as yet unresolved problem concerns the nature of the newly synthesized RNA and protein in evoked and differentiating apices. Are new molecular species of RNA and protein synthesized, or does the increased level merely represent more of the same macromolecules already present in vegetative apices? A priori, it would appear that the transition from the vegetative to the flowering state requires expression of new genetic information, although it is not obvious what type of enzymes would bring about this change. Due to the extremely small amounts of tissues involved, the presently available techniques to detect minor differences in the RNA and protein patterns have not yet been fully utilized. In the case of tulip there is evidence that progression of the apical meristem from the vegetative to the flowering condition was associated with marked changes in the protein composition (11, 249). These changes, however, may be merely the biochemical expression rather than the cause of morphogenetic events.

Clearly, work on the early events in evoked apices has been dominated by the current dogma of molecular biology, with most attention centered on nucleic acids and proteins. An alternative hypothesis (90) is that floral initiation is the result of a general activation and reorganization of the vegetative shoot apex without prior switching-on of particular genes. Analysis during evocation of the changes in rates and distributions of meristematic activity in the shoot tip, as proposed for woody species (229), might also provide valuable information on herbaceous plants.

Effects of Hormones

IAA had a dual effect on flower formation in *Chenopodium.* When applied during induction, it inhibited flowering; when given as a postinductive treatment, it stimulated flower formation (152). Auxin acted in the shoot tip (176, 222) by suppressing the axillary meristems which in *Chenopodium* are released from apical dominance by SD treatment, thus promoting development of the terminal bud (242). It is possible that this auxin effect was due to auxin-induced ethylene production since the ethylene-releasing chemical, 2-chloroethylphosphonic acid, also inhibited flowering in *Chenopodium* (75).

Experiments dealing with the effects of GA on stem growth, flowering, and the spatial distribution of mitotic activity within the shoot tip of the LD rosette plant *Rudbeckia* and the SDP *Perilla,* originally performed by Bernier et al (18), have been repeated by Chailakhyan et al (49, 107, 200). In both species an increase in mitotic activity in the subapical region was observed, resulting in a marked increase in stem elongation. In *Rudbeckia* under SD GA activated the central zone, although this occurred somewhat later than when flowering was induced by LD (49). Mitotic activity in the peripheral zone of *Perilla* was stimulated by GA, but virtually no mitoses were observed in the central zone and no flowering took place under LD (107). With subthreshold induction GA promoted flower formation and also enhanced mitotic activity in the central zone (200). In Chailakhyan's view (45) the action of GA is localized in the subapical region and that of the floral stimulus in the central zone of the shoot tip. It is doubtful, however, that the site of GA action can be so sharply delineated in all species. For example, in the LD rosette plant *Hieracium pratense* GA caused stem growth but no flower formation. Nevertheless, mitotic activity was stimulated in the entire apical region (215). It would be worthwhile to reinvestigate this problem using different strains of *Silene armeria* which respond to GA either with stem growth only or with both stem growth and flower formation (285).

IN VITRO FLOWER FORMATION

Under this heading come various experiments examining flower initiation of isolated plant parts cultured in vitro (76, 211). Stem tips excised from vegetative plants were used in many studies. Taken as a whole this approach has added little to our knowledge of the flowering process, because as soon as leaf primordia reached a certain size, the explants became photoperiodically sensitive and responded as whole plants (57, 68, 73, 112, 131, 132). In a variation of this approach, plants were first induced before the apices were excised (22–24, 35, 58, 74, 93). These studies established that once an apex is committed to flowering, contact with the rest of the plant is no longer necessary for floral differentiation to proceed to completion.

In vitro flower formation is also possible by de novo bud formation on tissues excised from flowering plants. Most interesting results have been obtained with dayneutral tobacco varieties. Stem segments taken from the inflorescence (3), or small explants from floral branches, regenerated flower buds (209, 257, 258). Aghion-Prat (3) established the existence of an apex-to-base gradient in the capacity of stem segments to produce flower buds in vitro. The axillary buds of an orchid (102) and of *Hieracium floribundum* (289) showed a similar gradient in the potential to flower. The flowering gradient in tobacco was paralleled by one in DNA content. The uppermost stem tissue of flowering tobacco plants contained ten times more DNA per gram fresh weight than tissue further down the stem (277). It is not clear whether this difference was due to cell size or ploidy level or both. Further work led to the startling finding that DNA isolated from the inflorescence region caused flower formation when applied to defoliated axillary buds of decapitated plants, whereas DNA prepared from vegetative plants had no flower-inducing activity. Thermal denaturation of the DNA increased the flower-inducing activity, while treatment with DNase completely eliminated it (276). However, the presence of DNase in tobacco cells (212) could be expected to lead to rapid degradation of externally added DNA molecules. The best approach to demonstrate conclusively the involvement of intact DNA in flowering would seem to lie in application of radioactive and density-labeled DNA, and to see if this DNA can be subsequently recovered intact from axillary buds (cf 185). Without such evidence, the claim that DNA, as opposed to a breakdown product or contaminant of the preparation, has flower-inducing activity (276), must be viewed with some caution.

Calluses derived from the basal and apical regions of tobacco stems retained the capacity to produce vegetative and floral buds, respectively. This origin-specific difference was passed through at least three subcultures (46, 47, 168, 277). The implication of this result is that the partly differentiated state in vitro was transmissible through mitotic cycles (cf 117). Expression of the generative capacity required a high sugar concentration in the medium and exposure to high light intensity (169). The ploidy level of both types of tissues fluctuated within the limits 2C and 4C (13) and no significant changes in the histone composition of vegetative and generative calluses could be detected (170, 203). In photoperiodically sensitive tobaccos the induced state is apparently highly labile since induced and subsequently de-budded plants, or stem segments excised from flowering plants, always regenerated vegetative buds under conditions unfavorable for flowering (3, 14, 46, 47).

CONCLUDING REMARKS

It is clear from the above discussion that more is known about the action of the floral stimulus than about its production and chemical nature. Although the early events in the apex following arrival of the floral stimulus have been described in great detail, some of the basic questions still remain unresolved. It can be expected, however, that further refinements of already available techniques for RNA and protein analysis will provide answers to some of these questions in the near future.

We are still pretty much in the dark about the inductive processes in the leaves. A bewildering variety of environmental conditions can cause flower formation, even within the same species, but there is at least circumstantial evidence that certain unifying principles are involved. For instance, both phytochrome and circadian rhythms appear to operate by causing changes in membrane permeability (119, 232).

The restraints imposed on flowering by the photoperiod often disappear under low or high temperatures. This phenomenon may also involve membrane changes since membrane fluidity is affected by temperature. Thus one can visualize that the flow of metabolites essential for floral induction is normally under phytochrome control, but at more extreme temperatures it would take place independently of light and darkness. Unfortunately, the idea that phytochrome regulates membrane permeability is rather general and vague, and no specific hypothesis has evolved to explain how changes in membrane properties of leaf cells can result in generation of the floral stimulus. It is unlikely that we will find out in biophysical and biochemical terms how phytochrome regulates floral induction until the exact mechanism of phytochrome action has been worked out in "simple" systems.

The question of the nature of the floral stimulus remains a central theme. Without knowing its identity, no progress can be expected in the study of its generation in the leaves of different photoperiodic response types, its transport, its continued production under noninductive conditions in such plants as *Perilla,* and its self-perpetuation in species with nonlocalized synthesis. Despite some limited success with extractions, the floral stimulus remains a physiological concept rather than a chemical reality. In fact, negative and nonreproducible results with extracts have led several workers (e.g. 63, 87, 88, 110, 231) to question or abandon the concept of a single substance being the limiting factor for flower formation. On the other hand, there is no evidence to date that precludes the existence of such a chemical. Sceptics of the flower hormone hypothesis would do well to recall that other hormones, with the exception of ABA, were not originally discovered by extraction from higher plants. Any worker attempting to extract and assay a flower-inducing substance faces many technical problems. Lack of a suitable assay, exceedingly low concentrations, and lability outside the plant all could be responsible for failure to isolate the stimulus. The time at which the induced material is harvested could also be critical. Furthermore, extraction with organic solvents would be favorable for isolating an acidic substance (182), but different procedures would be required if one were to isolate, for example, a peptide or steryl glycoside.

Contrary to the idea of a single substance controlling flowering, several authors (e.g. 87, 110, 129, 145, 147, 270) have proposed that flower formation is the result of a specific balance of hormones acting in the shoot apex. This hypothesis is readily applicable to woody perennials, but is less attractive to explain flower formation in herbaceous plants. For example, how could induction of a single leaf on a photoperiodic plant establish and maintain such a balance in the apex in the presence of several other noninduced leaves? Other workers have associated the floral stimulus with rhythmicity and postulated that a fluctuating supply of essential metabolites by the leaves to the apex (287), or sequential arrival in the apex of various chemicals, will bring about flower initiation. It would be extremely difficult to demonstrate such fluctuations by analyses of shoot apices at different times during induction and evocation, but the composition of honeydew collected from aphids feeding on petioles of induced leaves would probably reflect such postulated fluctuations. However, the fact that induced *Perilla* leaves, transferred to continuous light and constant temperature, continued to export floral stimulus for at least 3 months (290), would seem to argue against the idea that the floral stimulus represents nothing more than rhythmic changes in chemicals exported from leaves.

In addition to extractions, collection of phloem sap would appear worthwhile pursuing. Foremost remains the detection of biological activity which might be difficult enough with a single substance, and perhaps impossible if a particular complex or sequence of hormones were required for flower formation. Clearly, discovering the nature of the floral stimulus is of great importance not only for fundamental work on flowering, but also for the applied plant sciences. By putting the various hypotheses and possible experimental approaches in focus, it is hoped that further research on this intriguing problem will be stimulated.

ACKNOWLEDGMENT

I am grateful to many of the authors cited in this review for providing unpublished data and manuscripts prior to publication. My research was supported by the US Energy Research and Development Administration under Contract E(11-1)-1338 and by the National Science Foundation under grant No. GB-31108.

Literature Cited

1. Abeles, F. B. 1973. In *Ethylene in Plant Biology.* New York: Academic. 302 pp.
2. Addicott, F. T., Lyon, J. L. 1969. *Ann. Rev. Plant Physiol.* 20:139–64
3. Aghion-Prat, D. 1965. *Physiol. Vég.* 3:229–303
4. Ahmed, G. E. D. F., Jacques, M. 1975. *C. R. Acad. Sci.* 280D:617–20
5. Ahmed, G. E. D. F., Jacques, M., Chouard, P. 1974. *C. R. Acad. Sci.* 279D: 1437–40
6. Aksenova, N. P., Bavrina, T. V., Konstantinova, T. N., Golyanovskaya, S. A., Solov'eva, M. B. 1973. *Dokl. Akad. Nauk SSSR* 210:1474–77
7. Alexander, A. G. 1973. In *Sugarcane Physiology,* 523–72. Amsterdam: Elsevier.
8. Arzee, T., Zilberstein, A., Gressel, J. 1975. *Plant Cell Physiol.* 16:505–11
9. Audus, L. J. 1972. In *Plant Growth Substances I,* 245–293. London: Hill
10. Bagnard, C., Bernier, G., Arnal, C. 1972. *Physiol. Vég.* 10:237–54
11. Barber, J. T., Steward, F. C. 1968. *Dev. Biol.* 17:326–49
12. Bassi, P. K., Tregunna, E. B., Purohit, A. N. 1975. *Plant Physiol.* 56:335–36
13. Bavrina, T. V., Golyanovskaya, S. A., Aksenova, N. P., Konstantinova, T. N., Milyaeva, E. L. 1974. *Sov. Plant Physiol.* 21:589–97
14. Bavrina, T. V., Konstantinova, T. N., Aksenova, N. P. 1973. *Sov. Plant Physiol.* 20:668–76
15. Bennink, G. J. H. 1974. In *Plant Growth Substances 1973,* 974–79. Tokyo: Hirokawa
16. Bernier, G. 1971. *Can. J. Bot.* 49: 803–19
17. Bernier, G., Bodson, M., Kinet, J. M., Jacqmard, A., Havelange, A. See Ref. 15, 980–86
18. Bernier, G., Bronchart, R., Jacqmard, A., Sylvestre, G. 1967. *Bull Soc. R. Bot. Belg.* 100:51–71
19. Bernier, G., Kinet, J. M., Bodson, M., Rouma, Y., Jacqmard, A. 1974. *Bot. Gaz.* 135:345–52
20. Bernier, G., Raju, M. V. S., Jacqmard, A., Bodson, M., Kinet, J. M., Havelange, A. 1974. In *Mechanisms of Regulation of Plant Growth,* ed. R. L. Bieleski, A. R. Ferguson, M. M. Creswell, 547–51. Bull. 12, R. Soc. N.Z., Wellington
21. Besemer, S. T., Furuta, T. 1970. *Florists' Rev.* 145(3761):18, 39–40
22. Bhar, D. S. 1970. *Can. J. Bot.* 48: 1355–58
23. Blake, J. 1966. *Nature* 211:990–91
24. Blake, J. 1969. *J. Exp. Bot.* 20:113–23
25. Blake, J. 1972. *Planta* 103:126–28
26. Blondon, F. 1971. *C. R. Acad. Sci.* 272D:2896–99
27. Ibid 1972. 274D:218–21
28. Blondon, F., Harada, H. 1972. *C. R. Acad. Sci.* 274D:2578–81
29. Blondon, F., Jacques, R. 1970. *C. R. Acad. Sci.* 270D:947–50

30. Bodson, M. 1975. *Ann. Bot. London* 39:547–54
31. Bose, K. K. 1974. *Untersuchungen an Arabidopsis Thaliana (L.) Heynh. über kinetische und biochemische Aspekte der Vernalisation.* Inaugural Dissertation, Univ. zu Köln, Köln. 88 pp.
32. Brede, J., Kobayashi, A., Zeevaart, J. A. D. 1974. *Plant Research '73, MSU/AEC Plant Res. Lab., Mich. State Univ.* 64–65
33. Bronchart, R., Bernier, G., Kinet, J. M., Havelange, A. 1970. *Planta* 91: 255–69
34. Brown, J. A. M., Klein, W. H. 1971. *Plant Physiol.* 47:393–99
35. Brulfert, J., Fontaine, D. 1967. *Biol. Plant.* 9:439–46
36. Brulfert, J., Guerrier, D., Queiroz, O. 1975. *Planta* 125:33–44
37. Carpenter, B. H., Lincoln, R. G. 1959. *Science* 129:780–81
38. Carr, D. J. 1967. *Ann. NY Acad. Sci.* 144:305–12
39. Cathey, H. M., Taylor, R. L. 1970. *Florists' Rev.* 146(3790):38–39; 82–86
40. Chacko, E. K., Kohli, R. R., Swamy, R. D., Randhawa, G. S. 1974. *Physiol. Plant.* 32:188–90
41. Chacko, E. K., Kohli, R. R., Randhawa, G. S. 1974. *Sci. Hortic.* 2:389–98
42. Chailakhyan, M. Kh. 1968. In *Biochemistry and Physiology of Plant Growth Substances,* ed. F. Wightman, G. Setterfield, 1317–40. Ottawa: Runge
43. Chailakhyan, M. Kh. 1971. *Sov. Plant Physiol* 18:348–57
44. Chailakhyan, M. Kh. 1975. *Bot. Rev.* 41:1–29
45. Chailakhyan, M. Kh. 1975. *Biol. Plant.* 17:1–11
46. Chailakhyan, M. Kh., Aksenova, N. P., Konstantinova, T. N., Bavrina, T. V. 1974. *Phytomorphology* 24:86–96
47. Chailakhyan, M. Kh., Aksenova, N. P., Konstantinova, T. N., Bavrina, T. V. 1975. *Proc. R. Soc. London B* 190: 333–40
48. Chailakhyan, M. Kh., Butenko, R. G. 1957. *Sov. Plant Physiol.* 4:450–62
49. Chailakhyan, M. Kh., Kakhidze, N. T., Milyaeva, E. L., Gukasyan, I. A., Yanina, L. I. 1969. *Sov. Plant Physiol.* 16:392–99
50. Chailakhyan, M. Kh., Khazhakyan, Kh. K. 1974. *Dokl. Akad. Nauk SSSR* 217:975–78
51. Chailakhyan, M. Kh., Khlopenkova, L. P. 1969. *Dokl. Akad. Nauk SSSR* 189:1400–3

52. Chailakhyan, M. Kh., Khlopenkova, L. P. 1972. *Sov. Plant Physiol.* 19:1002–10
53. Chailakhyan, M. Kh., Khlopenkova, L. P., Khazhakyan, Kh. K. 1974. *Dokl. Akad. Nauk SSSR* 215:484–87
54. Chailakhyan, M. Kh., Yanina, L. I. 1971. *Dokl. Akad. Nauk SSSR* 199: 234–37
55. Ibid 1973. 208:749–52
56. Chailakhyan, M. Kh., Yanina, L. I., Frolova, I. A. 1970. *Sov. Plant Physiol.* 17:709–11
57. Choshi, A. 1970. *Rep. Fac. Sci. Shizuoka Univ.* 5:55–61
58. Ibid 1971. 6:87–94
59. Chouard, P. 1957. *C. R. Acad. Sci.* 245B:2520–22
60. Chrominski, A., Rozej, B. 1973. *Acta Agron. Acad. Sci. Hung.* 22:27–29
61. Cleland, C. F. See Ref. 20, 553–57
62. Cleland, C. F. 1974. *Plant Physiol.* 54:899–903
63. Cleland, C. F. 1975. *What's New in Plant Physiology,* ed. G. J. Fritz, 7(6): 1–4
64. Cleland, C. F., Ajami, A. 1974. *Plant Physiol.* 54:904–6
65. Cleland, C. F., Zeevaart, J. A. D. 1970. *Plant Physiol.* 46:392–400
66. Cline, M. G., Agatep, A. O. 1970. *Physiol. Plant.* 23:993–1003
67. Croes, A. F., Claessen, H. J. M., Wellensiek, S. J. 1973. *Z. Pflanzenphysiol.* 68:391–96
68. Culafić, L. 1973. *Bull. Inst. Jard. Bot. Univ. Beograd.* 8:53–56
69. Dass, H. C., Randhawa, G. S., Negi, S. P. 1975. *Sci. Hortic.* 3:231–38
70. de Fossard, R. A. 1967. *Aust. J. Sci.* 29:427–28
71. de Fossard, R. A. 1967. *Lab. Pract.* 16:1232–35
72. Ibid, 1360–66
73. de Fossard, R. A. 1972. *Bot. Gaz.* 133:341–50
74. Ibid 1973. 134:11–16
75. Ibid, 103–17
76. de Fossard, R. A. 1974. In *Tissue Culture and Plant Science,* ed. H. E. Street, 193–212. London: Academic
77. Deronne, M., Blondon, F. 1973. *C. R. Acad. Sci.* 276D:3021–24
78. Ibid. 277D:1013–16
79. Diomaiuto-Bonnand, J. 1969. *C. R. Acad. Sci.* 268D:51–54
80. Ibid 1972. 274D:372–75
81. Ibid 1974. 278D:49–52
82. Ibid 1975. 280D:1365–68
83. Doss, R. P. 1975. *Plant Physiol.* 56: 360–63

84. Durley, R. C., Pharis, R. P., Zeevaart, J. A. D. 1975. *Planta* 126:139–49
85. Eichhoff, E., Rau, W. 1969. *Planta* 87:290–303
86. El Hattab, A. H. 1968. *Meded. Landbouwhogesch. Wageningen:* 68(12): 1–111
87. Evans, L. T. 1969. In *The Induction of Flowering. Some Case Histories,* ed. L. T. Evans, 457–80. Ithaca, NY: Cornell
88. Evans, L. T. 1971. *Ann. Rev. Plant Physiol.* 22:365–94
89. Evans, L. T. 1975. *Can. J. Bot.* 53: 590–91
90. Evans, L. T. 1975. *Daylength and the Flowering of Plants.* Menlo Park, Calif.: Benjamin. 122 pp.
91. Evans, L. T. 1976. *Aust. J. Plant Physiol.* In press
92. Evans, L. T., King, R. W. 1969. *Z. Pflanzenphysiol.* 60:277–88
93. Fontaine, D. 1970. *Bull. Soc. Bot. Fr.* 117:297–304
94. Fontaine, D. 1972. *C. R. Acad. Sci.* 274D:58–61
95. Ibid., 2984–87
96. Fontaine, D., Lacombe, N., Brulfert, J. 1973. *C. R. Acad. Sci.* 277D:2001–4
97. Fontes, M. R., Ozbun, J. L., Powell, L. E. 1970. *Nature* 228:82–83
98. Friend, D. J. C. 1975. *Physiol. Plant.* 35:286–96
99. Gibby, D. D. 1973. *Xanthium strumarium* L.: *Extraction and assay of floral promotive principles and additional investigations into inhibition of flowering.* PhD thesis. Utah State Univ., Logan. 51 pp.
100. Gibby, D. D., Salisbury, F. B. 1971. *Plant Physiol.* 47:784–89
101. Gifford, E. M. Jr., Corson, G. E. Jr. 1971. *Bot. Rev.* 37:143–229
102. Goh, C. J. 1975. *Ann. Bot. London* 39:931–34
103. Goh, C. J., Seetoh, H. C. 1973. *Ann. Bot. London* 37:113–19
104. Goldschmidt, E. E., Monselise, S. P. 1972. In *Plant Growth Substances 1970,* ed. D. J. Carr, 758–66. Berlin: Springer
105. Gressel, J., Zilberstein, A., Arzee, T. 1970. *Dev. Biol.* 22:31–42
106. Groves, R. H., Lang, A. 1970. *Planta* 91:212–19
107. Gukasyan, I. A., Chailakhyan, M. Kh., Milyaeva, E. L. 1970. *Sov. Plant Physiol.* 17:63–70
108. Halaban, R., Hillman, W. S. 1970. *Plant Physiol.* 46:641–44
109. Ibid 1971. 48:760–64
110. Halevy, A. H. 1972. *Proc. 18th Int. Hortic. Congr. Tel Aviv, 1970* 5:187–98

111. Hanks, G. R. 1974. *Z. Pflanzenphysiol.* 71:63–66
112. Harada, H. 1967. *Nature* 214:1027–28
113. Harada, H., Bose, T. K., Cheruel, J. 1971. *Z. Pflanzenphysiol.* 64:267–69
114. Havelange, A., Bernier, G. 1974. *J. Cell Sci.* 15:633–44
115. Havelange, A., Bernier, G., Jacqmard, A. 1974. *J. Cell Sci.* 16:421–32
116. Henson, I. E., Wareing, P. F. 1974. *Physiol. Plant* 32:185–87
117. Heslop-Harrison, J. 1967. *Ann. Rev. Plant Physiol.* 18:325–48
118. Hillman, W. S. 1967. *Plant Cell Physiol.* 8:467–73
119. Hillman, W. S. 1976. *Ann. Rev. Plant Physiol.* 27:159–79
120. Hillman, W. S., Posner, H. B. 1971. *Plant Physiol.* 47:586–87
121. Hodson, H. K. 1970. *Floral-inducing extracts from Xanthium.* PhD thesis. Univ. California, Los Angeles. 148 pp.
122. Hodson, H. K., Hamner, K. C. 1970. *Science* 167:384–85
123. Hodson, H. K., Hamner, K. C. 1971. *Plant Physiol.* 47:726–28
124. Holland, R. W. K., Vince, D. 1971. *Planta* 98:232–43
125. Imhoff, C. 1973. *C. R. Acad. Sci.* 276D:3303–6
126. Imhoff, C., Brulfert, J., Jacques, R. 1971. *C. R. Acad. Sci.* 273D:737–40
127. Ishiguri, Y., Oda, Y. 1972. *Plant Cell Physiol.* 13:131–38
128. Ibid 1976. In press
129. Jackson, D. I., Sweet, G. B. 1972. *Hortic. Abstr.* 42:9–24
130. Jacobs, W. P. 1972. *Am. J. Bot.* 59:437–41
131. Jacobs, W. P., Suthers, H. B. 1971. *Am. J. Bot.* 58:836–43
132. Ibid 1974. 61:1016–20
133. Jacqmard, A., Miksche, J. P. 1971. *Bot. Gaz.* 132:364–67
134. Jacqmard, A., Miksche, J. P., Bernier, G. 1972. *Am. J. Bot.* 59:714–21
135. Jacqmard, A., Raju, M. V. S., Kinet, J. M., Bernier, G. 1976. *Am. J. Bot.* 63:166–74
136. Jacques, M. 1969. *C. R. Acad. Sci.* 268D:1045–47
137. Jacques, M. 1971. *Physiol. Vég.* 9: 461–74
138. Jacques, M. 1973. *C. R. Acad. Sci.* 276D:1705–8
139. Jacques, M., Jacques, R. 1969. *C. R. Acad. Sci.* 269D:2107–9
140. Julien, M. H. R. 1973. *J. Exp. Bot.* 24:549–57
141. Julien, R. 1969. *Rep. Maurit. Sug. Ind. Res. Inst.* 16:37–42

142. Kandeler, R. 1970. *Planta* 90:203–7
143. Kandeler, R. 1971. *Z. Pflanzenphysiol.* 64:278–80
144. Ibid 1972. 67:86–92
145. Kandeler, R. 1974. *Ber. Dtsch. Bot. Ges.* 87:71–81
146. Kandeler, R., Hügel, B. 1973. *Plant Cell Physiol.* 14:515–20
147. Kandeler, R., Hügel, B., Rottenburg, Th. 1975. In *Environmental and Biological Control of Photosynthesis,* ed. R. Marcelle, 161–69. The Hague: Dr. W. Junk
148. Katayama, T. C. 1971. *Mem. Fac. Agric. Kagoshima Univ.* 8:299–320
149. Katayama, T. C. 1974. *Proc. Crop Sci. Soc. Jpn.* 43:224–36
150. Kende, H., Baumgartner, B. 1974. *Planta* 116:279–89
151. Ketellapper, H. J., Barbaro, A. 1966. *Phyton* 23:33–41
152. Khatoon, S., Seidlová, F., Krekule, J. 1973. *Biol. Plant.* 15:361–63
153. Khudairi, A. K., Hemberg, T. 1974. *J. Exp. Bot.* 25:740–44
154. Khudairi, A. K., Maeng, J. 1973. *Physiol. Plant.* 28:271–77
155. Kimura, Y., Brede, J., Zeevaart, J. A. D. 1973. *Plant Research '72, MSU/AEC Plant Res. Lab., Mich. State Univ.* 40–44
156. Kinet, J. M. 1975. *New Phytol.* 74:25–32
157. Kinet, J. M., Bernier, G., Bodson, M., Jacqmard, A. 1973. *Plant Physiol.* 51:598–600
158. Kinet, J. M., Bodson, M., Alvinia, A. M., Bernier, G. 1971. *Z. Pflanzenphysiol.* 66:49–63
159. King, R. W. 1972. *Can. J. Bot.* 50:697–702
160. King, R. W. 1974. *Aust. J. Plant Physiol.* 1:445–47
161. King, R. W. 1975. *Can. J. Bot.* 53:2631–38
162. King, R. W., Cumming, B. G. 1972. *Planta* 108:39–57
163. King, R. W., Zeevaart, J. A. D. 1973. *Plant Physiol.* 51:727–38
164. Klautke, S., Rau, W. 1973. *Planta* 112:25–34
165. Klautke, S., Rau, W. 1973. *Ber. Dtsch. Bot. Ges.* 86:571–76
166. Kochankov, V. G. 1971. *Dokl. Akad. Nauk SSSR* 198:959–62
167. Ibid. 199:485–88
168. Konstantinova, T. N., Aksenova, N. P., Bavrina, T. V., Chailakhyan, M. Kh. 1969. *Dokl. Akad. Nauk SSSR* 187:466–69
169. Konstantinova, T. N., Bavrina, T. V., Aksenova, N. P., Golyanovskaya, S. A. 1972. *Sov. Plant Physiol.* 19:89–98
170. Konstantinova, T. N., Gofshtein, L. V., Molodyuk, O. I., Bavrina, T. V., Aksenova, N. P. 1974. *Dokl. Akad. Nauk SSSR* 216:226–28
171. Kopcewicz, J. 1970. *Naturwissenschaften* 57:136–37
172. Kopcewicz, J. 1972. *New Phytol.* 71:129–34
173. Kopcewicz, J. 1972. *Z. Pflanzenphysiol.* 67:373–76
174. Kopcewicz, J., Porazinski, Z. 1974. *Biol. Plant.* 16:132–35
175. Krekule, J., Horavka, B. 1972. *Biol. Plant.* 14:254–59
176. Krekule, J., Přivratský, J. 1974. *Z. Pflanzenphysiol.* 71:345–48
177. Krekule, J., Ullman, J. 1971. *Biol. Plant.* 13:60–63
178. Lang, A. 1952. *Ann. Rev. Plant Physiol.* 3:265–306
179. Lang, A. 1965. *Encyclopedia of Plant Physiology,* ed. W. Ruhland, 15/1:409–23. Berlin: Springer
180. Ibid, 1380–1536
181. Lincoln, R. G., Cunningham, A., Carpenter, B. H., Alexander, J., Mayfield, D. L. 1966. *Plant Physiol.* 41:1079–80
182. Lincoln, R. G., Cunningham, A., Hamner, K. C. 1964. *Nature* 202:559–61
183. Lincoln, R. G., Mayfield, D. L., Cunningham, A. 1961. *Science* 133:756
184. Lona, F. 1972. In *Hormonal Regulation in Plant Growth and Development,* ed. H. Kaldewey, Y. Vardar, 423–29. Weinheim: Verlag Chemie
185. Lurquin, P. F., Hotta, Y. 1975. *Plant Sci. Lett.* 5:103–12
186. McMillan, C. 1973. *Am. J. Bot.* 60:397–405
187. McMillan, C. 1974. *Nature* 249:183–86
188. McMillan, C. 1974. *Bot. Mag.* 87:261–69
189. McMillan, C. 1974. *Can. J. Bot.* 52:1779–91
190. McMillan, C. 1975. *Am. J. Bot.* 62:41–47
191. Maeng, J., Khudairi, A. K. 1973. *Physiol. Plant.* 28:264–70
192. Melchers, G. 1939. *Ber. Dtsch. Bot. Ges.* 57:29–48
193. Miginiac, E. 1971. *Physiol. Plant.* 25:234–39
194. Miginiac, E. 1972. *Physiol. Vég.* 10:627–36
195. Miginiac, E. See Ref. 20, 539–45
196. Miginiac, E., Lacombe, N. 1973. *Can. J. Bot.* 51:465–73

197. Miller, M. B., Lyndon, R. F. 1975. *Planta* 126:37–43
198. Miller, M. B., Lyndon, R. F. 1976. *J. Exp. Bot.* In press
199. Ibid. In press
200. Milyaeva, E. L., Gukasyan, I. A., Chailakhyan, M. Kh. 1970. *Dokl. Akad. Nauk SSSR* 194:970–73
201. Miyoshi, Y., Furuya, M., Takimoto, A. 1974. *Plant Cell Physiol.* 15:1115–23
202. Molder, M., Owens, J. N. 1974. *Can. J. Bot.* 52:1249–58
203. Molodyuk, O. I., Konstantinova, T. N., Bavrina, T. V., Aksenova, N. P. 1974. *Sov. Plant Physiol.* 21:927–30
204. Monselise, S. P., Hubermann, M. 1973. *Sci. Hortic.* 1:171–76
205. Moshkov, B. S., Odumanova-Dunaeva, G. A. 1972. *Dokl. Akad. Nauk SSSR* 203:714–16
206. Nakayama, S., Hashimoto, T. 1973. *Plant Cell Physiol.* 14:419–22
207. Nanda, K. K., Kumar, M., Sawhney, S., Sawhney, N. 1973. *Ann. Bot. London* 37:107–11
208. Napp-Zinn, K. 1973. In *Temperature and Life*, ed. H. Precht et al, 171–94. New York: Springer
209. Nguyen Thi Dien, Tran Thanh Van, M. 1974. *Can. J. Bot.* 52:2319–22
210. Nicholls, P. B. See Ref. 20, 305–9
211. Nitsch, C. See Ref. 184, 413–21
212. Oleson, A. E., Janski, A. M., Clark, E. T. 1974. *Biochim. Biophys. Acta* 366:89–100
213. Oota, Y. 1972. *Plant Cell Physiol.* 13:195–99
214. Ibid 1974. 15:63–68
215. Peterson, R. L., Yeung, E. C. 1972. *Bot. Gaz.* 133:190–98
216. Pharis, R. P. 1972. *Planta* 105:205–12
217. Pharis, R. P., Kuo, C. G. 1976. *Can. J. For. Res.* In press
218. Phillips, D. A., Cleland, C. F. 1972. *Planta* 102:173–78
219. Posner, H. B. 1971. *Plant. Physiol.* 48:361–65
220. Posner, H. B. 1973. *Plant Cell Physiol.* 14:1031–33
221. Ibid, 1199–1200
222. Přivratský, J., Tykva, R., Krekule, J. 1976. *Z. Pflanzenphysiol.* In press
223. Pryce, R. J. 1972. *Phytochemistry* 11:1911–18
224. Ibid 1973. 12:507–14
225. Ibid, 1745–54
226. Ibid 1974. 13:2377–81
227. Purohit, A. N., Tregunna, E. B. 1974. *Can. J. Bot.* 52:1146–48
228. Ibid, 1283–91
229. Romberger, J. A., Gregory, R. A. 1974. In *Proc. Third North American Forest Biology Workshop*, ed. C. P. P. Reid, G. H. Fechner, 132–47. Fort Collins: Colorado State Univ.
229a. Ross, S. D., Pharis, R. P. 1976. *Physiol. Plant.* 36:182–86
230. Sachs, R. M. See Ref. 87, 424–34
231. Sachs, R. M., Hackett, W. P. 1969. *HortScience* 4:103–7
232. Satter, R. L., Galston, A. W. 1973. *BioScience* 23:407–16
233. Sawhney, R., Cumming, B. G. 1971. *Can. J. Bot.* 49:2233–37
234. Ibid 1975. 53:512–16
235. Schwabe, W. W. 1971. In *Plant Physiology—A Treatise*, Vol. 7 A, ed. F. C. Steward, 233–411. New York: Academic
236. Schwabe, W. W. 1972. *Planta* 103:18–23
237. Schwabe, W. W., Al-Doori, A. H. 1973. *J. Exp. Bot.* 24:969–81
238. Schwabe, W. W., Wimble, R. H. 1976. In *Perspectives in Experimental Biology, Vol. 2 Botany*, ed. N. Sunderland, 41–57. Oxford: Pergamon
239. Searle, N. E. 1965. *Plant Physiol.* 40:261–67
240. Seidlova, F. 1972. *Biol. Plant.* 14:241–48
241. Seidlova, F. 1974. *Z. Pflanzenphysiol.* 73:394–404
242. Seidlova, F., Khatoon, S. 1976. *Ann. Bot. London.* 40:37–42
243. Sengupta, S. K., Rogers, M. N., Lorah, E. J. 1974. *J. Am. Soc. Hortic. Sci.* 99:416–20
244. Sherwood, S. B., Evans, J. O., Ross, C. 1971. *Plant Cell Physiol.* 12:111–16
245. Shinozaki, M. 1972. *Plant Cell Physiol.* 13:391–93
246. Shinozaki, M. See Ref. 20, 299–303
247. Sotta, B., Miginiac, E. 1975. *C. R. Acad. Sci.* 281D:37–40
248. Spiker, S., Krishnaswamy, L. 1973. *Planta* 110:71–76
249. Steward, F. C., Barber, J. T., Bleichert, E. F., Roca, W. M. 1971. *Dev. Biol.* 25:310–35
250. Suge, H. 1971. *Proc. Crop Sci. Soc. Jpn.* 40:115–19
251. Suge, H. 1972. *Plant Cell Physiol.* 13:1031–38
252. Suge, H. See Ref. 15, 960–66
253. Taillandier, J. 1971. *C. R. Acad. Sci.* 272D:219–22
254. Ibid, 557–60
255. Ibid 1972. 275D:1115–18
256. Takimoto, A., Tanaka, O. 1973. *Plant Cell Physiol.* 14:1133–41

257. Tran Thanh Van, M. 1973. *Planta* 115:87–92
258. Tran Thanh Van, M., Nguyen Thi Dien, Chlyah, A. 1974. *Planta* 119: 149–59
259. Tse, A. T. Y., Ramina, A., Hackett, W. P., Sachs, R. M. 1974. *Plant Physiol.* 54:404–7
260. van den Ende, H., Zeevaart, J. A. D. 1971. *Planta* 98:164–76
261. van de Pol, P. A. 1971. *K. Ned. Akad. Wet. Proc. Ser. C* 74:449–54
262. van de Pol, P. A. 1972. *Meded. Landbouwhogesch. Wageningen* 72(9):1–89
263. van Staden, J., Wareing, P. F. 1972. *Physiol. Plant.* 27:331–37
264. van de Vooren, J. 1969. *Z. Pflanzenphysiol.* 61:135–39
265. Ibid, 332–37
266. Ibid 1971. 64:52–59
267. Ibid, 414–17
268. Vergara, B. S., Chang, T. T., Lilis, R. 1969. *Int. Rice Res. Inst. Tech. Bull.* (Manila, Philippines) 8:1–31
269. Vince, D. 1972. In *Phytochrome,* ed. K. Mitrakos, W. Shropshire Jr., 257–91. New York: Academic
270. Vince-Prue, D. 1975. *Photoperiodism in Plants.* London: McGraw-Hill. 444 pp.
271. Vince-Prue, D. 1976. *Phytochrome and Photoperiodism.* Proc. 22nd Easter Sch. Agric. Sci., Univ. Nottingham, ed. H. Smith. London: Butterworths. In press
272. Vince-Prue, D., Guttridge, C. G. 1973. *Planta* 110:165–72
273. Wada, K. 1973. *Rep. Fac. Sci. Shizuoka Univ.* 8:149–55
274. Wada, K. 1974. *Plant Cell Physiol.* 15:381–84
275. Wall, P. C., Cartwright, P. M. 1974. *Ann. Appl. Biol.* 76:299–309
276. Wardell, W. L. 1976. *Plant Physiol.* In press
277. Wardell, W. L., Skoog, F. 1973. *Plant Physiol.* 52:215–20
278. Wellensiek, S. J. 1966. *Z. Pflanzenphysiol.* 55:1–10
279. Ibid 1967. 56:33–39
280. Ibid 1969. 61:462–71
281. Ibid 1970. 63:25–30
282. Wellensiek, S. J. 1972. *K. Ned. Akad. Wet. Proc. Ser. C* 75:179–84
283. Wellensiek, S. J. 1972. *Acta Bot. Neerl.* 21:285–91
284. Wellensiek, S. J. 1973. *Neth. J. Agric. Sci.* 21:163–66
285. Ibid, 245–55
286. Wellensiek, S. J., van Brenk, G. 1971. *Z. Pflanzenphysiol.* 64:270–73
287. Went, F. W. 1959. In *Photoperiodism and Related Phenomena in Plants and Animals,* ed. R. B. Withrow, 551–64. Washington: Am. Assoc. Adv. Sci.
288. Williams, M. W. 1972. *J. Am. Soc. Hortic. Sci.* 97:210–12
289. Yeung, E. C., Peterson, R. L. 1972. *Can. J. Bot.* 50:73–78
290. Zeevaart, J. A. D. 1958. *Meded. Landbouwhogesch. Wageningen* 58(3):1–88
291. Zeevaart, J. A. D. See Ref. 87, 435–56
292. Zeevaart, J. A. D. 1971. *Planta* 98: 190–94
293. Zeevaart, J. A. D. 1971. *Plant Physiol.* 47:821–27
294. Ibid 48:86–90
295. Zeevaart, J. A. D. 1973. *Planta* 114: 285–88
296. Zeevaart, J. A. D. 1974. *Plant Physiol.* 53:644–48
297. Zeevaart, J. A. D. See Ref. 15, 1175–81
298. Zeevaart, J. A. D. 1976. In *Plant Hormones and Related Compounds,* ed. D. S. Letham et al. Amsterdam: ASP Biol. Med. In press
299. Zeevaart, J. A. D., Lang, A. 1962. *Planta* 58:531–42
300. Zilberstein, A., Arzee, T., Gressel, J. 1973. *Cell Differ.* 2:213–20

Ann. Rev. Plant Physiol. 1976. 27:349-74

POST-TRANSLATIONAL MODIFICATION OF PROTEINS BY PHOSPHORYLATION

❖7613

Anthony Trewavas

Department of Botany, University of Edinburgh, King's Buildings, Mayfield Road, Edinburgh, Scotland

CONTENTS

INTRODUCTION

How do living organisms control their growth and differentiation? Biologists of different disciplines would certainly give no uniform answer to this question. It is a general biochemical contention that the process involves changes in the pattern of enzyme activities. If we accept this to be the case, how then can cells regulate their enzyme activities? Work on bacteria provided the earliest answers. These suggested that the catalytic activity of enzymes could be modified allosterically or that the number of catalytic molecules could be changed by altering protein synthesis. There is little doubt that eukaryote cells can use both of these forms of regulation, but there are available to the eukaryotic cell other ways of regulating enzyme activities which appear to be almost insignificant in prokaryotes. Chief among these are the control of protein degradation and the post-translational modification of proteins. Undoubtedly the new regulatory requirements issuing from the evolution of highly complex and organized systems has ensured their retention and development in the eukaryotic cell. As is now becoming clear, the chemical modification of proteins and enzymes may represent the molecular mechanism by which the majority of animal hormones operate, and hormones are the necessary adjuncts to any multicellular system.

Enzymes and proteins can be modified chemically in a number of ways: methylation, acetylation, thiolation, ribosylation, adenylation, and phosphorylation are all known. Virtually all of present-day interest is limited to phosphorylation. It had been my intention in this review to deal with all forms of post-translational modification. Instead, I have confined it to phosphorylation not only for the above reason, but because the state of knowledge in this area indicates that we are poised for a most dramatic breakthrough in regulatory understanding.

Proteins are phosphorylated by protein kinases and dephosphorylated by protein phosphatases. Although plants certainly contain both of these enzymes, the evidence on plant protein phosphorylation is very limited and fragmentary and so the substance of this review must deal primarily with work on animals. This field does hold out great promise for the would-be plant investigator, however. The regulation of cell division, genome activity, protein synthesis, membrane permeability, and the molecular basis of cell polarity are all of vital importance in understanding plant growth and differentiation. Answers to all of those outstanding problems in animals are being sought for and found in protein phosphorylation. Clearly this is a field which no plant physiologist can afford to ignore!

How Protein Phosphorylation Came to be Recognized as an Important Control Phenomenon

All of the earliest reports concerning phosphorylated proteins dealt with vitellin and ovalbumin in egg yolk and casein in milk. The oldest is probably that of Meischer (218), who reported in 1870 the presence of phosphopeptides in egg yolk. The detection of phosphorus in casein preparations (23, 250, 278) and ovalbumin (232) followed about the turn of the century, but phosvitin was not noted until much later (217). Isolation of serine phosphate from vitellin and casein was first reported about 1930 (194, 252). Exhaustive chemical evidence for the presence of serine and threonine phosphates in casein was only published in the early 1950s (2, 65).

With the ready availability of $^{32}P_i$ from 1942 onwards (47) there came the realization that phosphorylated proteins were present in many tissues and tumors (59, 86, 130, 148, 208, 336) and that the phosphate moieties on these proteins showed high rates of turnover. These reports culminated in the first clear demonstration of protein kinase activity in liver in 1954 (37). The detection of phosphoprotein phosphatase was first published in 1946 (115), and was quickly followed by a spate of reports showing the widespread distribution of these enzymes in animals and plants (10, 78, 242, 292, 306). Doubt was expressed at the time, however, as to the exact specificity and function of such enzymes (242, 292).

Contrary to popular belief, the first phosphorylated enzyme reported was probably pepsin (242). Phosphorylation does not alter pepsin catalytic activity, and this may explain why it has been generally forgotten. The detection of two forms of muscle phosphorylase, an active or *a* form and an inactive or *b* form, was first published in 1943 (54). It was not until 1955 that Sutherland and co-workers (256, 309) showed that the *a* form was phosphorylated and the *b* form dephosphorylated. Concurrent with this, Fischer and co-workers (79, 165) reported the isolation of the highly specific protein kinase (phosphorylase *b* kinase) which together with ATP phosphorylated phosphorylase *b*. Sutherland's interest in phosphorylase arose from studies on the hypoglycemic effects of adrenalin and glucagon. It was found that both of these hormones induced the degradation of glycogen by increasing the catalytic activity of phosphorylase. This was the result of a switch from the inactive, dephosphorylated form to the active, phosphorylated form. In 1957 Sutherland & Rall (308; see also 52) were able to report that this action of adrenalin was mediated by the intracellular production of cyclic AMP (cAMP). As is now known, many animal hormones use the cAMP system as a second intracellular messenger. At the latest count the effects of 19 different animal hormones in some 29 different animal tissues are mediated by the adenyl cyclase/cyclic AMP system (133). An understanding of the biochemical mode of action of cAMP therefore becomes a necessary prerequisite for hormone theory.

The reported detection of other phosphorylated enzymes came slowly with glycogen synthetase in 1962 (87) and phosphorylase *b* kinase (163, 164) in 1966. [The interconversions of all of these enzymes in glycogen metabolism have been neatly summarized in a diagram published by Holzer & Duntze (120).] In 1968, however, it was reported that the inactive form of phosphorylase *b* kinase could be phosphorylated and activated by another relatively nonspecific protein kinase from muscle (327). Furthermore, this protein kinase was directly dependent upon added cAMP for catalytic activity. Within a year it had been shown that cAMP-dependent protein kinases could be detected in at least 15 different mammalian tissues (53, 170, 180, 220) and 8 invertebrate phyla (170) [although it was also claimed at the time to be present in *E. coli* (169), this now looks extremely doubtful (255)]. This widespread distribution enabled Kuo & Greengard (170) to postulate that all of the biochemical effects of cAMP were mediated through cAMP-dependent protein kinases.

This simplifying theory led to a veritable explosion of research, which is recounted in the subsequent pages of this review. It was designed initially to answer one question: which cellular proteins are phosphorylated and so have their biological activity modulated by protein kinases and cAMP. Time, however, has seen a modification of these ambitions. Although the concept of cAMP control of phosphorylation provided much of the original impetus, many cAMP-independent protein kinases have been detected and studied (184). Thus the function of protein phosphorylation has grown into a field in its own right independent of studies on cAMP.

A recent symposium on protein phosphorylation (5) and two recent reviews (272, 310) represent the only useful source books available. This article does not deal directly either with protein kinases or with cAMP, but it would be impossible to discuss protein phosphorylation without mentioning either of them. Reviews on protein kinases (162, 184) and cAMP (133, 307) deal in depth with these two topics.

Phosphorylation of Enzymes

Holzer & Duntze (120) reviewed enzyme modification in 1971. They concluded that there was exacting evidence showing that phosphorylation activated phosphorylase *b* and phosphorylase *b* kinase, but inactivated pyruvate dehydrogenase, fructose 1,6-diphosphatase, and glycogen synthetase. They noted that while palmityl CoA synthetase and phosphorylase *a* phosphatase may also be activated by phosphorylation, the phosphorylated enzyme had not been isolated. A crucial piece of evidence was and still is lacking for these two enzymes.

Other enzymes can now be added to the above list. Critical evidence shows that lipase (302), carbonic anhydrase (227), and liver RNA polymerase (209) are activated while cell surface alkaline phosphatase (103) and acetyl CoA carboxylase (38, 270) are inactivated by phosphorylation. It is interesting that the push-pull mechanism in which the degradative enzyme is activated at the same time as the synthetic enzyme is inactivated operates for both glycogen and fat metabolism. Phosphorylation activates lipase and palmityl CoA synthetase and inactivates acetyl CoA carboxylase, the first enzyme in fatty acid biosynthesis.

Evidence has also appeared indicating that plasma membrane-bound adenyl cyclase may be inactivated by phosphorylation (51). The critical step, isolation of the phosphorylated enzyme, has not yet been accomplished. Bovine heart and brain protein kinases (76, 203) have also been shown very intriguingly to be phosphorylated enzymes. Although it appears to be the regulatory subunit which is phosphorylated, there is no clear evidence relating phosphorylation to enzymatic function. Tyrosine amino-transferase (187) joins pepsin (242) as enzymes which are phosphorylated but in which the phosphorylation does not alter catalytic activity.

Phosphorylation of Nuclear Acidic Proteins:
The Key to Genomic Control?

The nucleus contains over half of the total cellular protein phosphate, and the ratio of protein phosphate to total protein is 25-fold higher in the nucleus than it is in the cytoplasm (179). Less than 10% of this protein phosphate is found in combination with the highly basic acid-soluble histones. The remaining 90% or so is found to be associated with the residual proteins, the so-called acidic protein fraction (179). As judged by isotopic labeling, phosphorylation of these proteins is rapid and is catalyzed by endogenous nuclear protein kinases (59, 130, 156, 283). Dephosphorylation is catalyzed by endogenous nuclear phosphatases (156, 179). The majority of the phosphate is attached to protein-bound serine (179). Electrophoretic profiles of phosphorylated proteins appear to be complex, with a minimum of at least 15–20 proteins phosphorylated (20, 46, 230, 248, 283, 315, 316, 324). It has been estimated that a quarter of the nuclear proteins are phosphorylated and that they contain an average of 4 phosphates per 100 amino acids (156, 179). The amount, rapidity, and complexity of phosphorylation and its enzymatic basis appear to be identical in both plants and animals (46, 324).

Specific gene regulation is a property of the acidic proteins rather than the histones (238, 301). It has been contended that the phosphorylated acidic proteins are regulators of specific gene activity and that phosphorylation provides the means for modulating the biological functions of these proteins (4, 5, 301). The isolation of any eukaryotic gene regulator protein has yet to be reported. The question as to whether phosphorylation modifies the function of gene regulatory proteins is still undetermined. We should then critically examine the reasons that have compelled some biologists to propose this hypothesis.

Much emphasis has been placed by exponents of the hypothesis (4, 5) on the rapidity of phosphorylation of nuclear phosphoprotein (20, 59, 130, 156–158, 283). It has been argued that this represents an important aspect of genetic control and that the ready reversibility of this process fits a cyclical mechanism for binding and release of regulatory proteins to DNA (5). It is pertinent to ask how rapid the rate of phosphorylation actually is. A recent measurement in *Hela* cells showed the half-life of protein-bound phosphate in individual proteins to range from 5 to 12 hours, with the average value being about 7 hours (144). This may be compared to the half-life of nuclear RNA (the molecules supposedly being regulated) which is about 0.5 hour (241) and the *Hela* cell cycle time of 12 hours (144). Such values hardly qualify for the description of rapid.

Correlations have been frequently observed between the levels of nuclear protein phosphate and the rates of RNA synthesis. For example, diffuse chromatin, which synthesizes RNA at a ten to twentyfold higher rate than dense chromatin, has a fourfold higher content of protein phosphate (85). Similar correlations have been observed in many developmental situations (92, 206, 283). The level of nuclear protein phosphate varies directly with the capacity of the tissue to make RNA, reflecting perhaps a changing balance between diffuse and dense chromatin. The higher levels of phosphoproteins in diffuse chromatin have been used to support the notion that they regulate gene activity (5). Diffuse chromatin, however, also has higher levels of both acidic proteins and acetylated histones (85). As has been pointed out, substantial evidence excludes histones from specific gene regulation (301). In that case the higher levels of phosphorylation in diffuse chromatin can hardly be used to support their putative gene regulating properties. It has also been claimed that when lymphocytes are induced to divide by phytohemagglutinins or other mitogens (127, 159), increased labeling of phosphoproteins can be detected prior to increased RNA synthesis. This, it is suggested, also supports the notion of phosphoproteins as gene regulator proteins (4, 5). We should be careful in the interpretation of such results. One event preceding another does not prove that the first event causes the second. In this lymphocyte system, increased acetylation of histones appears to precede increased phosphorylation of acidic proteins (4, 251); however, it has not been argued that increased histone acetylation causes increased protein phosphorylation (4). The very fine analysis by Berlin & Schimke (22) illustrates the difficulties facing experimenters in determining the apparent time of initiation of changes in macromolecule populations. As can be deduced from their paper (22), differential turnover rates may account for the apparent sequence of events in the lymphocyte system.

It has been reported that RNA synthesis in in vitro RNA synthesizing systems can be stimulated by added phosphoproteins (142, 143, 179, 264, 315), and it has been argued that this also supports their gene regulating properties (301). Such stimulations are often small and are complicated first by the formation of insoluble complexes between phosphoproteins and histones (179) and second by the demonstration that RNA polymerase activity is greatly increased by protein kinases (209–211, 214), enzymes found in the acidic protein fraction (156, 179). Furthermore, the phosphoprotein fractions used in these experiments are of undetermined purity and probably contain substantial levels of other unphosphorylated acidic proteins (301). Acidic proteins have been reported to have the same but very much larger stimulatory capacity on in vitro RNA synthesis (238, 264). It has been claimed in one case (281) that the stimulatory effect of phosphoprotein can be abolished by prior treatment with phosphatase. However, it seems likely that this was the result of continued phosphatase action during in vitro RNA synthesis.

Phosphorylated nuclear proteins have been shown to bind to DNA, and such binding preferentially occurs on homologous DNA (155, 160, 315, 316), thus inviting comparisons with bacterial repressor proteins (301). In this respect again they appear to be no different then other acidic proteins which also bind to DNA (301). Thus there seems little reason to believe that the DNA binding is the result of phosphorylation. The binding of phosphoproteins to DNA is also extremely weak and certainly of insufficient strength to modify the much stronger binding of histones to DNA, an oft-quoted function of phosphoproteins (179).

It has been reported that there are multiple nuclear protein kinases. At least 12 have been separated by column chromatography; some of these were found to be activated, some were inhibited, and others were insensitive to AMP (152, 275, 312). It has been argued that this provides the means whereby animal hormones may modulate the phosphorylation of specific proteins and thus gene activity (152, 301). The claimed multiplicity must surely be open to doubt since the demonstration by Abou-Issa et al (1) that protein kinases are frequently isolated as enzyme-substrate complexes. The apparent nuclear protein kinase multiplicity may in part arise from a combination of one or a few kinases with the numerous substrates in the nucleus. The cAMP sensitivity of nuclear protein kinases is certainly still highly contentious and has sometimes been undetectable (104, 265, 275, 312) or extremely small (118, 210) and therefore of dubious significance.

Gel electrophoretic profiles of phosphorylated chromatin proteins have frequently been reported to be tissue specific (5, 80, 248, 263, 315). It has been argued that this supports the notion that such proteins are concerned with the specific manipulation of the genome during differentiation (301). There is little doubt that this is also a contentious area of research. A careful two-dimensional gel analysis of phosphoproteins in the chromatins of various rat tissues has revealed only minor tissue differences (201). Much of the earlier work which indicated substantial tissue differences used phenol-extracted chromatin phosphoproteins for analysis. Different tissues probably contain the same phosphoproteins, but the spectrum of phosphoproteins extracted by phenol varies from tissue to tissue (201, 263).

Finally, changes in the electrophoretic profiles of phosphorylated nuclear proteins have been observed during different cell divison phases and during sea urchin development or after hormone, drug or cAMP treatments (25, 49, 127, 131, 136, 141, 144, 247, 249). In plants the profiles change during seed germination and after growth substance treatment (46). It has been argued that since the activity of the genome is likely to alter after these developmental perturbations, changes in phosphorylated proteins would be in agreement with their putative gene regulatory function (301). One objection is that many of these observed changes are relatively trivial, being limited to one or a few proteins. Also, such changes are of unknown significance since the biological function of these proteins is still a matter for conjecture. There is one exception to this criticism (136). Good evidence now shows that at least one of the phosphorylated acidic proteins is DNA-dependent RNA polymerase. Phosphorylation increases the catalytic activity of the enzyme six to ninefold (135, 209–211). The biological significance of this phosphorylation has been strikingly demonstrated in ovarian tissue. Chorionic gonadotrophin increases ovarian cell RNA synthesis about 10 min after treatment (135). Preceding this, cellular cAMP levels are elevated by the hormone. A cytoplasmic protein kinase combines with the cAMP and may be translocated to the nucleus (134). Three nuclear proteins are specifically phosphorylated by this protein kinase, and these are identical with the three ovarian polymerases Ia, Ib, and II (135–137). The activity of all three polymerases is increased between three and ninefold after phosphorylation and ovarian RNA synthesis is increased.

Does the evidence indicate that nuclear phosphoproteins control specific gene activity? They do have a number of properties which could be construed as indicating this possibility. In all respects these properties seem to be shared by other unphosphorylated acidic proteins (301). There is no piece of evidence which can be marked out as indicating unequivocally that phosphorylation controls the putative regulatory nature of these proteins.

There is no doubt that nuclear protein phosphorylation is of importance, but not in the way envisaged by the proponents of the protein phosphorylation/specific gene regulatory theory. The phosphorylation of RNA polymerase represents an important step forward in our understanding of the control of nuclear activity. If it is a model for the future, it suggests that other, perhaps all, of the nuclear phosphoproteins may be enzymes. The recent demonstration that histone deacetylase, a nuclear acidic protein, is also phosphorylated is strong support for this proposal (326). However, recent work may suggest other functions. Ribonucleoprotein particles containing DNA-like RNA can be isolated from nuclei. Some of these proteins are phosphorylated and the particles contain protein kinase activity (27, 88, 212). Future experiments may show the relationship of this modification to the selection and processing of messenger RNA.

Histone Phosphorylation and the Regulation of Cell Division

The histones are a group of highly basic acid-soluble proteins found in association with DNA (119). They are of limited heterogeneity, generally only five groups being recognized in most animals and plants. These groups are the very lysine-rich histone F1, the slightly lysine-rich histones, F2a2 and F2b, and the arginine-rich histones, F2a1 and F3. The current view is that the primary structure of the histones except histone F1 has been highly conserved during evolution (60, 234, 236). Histone F1 in contrast may even exhibit tissue specificity in its primary structure (234).

The well-known capacity of histone to repress RNA transcription from DNA formed much of the original basis of research (30, 60, 119). The limited heterogeneity of these molecules and the substantial evidence in favor of nuclear acidic proteins regulating genomic activity (301) has reduced interest in histone research. To some extent this has revived with the detection of considerable post-translational modification of histones. Acetylation, methylation, thiolation, ribosylation, and phosphorylation have all been reported. Hnilica (119) and Delange & Smith (60) have satisfactorily reviewed the literature on modification up to the end of 1971.

A substantial body of evidence has shown that there is a good correlation between the level of histone F1 phosphorylation and cell division. Thus comparisons have been made between dividing and nondividing tissues of calf (235) and mouse (285); between fetal, regenerating, and mature rat liver (11, 14, 231); between stationary and exponentially growing hepatomas (14, 229); between tumorous and normal tissues in the rat and mouse (12, 285); and between cell cultures growing at different rates (12). In every case 1–15% of histone F1 is phosphorylated in the nondividing cells and between 50–80% in the dividing cells with the final level being correlated directly with the rate of division (12). A further conclusion which can be drawn from these papers is that significant levels of phosphorylation are usually only found in one histone, F1.

Synchronous cultures of Chinese hamster cells (106, 107, 109–111, 177, 178, 284), *Hela* (178, 207), *Physarum* (33–35), and HTC cells and the partially synchronous regenerating liver (16, 240, 290) and the lymphocyte (56) have been used to examine the temporal alteration of histone F1 phosphorylation during the cell cycle. Low but detectable histone F1 phosphorylation has been observed in late G1 (13, 110, 111). Phosphorylation is higher in S (13, 16, 56, 110, 207, 229, 240, 290), and even higher again in G2, but declines—sometimes dramatically—as cells go into M and back into G1 (33–35, 106–11, 177, 207). Although it has been argued (17, 199, 314) that S phase phosphorylation of a newly synthesised histone F1 is of importance and concerned with the final organization and packing of newly synthesised DNA, there are several lines of evidence which suggest this may not be the case.

First, even in nondividing cells a small proportion of histone F1 is phosphorylated (235). Histone F1 phosphorylation in the S phase of the cell cycle has been invariably detected by pulse labeling with $^{32}P_i$. The synthesis of histones is confined to the S phase of the cell cycle (119). Incorporation of $^{32}P_i$ must accompany histone synthesis in order to maintain a resting level of phosphorylation. In *Physarum* (33–35) the ratio of total histone F1 to phosphorylated histone F1 is invariant during G1, S, and early G2.

Second, while hydroxyurea and cycloheximide can effect a rapid and almost total inhibition of DNA synthesis in HTC cells, the rate of histone phosphorylation only declines slowly to a value about 50% lower than that in uninhibited cells (17, 314). Such results do not suggest a strong coupling between DNA synthesis and histone phosphorylation. Furthermore, the histone F1 phosphorylation observable in late G1 represents phosphorylation of histones synthesized in previous cell cycles (110, 111). It is unaffected by inhibitors of DNA synthesis and presumably reflects the opening up of chromatin structure in preparation for replication, thus permitting entry of kinases and phosphatases. A similar possibility is equally applicable to the S phase of the cell cycle (314).

Third, studies on *Physarum* have shown convincingly that the level of phosphorylated histone F1 increases sixfold during middle and late G2. Phosphorylation peaks at the time of maximum chromosome condensation and then declines dramatically just prior to M (33–35). Histone and DNA synthesis are of course absent during G2 (35). *Physarum* is a highly synchronous system. The 10^8 nuclei in each coenocytic plasmodium all divide within a 5 min period out of a total cell cycle time of 10 hr (35). Compared to *Physarum* the animal cell lines used for cell cycle studies, and in which significant S phase F1 phosphorylation has been reported, are only weakly synchronous. The M period, for example, may take up to several hours (13, 56, 110, 207, 240, 290). The phases of such cell cultures would be better referred to as S rich, M rich, etc. An increase in histone F1 phosphate located in late G2 in a highly synchronous system like *Physarum* would in a weakly synchronous system spread into the S rich and M rich phases of the cell cycle. The degree of spread would depend upon the degree of synchrony.

Fourth, there is good evidence for high significance to be placed on histone F1 phosphorylation during G2 rather than S.

A histone kinase has been detected in Chinese hamster and *Hela* cells (174–176, 178) and *Physarum* (33, 34), which is highly specific for histone F1 (histone F1 kinase). This enzyme increases twenty to fortyfold and then decreases during late G2 (33, 34) and is responsible for the large increase in F1 phosphorylation seen at this time (33, 34, 176, 178). The enzyme activity is extremely labile in vivo and was only detected in animal cells by holding them at metaphase with vinblastine (178). Other histone kinases have been detected in Chinese hamster and *Hela* cells (174–176, 178) which will phosphorylate F1. In contrast to F1 kinase, they have a low specificity for histone F1, are activated by cAMP, and phosphorylate F1 at different sites as demonstrated by tryptic peptide analysis (176). The crowning achievement of this area of work has been the demonstration that treatment of *Physarum* with heterologous F1 kinase can actually alter the time of mitosis (34) by up to 40 minutes. Bradbury and associates (33–35) have discussed in some detail the concept of the mitotic trigger which has been developed from plasmodial fusion experiments. They have concluded that the trigger is probably histone F1 kinase and they have indicated how phosphorylation of histone F1 may initiate chromosome condensation.

These concepts have been criticized recently (97). It has been shown that the amitotic nucleus of *Tetrahymena*, which undergoes no chromosome condensation during the cell cycle, has a high level of histone F1 phosphorylated in rapidly growing cells. While this certainly raises difficulties, it must be recalled that there are at least two types of histone kinase, only one of which is concerned with the putative role of histone F1 in chromosome condensation. It is not known which histone kinase is responsible for the high level of histone F1 phosphate in *Tetrahymena*. A further report (321) which indicates that avian erythrocyte histone F1 cannot be phosphorylated in vivo or in vitro also raises other difficulties and indicates that work in this area is far from over.

In contrast to the massive phosphorylation of histone F1 which occurs during cell division, the phosphorylation of F1 in adult rat liver probably involves about 1% of the total histone (183). This phosphorylation is catalyzed by two histone kinases which phosphorylate single but different serine residues in histone F1. They also exhibit differing sensitivities to cAMP (181–183, 205). Langan (183) has suggested that this low but highly specific level of F1 phosphorylation may be related to the regulation of gene activity. A certain amount of evidence supports this hypothesis. For example, increased histone phosphorylation precedes increased RNA synthesis induced by hormone treatment or during liver regeneration (36, 66, 114, 322), DNA conformation in vitro is less altered by phosphorylated than dephosphorylated histone F1 (3), phosphorylated histone F1 is less effective than dephosphorylated histone in repressing in vitro RNA synthesis (185, 303; but see 43 for opposing view), and F1 phosphorylation is possibly tissue specific (126, 234). However, critical experiments supporting this theory are still lacking, and the much stronger evidence indicating that only the nuclear acidic proteins regulate gene activity (301) shows that considerable caution must be exercised concerning such hypotheses.

Although most interest has centered on histone F1 phosphorylation, studies have been made on the other histones. There have been a number of reports which show that histone F2a2 is phosphorylated (13, 15, 105, 106, 109, 110, 178, 200), but the rate of phosphorylation is invariant through the cell cycle. Furthermore, only a small proportion (10–15%) of the histone is phosphorylated at any one time (14,- 200). The kinetics of labeling with $^{32}P_I$ appear to be identical in both *Hela* cells (207) and trout testes (200). These suggest a very rapid turnover of the phosphate group. It has been suggested (199) that perhaps phosphorylation is concerned with the placing of histone in the right conformation on DNA. However, the continued phosphorylation of F2a2 in G1 and G2 (106, 109, 110) would seem to obviate this possibility.

The phosphorylation of histone F2b (77, 200, 207), F2a1 (197, 199), and F3 (109, 111, 199) have all been reported, but the significance of the phosphorylation, if any, is not known. However, Dixon and his collaborators (199) have shown that protamines appear to undergo an obligatory sequence of phosphorylation and dephosphorylation during the maturation of the trout sperm head. They suggest that the dephosphorylation of the protamine is involved in the gradual condensation of chromatin as the sperm matures. Somewhat by analogy, Louie & Dixon (198) have proposed that the interconversion of diffuse and dense chromatin may be regulated by histone phosphorylation and dephosphorylation. This view has been strongly criticized and is probably untenable (33).

Probably all of the work quoted in this section has been concerned with the phosphorylation of serine and threonine residues in histones and protamines (158). Three recent papers (48, 294, 295) show that there are histone kinases in liver and tumor cells which can phosphorylate lysine and histidine residues in histones. Since lysine and histidine phosphates are acid-labile, they will probably have been missed by most investigators. This does indicate that some reappraisal of our present understanding of histone phosphorylation may have to be undertaken.

Microtubule Phosphorylation and Aggregation

Microtubules are recognized to be ubiquitous entities in eukaryotic cells. Their probable functions in plants include spindle formation, determination of the plane of division, and the orientation of microfibril deposition and secondary thickening in cell walls (117). Microtubules are aggregates of a protein called tubulin which consists of two polypeptide chains with molecular weights each about 55,000. Traces of other proteins are frequently encountered in microtubule preparations (117).

Much of the interest in microtubules hinges around the problem of the cellular regulation of aggregation from tubulin. Eipper (73) has summarized the evidence which shows that some cAMP effects on secretion, cell growth, and cell shape can be inhibited by colchicine, an alkaloid which inhibits microtubule aggregation. The possibility that microtubule aggregation may be regulated by cAMP-dependent protein kinases has to be considered seriously.

Eipper (72) has shown convincingly that brain tubulin contains about one molecule of covalently bound phosphate per molecule of tubulin. By $^{32}P_i$ labeling in vivo it was shown that all the radioactivity was located in one tryptic peptide and attached to serine phosphate (73). These results have been confirmed for chick muscle and *Hela* cell tubulin (244), but *Chlamydomonas* tubulin apparently contains no detectable phosphate (273). Sloboda et al (293) detected two proteins (molecular weights about 3×10^5) in microtubule preparations which represent only 5% of the total protein but whose labeling was three to fourfold higher than tubulin itself. They suggest that these proteins may be proper components of the microtubule and concerned with axoplasmic transport although there is little to sustain this latter suggestion.

Isolated microtubule preparations frequently have been found to contain endogenous protein kinase activity (72–74, 95, 173, 189, 226, 244, 260, 293, 296) which is separable from tubulin itself (73, 74). There is still considerable contention as to whether tubulin itself becomes labeled in vitro with ^{32}P-ATP (73, 95, 173, 226, 244) or whether it is associated with proteins which become labeled (189, 293). The attached protein kinase has been reported by some to be cAMP sensitive (95, 173, 189, 260, 293) and by others insensitive (73, 74, 226, 244, 296). Eipper (73, 74) and Leterrier et al (189) discuss reasons for both these controversies but the latter difficulty may result from variable contamination by cAMP dependent (128) or independent (121) protein kinases both of which are found in the brain, the main source of tubulin.

There is little in the present published work which would support a relationship of phosphorylation to tubulin aggregation. Vinblastine, colchicine, and Ca^{2+} ions, all inhibitors of aggregation, fail to affect in vitro phosphorylation (95, 244, 296). Aggregation of tubulin can take place in the absence of ATP or GTP (282), but the rate of polymerization is certainly accelerated by both these substances. It is more probable that the cAMP effects on Ca^{2+} flux (261) account for the colchicine-inhibitable cAMP responses described earlier (73). Piras & Piras (244) have indicated that there are dramatic changes in tubulin phosphorylation during embryonic development which may reflect protein kinase changes (245). There are also two reports that adult tubulin is more difficult to phosphorylate than embryonic tubulin (73, 74, 244), but the significance of this remains to be established.

The Enigma of Ribosomal Protein Phosphorylation

Much of the impetus for an examination of ribosomal protein phosphorylation followed from the observations made by Garren, Ney & Davis (91). They showed that the increased production of corticosterone, induced by ACTH in the adrenal cortex, could be inhibited by cycloheximide but not by actinomycin D. Although at the time this was interpreted as indicating ACTH regulation at the translational level of protein synthesis, it would be treated more sceptically now. The ACTH effect is mediated by cAMP and there is other evidence, summarized in (133), relating cAMP to translational control of protein synthesis. An examination of the possible presence and function of ribosomal protein phosphorylation can certainly be justified.

The presence of phosphorylated ribosomal proteins has been detected in many animal and plant tissues. Animal tissues include the adrenal cortex (93, 328), testis (124), reticulocytes (42, 50), 81, 138–140, 213, 317), fibroblasts (190), liver (28, 55, 69–71, 101, 125, 196, 243, 299), mammary gland (204), thyroid (239), anterior pituitary gland (18), and numerous tumor tissues (24, 68, 243, 253); plant tissues include pea stem (147), *Lemna* (147, 319), chinese cabbage leaf (257), wheat embryo (40), and yeast (98). It has been established numerous times (e.g. 18, 125, 138, 147, 204, 253, 319) that some or all of the phosphate groups are attached to serine and threonine residues. In a single study (96) the absence of phosphorylated ribosomal protein in *E. coli* has been recorded, but it can be detected after T7 phage infection (254).

Isolated ribosomes usually have attached protein kinase activity of which some 70–90% may be released by washing ribosomes in 0.25–0.5 M KCl (69, 81, 98, 124, 125, 139, 147). Substantially all of the associated protein kinase can be removed by converting ribosomes to their subunits (69, 213, 316, 329). It has been suggested that the weakness of the attachment of the protein kinase for the ribosome indicates that it may be a contaminant from the cytoplasm acquired during isolation (70, 139). However, it has been shown that the loosely attached ribosomal kinase is recognizably different from cytoplasmic kinases (98, 124), or is in the cytoplasm in very low amounts compared to that attached to the ribosome (125), or that it is apparently similar to only one of a number of supernatant kinases (81, 147, 317), suggesting possible specificity of attachment. Ribosomes occasionally have been reported to have associated protein phosphatase activity (125, 139). The majority of endogenous animal ribosomal kinases are activated severalfold by cAMP (18, 42, 69, 70, 81, 125, 196, 328, 329) whereas the plant ribosomal kinases are totally insensitive to cAMP (40, 98, 147, 257).

Many investigators have made use of the ribosomal kinase to examine which proteins are labeled when ribosomes are incubated in ^{32}P-ATP (18, 61, 93, 125, 139, 147, 207, 328) or when purified subunits are phosphorylated with exogenous kinase (69, 70, 299, 317, 325). The numbers of ribosomal proteins phosphorylated range from 3 to 14 (averaging about 8) with the majority being located in the large ribosomal subunit. This is in marked contrast to in vivo labeling with ^{32}P$_i$ where in ascites tumor (259), liver (28, 101, 102, 196, 243), novikoff hepatoma (253), anterior pituitary gland (18), reticulocyte (42), and *Lemna* (319) highly purified ribosomes are found to have 80–90% of their bound radioactivity in one protein located in the small ribosomal subunit. There is evidence that this protein may accept up to four or five phosphates per molecule (101). Other labeled proteins can be found in less highly purified ribosomes (24, 42, 319). There may be many reasons for the differences between in vivo and in vitro labeling. The intactness of the ribosome (299) and ribosomal purity (213, 317) both affect the types of protein labeled in vitro. The above contrast does suggest that great caution must be exercised concerning the significance of in vitro ribosomal protein phosphorylation. Martini & Gould (213), however, have discussed the possible use of in vitro protein phosphorylation as a probe for ribosomal topography.

Is there any evidence to relate ribosomal protein phosphorylation to the protein synthesizing function of the ribosome? In any discussion of this topic the following results are of direct relevance.

Only slight (140, 213) or negligible differences (101, 319) have been observed between the levels of phosphorylation in polysomes and "inactive monosomes." Although it was originally reported that one phosphorylated ribosomal protein was found only in monosomes (138), subsequent work (140) did not find this correlation to be particularly compelling. Inactive ribosomes isolated from dormant wheat embryos have the same level of attached protein kinase as active ribosomes isolated from embryos germinated for 24 hours (Trewavas, unpublished data).

Sodium fluoride, puromycin, and cycloheximide, all inhibitors of protein synthesis, induce dramatic increases in ribosomal protein phosphorylation (42, 102). However, each of these substances inhibits protein synthesis in a different way (102). Their apparent uniformity of effect on ribosomal protein phosphorylation has led Gressner & Wool (102) to suggest that the increased protein phosphorylation is the result of higher cAMP levels. Apparently all three inhibitors enhance adenyl cyclase activity as a side effect.

A series of careful measurements has enabled Kabat (140) to make accurate estimates of the turnover time of ribosomal protein phosphorylation in reticulocytes. The replacement rate of the phosphate is about 3% min^{-1} (a half-life of just over 20 min). This is very much slower than the time required to make a globin chain which is 0.25 to 0.4 min (140). These measurements at least show that phosphorylation/dephosphorylation of ribosomal protein is not an obligatory reaction of reticulocyte protein synthesis. A half-life of liver ribosomal protein phosphorylation may be estimated from the data of Correze, Pinell & Nunez (55) and is a figure of at least 30 min, reinforcing the above conclusion. There have been several reports (122, 317, 325) of protein kinases using GTP for ribosomal protein phosphorylation with the scarcely veiled hint that these may explain the requirement for GTP in protein synthesis. The above measurements of turnover rates would tend to obviate this possibility.

Two studies have shown that purified initiation factors have negligible protein kinase activity (81, 325).

Eil & Wool (71) have examined the ability of ribosomal subunits phosphorylated with exogenous protein kinase to participate in in vitro protein synthesis. Compared to unphosphorylated controls, there were negligible differences in elongation rates, aminoacyl-tRNA binding and translation rates of viral mRNA. Functions which were not tested and may yet prove to be modified by phosphorylation include translation of specific cellular mRNAs and termination. It has been reported (222) that inclusion of protein kinase in an in vitro synthesizing system inhibits protein synthesis. The stepwise inhibition noted with increasing increments of protein kinase suggests that the inhibition is not produced as a result of the catalytic activity of the enzyme.

Several studies have investigated the possibility that ribosomal protein phosphorylation may be related to the binding of ribosomes to membranes. Although attached protein kinase is found in generally higher levels in membrane-bound polysomes (18, 125, 239, 329) than in free ribosomes, the in vivo phosphorylation is higher in free ribosomes (19). Minor differences have been noted between phosphorylated proteins of free and bound polysomes (125, 243). There is little in this present work to convince one that protein kinase plays a key role in ribosome binding. Furthermore, the critical experiments to show such a relationship have not yet been performed even though they are technically feasible.

Insulin, prolactin, glucagon, and thyroid hormone are all capable of altering the rate of protein synthesis in various tissues (28, 55, 204). Although all of these hormones also alter the phosphorylation of ribosomal protein (28, 55, 204), it seems likely that some of these changes reflect simple alterations in nucleotide pool size (42). Correze, Pinell & Nunez (55), in a more critical study, concluded that the thyroxine-induced increase in liver ribosomal protein phosphorylation more accurately reflected altered protein kinase levels than changes in the levels of polysomes. In plants the rather trivial effects of abscisic acid and cytokinins on ribosomal protein phosphorylation do little to encourage the belief that these represent the molecular basis of their action upon plant growth (147, 257, 319).

When all of these facts are considered together they would suggest that there may be no relationship between ribosomal protein phosphorylation and protein synthesis. In that case, the function of ribosomal protein phosphorylation remains very much an enigma.

There are, however, two observations which must be considered in any total evaluation of this field. First, ribosomal protein phosphorylation is increased some tenfold during liver regeneration (181). Perhaps ribosomal protein phosphorylation performs some function during the increased synthesis and processing of ribosomes which occurs at this time. Second, it has been shown (68, 89, 223) that reticulocyte informosomes contain at least one phosphorylated protein. The messenger ribonucleoprotein particles which can be derived from polysomes contain at least three phosphorylated proteins (9, 89, 223). A poly-A binding protein has also been shown to be phosphorylated (26). This type of result is suggesting a possible function of protein phosphorylation at the level of mRNA selection. At the moment however, they are merely correlative findings; a considered judgment must await the publication of the critical experiments.

Membrane Protein Phosphorylation: A Possible Basis for Cell Polarity

Cyclic AMP has been shown to regulate the flux of water, ions, and amino acids across membranes and the secretion of enzymes, hormones, and neurotransmitters (307). The possibility that these effects are mediated by membrane-bound protein kinases is under active consideration.

The following membrane types have been shown to contain phosphorylated proteins or to have proteins which can be phosphorylated by protein kinases: plasma membranes from liver (128, 289), rod outer segments (128), synaptic tissue (128), various kidney cell types (67, 82, 83, 280), fat cells (44, 45), ovary cells (262), various smooth muscle tissues (6, 41), anterior pituitary gland (188), mammary gland (204), erythrocytes (112, 267–269, 272, 276, 287), and *Hela* cells (149). Other membranes containing phosphorylated proteins which may be plasma membranes but whose subcellular origin is incompletely characterized are from synaptosomes in guinea pig, rat, and ox (100, 129, 132, 317, 331–334), leucocyte and platelets (51), and bladder mucosal epithelial cells (62, 63, 123, 195). Intracellular phosphorylated membrane proteins have been detected in microsomal membranes from heart (64, 150, 151, 337), brain (132, 202, 317, 331), bladder (195), and liver (338); mitochondrial and lysosomal membranes from liver (224, 338); and secretory granule membrane from the anterior pituitary (172) and pancreas (214).

In the majority of these membrane systems (41, 44, 82, 151, 172, 188, 195, 224, 271, 280, 318, 333) phosphorylation of membrane-bound proteins has been shown to be catalyzed by endogenously bound protein kinases. Most of these have their activity modulated by cAMP (41, 44, 82, 129, 151, 188, 195, 271, 280). The presence of phosphoprotein phosphatase in bladder, synaptosomal, and blood cell membranes has been reported (62, 63, 100, 186, 195, 332), and this enzyme may be regulated in the bladder by cAMP (195).

The number of proteins which are labeled with $^{32}P_i$ in each membrane type may vary from 3 up to 20. It is usually the phosphorylation of only one or two proteins which can be modulated by cAMP (41, 44, 63, 100, 112, 129, 195, 272, 276, 287, 323). These membrane-bound kinases will also catalyze cAMP-dependent phosphorylation of exogenously added histone and protamine (100, 267). Thus the selective effect of cAMP upon one or two proteins probably indicates a close association of kinase and substrate in the membrane itself.

There are many reports that the catalytic activities of the membrane-bound kinases are inhibited by low concentrations of calcium ions (6, 45, 112, 172, 188, 203, 269, 323, 333, 334, 337). There is an almost total lack of awareness of the complications that calcium-activated ATPases can introduce into kinase assays, and thus the validity of the inhibition may be in some doubt.

Most papers have been concerned with relating membrane protein phosphorylation to some physiological effect of cAMP. The suggested functions of phosphorylation are: regulation of sodium and water permeability (62, 63, 67, 195, 276, 280), glucose and P_i transport (44), pyruvate transport into mitochondria (338), hormone secretion (172, 188), synaptic transmission (100), Ca^{2+} uptake and muscle contraction (151), and lysosomal swelling (338). Unfortunately, most of these represent little more than unsubstantiated speculation. We need only consider those for which there may be some substance to the proposed function.

Glucose is transported into fat cells by a carrier-mediated facilitated diffusion mechanism (44). Insulin (which inhibits adenyl cyclase activity) can increase the affinity of the carrier for glucose, thus increasing glucose transport (44, 45). Exogenously added ATP at very low concentrations blocks the insulin-stimulated glucose transport. ATP analogs which cannot function as phosphorylating agents are unable to inhibit this insulin effect. A cAMP-dependent protein kinase in the fat cell membrane together with ATP catalyzes the phosphorylation of two membrane proteins. Phloretin, a competitive inhibitor of glucose transport, also inhibits the phosphorylation of these two proteins and protects the fat cell membranes from the ATP effect (44, 45).

Intracellular uptake and release of Ca^{2+} from the sarcoplasmic reticulum is an important regulatory factor in muscle contraction (166, 261). Cyclic AMP is able to increase calcium uptake by the sarcoplasmic reticulum (337). This effect can be duplicated by simply adding exogenous protein kinase to the sarcoplasmic reticulum (150). In fact, a linear relationship was found between the level of sarcosomal protein phosphorylation and the level of calcium uptake (150). The sarcoplasmic reticulum contains an endogenous protein kinase which can be activated by cAMP (150, 337). It phosphorylates a single protein which is not apparently an ion-stimulated ATPase (311). In uterine muscle, more intriguingly, cAMP treatment leads to a translocation of protein kinase from the cell sap to the microsomal fraction accompanying an increased accumulation of calcium in the microsomes (161).

Greengard and co-workers (62, 63, 195) have shown that vasopressin and aldosterone, which regulate sodium and water movement through the mucosal epithelium of the toad bladder, promote the dephosphorylation of a single membrane-bound protein in this tissue by activating a phosphoprotein phosphatase. The effects can be mimicked by cAMP. Substances which antagonize the hormonal effect on sodium transport (e.g. spironolactone, cycloheximide, etc) also inhibit the dephosphorylation of this protein. In the avian erythrocyte (276) a similar correlation between sodium transport, protein phosphorylation, and substances promoting or inhibiting sodium transport has been detected.

These and other attempts to demonstrate a relationship between membrane protein phosphorylation and the cAMP control of permeability have to contend with three difficulties. First, it will be recalled that in many cases cAMP alters the phosphorylation of only one or two proteins. It must be demonstrated convincingly that one of these proteins is not a Na^+/K^+ or Ca^{2+} stimulated ATPase. These enzymes are widely distributed and have an acyl phosphate as an intermediate (57). Increased sodium flux induced by cAMP (307), for example, must most certainly involve increased turnover and thus increased phosphorylation of the ATPase. Notice that this effect does not necessarily involve changes in protein kinase activity. It has been reported that membrane protein phosphate is attached to serine or threonine (for example 45, 63, 132, 188, 332) and that phosphorylation is insensitive to oubain and sodium or potassium ions (44, 63, 269, 276, 337). These analyses are usually carried out on total membrane phosphorylation, and it would be easy to miss protein-bound acyl phosphate on one protein compared to serine phosphate on seven or eight.

Second, there is now good evidence that one phosphorylated protein in erythrocyte and brain membranes is the protein kinase itself (112, 113, 203). It is the regulatory subunit which is phosphorylated and cAMP can alter this phosphorylation. The significance of this is not understood. It does show, however, that there is a membrane protein whose phosphorylation can be altered by cAMP without necessarily involving changes in membrane permeability.

A final difficulty arises from observations that some hormones can induce substantial changes in the conformation of membrane-bound proteins (171, 298). Although the generality of this phenomenon still remains a matter for conjecture, the possibility that a conformational change will expose previously protected protein-bound serines to phosphorylation by kinases must be seriously entertained. On this basis changes in phosphorylation patterns become a reflection rather than a cause of altered membrane phenomena.

Despite these objections, two recent publications (280, 288) have provided the most exciting results yet published in this field and represent the strongest of reasons for supposing that membrane protein phosphorylation may be a significant event in the control of permeability.

The cortical collecting tubule in the kidney is lined by a single layer of epithelial cells. Studies of perfused tubules (90) have shown that the plasma membrane on the blood surface of the cells (so-called basal membrane) is freely permeable to water. The plasma membrane on the urinary surface (the so-called apical membrane) is normally impermeable. After addition of vasopressin (an antidiuretic hormone) the apical plasma membrane becomes freely permeable to water and transport of water from urine to blood commences. The movement of water through the apical cells is accompanied by the formation of vacuoles and bulging of the apical membrane into the tubule lumen. Other studies (21) have shown that the water permeability of these cells can only be manipulated by hormones applied to the basal surface and that the effect of antidiuretic hormone is mediated by cAMP.

Separation of the apical and basal plasma membranes of these kidney tubule cells has now been achieved in rat and ox (280, 288). In both cases hormone-sensitive adenylate cyclase was found only in the basal plasma membrane. In contrast, cAMP-dependent protein kinase activity was found only in the apical plasma membrane. The membrane-bound kinase catalyzes the phosphorylation of endogenous membrane proteins. These very exciting results show that the protein kinase is only located in the membrane whose water permeability is modulated by cAMP. The adenylate cyclase, on the other hand, is located in the membrane sensitive to added hormones. The polar distribution of such important regulatory enzymes suggest intriguing possibilities for future work.

Phosphorylation of Organ-Specific Proteins

Numerous reports show that various muscle proteins, including parvalbumins (29), troponin (75, 166), myosin (216, 246), sarcolemma proteins (305), and uncharacterized muscle proteins (279), brain myelin-basic protein (39, 58, 219, 221, 300), and rhodopsin (31, 84, 167, 168, 286, 335) are all phosphorylated by endogenous kinases. Although there is correlative evidence relating troponin phosphorylation to muscle contraction (75) and light stimulated rhodopsin phosphorylation (31, 84, 335), it would be premature to assume that phosphorylation controls the biological activity of these proteins.

Are Protein Kinases and Protein Phosphorylation Essential for Viral Infection?

Probably one of the most unexpected findings of protein phosphorylation studies has been the convincing demonstration (254, 255) that a protein kinase is a T7 phage gene product. The enzyme is synthesized in the host, *E. coli,* 4 to 5 min after phage infection. It has been mapped as being adjacent to RNA polymerase on the phage genome. Although the function of the protein kinase for the infective process is unknown, host ribosomal proteins, (254) and RNA polymerase (339) are rapidly phosphorylated after de novo synthesis of the protein kinase. Probably another highly significant finding in this connection is that uninfected *E. coli* has no detectable protein kinase activity (255) despite earlier reports (169). A possible solution to this dilemma comes from the work of Li & Brown (191). They showed that a polyphosphate kinase from *E. coli* is stimulated by histone, a frequently used substrate for detecting protein kinase activity (169). Polyphosphate kinase could easily be mistaken for protein kinase in the absence of sufficient characterization.

Numerous reports indicate that viruses may have associated protein kinases in the envelope or that some of the envelope proteins are phosphorylated. This has been shown for vaccinia virus (153, 154, 237, 266, 330), herpes virus (258, 274), vesicular stomatitis virus (225, 297, 304, 330), RNA tumor virus (116, 304), frog polyhedral cytoplasmic deoxyribovirus (99, 291), influenza, parrainfluenza virus (116), rhabdoviruses (297), adenovirus (277), and simian virus 40 (313). Evidence indicating a requirement for the envelope-associated protein kinase for infectivity (99) and for RNA synthesis by the viral RNA polymerase (330) is unfortunately rather weak. Moyer & Summers (225) have argued that the envelope protein may even represent a contaminant acquired from the host during maturation. The envelope-attached protein kinase is probably not responsible for the phosphorylation of coat proteins (225, 277, 313).

Is There Cyclic AMP in Plants?

I have endeavored to do two things in this review. First, I have tried to present an overall picture of protein phosphorylation and thereby to convince plant scientists of its importance. Second, I have tried to provide a somewhat critical appraisal of the actual extent of knowledge in the more exciting areas of work. Since virtually all of the described work is on animals, the botanist is perfectly entitled to ask what relevance all this has to his own chosen organism, the plant.

Plants certainly have protein kinases. They have been detected in pea shoot (146, 147), *Lemna* (147), barley (324), and wheat embryos (40), tobacco and chinese cabbage leaf (257), and carrot root (257). They have been detected in nuclei (257, 324), chloroplasts (257), ribosomes (40, 147, 257), and cytoplasmic fractions (40, 146). In particular aspects, protein phosphorylation is very similar in plants and animals. Two-dimensional gel electrophoresis has revealed that there are at least 20 phosphorylated proteins in barley nuclei (Trewavas unpublished data) which compares very favorably with the complexity in liver (201). The total amount of inorganic phosphate attached to nuclear proteins is similar in *Lemna* and liver (46). Gressner & Wool (101) have commented on the very considerable similarity of ribosomal protein phosphorylation in *Lemna* (319) and liver (101), one small subunit protein of almost identical molecular weight being phosphorylated in both cases. A single protein kinase may be eluted with low salt concentrations from ribosomes of reticulocytes (81) or peas (147).

There is one pronounced difference. Many but not all animal protein kinases are cAMP-dependent (162). No plant protein kinase yet tested shows any sensitivity to cAMP (40, 146, 147, 324). This contrast is emphasized in ribosomal protein phosphorylation where the animal ribosomal kinase is activated three to fourfold cAMP (81), but the equivalent pea ribosomal kinase is insensitive. It can be argued that it is just a matter of assaying the right plant protein kinase and cAMP sensitivity will appear. However, it is more pertinent to ask whether plants possess a functioning adenyl cyclase and thus use the second messenger cAMP to mediate growth substance action. In my own view they probably do not and for the following reasons:

1. As pointed out by Lin (192), many of the purported demonstrations of cAMP in plants [these are all summarized in (192)] suffer from the following serious defects. The use of contaminated plants, inadequate characterization of supposed cAMP, contamination by other unknown nucleotides particularly in labeling experiments, and the use of an assay system which has the unfortunate property of giving a positive result with interfering substances (94). Much of the early work which claimed to show the presence of cAMP in plants has been thoroughly discredited by more exacting analyses (8, 145, 228, 233, 257). There has been no satisfactory demonstration of adenyl cyclase in any plant tissue (192).

2. Numerous claims have been made that added cAMP affects many plant physiological processes (the references are listed in 8 and 192). Many adenine derivatives are cytokinins, and it would be difficult to discriminate a genuine cAMP effect from a cytokinin-like action. Plants can also convert the dibutyryl derivative of cAMP into an active cytokinin (257).

3. Plant nucleotide phosphodiesterase is capable of hydrolyzing 2'3' cyclic nucleotide phosphates as well as 3'5' cyclic nucleotide phosphates unlike the animal enzyme which is specific for the latter substrate (7, 193). Such a property suggests a role in RNA degradation rather than specific cAMP hydrolysis.

4. Even if cAMP is present in plants and we can accept the detected levels as being genuine, they are much lower than those found in animal systems and offend the general principle of amplification inherent in cAMP control (8, 32).

5. As quoted above, no plant protein kinase has yet been shown to be sensitive to cAMP.

6. The concept of cAMP in animal systems is that it acts as a second messenger between a hormone circulating in the blood stream, and therefore on the outside of the cell, and intracellular receptor systems which carry out hormonally controlled metabolic changes. There is every reason to believe that plant growth substances can and do move intracellularly in their target tissue and thus a second messenger requirement is obviated. I have recently discussed this point at some length (320), together with other evidence indicating that animal hormones and plant growth substances fulfill basically different requirements in their respective organisms.

If plants do not possess an adenyl cyclase system do they regulate the activity of their protein kinases? There is little literature on the subject at present and that which has been published does not suggest direct regulation of kinases by growth substances (147, 257). However, recently we have able to show that dividing artichoke cells have a higher level of phosphorylated histone F1 than their nondividing counterparts (Stratton and Trewavas, unpublished data) exactly as in animal systems. There is no evidence to show that histone F1 kinase is regulated by cAMP in animal systems, and thus there are most certainly alternatives to cAMP for protein kinase regulation. It should be remembered, of course, that many animal protein kinases are cAMP-independent. McMahon (215) has summarized some of the evidence showing regulation of kinase activity by Ca^{2+}, K^+ etc, and other more recent examples have been mentioned in this chapter. This and the evidence relating growth substances to permeability phenomena (320) suggests one direction in which research could advance. The most promising development would of course be the detection of a plant enzyme whose catalytic activity could be modulated by phosphorylation. To some this may seem like looking for a needle in a haystack, but the rewards of such an enterprise would surely far outweigh the cost.

Literature Cited

1. Abou-Issa, H., Kratowich, N., Mendicino, J. 1974. *Eur. J. Biochem.* 42: 461–71
2. Agren, G., DeVerdier, C. H., Glomset, J. 1951. *Acta Chem. Scand.* 5:324–25
3. Adler, A. J., Schaffhausen, B., Langan, T. A., Fasman, G. D. 1971. *Biochemistry* 10:909–13
4. Allfrey, V. G. 1970. *Fed. Proc.* 29: 1447–60
5. Allfrey, V. G., Johnson, E. M., Karn, J., Vidali, G. 1973. *Protein Phosphorylation in Control Mechanisms,* ed. F. Huijing, E. Y. C. Lee, 217–44. New York: Academic. 317 pp.
6. Andrew, G. C., Roses, A. D., Almon, R. R., Appel, S. H. 1973. *Science* 182:927–29
7. Amrhein, N. 1974. *Z. Pflazenphysiol.* 72:249–59
8. Amrhein, N. 1974. *Planta* 118:241–58
9. Auerbach, S., Pederson, T. 1975. *Biochem. Biophys. Res. Commun.* 63:149–56
10. Axelrod, B. 1947. *J. Biol. Chem.* 167: 57–67
11. Balhorn, R., Balhorn, M., Chalkley, R. 1972. *Dev. Biol.* 29:199–211
12. Balhorn, R., Balhorn, M., Morris, H., Chalkley, R. 1972. *Cancer Res.* 32: 1775–80
13. Balhorn, R., Bordwell, J., Sellers, L., Granner, D., Chalkley, R. 1972. *Biochem. Biophys. Res. Commun.* 46: 1326–33
14. Balhorn, R., Chalkley, R., Granner, D., 1972. *Biochemistry* 11:1094–98
15. Balhorn, R., Oliver, D., Hohmann, P., Chalkley, R., Granner, D. 1972. *Biochemistry* 11:3915–21
16. Balhorn, R., Rieke, W., Chalkley, R. 1971. *Biochemistry* 10:3952–59
17. Balhorn, R., Tanphaichitr, N., Chalkley, R., Granner, D. 1973. *Biochemistry* 12:5146–50
18. Barden, N., Labrie, F. 1973. *Biochemistry* 12:3096–3102
19. Barela, T. D., Kizer, D. E. 1974. *Biochim. Biophys. Acta* 335:218–24
20. Benjamin, W. B., Gellhorn, A. 1968. *Proc. Natl. Acad. Sci. USA* 59:262–68
21. Bentley, P. J. 1966. *Biol. Rev. Cambridge Philos. Soc.* 41:275–316
22. Berlin, C. M., Schimke, R. T. 1965. *Mol. Pharmacol.* 1:149–58
23. Biffi, U. 1898. *Virchows Arch.* 152:130
24. Bitte, L., Kabat, D. 1972. *J. Biol. Chem.* 247:5345–50
25. Blankenship, J., Bresnick, E. 1974. *Biochim. Biophys. Acta* 340:218–26
26. Blanchard, J. M., Brissac, C., Jeanteur, P. H. 1974. *Proc. Natl. Acad. Sci. USA* 71:1882–86
27. Blanchard, J. M., Ducamp, C. H., Jeanteur, P. H. 1975. *Nature* 253:467–68
28. Blat, C., Loeb, J. E. 1971. *FEBS Lett.* 18:124–26
29. Blum, H. E., Pocinwong, S., Fischer, E. H. 1974. *Proc. Natl. Acad. Sci. USA* 71:2198–2202

30. Bonner, J. et al 1973. *Cold Spring Harbor Symp. Quant. Biol.* 38:303–10
31. Bownds, D., Dawes, J., Miller, J., Stahlman, M. 1972. *Nature New Biol.* 237:125–27
32. Bowness, J. M. 1966. *Science* 152:1370–71
33. Bradbury, E. M., Inglis, R. J., Matthews, H. R. 1974. *Nature* 247:257–61
34. Bradbury, E. M., Inglis, R. J., Matthews, H. R., Langan, T. A. 1974. *Nature* 249:553–55
35. Bradbury, E. M., Inglis, R. J., Matthews, H. R., Sarner, N. 1973. *Eur. J. Biochem.* 33:131–39
36. Buckingham, R. H., Stocken, L. A. 1970. *Biochem. J.* 117:157–60
37. Burnett, G., Kennedy, E. P. 1954. *J. Biol. Chem.* 211:969–81
38. Carlson, C. A., Kim, K. H. 1973. *J. Biol. Chem.* 248:378–80
39. Carnegie, P. R., Dunkley, P. R., Kemp, B. E., Murray, A. W. 1974. *Nature* 249:147–50
40. Carratu, G., Manzocchi, L. A., Lanzani, G. A., Giannattasio, M. 1974. *Plant Sci. Lett.* 3:313–21
41. Casnellie, J. E., Greengard, P. 1974. *Proc. Natl. Acad. Sci. USA* 71:1891–95
42. Cawthorn, M. L., Bitte, L. F., Krystosek, A., Kabat, D. 1974. *J. Biol. Chem.* 249:275–78
43. Chae, C. B., Smith, M. C., Irvin, J. L. 1972. *Biochim. Biophys. Acta* 287:134–39
44. Chang, K. J., Cuetracasas, P. 1974. *J. Biol. Chem.* 249:3170–80
45. Chang, K. J., Marcus, N. A., Cuatracasas, P. 1974. *J. Biol. Chem.* 249:6854–65
46. Chapman, K. S. R., Trewavas, A. J., Van Loon, L. C. 1975. *Plant Physiol.* 55:293–96
47. Chargaff, E. 1942. *J. Biol. Chem.* 142:505–14
48. Chen, C. C., Smith, D. L., Bruegger, B. B., Halpern, R. M., Smith, R. A. 1974. *Biochemistry* 13:3785–89
49. Chiu, J. F., Craddock, C., Getz, S., Hnilica, L. S. 1973. *FEBS Lett.* 33:247–50
50. Comorosan, S., Lugojan, P. 1968. *Eur. J. Biochem.* 6:460–66
51. Constantopoulos, A., Najjar, V. A. 1974. *Biochem. Biophys. Res. Commun.* 53:794–99
52. Cook, W. H., Lipkin, D., Markham, R. 1957. *J. Am. Chem. Soc.* 79:3607
53. Corbin, J. D., Krebs, E. G. 1969. *Biochem. Biophys. Res. Commun.* 36:328–36
54. Cori, G. T., Green, A. A. 1943. *J. Biol. Chem.* 151:31–43
55. Correze, L., Pinell, P., Nunez, J. 1972. *FEBS Lett.* 23:87–91
56. Cross, M. E., Ord, M. G. 1970. *Biochem. J.* 118:191–93
57. Dahl, J. L., Hokin, L. E. 1974. *Ann. Rev. Biochem.* 43:327–56
58. Daile, P., Carnegie, P. R. 1974. *Biochem. Biophys. Res. Commun.* 61:852–58
59. Davidson, J. N., Frazer, S. C., Hutchison, W. C. 1951. *Biochem. J.* 49:311–18
60. DeLange, R. J., Smith, E. L. 1971. *Ann. Rev. Biochem.* 40:279–314
61. Delaunay, J., Loeb, J. E., Pierre, M., Schapira, G. 1973. *Biochim. Biophys. Acta* 312:147–51
62. Delorenzo, R. J., Greengard, P. 1973. *Proc. Natl. Acad. Sci. USA* 70:1831–35
63. Delorenzo, R. J., Walton, K. G., Curran, P. F., Greengard, P. 1973. *Proc. Natl. Acad. Sci. USA* 70:880–84
64. Demeis, L., Demello, M. C. F. 1973. *J. Biol. Chem.* 248:3691–3701
65. DeVerdier, C. H. 1953. *Acta Chem. Scand.* 7:192–93
66. Devilliers-Graaff, G., Von Holt, C. 1973. *Biochem. Biophys. Acta* 299:480–84
67. Dousa, T., Sands, H., Hechter, O. 1971. *Fed. Proc.* 30:200 (Abstr.)
68. Egly, J. M., Johnson, B. C., Stricker, C., Mandel, P., Kempf, J. 1972. *FEBS Lett.* 22:181–84
69. Eil, C., Wool, I. G. 1971. *Biochem. Biophys. Res. Commun.* 43:1001–9
70. Eil, C., Wool, I. G. 1973. *J. Biol. Chem.* 248:5122–29
71. Ibid, 5130–36
72. Eipper, B. A. 1972. *Proc. Natl. Acad. Sci. USA* 69:2283–87
73. Eipper, B. A. 1974. *J. Biol. Chem.* 249:1398–1406
74. Ibid, 1407–16
75. England, P. J. 1975. *FEBS Lett.* 50:57–60
76. Erlichman, J., Rosenfeld, R., Rosen, O. M. 1974. *J. Biol. Chem.* 249:5000–3
77. Farago, A., Romhanyi, T., Antoni, F., Takats, A., Fabian, F. 1975. *Nature* 254:88
78. Feinstein, R. N., Volk, M. E. 1949. *J. Biol. Chem.* 177:339–51
79. Fischer, E. H., Krebs, E. G. 1955. *J. Biol. Chem.* 216:121–26
80. Fleischer-Lambropoulos, H., Sarkander, H. I., Brade, W. P. 1974. *FEBS Lett.* 45:329–32
81. Fontana, J. A., Picciano, O., Loven-

berg, W. 1972. *Biochem. Biophys. Res. Commun.* 49:1225–32

82. Forte, L. R., Byington, K. H. 1973. See Ref. 5, 303

83. Forte, L. R., Chao, W. T. H., Walkenbach, R. J., Byington, K. H. 1972. *Biochem. Biophys. Res. Commun.* 49: 1510–17

84. Frank, R. W., Cavanagh, H. D., Kenyon, K. R. 1973. *J. Biol. Chem.* 248: 596–609

85. Frenster, J. H. 1965. *Nature* 206: 680–83

86. Friedkin, M., Lehninger, A. L. 1949. *J. Biol. Chem.* 177:775–84

87. Friedman, D. L., Larner, J. 1962. *Biochim. Biophys. Acta* 64:185–86

88. Gallinaro-Matringe, H., Jacob, M. 1973. *FEBS Lett.* 36:105–8

89. Gander, E. S., Stewart, A. C., Morel, C. M., Scherrer, K. 1973. *Eur. J. Biochem.* 38:443–52

90. Ganote, C. E., Grantham, J. J., Moses, H. L., Burg, M. B., Orloff, J. 1968. *J. Cell Biol.* 36:355–67

91. Garren, L. D., Ney, R. L., Davis, W. W. 1965. *Proc. Natl. Acad. Sci. USA* 53:1443–50

92. Gershey, E. L., Kleinsmith, L. J. 1969. *Biochim. Biophys. Acta* 194:519–25

93. Gill, G. N., Walton, G. M., Holdy, K. E., Mariash, C. N., Kalstrom, J. B. 1973. See Ref. 5, 175–87

94. Gilman, A. G. 1970. *Proc. Natl. Acad. Sci. USA* 67:305–12

95. Goodman, D. B. P., Rasmussen, H., Dibrella, F., Guthrow, C. E. 1970. *Proc. Natl. Acad. Sci. USA* 67:652–59

96. Gordon, J. 1971. *Biochem. Biophys. Res. Commun.* 44:579–86

97. Gorovsky, M. A., Keevart, J. B., Pleger, G. L. 1974. *J. Cell Biol.* 61:134–45

98. Grankowski, N., Kudlicki, N., Gasior, E. 1974. *FEBS Lett.* 47:103–6

99. Gravell, M., Cromeans, T. L. 1972. *Virology* 48:847–51

100. Greengard, P. 1973. See Ref. 5, 145–74

101. Gressner, A. M., Wool, I. G. 1974. *J. Biol. Chem.* 249:6917–25

102. Gressner, A. M., Wool, I. G. 1974. *Biochem. Biophys. Res. Commun.* 760: 1482–90

103. Griffin, M. J., Price, G. H., Tu, S. 1973. See Ref. 5, 301

104. Grummt, I. 1974. *FEBS Lett.* 39: 125–28

105. Gurley, L. R., Walters, R. A. 1974. *Biochem. Biophys. Res. Commun.* 55:697–703

106. Gurley, L. R., Walters, R. A., Tobey, R. A. 1973. See Ref. 5, 297

107. Gurley, L. R., Walters, R. A., Tobey, R. A. 1973. *Biochem. Biophys. Res. Commun.* 50:744–50

108. Gurley, L. R., Walters, R. A., Tobey, R. A. 1973. *Arch. Biochem. Biophys.* 154:212–18

109. Gurley, L. R., Walters, R. A., Tobey, R. A. 1973. *Fed. Proc.* 32:587

110. Gurley, L. R., Walters, R. A., Tobey, R. A. 1974. *Arch. Biochem. Biophys.* 164:469–77

111. Gurley, L. R., Walters, R. A., Tobey, R. A. 1974. *J. Cell Biol.* 60:356–64

112. Guthrow, C. E., Allen, J. E., Rasmussen, H., 1972. *J. Biol. Chem.* 247:8145–53

113. Guthrow, C. E., Brunswick, D. J., Cooperman, B. S., Rasmussen, H. 1973. See Ref. 5, 319

114. Gutierrez-Cernosek, R. M., Hnilica, L. S. 1971. *Biochim. Biophys. Acta* 247:348–54

115. Harris, D. L. 1946. *J. Biol. Chem.* 165:541–51

116. Hatanaka, M., Twiddy, E., Gilden, R. V. 1972. *Virology* 47:536–38

117. Hepler, P. K., Palevitz, B. A. 1974. *Ann. Rev. Plant Physiol.* 25:309–62

118. Higashino, N., Takeda, M. 1974. *J. Biochem.* 75:189–91

119. Hnilica, L. S. 1972. *The Structure and Biological Functions of Histones.* CRC Press. 214 pp.

120. Holzer, H., Duntze, W. 1971. *Ann. Rev. Biochem.* 40:345–74

121. Inoue, Y., Yamamura, H., Nishizuka, Y. 1973. *Biochem. Biophys. Res. Commun.* 50:228–36

122. Issinger, O. G., Traut, R. R. 1974. *Biochem. Biophys. Res. Commun.* 59: 829–36

123. Jard, S., Bastide, F. 1970. *Biochem. Biophys. Res. Commun.* 39:559–66

124. Jergil, B., Ohlsson, R., 1972. *Eur. J. Biochem.* 28:546–54

125. Ibid 1974. 46:13–21

126. Jergil, B., Sung, M., Dixon, G. H. 1970. *J. Biol. Chem.* 245:5867–70

127. Johnson, E. M., Karn, J., Allfrey, V. G. 1974. *J. Biol. Chem.* 249:4991–99

128. Johnson, E. M., Maeno, H., Greengard, P. 1971. *J. Biol. Chem.* 246:7331–39

129. Johnson, E. M., Ueda, T., Maeno, H., Greengard, P. 1972. *J. Biol. Chem.* 247:5650–52

130. Johnson, R. M., Albert, S. 1953. *J. Biol. Chem.* 200:335–44

131. Jolicoeur, P., Labrie, F. 1974. *Eur. J. Biochem.* 48:1–6

132. Jones, D. A., Rodnight, R. 1971. *Biochem. J.* 121:597–600

133. Jost, J. P., Rickenberg, H. V. 1971. *Ann. Rev. Biochem.* 40:741–74
134. Jungmann, R. A., Hiestand, P. C., Schweppe, J. S. 1974. *Endocrinology* 94:168
135. Jungmann, R. A., Hiestand, P. C., Schweppe, J. S. 1974. *J. Biol. Chem.* 249:5444–51
136. Jungmann, R. A., Schweppe, J. S. 1972. *J. Biol. Chem.* 247:5535–42
137. Ibid, 5543–48
138. Kabat, D. 1970. *Biochemistry* 9: 4160–75
139. Ibid 1971. 10:197–203
140. Kabat, D. 1972. *J. Biol. Chem.* 247: 5338–44
141. Kadohama, N., Turkington, R. W. 1974. *J. Biol. Chem.* 249:6225–33
142. Kamiyama, M., Dastugue, B., Defer, N., Kruh, J. 1972. *Biochim. Biophys. Acta* 277:576–81
143. Kamiyama, M., Dastugue, B., Kruh, J. 1971. *Biochem. Biophys. Res. Commun.* 44:1345–50
144. Karn, J., Johnson, E. M., Vidali, G., Allfrey, V. G. 1974. *J. Biol. Chem.* 249:667–77
145. Keates, R. A. B. 1973. *Nature* 244: 355–57
146. Keates, R. A. B. 1973. *Biochem. Biophys. Res. Commun.* 54:655–61
147. Keates, R. A. B., Trewavas, A. J. 1974. *Plant Physiol.* 54:95–99
148. Kennedy, E. P., Smith, S. W. 1954. *J. Biol. Chem.* 207:153–65
149. Kinzel, V., Mueller, G. C. 1973. *Biochim. Biophys. Acta* 322:337–51
150. Kirchberger, M. A., Tada, M., Katz, A. M. 1974. *J. Biol. Chem.* 249:6166–73
151. Kirchberger, M. A., Tada, M., Yoshioka, S., Katz, A. M. 1973. See Ref. 5, 309
152. Kish, V. M., Kleinsmith, L. J. 1974. *J. Biol. Chem.* 249:750–60
153. Kleiman, J. H., Moss, B. 1975. *J. Biol. Chem.* 250:2420–29
154. Ibid, 2430–37
155. Kleinsmith, L. J. 1973. *J. Biol. Chem.* 248:5645–53
156. Kleinsmith, L. J., Allfrey, V. G. 1969. *Biochim. Biophys. Acta* 175:123–35
157. Ibid, 136
158. Kleinsmith, L. J., Allfrey, V. G., Mirsky, A. E. 1966. *Proc. Natl. Acad. Sci. USA* 55:1182–89
159. Kleinsmith, L. J., Allfrey, V. G., Mirsky, A. E. 1966. *Science* 154:780–81
160. Kleinsmith, L. J., Hiedema, J., Carroll, A. 1970. *Nature* 226:1025–26
161. Korenman, S. G., Bhalla, R. C., Sanborn, B. M., Stevens, R. H. 1974. *Science* 183:430–32
162. Krebs, E. G. 1972. *Curr. Top. Cell. Regul.* 5:99–131
163. Krebs, E. G., 1964. *Biochemistry* 3:1022–33
164. Krebs, E. G., DeLange, R. J., Kemp, R. G., Riley, W. D. 1966. *Pharmacol. Rev.* 18:163–75
165. Krebs, E. G., Fischer, E. H. 1956. *Biochim. Biophys. Acta* 20:150–55
166. Krebs, E. G. et al 1973. See Ref. 5, 31–47
167. Kuhn, H. 1974. *Nature* 250:588–90
168. Kuhn, H., Dreyer, W. J. 1972. *FEBS Lett.* 20:1–6
169. Kuo, J. F., Greengard, P. 1969. *J. Biol. Chem.* 244:3417–19
170. Kuo, J. F., Greengard, P. 1969. *Proc. Natl. Acad. Sci. USA* 64:1349–55
171. Kury, G., Ramwell, P. W., McConnell, H. M., 1974. *Biochem. Biophys. Res. Commun.* 56:478–83
172. Labrie, F., Lemaire, S., Poirier, G., Pelletier, F., Boucher, R. 1971. *J. Biol. Chem.* 246:7311–17
173. Lagnado, J. R., Lyons, C. A., Weller, M., Philipson, O. 1972. *Biochem. J.* 128:95
174. Lake, R. S. 1973. See Ref. 5, 295
175. Lake, R. S. 1973. *Nature* 242:145–46
176. Lake, R. S. 1973. *J. Cell Biol.* 58: 317–31
177. Lake, R. S., Goidl, J. A., Salzman, N. P. 1972. *Exp. Cell Res.* 73:113–21
178. Lake, R. S., Salzman, N. P. 1972. *Biochemistry* 11:4817–26
179. Langan, T. A. 1967. *Regulation of Nucleic Acid and Protein Biosynthesis*, ed. V. V. Koningsberger, L. Bosch, 10:233–43. B. B. A. Library Ser. Amsterdam: Elsevier
180. Langan, T. A. 1968. *Science* 162: 579–80
181. Langan, T. A. 1969. *J. Biol. Chem.* 244:5763–65
182. Langan, T. A. 1969. *Proc. Natl. Acad. Sci. USA* 64:1276–83
183. Langan, T. A. 1971. *Ann. NY Acad. Sci.* 185:166
184. Langan, T. A. 1973. *Adv. Cyclic Nucleotide Res.* 3:99–151
185. Langan, T. A. 1973. See Ref. 5, 287–91
186. Layne, P., Constantopoulos, A., Judge, J. F., Rauner, R., Najjar, V. A. 1973. *Biochem. Biophys. Res. Commun.* 53: 800–5
187. Lee, K. L., Nickol, J. M. 1974. *J. Biol. Chem.* 249:6024–26
188. Lemay, A. et al 1974. *J. Biol. Chem.* 249:323–28

189. Leterrier, J. F., Rappaport, L., Nenez, J., Osty, J. 1974. *FEBS Lett.* 46:285–88
190. Li, C. C., Amos, H. 1971. *Biochem. Biophys. Res. Commun.* 45:1398–1407
191. Li, H. C., Brown, G. G. 1973. *Biochem. Biophys. Res. Commun.* 53:875–81
192. Lin, P. P. C. 1974. *Adv. Cyclic Nucleotide Res.* 4:439–61
193. Lin, P. P. C., Varner, J. E. 1972. *Biochim. Biophys. Acta* 276:454–74
194. Lipmann, F. A., Levene, P. A. 1932. *J. Biol. Chem.* 98:109–17
195. Liu, A. Y. C., Greengard, P. 1974. *Proc. Natl. Acad. Sci. USA* 71:3869–73
196. Loeb, J. E., Blat, C. 1970. *FEBS Lett.* 10:105–8
197. Louie, A. J., Dixon, G. H. 1972. *Proc. Natl. Acad. Sci. USA* 69:1975–79
198. Louie, A. J., Dixon, G. H. 1973. *Nature New Biol.* 243:164–68
199. Louie, A. J., Landido, E. P. M., Dixon, G. H. 1973. *Cold Spring Harbor Symp. Quant. Biol.* 38:803–19
200. Louie, A. J., Sung, M. T., Dixon, G. H. 1973. *J. Biol. Chem.* 248:3335–40
201. MacGillivray, A. J., Rickwood, D. 1974. *Eur. J. Biochem.* 41:181–89
202. Maeno, H., Johnson, E. M., Greengard, P. 1971. *J. Biol. Chem.* 246:134–42
203. Maeno, H., Reyes, P. L., Ueda, T., Rudolph, S. A., Greengard, P. 1974. *Arch. Biochem. Biophys.* 164:551–59
204. Majunder, G. C., Turkington, R. W., 1972. *J. Biol. Chem.* 247:7207–17
205. Mallette, L. E., Neblett, M., Exton, J. H., Langan, T. A. 1973. *J. Biol. Chem.* 248:6289–91
206. Man, N. T., Norris, G. E., Cole, R. J. 1974. *FEBS Lett.* 42:257–61
207. Marks, D. B., Woon, K. P., Borun, T. W. 1973. *J. Biol. Chem.* 248:5660–67
208. Marshak, A., Calvet, F. 1949. *J. Cell. Comp. Physiol.* 34:451–61
209. Martelo, O. J. 1973. See Ref. 5, 199–219
210. Martelo, O. J., Hirsch, J. 1974. *Biochem. Biophys. Res. Commun.* 58: 1008–15
211. Martelo, O. J., Wood, S. L. C., Davie, E. W. 1974. *J. Mol. Biol.* 87:685–96
212. Martin, T. et al 1973. *Cold Spring Harbor Symp. Quant. Biol.* 38:921–32
213. Martini, O. H. W., Gould, H. J. *Biochim. Biophys. Acta* 295:621–29
214. McDonald, R. J., Ronzio, R. A. 1974. *FEBS Lett.* 40:203–6
215. McMahon, D. 1974. *Science* 185: 1012–21
216. McPherson, J., Fenner, C., Smith, A., Mason, D. T., Wikman-Coffelt, J. 1974. *FEBS Lett.* 47:149–54

217. Mecham, D. K., Olcott, H. S. 1949. *J. Am. Chem. Soc.* 71:3670–89
218. Meischer, F. 1870. *Med.-Chem. Untersuch.* 4:502
219. Miyamato, E., Kakiuchi, S., Kakimoto, Y. 1974. *Nature* 249:150–51
220. Miyamoto, E., Kuo, J. F., Greengard, P. 1969. *Science* 165:63–65
221. Miyamoto, E., Shiro, K. 1974. *J. Biol. Chem.* 249:2769–77
222. Monier, D., Santhanam, K., Wagle, S. R. 1972. *Biochem. Biophys. Res. Commun.* 46:1881–86
223. Morel, C., Gander, E. S., Herzeberg, M., Dubochet, J., Scherrer, K. 1973. *Eur. J. Biochem.* 36:455–64
224. Moret, V., Clari, G., Pinna, L. A. 1975. *Biochem. Biophys. Res. Commun.* 62:1011–17
225. Moyer, S. A., Summers, D. F. 1974. *J. Virol.* 13:455–65
226. Murofushi, H. 1973. *Biochim. Biophys. Acta* 327:354–64
227. Narumi, S., Miyamoto, E. 1974. *Biochim. Biophys. Acta* 350:215–24
228. Niles, R. M., Mount, M. S. 1974. *Plant Physiol.* 54:372–73
229. Oliver, D., Balhorn, R., Granner, D., Chalkley, R. 1972. *Biochemistry* 11: 3921–25
230. Olson, M. O., Orrick, L. R., Jones, C., Busch, H. 1974. *J. Biol. Chem.* 249:2823–27
231. Ord, M. G., Stocken, L. A. 1969. *Biochem. J.* 112:81–89
232. Osborne, T. B., Campbell, G. F. 1900. *J. Am. Chem. Soc.* 22:422–42
233. Ownby, J. D., Ross, C. W., Key, J. L. 1975. *Plant Physiol.* 55:346–51
234. Panyim, S., Bilek, D., Chalkley, R. 1971. *J. Biol. Chem.* 246:4206–15
235. Panyim, S., Chalkley, R. 1969. *Biochemistry* 8:3972–79
236. Panyim, S., Chalkley, R., Spiker, S., Oliver, D. 1970. *Biochim. Biophys. Acta* 214:216–22
237. Paoletti, E., Moss, B. 1972. *J. Virol.* 10:417–24
238. Paul, J., Gilmour, S. 1968. *J. Mol. Biol.* 34:305–16
239. Pavlovic-Hournac, M., Delbauffe, D., Virion, A., Nunez, J. 1973. *FEBS Lett.* 33:65–69
240. Pawse, A. R., Ord, M. G., Stocken, L. A. 1971. *Biochem. J.* 122:713–19
241. Penman, S., Vesco, C., Penman, M. 1968. *J. Mol. Biol.* 34:49–69
242. Perlmann, G. 1955. *Adv. Protein Chem.* 10:1–32
243. Pierre, M., Creuzet, C., Loeb, J. 1974. *FEBS Lett.* 45:88–91

244. Piras, M. M., Piras, R. 1974. *Eur. J. Biochem.* 47:443–49
245. Piras, M. M., Staneloni, R., Leiderman, B., Piras, R. 1972. *FEBS Lett.* 23:199–202
246. Pires, E., Perry, S. V., Thomas, M. A. W. 1974. *FEBS Lett.* 41:292–96
247. Platz, R. D., Hnilica, L. S. 1973. *Biochem. Biophys. Res. Commun.* 54:222–27
248. Platz, R. D., Kish, V. M., Kleinsmith, L. J. 1970. *FEBS Lett.* 12:38–40
249. Platz, R. D., Stein, G. S., Kleinsmith, L. J. 1973. *Biochem. Biophys. Res. Commun.* 51:735–40
250. Plimmer, R. H., Bayliss, W. M. 1906. *J. Physiol.* 33:439–46
251. Pogo, B. G. T., Allfrey, V. G., Mirsky, A. E. 1966. *Proc. Natl. Acad. Sci. USA* 55:805–12
252. Posternak, S. 1927. *Biochem. J.* 21:289
253. Prestayko, A. W., Olson, M. O. J., Busch, H. 1974. *FEBS Lett.* 44:131–35
254. Rahmsdorf, H. J., Herrlich, P., Pai, S. H., Schweiger, M., Wittman, H. G. 1973. *Mol. Gen. Genet.* 127:259–71
255. Rahmsdorf, H. J. et al 1974. *Proc. Natl. Acad. Sci. USA* 71:586–89
256. Rall, T. W., Sutherland, E. W., Wosilait, W. D. 1956. *J. Biol. Chem.* 218:483–92
257. Ralph, R. K., McCombs, P. J. A., Tener, G., Wojcik, S. J. 1972. *Biochem. J.* 130:901–11
258. Randall, C. C., Rogers, H. W., Downer, D. N., Gentry, G. A. 1972. *J. Virol.* 9:216–22
259. Rankine, A. D., Leader, D. P. 1975. *FEBS Lett.* 52:284–87
260. Rappaport, L., Leterrier, J. F., Nunez, J. 1972. *FEBS Lett.* 26:349–52
261. Rasmussen, H., Goodman, D. B. P., Tenenhouse, A. 1972. *CRC Crit. Rev. Biochem.* 1:95–161
262. Reiber, M., Bacalao, J. 1973. *Biochem. J.* 131:641–44
263. Rickwood, D., Riches, P. G., MacGillivray, J. A. 1973. *Biochim. Biophys. Acta* 299:162–71
264. Rickwood, D., Threlfall, G., MacGillivray, A. J., Paul, J. 1972. *Biochem. J.* 129:50p
265. Rikans, L. E., Ruddon, R. W. 1973. *Biochem. Biophys. Res. Commun.* 54:387–94
266. Rosemond, H., Moss, B. 1973. *J. Virol.* 11:961–70
267. Rosen, O. M., Rubin, C. S., Erlichman, J. 1973. See Ref. 5, 67–81
268. Roses, A. D., Appel, S. H. 1973. *Proc. Natl. Acad. Sci. USA* 70:1855–59
269. Roses, A. D., Appel, S. H. 1973. *J. Biol. Chem.* 248:1408–11
270. Rous, S. 1974. *FEBS Lett.* 44:55–58
271. Rubin, C. S., Rosen, O. M. 1973. *Biochem. Biophys. Res. Commun.* 50:421–29
272. Rubin, C. S., Rosen, O. M. 1975. *Ann. Rev. Biochem.* 44:831–87
273. Rubin, P., Filner, P. 1973. *J. Cell Biol.* 56:628–35
274. Rubinstein, A. S., Gravell, M., Darlington, R. 1972. *Virology* 50:287–90
275. Ruddon, R. W., Anderson, S. L. 1972. *Biochem. Biophys. Res. Commun.* 46:1499–1508
276. Rudolph, S. A., Greengard, P. 1974. *J. Biol. Chem.* 249:5684–87
277. Russell, W. C., Skehel, J. J., Machado, R., Pereira, H. G. 1972. *Virology* 50:931–34
278. Salkowski, E. 1893. *C.F.D. Med. Wiss.* 23:28
279. Sands, H., Meyer, T. A. 1973. *Biochim. Biophys. Acta* 321:489–95
280. Schwartz, I. L., Shlatz, L. J., Kinne-Saffran, E., Kinne, R. 1974. *Proc. Natl. Acad. Sci. USA* 71:2595–99
281. Shea, M., Kleinsmith, L. J. 1973. *Biochem. Biophys. Res. Commun.* 50:473–77
282. Shelanski, M. L., Gaskin, F., Cantor, C. R. 1973. *Proc. Natl. Acad. Sci. USA* 70:765–68
283. Shelton, K. R., Seligy, V. L., Neelin, J. M. 1972. *Arch. Biochem. Biophys.* 153:375–83
284. Shepherd, G. R., Noland, B. J., Hardin, J. M. 1971. *Exp. Cell Res.* 67:474–77
285. Sherod, D., Johnson, G., Chalkley, R. 1970. *Biochemistry* 9:4611–15
286. Shichi, H., Somers, R. L., O'Brien, P. J. 1974. *Biochem. Biophys. Res. Commun.* 61:217–21
287. Shimomura, R., Matsumura, S., Nishizuka, Y. 1975. *J. Biochem.* 75:1–10
288. Shlatz, L. J., Kinne, R., Kinne-Saffran, E., Schwartz, I. L. 1973. *Physiologist* 16:451
289. Shlatz, L. J., Marinetti, G. V. 1971. *Biochem. Biophys. Res. Commun.* 45:51–56
290. Siebert, G., Ord, M. G., Stocken, L. A. 1971. *Biochem. J.* 122:721–25
291. Silberstein, H., August, J. T., 1973. *J. Virol.* 12:511–22
292. Singer, M. F., Fruton, J. S. 1957. *J. Biol. Chem.* 229:111–20
293. Sloboda, R. D., Rudolph, S. A., Rosenbaum, J. L., Greengard, P. 1975. *Proc. Natl. Acad. Sci. USA* 72:177–81

294. Smith, D. L., Bruegger, B. B., Halpern, R. M., Smith, R. A. 1973. *Nature* 246:103–4
295. Smith, D. L. et al 1974. *Biochemistry* 13:3280–85
296. Soifer, D., Laszlo, A. H., Scotto, J. M. 1972. *Biochim. Biophys. Acta* 271:182–92
297. Sokol, F., Clark, H. F. 1973. *Virology* 52:246–63
298. Sonenburg, M. 1971. *Proc. Natl. Acad. Sci. USA* 68:1051–55
299. Stahl, J., Welfle, H., Bielka, H. 1972. *FEBS Lett.* 26:233–36
300. Steck, A. J., Appel, S. H. 1974. *J. Biol. Chem.* 249:5416–20
301. Stein, G. S., Spelsberg, T., Kleinsmith, L. J. 1974. *Science* 183:817–24
302. Steinberg, D. 1973. See Ref. 5, 47–61
303. Stevely, W. S., Stocken, L. A. 1968. *Biochem. J.* 110:187–91
304. Strand, M., August, J. T. 1971. *Nature New Biol.* 233:137–40
305. Sulakhe, P. V., Drummond, G. I., 1974. *Arch. Biochem. Biophys.* 161:448–55
306. Sundararajan, T. A., Sarma, P. S. 1954. *Biochem. J.* 56:125
307. Sutherland, E. W. 1973. See Ref. 5, 1–10
308. Sutherland, E. W., Rall, T. W. 1957. *J. Am. Chem. Soc.* 79:3608
309. Sutherland, E. W., Wosilait, W. D. 1955. *Nature* 175:169–70
310. Taborsky, G. 1974. *Adv. Protein Chem.* 28:1–210
311. Tada, M., Kirchberger, M. A., Katz, A. M. 1975. *J. Biol. Chem.* 250:2640–47
312. Takeda, M., Yamamura, H., Ohga, Y. 1971. *Biochem. Biophys. Res. Commun.* 42:103–10
313. Tan, K. B., Sokol, F. 1972. *J. Virol.* 10:985–94
314. Tanphaichitr, N., Balhorn, R., Granner, D., Chalkley, R. 1974. *Biochemistry* 13:4249–54
315. Teng, C. T., Teng, C. S., Allfrey, V. G. 1970. *Biochem. Biophys. Res. Commun.* 41:690–96
316. Teng, C. S., Teng, C. T., Allfrey, V. G. 1971. *J. Biol. Chem.* 246:3597–3609
317. Traugh, J. A., Mumby, M., Traut, R. R. 1973. *Proc. Natl. Acad. Sci. USA* 70:373–76
318. Trevor, A. J., Rodnight, R. 1965. *Biochem. J.* 95:889–96
319. Trewavas, A. J. 1973. *Plant Physiol.* 51:760–65
320. Trewavas, A. J. 1976. *Molecular Biology of Plants*, ed. J. Bryant. New York: Academic. In press
321. Tsuzuki, J., Loeb, J. 1974. *Exp. Cell Res.* 88:303–10
322. Turkington, R. W., Riddle, M. 1969. *J. Biol. Chem.* 244:6040–46
323. Ueda, T., Maeno, H., Greengard, P. 1973. *J. Biol. Chem.* 248:8295–8305
324. Van Loon, L. C., Trewavas, A. J., Chapman, K. 1975. *Plant Physiol.* 55:288–92
325. Ventimiglia, F. A., Wool, I. G. 1974. *Proc. Natl. Acad. Sci. USA* 71:350–54
326. Vidali, G., Boffa, L. C., Allfrey, V. G. 1972. *J. Biol. Chem.* 247:7365–73
327. Walsh, D. A., Perkins, J. P., Krebs, E. G. 1968. *J. Biol. Chem.* 243:3763–74
328. Walton, G. M., Gill, G. N. 1973. *Biochemistry* 12:2604–11
329. Walton, G. M., Gill, G. N., Abrass, I. B., Garren, L. D. 1971. *Proc. Natl. Acad. Sci. USA* 68:880–84
330. Watanabe, Y., Sakuma, S., Tanaka, S. 1974. *FEBS Lett.* 41:331–34
331. Weller, M., Rodnight, R. 1970. *Nature* 225:187–88
332. Weller, M., Rodnight, R. 1971. *Biochem. J.* 124:393–406
333. Ibid 1973. 132:483–92
334. Ibid 1974. 142:605–9
335. Weller, M., Virmaux, N., Mandel, P. 1975. *Proc. Natl. Acad. Sci. USA* 72:381–85
336. Williams-Ashman, H. G., Kennedy, E. P. 1952. *Cancer Res.* 12:415–19
337. Wray, H. L., Gray, R. R., Olsson, R. A. 1973. *J. Biol. Chem.* 248:1496–98
338. Zahlten, R. N., Hochberg, A. A., Stratman, F. W., Lardy, H. A. 1972. *Proc. Natl. Acad. Sci. USA* 69:800–4
339. Zillig, W. et al 1975. *Proc. Natl. Acad. Sci. USA* 72:2506–10

Ann. Rev. Plant Physiol. 1976. 27:375–83

PARAMAGNETIC INTERMEDIATES IN PHOTOSYNTHESIS

♦7614

James R. Bolton

Department of Chemistry, Photochemistry Unit,[1] The University of Western Ontario, London, Ontario N6A 5B7, Canada

Joseph T. Warden

Biochemistry Program, Department of Chemistry, Rensselaer Polytechnic Institute, Troy, New York 12181

CONTENTS

INTRODUCTION

Photosynthetic applications of electron spin resonance (ESR) was last reviewed in this series by Weaver (80), to whose work the reader is referred for references prior to 1968. Since then other reviews have appeared on this subject by Kohl (47), Weaver & Weaver (81) and by Warden & Bolton (77). Also, Bearden & Malkin have reviewed primary photochemical reactions in chloroplast photosynthesis (6), and Clayton has produced a similar review for bacteria (13). We believe that the literature through 1973 has been covered adequately in these reviews; hence the bulk of our references will cover the period from January 1974 to August 1975. The approach we have adopted is somewhat unique, in that rather than treating each system separately [e.g. bacteria, Photosystem I (PSI) and Photosystem II (PSII)], we have chosen to analyze the primary photochemistry of the reaction center

[1]Publication No. 146

complex in terms of its components (primary donors, primary acceptors, and secondary components). Thus we wish to emphasize the salient similarities among the different photosystems. We will treat only paramagnetic centers which are primary or secondary to the photochemical process.

The principal technique of interest in this review will be ESR spectroscopy. Several general treatments of ESR are available (71, 82). Likewise, a good general introduction to the study of photosynthesis is provided by the books of Govindjee (30) and Rabinowich & Govindjee (67). One might ask why ESR is so important in photosynthesis studies. It is now clear that almost all photosynthetic photochemistry involves a photochemical electron transfer from a special chlorophyll (or bacteriochlorophyll) species to an electron acceptor. By its very nature this process produces changes in the paramagnetism of the donor and acceptor species; and indeed almost all primary donor and acceptor entities have now been detected by ESR. ESR is quite sensitive and has the additional advantage of being able to ignore all diamagnetic molecules. Additionally, transient techniques are now available which permit detection of paramagnetic intermediates with lifetimes as short as a few microseconds (11).

Primary Donors

The primary photochemical process in photosynthesis originates from a structurally unique chlorophyll species which we designate P. It should be noted that only 1% or less of the chlorophyll is photochemically active (30), the remainder being involved in the light-harvesting process. Much of the recent work in photosynthesis has focused on the elucidation of the chemical, physical, and biological nature of P and additionally the photophysical processes which precede photochemistry at P.

It is now well established that the primary photochemical step in photosynthetic systems involves a one-electron transfer from P to a primary acceptor which we denote as A_1(69). This leaves P in the state P^+ which is paramagnetic and gives rise to an ESR signal which has a characteristic g-factor (2.0025 ± 0.0001) and lineshape consistent with an immobilized chlorophyll cation (57, 77). The evidence linking the ESR signal with P^+ has been covered well in earlier reviews (6, 77, 81). However, the ESR signals of P^+ observed in vivo are narrower than those observed from chlorophyll cations in vitro by a factor of $\sqrt{2}$ which reflects the delocalization of the unpaired electron in vivo over a *special pair* of chlorophyll molecules (38, 60). The chemical nature of the *special pair* is ambiguous at present; however, in vitro experiments suggest that water or some other bifunctional molecule may form a bridge linking two chlorophylls in a parallel orientation (38) to permit pi-pi overlap between the two chlorophylls.

The strongest evidence for the *special pair* comes from electron nuclear double resonance (ENDOR) studies which indicate that the proton hyperfine couplings for the in vivo chlorophyll species are reduced by about a factor of *two* from those found in an in vitro solution of chlorophyll monomer cations (24, 59). These data are best interpreted as supporting the sharing of one unpaired electron between two chlorophyll species. Other evidence is provided by difference circular dichroism measurements for P (65) which reveal exciton components arising from the intimate interaction of several chlorophylls. The evidence for a *special pair* of chlorophylls is very good for P_{865} in bacteria and P_{700} in PSI of green plants and algae, but it is less complete for P_{680} in PSII. Here the only evidence is that the ESR linewidth in vivo is about the same as that of P^+_{700} (55).

If one accepts that P is composed of a chlorophyll dimer [Chl • X • Chl] where X is the linking ligand, then it is strange that this one structural species could have a widely varying redox potential in the various photosystems: P_{680} ($\gtrsim +800mV$) (55), P_{700} ($\sim +500mV$) (46) and P_{865} in bacteria ($\sim +450mV$) (64). We may speculate that environmental factors play an important role in altering redox potentials, particularly the hydrophobicity of the environment. In this regard Kassner has shown that the redox potentials of porphyrins are strongly influenced by the nature of the solvent (44). Additionally, the nature of the electron acceptor and the presence of transition metal ions in close proximity to P could also perturb redox potentials. This point could be particularly important in the case of P_{680} due to the high concentration of manganese and iron proteins in PSII.

Recent experiments suggest that a triplet intermediate may be involved in the primary photochemistry at P. When the primary acceptor is reduced so as to prevent photochemistry, then light-induced triplet chlorophyll ESR signals are observable in green plant, algal and bacterial systems at cryogenic temperatures (18, 50, 73). The signals are formed with a quantum yield near unity (84) and the zero-field splitting parameters D and E are significantly smaller than for chlorophyll triplets in vitro (50, 61, 73). In a previous review (77) we suggested that this difference in zero-field splitting factors was a consequence of the *special pair* model. Similar interpretations have been proposed by others (50, 73). An additional feature of the triplet ESR signals is that very strong spin polarization is observed both in vivo and in vitro (12, 45, 50, 51, 73). However, the nature of this polarization is quite different between the in vivo signals and the in vitro signals (12, 45, 51, 61) which may arise from the *special pair* nature of the in vivo signal. Further clarification of the nature of the dynamic spin polarization process will require detailed kinetic measurements of the population and decay rates for the various triplet sublevels. Additionally, the role of the acceptor in the spin polarization process in vivo needs to be ascertained.

The observation of triplet state ESR signals in photosynthetic systems has rekindled interest in the role of ^{3}Chl in the primary electron transfer process (28). It is worth noting in this regard that chlorophyll- (or bacteriochlorophyll-) sensitized electron transfer to quinones in protic solvents is mediated by ^{3}Chl (83). However, in aprotic solvents (e.g. dry acetone) it appears that electron transfer proceeds through the first excited singlet state of chlorophyll (34). Additionally, recent experiments seem to indicate that the formation of ^{3}Chl in vivo is probably a side reaction which only occurs when photochemistry is blocked. Picosecond measurements (39, 68) suggest that electron transfer occurs from a state having a lifetime of ~ 240 ps. The short lifetime of this state is consistent with a singlet rather than a triplet intermediate. A possible model for this intermediate is one in which the initial charge transfer occurs between the two molecules of the *special pair* or with one or more chlorophyll or perhaps pheophytin molecules nearby. The bacterial reaction center protein contains two bacteriochlorophyll molecules and two bacteriopheophytin molecules in addition to the *special pair* of bacteriochlorophylls in the P_{865} center. These additional molecules may form an overlapping chain which would aid in the transfer of the electron from P to A_1.

Primary Acceptors

For many years following the first observations of light-induced ESR signals in photosynthetic systems no signal was detected which could be ascribed to a primary acceptor species. This presented a paradox as, if it is accepted that the primary photochemical event involves a one-electron transfer reaction from P, then a change in the paramagnetism of the primary acceptor must also occur. Finally in 1971 Feher (23) detected a broad absorption ESR signal at 1.4K and ascribed it to the bacterial primary acceptor. Leigh & Dutton subsequently confirmed this assignment (49), obtaining a first derivative ESR spectrum with g components at 1.82 and 1.68. Feher et al (25) subsequently demonstrated that their absorption mode signal is mathematically equivalent to the first derivative signal of Dutton and Leigh. Similarly, in 1971 Malkin & Bearden (53) reported the detection in green plant photosystem I of a broad, ferredoxin-like ESR signal ($g \sim 2.04$, 1.94, and 1.86) which was irreversibly formed by light at low temperatures.

Since iron is the only transition metal present in significant amounts in bacterial reaction centers (23, 52), it is natural to assume that iron might be the primary acceptor. This assignment is supported by observation that the iron chelator o-phenanthroline binds specifically to reaction centers and inhibits secondary electron transport (32, 36). Additionally, o-phenanthroline alters the redox potential of the primary acceptor (15, 37). However, there are several observations which suggest that iron alone is not the primary acceptor: (*a*) replacement of iron by Mn yields photoactive reaction centers with unaltered back electron transfer kinetics (25); and (*b*) Mossbauer determinations with ^{57}Fe-enriched reaction centers indicate that iron exists in a +2 state regardless of the redox state of the primary acceptor (16).

Photoactive iron-free reaction centers exhibit a narrow, light-induced signal ($g = 2.0050$) (52), which has been identified as the anion radical of ubiquinone (27). These observations suggest that ubiquinone (UQ) is a primary acceptor in bacteria. Additional evidence for the primacy of UQ is the observed inhibition of photochemistry when quinone is extracted from reaction center preparations of *R. spheroides* (14, 62). However, some investigators see no inhibition of photochemistry with complete UQ removal (32, 42, 72). Furthermore, the broad in vivo ESR spectrum is totally different from that of in vitro UQ$^-$.

Since it appears that neither iron nor UQ function alone as the primary acceptor, the alternative explanation is that they function together as a complex or tightly coupled unit (10, 26). Thus although UQ may act as the primary electron acceptor (70), the close proximity of the paramagnetic iron would perturb the magnetic environment of the UQ$^-$ so as to produce the very broad ESR spectrum.

In contrast to the bacterial system where the structure and identity of the primary acceptor should be elucidated in the near future, the situation in algal and green plant systems is much less optimistic (40). The early observations of Bearden & Malkin (5) that a broad iron-sulfur type signal occurs in stoichiometric proportion to P^+_{700}, along with other supporting data (4, 22), implicated a bound ferredoxin as the PSI primary acceptor. In fact, it appears that there are at least two bound ferredoxin components (20, 43). However, Warden et al (79) noted that the kinetics of P_{700} oxidation and reduction exhibited significant reversibility (5–30%) at low temperatures. Subsequently, McIntosh et al (58) demonstrated that although the bound ferredoxin lacked a low temperature reversible component, a weak broad resonance ($g = 1.75$ and 2.07) possessed identical kinetics to that of P^+_{700}. This new broad signal was proposed as reflecting the PSI primary acceptor which mediates electron transfer between P_{700} and bound ferredoxin (58). In support for this model, Evans & Cammack (19) observed that reduction of the bound ferredoxins by dithionite produces an enhancement of the reversible photooxidation of P_{700} at low temperatures. Evans et al (21) have been able to confirm the resonance at $g = 1.76$ and present a spectrum of that component. Nevertheless, other investigators have been unable to demonstrate the low temperature reversible P_{700} kinetics (55, 75). Additionally, Ke et al (41) indicate that the kinetics of appearance and disappearance of P^+_{700} and the bound ferredoxin signal are identical at low temperatures; however, the time resolution of their instrument may have precluded a valid comparison. Clearly further work is needed before this controversy will be resolved.

To date no ESR signal has been detected due to the primary acceptor of photosystem II (PSII), although from optical difference spectra (29, 66) it would appear that the primary photoreduction involves the formation of a bound plastosemiquinone anion. The absence of an ESR spectrum may be understood if a paramagnetic transition metal (Fe?) resides close by to strongly distort the magnetic environment of the anion radical.

It is tempting to compare the primary acceptor species in bacteria, PSI, and PSII. The g-factors (1.76 and 2.07) reported by McIntosh et al (58) and Evans et al (21) for the PSI component bear some resemblance to those reported (49) for the bacterial primary acceptor (1.68, 1.82, and 2.0). Similarly, quinones have been assigned a definite role in bacterial and PSII primary acceptors; the extent of their participation in PSI photochemistry remains to be ascertained.

Secondary Components

Although our approach thus far has emphasized the similarity in the primary photochemistry of photosynthesis among the various photosystems, this methodology breaks down when we consider secondary donors and acceptors. Nevertheless some similarities still exist between the donors for PSI and bacteria. A cytochrome c appears to be the immediate donor to P^+_{865} in bacteria (64). In PSI of green plants the situation is more confused. Two metalloproteins have been implicated as donors to P^+_{700}: cytochrome f, a c-type cytochrome, and plastocyanin, a copper-containing protein (7). Unfortunately, the low temperatures required to observe the ESR spectra of these donors and the breadth of their spectra mitigate against the use of ESR to probe these components. Thus optical difference spectroscopy has dominated the study of donor oxidation in both bacteria and green plants.

The reduction time of P^+ by the secondary donor must be rapid to compete with charge recombination between P^+ and A^-_1. In bacteria cytochrome c oxidation occurs in 2–10 μs at room temperature and in 2 ms at 77K (17), whereas the charge recombination time is $\sim$120 ms at room temperature and $\sim$30 ms at 77K (36, 57). However, in PSI three reduction phases for P^+_{700} have been seen in flash spectroscopy: 20 μs (31), 200–400 μs (31) and $\sim$20 ms (78). The last component is thought to represent electrons transferred from the plastoquinone pool situated between PSII and PSI. The two rapid components have been attributed to the postulated primary donors, plastocyanin and cytochrome f, respectively (31). The 200–400 μs component is assigned to cytochrome f oxidation on the basis of the 300 μs oxidation time for cytochrome f as determined by Hildreth (35). Warden (unpublished results) has recently carried out a kinetic analysis of P^+_{700} reduction monitored by ESR following a 10 μs flash and has confirmed the 200–400 μs decay component reported by Haehnel. Warden also finds that the redox potential of this component corresponds with that of cytochrome f in vivo. Also, irreversible inhibition of plastocyanin eliminates the 200–400 μs decay component. This work supports the assertion that plastocyanin is the immediate donor to P^+_{700} and is situated between cytochrome f and P_{700}. ESR detection of plastocyanin in vivo at 20–30K has recently been reported (54, 74), supporting the concept that plastocyanin functions as an electron carrier between the two photosystems. In addition, experiments with intact cells indicate that plastocyanin also participates in cyclic electron transport around PSI (74).

The ultimate electron donor to PSII is water via the oxygen-evolving complex. The high redox potential of P^+_{680} as well as the rapid charge recombination time ($\sim$5 ms at 77K) (55, 56) necessitate a highly efficient, organized electron transfer complex to deliver electrons from water to P^+_{680}. Recent observations suggest that quinones or quinone derivatives might function on the oxidizing as well as the reducing side of PSII. In this regard Signal II, attributed to a plastochromanoxyl radical by Kohl & Wood (48), seems to reflect the state of secondary donors and perhaps acceptors for PSII (1, 77). Flash photolysis studies indicate also that the Signal II moiety is closely linked to the oxygen evolution process (2). Additionally, hexane extraction of plastoquinone disrupts electron flow from water to P_{680}, and reconstitution with isolated plastoquinone partially restores the electron donation from diphenylcarbazide to P^+_{680} (63).

Examination of oxygen-evolving chloroplasts at room temperature has revealed a rapidly decaying light-induced transient ($t_{1/2}\sim$600 μs) with $g = 2.0045$ and a linewidth $\Delta H_{pp} \sim 20$ G (8, 76). The spectrum of this signal labeled Signal II$_{vf}$, is very similar to that of Signal II and cannot be assigned to an immobilized plastosemiquinone since an in vitro frozen solution of plastosemiquinone has a symmetric single-line ESR spectrum with $g \approx 2.0045$ but with a linewidth ΔH_{pp} of only $\sim$13G (Warden, unpublished results). Signal II$_{vf}$ is formed at wavelengths ($\lambda < 680$ nm) which activate PSII and is eliminated by the PSII inhibitor DCMU [3-(3,4-dichlorophenyl)-1,1'-dimethylurea]. Treatments which inhibit electron transport on the oxidizing side of PSII (e.g. tris-washing, heating, high concentrations of Mg^{2+}) greatly retard the decay of Signal II$_{vf}$ (2, 76). The effect of lipophilic electron donors (e.g. benzidene) (3) and the lack of inhibition of Signal II$_{vf}$ by dibromothymoquinone, an inhibitor of electron transport on the reducing side of PSII, suggest that Signal II_{vf} arises from the physiological donor to P^+_{680} (76).

If the Signal II_{vf} species is the immediate donor to P^+_{680} and if Signal II_{vf} arises from a plastoquinone derivative, then it is hard to explain the high redox potential for Signal II_{vf} if it lies between water and P_{680}. This high potential may be brought about by a strong interaction with bound manganese associated with the oxygen-evolving complex. This contention is supported by the observation that Signal II_{vf} in oxygen-evolving chloroplasts is difficult to microwave power saturate even at 200 mW. However, upon tris washing, a treatment which releases manganese from the oxygen evolving system (9), Signal II_{vf} becomes readily saturable (76). The nonsaturating state probably arises from dipolar relaxation by manganese close to the Signal II_{vf} center. The interesting observation by Harbour & Tollin (33) that chlorophyll can sensitize a benzoquinone-mediated oxidation of water is intriguing with regard to quinone participation on the oxidizing side of PSII. Indeed, one might speculate that a manganese-quinone complex is requisite for and participates in the liberation of oxygen from water.

CONCLUSION

This review emphasizes chemical and mechanistic similarities among the reaction center systems of the various photosystems. We believe that future research will unearth many more similarities showing that Nature has used basically the same process in each of the photosystems, the difference being of environmental origin rather than of basic mechanism. Future ESR studies will likely continue to focus on the primary donor and acceptor entities as much work remains to be done in identifying and characterizing these components and their interactions. The use of low temperatures (1–10K) and rapid transient detection techniques should prove invaluable in these studies.

Literature Cited

1. Babcock, G. T., Sauer, K. 1973. *Biochim. Biophys. Acta* 325:483–503
2. Ibid 1975. 376:315–28
3. Ibid. 396:48–62
4. Bearden, A. J., Malkin, R. 1972. *Biochem. Biophys. Res. Commun.* 46: 1299–1305
5. Bearden, A. J., Malkin, R. 1972. *Biochim. Biophys. Acta* 283:456–68
6. Bearden, A. J., Malkin, R. 1975. *Q. Rev. Biophys.* 7:131–77
7. Bishop, N. I. 1971. *Ann. Rev. Biochem.* 40:197–226
8. Blankenship, R. E., Babcock, G. T., Warden, J. T., Sauer, K. 1975. *FEBS Lett.* 51:287–93
9. Blankenship, R. E., Sauer, K. 1974. *Biochim. Biophys. Acta* 357:252–66
10. Bolton, J. R., Cost, K. 1973. *Photochem. Photobiol.* 18:417–21
11. Bolton, J. R., Warden, J. T. 1974. In *Creation and Detection of the Excited State,* ed. W. R. Ware, 2:63–97. New York: Dekker
12. Clarke, R. H., Hofeldt, R. H. 1974. *J. Chem. Phys.* 61:4582–87
13. Clayton, R. K. 1973. *Ann. Rev. Biophys. Bioeng.* 2:131–56
14. Cogdell, R. J., Brune, D. C., Clayton, R. K. 1974. *FEBS Lett.* 45:344–47
15. Cogdell, R. J., Crofts, A. R. 1972. *FEBS Lett.* 27:176–78
16. Debrunner, P. G., Schultz, C. E., Feher, G., Okamura, M. Y. 1975. *Biophys. J.* 15:226a

17. Dutton, P. L., Kihara, T., McCray, J. A., Thornber, J. P. 1971. *Biochim. Biophys. Acta* 226:81–87
18. Dutton, P. L., Leigh, J. S., Seibert, M. 1972. *Biochem. Biophys. Res. Commun.* 46:406–13
19. Evans, M. C. W., Cammack, R. 1975. *Biochem. Biophys. Res. Commun.* 63:187–93
20. Evans, M. C. W., Reeves, S. G., Cammack, R. 1974. *FEBS Lett.* 49:111–14
21. Evans, M. C. W., Sihra, C. K., Bolton, J. R., Cammack, R. 1975. *Nature* 256:668–69
22. Evans, M. C. W., Telfer, A., Lord, A. V. 1972. *Biochim. Biophys. Acta* 267:530–37
23. Feher, G. 1971. *Photochem. Photobiol.* 14:373–87
24. Feher, G., Hoff, A. J., Isaacson, R. A., Ackerson, L. C. 1975. *Ann. NY Acad. Sci.* 242:293
25. Feher, G., Isaacson, R. A., McElroy, J. D., Ackerson, L. C., Okamura, M. Y. 1974. *Biochim. Biophys. Acta* 368:135–39
26. Feher, G., Okamura, M. Y., McElroy, J. D. 1972. *Abstr. Biophys. Soc.* FPM-J17
27. Feher, G., Okamura, M. Y., McElroy, J. D. 1972. *Biochim. Biophys. Acta* 267:222–26
28. Fong, F. K. 1974. *Proc. Natl. Acad. Sci. USA* 71:3692–95
29. van Gorkom, H. J. 1974. *Biochim. Biophys. Acta* 347:439–42
30. Govindjee, Govindjee, R. 1975. *Bioenergetics of Photosynthesis*, ed. Govindjee, 2–50. New York: Academic
31. Haehnel, W., Doring, G., Witt, H. T. 1971. *Z. Naturforsch.* 266:1171–74
32. Halsey, Y. D., Parson, W. W. 1974. *Biochim. Biophys. Acta* 347:404–16
33. Harbour, J. R., Tollin, G. 1974. *Photochem. Photobiol.* 20:271–77
34. Ibid. 19:69–74
35. Hildreth, W. W. 1968. *Biochim. Biophys. Acta* 153:197–202
36. Hsi, E. S. P., Bolton, J. R. 1974. *Biochim. Biophys. Acta* 347:126–33
37. Jackson, J. B., Cogdell, R. J., Crofts, A. R. 1973. *Biochim. Biophys. Acta* 292:218–25
38. Katz, J. J., Norris, J. R. 1973. *Curr. Top. Bioenerg.* 5:41–75
39. Kaufmann, K. J., Dutton, P. L., Netzel, T. L., Leigh, J. S., Rentzepis, P. M. 1975. *Science* 188:1301–4
40. Ke, B. 1973. *Biochim. Biophys. Acta* 301:1–33
41. Ke, B. et al 1974. *Biochim. Biophys. Acta* 368:401–8
42. Ke, B., Garcia, A. F., Vernon, L. P. 1973. *Biochim. Biophys. Acta* 292:226–36
43. Ke, B., Hansen, R. E., Beinert, H. 1973. *Proc. Natl. Acad. Sci. USA* 70:2941–45
44. Kassner, R. J. 1972. *Proc. Natl. Acad. Sci. USA* 60:2263–67
45. Kleibeuker, J. F., Schaafsma, T. J. 1974. *Chem. Phys. Lett.* 29:116–22
46. Knaff, D. B., Malkin, R. 1974. *Arch. Biochem. Biophys.* 159:555–62
47. Kohl, D. H. 1972. *Biological Applications of Electron Spin Resonance*, ed. H. M. Swartz, J. R. Bolton, D. C. Borg, 213–64. New York: Wiley-Interscience
48. Kohl, D. H., Wood, P. M. 1969. *Plant Physiol.* 44:1439–45
49. Leigh, J. S., Dutton, P. L. 1972. *Biochem. Biophys. Res. Commun.* 46:414–21
50. Leigh, J. S., Dutton, P. L. 1974. *Biochim. Biophys. Acta* 357:67–77
51. Levanon, H., Scherz, A. 1975. *Chem. Phys. Lett.* 31:119–24
52. Loach, P. A., Hall, R. L. 1972. *Proc. Natl. Acad. Sci. USA* 69:786–90
53. Malkin, R., Bearden, A. J. 1971. *Proc. Natl. Acad. Sci. USA* 68:16–19
54. Malkin, R., Bearden, A. J. 1973. *Biochim. Biophys. Acta* 292:169–85
55. Malkin, R., Bearden, A. J. 1975. *Biochim. Biophys. Acta* 396:250–59
56. Mathis, P., Vermeglio, A. 1974. *Biochim. Biophys. Acta* 368:130–34
57. McElroy, J. D., Mauzerall, D. C., Feher, G. 1974. *Biochim. Biophys. Acta* 333:261–77
58. McIntosh, A. R., Chu, M., Bolton, J. R. 1975. *Biochim. Biophys. Acta* 376:308–14
59. Norris, J. R., Scheer, H., Druyan, M. E., Katz, J. J. 1974. *Proc. Natl. Acad. Sci. USA.* 71:4897–4900
60. Norris, J. R., Uphaus, R. A., Crespi, H. L., Katz, J. J. 1971. *Proc. Natl. Acad. Sci. USA* 68:625–28
61. Norris, J. R., Uphaus, R. A., Katz, J. J. 1975. *Chem. Phys. Lett.* 31:157–61
62. Okamura, M. Y., Isaacson, R. A., Feher, G. 1975. *Proc. Natl. Acad. Sci. USA.* In press
63. Okayama, S. 1974. *Plant Cell Physiol.* 15:95–101
64. Parson, W. W., Cogdell, R. J. 1975. *Biochim. Biophys. Acta* 416:105–49
65. Phillipson, K. D., Sato, V. L., Sauer, K. 1972. *Biochemistry* 11:4591–95
66. Pulles, M. P. J., Kerkhof, P. L. M., Amesz, J. 1974. *FEBS Lett.* 47:143–45

67. Rabinowich, E., Govindjee 1969. *Photosynthesis.* New York: Wiley. 273pp.
68. Rockley, M. G., Windsor, M. W., Cogdell, R. J., Parson, W. W. 1975. *Proc. Natl. Acad. Sci. USA* 72:2251–55
69. Sauer, K. 1975. *Bioenergetics of Photosynthesis,* ed. Govindjee, 115–81. New York: Academic
70. Slooten, L. 1972. *Biochim. Biophys. Acta* 275:208–18
71. Swartz, H. M., Bolton, J. R., Borg, D. C. 1972. *Biological Applications of Electron Spin Resonance.* New York: Wiley Interscience (see especially chapters 1 and 2)
72. Takamiya, K-I., Nishimura, M. 1975. *Biochim. Biophys. Acta* 396:93–103
73. Uphaus, R. A., Norris, J. R., Katz, J. J. 1974. *Biochem. Biophys. Res. Commun.* 61:1057–63
74. Visser, J. W. M., Amesz, J., van Gelder, B. F. 1974. *Biochim. Biophys. Acta* 333:279–87
75. Visser, J. W. M., Rijgersberg, K. P., Amesz, J. 1974. *Biochim. Biophys. Acta*
76. Warden, J. T., Blankenship, R. E., Sauer, K. 1976. *Biochim. Biophys. Acta* 423:462–78
77. Warden, J. T., Bolton, J. R. 1974. *Accounts Chem. Res.* 7:189–95
78. Warden, J. T., Bolton, J. R. 1974. *Photochem. Photobiol.* 20:263–69
79. Warden, J. T., Mohanty, P., Bolton, J. R. 1974. *Biochem. Biophys. Res. Commun.* 59:872–78
80. Weaver, E. C. 1968. *Ann. Rev. Plant Physiol.* 19:283–94
81. Weaver, E. C., Weaver, H. E. 1972. *Photophysiology* 7:1–32
82. Wertz, J. E., Bolton, J. R. 1972. *Electron Spin Resonance—Elementary Theory and Practical Applications.* New York: McGraw-Hill. 497 pp.
83. White, R. A., Tollin, G. 1971. *Photochem. Photobiol.* 14:15–42
84. Wraight, C. A., Leigh, J. S., Dutton, P. L., Clayton, R. K. 1974. *Biochim. Biophys. Acta* 333:401–8

368:235–46

Ann. Rev. Plant Physiol. 1976. 27:385–406

GEOTROPISM

❖7615

Barrie E. Juniper

School of Botany, University of Oxford, Oxford OX1 3RA, England

CONTENTS

Since the last review of this subject (135) the greater volume of work and revision of established ideas has concerned roots rather than shoots. The emphasis here will reflect this preponderence, but relevant work on shoots will not be ignored.

Terminology

Many terms have been used in the literature to describe aspects of geotropism. The following terms, briefly defined below, will be used in this review.

Geotropism, the response of a plant organ to gravity, is assumed to comprise a reaction chain. It is also assumed, but not yet proven beyond all doubt, that the opening phase, i.e. the receipt of the stimulus, is a physical phase. This is commonly termed the *stimulation*. An altered physical state is assumed to pass into the first physiological phase which is termed *perception*. The perceived stimulus is then assumed to pass in *transmission* in the form of some *signal* to the site of the *reaction*, which in geotropism is normally a curvature. Any geotropically perceptive organ must be given a certain minimal stimulus over a given time before a reaction will take place: $t \times g = k$. The duration of this stimulus where $1 \times g$ is the norm is the *presentation time*. The period between the end of the presentation time and the beginning of the reaction is called the *latent period*. The term *statolith* will be used to describe those geotropically sensitive masses of high specific weight occurring in the perceptive cells of the plant organ. The cells in which these statoliths occur are termed *statocytes*. A common misunderstanding in descriptions of geotropism arises from the use of the word starch grain, as if such an object were an independent cell organelle. Under normal conditions, starch grains never occur free in a cell. They are found, from two to several in number, within the bounding membranes of a modified plastid called an *amyloplast*. Amyloplasts may function as statoliths, some other objects and substances may function similarly, but starch grains by themselves never do. The verb *"decapping"* will be used in this review to describe the surgical removal of the root cap only. *"Decapitating"* will be used to describe the removal of the distal tip of a root or shoot which in a root includes not only all the cap, but some or all of the meristematic region and possibly part of the elongating zone as well.

Introduction

Several aspects of geotropism have, in the last few years, received particular attention: (*a*) the mechanisms of graviperception; (*b*) the various growth controlling substances connected with geotropism; and (*c*) the movement of these substances in the various tissues of the plant. The one fundamental shift in the pattern of research has been the belated recognition that at least the intermediate mechanisms of geotropism in the shoot and root are more different than was once supposed.

The sunlight falling on the earth is intercepted by orientated solar receivers (leaves) positioned to accept the maximum number of quanta. Without positive and negative geotropism, plants would be restricted to the much smaller amount of energy that could be received by thalloid layers coating the surface of the earth. The negatively geotropic stem of the ideal higher plant supports flexible, movable, diageotropic leaves; each leaf is developed in a given acropetal succession to a precise phyllotaxy, bringing about the minimum mutual shading. The stem structure is held erect by a positively geotropic and diageotropic root system.

The shoot and root structure must, in evolutionary time, have developed in coordinated sequence, and it was natural that a synthetic system of control based on the recently discovered growth controlling compounds should have been proposed for both systems (21, 22, 131). The Cholodny-Went hypothesis of a common but mirror mechanism for both root and shoot has held the stage for over 50 years, but although it still has value in investigations into shoots, its basic tenet, a major role for indole-3yl-acetic acid (IAA) in roots can no longer be sustained. The Cholodny-Went hypothesis in its modern form states that in the shoot tip IAA is present in optimal or near optimal amounts, and under the influence of gravity, i.e. when a shoot is laid horizontally, the IAA will migrate by lateral transport to the lower side and will bring about an increase in growth. In roots it is proposed that IAA in the tip is present in growth-inhibiting amounts; the consequence of gravity is further to inhibit growth of the lower half in a horizontally displaced root by bringing about an increase of IAA in the lower half. The distribution is again supposed to be brought about by lateral transport.

The Graviperception Mechanism

Graviperception in plants possesses a number of specific characteristics and any proposed model mechanism must accommodate to these features. (*a*) The minimum stimulus has a precise threshold and below this threshold no reaction whatsoever will take place. (*b*) There is an inverse correlation between the force and the exposure time required to bring about this threshold stimulus, i.e. $t \times g = k$. (*c*) A number of subthreshold stimuli can be summed to cause a reaction, provided that the periods between the end of one stimulation and the beginning of the next do not exceed the stimulation times by more than 10 times. (*d*) In certain plant organs only particular cells (and in one well-documented case a single cell) are capable of receiving a stimulus. (*e*) Relatively immature organs, e.g. roots emerging from the grain and regenerating root tips, may be able to perceive a stimulus.

THE FINE STRUCTURE OF THE CELLS THAT PERCEIVE GRAVITY   There does not seem to have been an intensive study of the fine structure of the statocyte cells in shoots, but a considerable body of observations on roots of different kinds now makes some synthesis possible (50, 59, 86, 91, 92). The perceptive cells of root caps of all the genera and species so far studied in detail, although expanding rapidly and of short life span, are more or less nonvacuolate (Figure 1). The impression of vacuolate cells given by earlier light microscope studies is erroneous, but the consistency of this observation suggests that the cytoplasm of cap cells may be peculiarly sensitive to some of the older fixatives. Cap cells only begin to vacuolate as they senesce and approach the margin (59, 62, 84). The perceptive cells are variable in shape (Figure 1), but usually about twice as long as broad, with very approximate dimensions of 35 μm $\times$ 18μm. They possess numerous mitochondria and Golgi bodies, variable in number but at least an order of magnitude larger than the amyloplasts which vary from 26 up to 50 or so (38, 60). The nuclei, which increase in size and become polyploid as the cells mature, are often amoeboid in shape (10, 60). The endoplasmic reticulum (ER) is variable in amount and distribution between the species, although consistent within the species. It may, as in the roots of grasses, be evenly and peripherally distributed in the cell (Figure 1), or it may, as in *Pisum* (56) and *Lepidium* (53, 125), be located in a precise pattern at the distal ends of the cells. The ER in some statocyte cells, e.g. *Zea, Triticum, Lens,* and *Vicia* (37, 56, 60, 86), moves when the root is given a geotropic stimulus; in others, e.g. *Pisum* and *Lepidium,* it does not. All the cells of the root cap have large numbers of plasmodesmata, and where they have been counted as in *Zea* and *Lens* (58; Perbal, personal communication), they are far more numerous in the transverse walls than in the longitudinal walls. Numerous plasmodesmata cross the boundary where this is present between the root cap and the root itself (58).

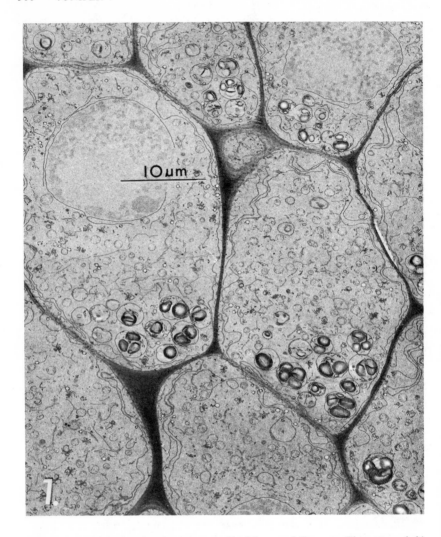

Figure 1   Longitudinal section through core cells of the cap of *Zea mays*. The root was held vertically for two hours prior to fixation, and during the fixation with glutaraldehyde/KMnO$_4$.

MECHANISMS OF PERCEPTION NOT BASED ON A STATOLITH SYSTEM
Kutschera-Mitter (71) has proposed a mechanism based on the difference in the rate of water loss and the movement of the cap mucilage across a horizontally oriented root. It is proposed that the transpiration of the upper side of a horizontal root will be greater than that on the lower side, mucilage will move to the lower side, both bringing about an earlier maturation and sloughing off of cap cells. This in its turn

will bring about an enhanced uptake of water and hence a greater rate of elongation on the upper side now exposed. However, this theory does not easily account for the very short presentation times of some species [18 sec for *Vicia* primary roots (7)] nor for summation of stimuli (17, 29) whereby a number of subliminal stimuli, if given within a limited period of time, can be "remembered" by the plant. Nor can it account for the observations that root cap peripheral cells are not required for an effective geotropic response (59, 61), and in certain circumstances the quiescent center of the root tip may be able to take over the geotropic functions of the cap (8, 9).

THE STATOLITH HYPOTHESIS   The most likely way for a plant organ to detect its orientation with respect to gravity is by the movement of one or more of its component parts. Mechanisms which invoke an overall distortion of the plant organ or cell have been suggested (93) but are difficult to comprehend or to test. Bodies which moved in cells under a gravitational stimulus were observed almost 120 years ago. The statolith theory, more or less as we currently understand it, was formulated 75 years ago. For a review of some of the early literature see Audus (6) and Wilkins (135). This theory has enjoyed fluctuating popularity through its long history. Many experiments have been performed in an attempt to destroy the basic tenet, which is that the sedimentation of amyloplasts, or similar heavy bodies, initiates the perception through the cytoplasm of the statocyte cells. Some of these early experiments have been reviewed and reinterpreted in the light of the latest evidence (7, 50). Reviews summarizing the evidence against the statolith theory have also appeared (117, 132). Only the most recent of these experiments will be reviewed here. The evidence supporting the statolith hypothesis is substantial but, on the whole, indirect. It can be summarized as follows: (*a*) There is a good correlation between the presence of statoliths of one form or another and the site of geotropic sensitivity. There is an equally good correlation between the recovery of geotropic sensitivity and the reformation of statoliths (8, 11, 16, 50, 61). (*b*) The statoliths, in this example amyloplasts, are the only organelles which show significant redistribution (sedimentation) in geostimulated root cap cells of several species of plants (37, 60, 86). (*c*) There is an approximate correlation between the amount or size of the statoliths and the efficiency of the geotropic response (8, 43, 85, 104). (*d*) There is a good inverse correlation between the presentation time and the extent of the development of the statocyte tissue (5). (*e*) There is a direct proportional relationship between size and asymmetric statolith distribution and the differential distribution of auxin in the shoots of certain cereal plants (27, 43). (*f*) Statocytes from whose amyloplasts the starch has been unequivocally removed do not appear to transmit a geotropic signal (49, 50).

The evidence against the statolith hypothesis can be summarized as follows: (*a*) The geotropism of roots and shoots is usually in opposite directions, although both are assumed to be stimulated by a common initial mechanism. This criticism has lost much of its early weight since it is now clear (see later) that the transmission and reaction to the stimulus are almost certainly based on different chemical messengers. (*b*) Experiments have been performed which sought to remove by chemical or physical methods the starch from amyloplast-statoliths. Several authors have claimed that, in the total absence of starch from these amyloplasts, geotropic perception was still possible. Any such experiments carried out before the advent of electron microscopy need no longer be considered seriously, since the size of residual starch grains within any amyloplast may lie well below the resolution of a light microscope. The most recent experiments (93), however, are a serious criticism of the basic statolith hypothesis. Iversen (49, 50) has repeated these experiments, both on *Triticum* coleoptiles as used by Pickard & Thimann (93) and on the roots of *Lepidium* and *Trifolium*. Under those conditions of chemical treatment (gibberellic acid plus kinetin = GA_3 + K) in which all the starch was removed from the amyloplasts, but which did not affect elongation of the organ, no geotropic reaction was observed. (*c*) There are many instances in both shoots and roots where it can be demonstrated that an organ possesses sedimenting statoliths yet no geotropic reaction is observed, e.g. mutants of *Oryza* and *Pisum* and the normal secondary roots of *Myosotis* and *Oxalis*. Such anomalies can for the moment be satisfactorily explained by assuming some failure in the transmission or reaction sequences. (*d*) There are two examples of amyloplast-free organs of higher plants which are geotropically sensitive: the perianth of *Clivia nobilis* and the aerial roots of the orchid *Laelia anceps* (5, 6). Neither of these particular organs has, to my knowledge, been examined in detail recently, and it is possible that organelles other than amyloplasts might serve as statoliths.

If the body of evidence supporting the general idea of the statolith theory is by now almost overwhelming, and becoming better substantiated as each year passes, we must at this moment agree with Perbal (89), who could find no direct link between amyloplast movement and geotropic response.

Before discussing the speculative schemes that purport to link amyloplast movement to the transmission of a message, it will be useful to look at the single-cell statocyte mechanism in the alga *Chara*.

THE STATOLITH SYSTEM IN *CHARA*   Giesenhagen (33) in 1901 proposed that the Glanzkörper (shining bodies), present in the unicellular rhizoids of the alga *Chara*, functioned as statoliths in a similar manner to the systems already proposed the year before for higher plants (6). Buder (16) and more recently Sievers and his co-workers (120–122, 124) have shown how this system works. The *Chara* rhizoids are about 30 μm across and reach a length of 6–9 cm without dividing. Between 30 and 60 statoliths about 1–2 μm across and now known to consist of barium sulfate (111) are normally found in a group between 10 and 20 μm above the tip of the cell. In the *Chara* rhizoid only the dome-shaped tip elongates. This it does at the rate of about 120 μm per hour at room temperature. The nucleus lies about 250 μm from the tip and only the older most basal part contains a vacuole. If the rhizoid is turned on its side, the statoliths begin to fall towards the lower part of the cell, reaching the plasmalemma in about 3 min (124). The latent period is about 15 min and then the tip of the cell begins to curve downwards. If by centrifugation the statoliths are displaced to a region above the nucleus, they remain there; the rhizoids grow a little more slowly than usual, but do not respond to gravity (16). A new quorum of statoliths is slowly reformed, and the ability to perceive gravity slowly returns.

In the normally orientated rhizoid a group of Golgi bodies, actively producing vesicles, lies just above the cluster of statoliths. The vesicles, when released, move downward towards the tip, passing between the mass of statoliths and the plasmalemma. In the tip region their membranes fuse with the plasmalemma and their contents are discharged into the cell wall. Assisted by the Golgi-derived material, the tip grows symmetrically in area. When a rhizoid is placed on its side, the cluster of statoliths blocks the movements of the Golgi vesicles towards that side. This region of the cell wall almost completely stops growing, whereas because of the arrival of a rather larger number of Golgi vesicles than usual, growth on the upper side increases. This causes the tip to curve downward and eventually to reach the vertical direction.

The *Chara* rhizoid statolith system has been described in detail, partly because it is the only geotropic system in plants which has been adequately explained, but also because its simplicity has led to extrapolations from this single cell system to multicellular systems which have been neither helpful nor stimulating.

THE STATOCYTE SYSTEM IN HIGHER PLANTS   It is possible that other geotropic systems in other single-celled organs will be found that work in a manner similar to that described in *Chara*. In higher plants geoperceptive zones are usually multicellular, frequently coordinated in their action, i.e. removal of a part renders the system inoperative or defective, and frequently the site of perception and response are separate.

In coleoptiles the movable statoliths are usually located just below the meristem in a "starch sheath" around the central cylinder. The greatest number of movable amyloplasts are in the solid extreme tip where curvature starts, although cell elongation is extremely slow. Movable amyloplasts are also present for some way down the hollow cylinder of the coleoptile where elongation is appreciable. Decapitating experiments indicate that geoperception is not confined to the tip, but the tip, apparently by supplying a growth-controlling substance, promotes a secondary geoperceptive system behind it (117).

In the primary roots of most plants, geoperception is thought to be localized in the root cap (61, 67, 95–97). The only mobile amyloplasts are located in the core cells of the cap which, although mature cells, are, like the rhizoids of *Chara,* essentially nonvacuolate (50, 59, 91, 92). Removal of this cap renders the root as a whole unable to perceive gravity until it has reformed a new perceptive tissue (8–11, 61, 95). Removal of the cap, although this point is in dispute, does not seem to alter the rate of elongation of the root. In all roots the principal site of reaction is some distance behind the cap in the elongating zone of the root.

POSSIBLE MODES OF ACTION OF THE STATOLITHS   There is an impressive weight of evidence correlating statolith movement and geoperception, but a correlation is not a cause. If we accept that the amyloplasts or their equivalents have some role in perception, how can they bring about the creation of a gradient of some growth controlling substance across the central zone of the particular organ, i.e. the cap? None of the current hypotheses have much experimental or observational evidence to support them, but some may be dismissed more easily than others. Hypotheses known to this author are listed below.

(*a*) the motion of the statoliths within the statocyte;

(*b*) the displacement of weight within the cap;

(*c*) asymmetrical distribution of or pressure upon the ER membranes by the statoliths;

(*d*) displacement of and/or asymmetrical function of the Golgi bodies (dictyosomes);

(*e*) asymmetrical pressure upon the plasmamembrane of the statocyte;

(*f*) asymmetrical distribution of enzyme activity(ies) upon the statocytes themselves, e.g. physiologically active sensors;

(*g*) the presence of the statoliths at a particular site (transport barriers);

(*h*) the interaction between statoliths and plasmodesmata to operate a valve mechanism.

Hypotheses a and b   These (93) are very difficult to confirm or to refute. However, both are subject to the same criticism, that presentation times in both shoot and root perception zones may be very short: *Osmunda* fronds in 30 sec (40), in *Avena* coleoptiles less than 30 sec (7, 55) in *Vicia* roots only 18 sec (7). Taking Hawker's times for the movement of amyloplasts through cytoplasm, which may be as little as 0.5 μm in a minute (41), the statoliths will move a very short distance indeed in the minimal presentation times given above. If statoliths move only 0.25 μm, not only will the displacement of weight within the statocyte be infinitesimally small, but the motion and the resulting disturbance within the statocyte will be equally minute.

Hypothesis c   The possible association of the movement of the statoliths with the ER membranes deserves and has received more extended attention.

The idea that the amyloplasts might bring about an asymmetrical distribution of the ER, or create a gradient by asymmetrical pressure on the ER, dates from the observations of Nemec in 1900, who noted that some other component of the cell, apart from the amyloplasts, redistributed under the influence of gravity. It is now appreciated that this material was probably ER. The observation was taken up and extended by Griffiths & Audus (37) in *Vicia* root caps, with the then recently available electron microscope techniques, and extended to other species of plants and in greater detail by others (56, 60, 86). There is no doubt now that in the caps of many species of plants a redistribution of the amyloplasts can bring about a redistribution of the ER. When the stimulus is withdrawn the ER may return relatively rapidly to its previous symmetrical position (56, 60). However, the ER of the statocytes is known not to move under a gravitational stimulus in *Lepidium* root caps (50, 123, 125, 129) and in *Pisum* root caps (56). A model based on the secondary movement of ER membranes to bring about lateral gradients would have to assume completely different mechanisms in relatively closely related species of higher plants—an evolutionary trend which seems unlikely.

Sievers and his co-workers (123, 125, 129) have proposed a variant on this idea, which is that changes of pressure on the asymmetrical ER groups of the root caps of *Lepidium,* with perception of a gravitational stimulus, would bring about biochemical or biophysical changes in the membranes of the ER, setting in motion the events of transmission. Such an hypothesis is attractive in that it would begin to operate within the very short presentation times known for some roots. Movements of only fractions of a micron would be sufficient to trigger the system. However, the ER pattern in *Lepidium* root caps and calyptras is very complex, the fine structure of the core cells of the cap is different, i.e. a mirror image of each other on either side of a central axis, and nothing comparable to such a situation has been found in those other species whose fine structure has been studied in detail, e.g. *Zea Hordeum, Triticum, Lens, Convolvulus,* and *Pisum.* Nor would Sievers & Volkmann's model explain why previously inverted roots responded almost identically to normally grown roots (50, 52). The problem of different model systems for different species remains.

Hypothesis d The asymmetric distribution of Golgi bodies or their products has been vindicated in the *Chara* rhizoid, and this has led to attempts to apply this principle to higher plants (77, 117, 118). The Golgi bodies, due to their relatively low density and dissected shape, cannot be considered as the primary perceivers of the stimulus. Nevertheless, there is no reason why they should not be moved in secondary fashion, like the ER in some root caps, by the statoliths. Shen-Miller & Miller (118), working with *Avena* coleoptiles, found significantly more Golgi bodies in the bottom halves of individual cells of the apex about 6 min after stimulation. Mitochondria showed a similar but slower trend (117, 119). Moreover, exclusively in the apical cells, the activity of the Golgi bodies, as measured by the numbers of vesicles they produce, is greater in the lower half. Shen-Miller and her co-workers have constructed a scheme (117, 118) incorporating the differential distribution of Golgi bodies and their vesicles, linking this with differential IAA gradient and differential cell expansion. It is possible that such a system could make a contribution in shoots, but unlikely that it is the primary mechanism. The presentation times in *Avena* coleoptiles are so short (ca 30 sec) that little or no secondary movement of Golgi, their vesicles, or the stimulation of their vesicles seems possible. It seems most unlikely that such a mechanism operates in roots. Only a very slight Golgi redistribution has been observed in root caps of *Vicia* after considerable stimulation (37). No redistribution was detected in *Zea* (60). No differential activity of the Golgi in any statocyte cell of *Zea* has been detected, nor, in a statocyte cell, the differential movement of vesicles to any preferred area of the plasmalemma.

Hypothesis e Hypothesis *e* has a longer history, probably originating with Haberlandt's (38) observations of the movement of the amyloplast towards the "physically lower portion of the ectoplast," now assumed to mean plasmalemma or adjacent cytoplasm. That amyloplasts come to rest against the plasmalemma and thereby alter its permeability in some way is an attractive hypothesis, but unfortunately there is no evidence that the amyloplasts of any statocyte cells ever come in contact with the plasmalemma at any time. The observations of all those workers who have studied statocyte cells under the EM are in agreement that the amyloplasts, regardless of their position in the cell, the degree of stimulus applied to that statocyte, or the species in which they are studied, lie at distances from 0.5 μm to several microns from the plasmalemma (37, 50, 53, 54, 59, 60, 86, 125, and Figure 1). The erroneous impression of statoliths lying against the lower walls seems to have come about from the use of thick sections in the light microscope. As Iversen (50) has shown, a comparison of light and electron micrographs of similar material indicates that statoliths which look as if they are in contact with the lower wall under the light microscope are invariably some distance away from it.

Moreover, direct observations on the development of the geotropic curvature in *Avena* coleoptiles indicate that it is not necessary for the statoliths to settle on the lateral cell wall for the reaction chain to start (3, 55). In fact, in *Lepidium* root caps the amyloplasts do not reach the lower wall for 15 min, which is much longer than the presentation time (54). Perbal (89, 90), who has studied this particular aspect of the problem in some detail, concludes that there is no correlation between curvature in its initial stage and the average number of amyloplasts per cell in section, their average volume, or the space they occupy in the statocyte. In short, there seems to be no way in which the statoliths in this system can operate by pressure on a sensitive surface.

It is possible to imagine that some indirect pressure is brought to bear on the plasmamembrane through pressure on the ER or other organelles (124). An examination of micrographs of normal and stimulated statocyte cells indicates, however, that the ER rarely if ever comes in contact with the plasmamembrane and the ER does not normally make connections with the plasmamembrane, but may make connections with the desmotubules (109) of the plasmodesmata. Little pressure in either case can be brought to bear directly on the plasmamembrane itself. Furthermore, the minimal presentation times are insufficient, as we have seen, for the amyloplasts to move more than a short distance across the cell.

Hypothesis f   Certain statoliths, e.g. the barium sulphate crystals in *Chara* rhizoids, are almost certainly chemically inert. However, the amyloplast statoliths in the shoots and roots of higher plants are certainly not; there is good evidence for chemical activity when at rest and for other changes when disturbed (1, 47, 50, 84). Hinchman & Gordon (46) have shown that the starch grains of the amyloplasts of horizontally rotated *Avena* coleoptiles are larger than those of control shoots. Increased levels of starch and sugar appear in the shoots of the rotated plants. The amyloplast statoliths of root caps are both highly resistant to the reduction of their starch by starvation (5, 6) and stable in appearance, but are in fact turning over starch monomers very rapidly (84); they are presumably then releasing sugars into the cytoplasmic medium and if supplied with external sugars will take them up. As the root cap cells approach the periphery of the cap, the supply of endogenous sugar presumably begins to fail and the amyloplasts begin to shrink (59, 62). Their capacity to export sugar apparently does not alter, and this contributes, via the enhanced activity of the peripheral cell Golgi bodies, to the mucilage surrounding the root cap (62, 84). In addition, it is now clear that IAA-oxidase is probably located on the membranes surrounding the amyloplasts and the rough ER of the cap statocytes of *Brassica* and *Zea* (1, 50). The amyloplasts are therefore sites of physiological activity in their own right. This activity cannot by itself be the initiator of the perception, but there seems no reason why it should not have a significant role in the modification or transmission of the perceived stimulus.

Hypothesis g   Statoliths as transport barriers are known to function in the *Chara* rhizoid. Here they function, *after* redistribution, as a block to the movement of Golgi material to the plasmalemma. Since the perception times in the apical tips of higher plants are so brief the statoliths cannot function in this way, but it is possible that they could function as a symmetrical block in the normal position, becoming, after the brief stimulation, an asymmetrical block to the movement of materials (75). This asymmetrical block could be coupled with asymmetrical physiological activity, as in hypothesis *f*. It is also well established that the physiological properties of the statoliths may change as they are redistributed in the cell. As we have seen, gravity compensation on a horizontal clinostat increases the diameter of the starch grains in the amyloplasts of the coleoptiles of *Avena* (46). However, we should note that in geotropically stimulated *Zea* coleoptiles lateral auxin asymmetry was not significantly different in a wild type and an amylo-maize mutant in which the amyloplasts had a chemically different starch composition (27).

Hypothesis h   The eighth hypothesis, based upon the idea that the amyloplasts and plasmodesmata might act in combination as a multiple valve system, is an attempt to construct a model compatible with the observed very brief presentation times and commensurate short displacements of the statoliths. The idea that plasmodesmata might act as valves is not a new one (30), and the idea that they might act in geotropism has already been put forward (4, 8, 57) and recently reviewed and extended by Audus (7). But so far no precise model has been proposed whereby a plasmodesmatal-statolith valve might function.

The transverse walls of the root cap columella statocyte cells of all species studied with the electron microscope are traversed by large numbers of plasmodesmata (see Figure 1; also 58, 59, 91, 92). Maize root caps have a maximum of about 1500 per 100 μm^2 to a minimum of about 500 per 100 μm^2. The longitudinal walls in the same cells had a maximum of 500 and a minimum of 45 over the same area, and a median cell of the columella (Figure 1) would have approximately 800 plasmodesmata on its transverse wall and 80 on its longitudinal walls per 100 μm^2. Virtually identical figures for the statocyte cells of the primary roots of *Lens culinaris,* 770 and 48 respectively, have been found by Perbal (personal communication, 1975).

So far as is known, all of these plasmodesmata possess a desmotubule (109) and the desmotubule, in some way not yet clear, joins the membranes of the ER (129). This attachment of the desmotubule to the ER on both sides of a wall (Figure 2A) probably explains why the movement of the amyloplasts displaces some but not all of the ER adjacent to the cell wall (50, 56, 60, 125). The loose "arms" of the ER membranes appear to be free to be moved under gravitational stimulus (37, 56, 60, 86). Commonly (56, 60, 129) there is a greater accumulation of ER membranes at the base of the cell and lesser amounts parallel to the longitudinal walls or to the transverse wall at the "top" end of the cell. At rest in the normal vertical growing position (Figure 1), the amyloplasts will lie on a heap of ER membranes and will never, in any statocyte cells so far studied, come in contact with the plasmalemma of the cell.

If the statoliths, of which there are upwards of 26 in most statocyte cells (38, 59), sat upon ER membranes which in turn were attached to desmotubules, they would constitute together a valve, valve guide, and pressure system (Figures 2A and 2B). Such a valve system would be sensitive to extremely small movements in position, capable of infinitely repeatable action, would function in the 90° inverted position, work in both directions, and presumably act with any potentially mobile compound which used the plasmodesmatal path.

It is the existence of a group of statocytes, whether in shoot or root, all of them presumably operating in the same way and all of them receiving an identical gravita-

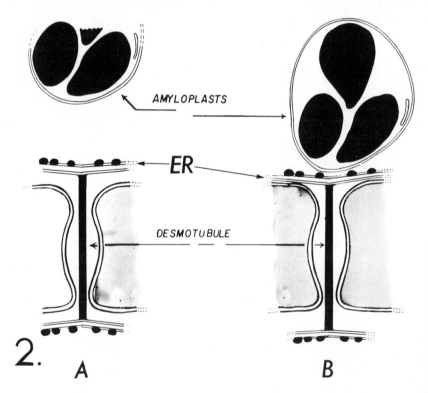

Figure 2   A model for the proposed amyloplasts/plasmodesmatal valve. A. Open. B. Closed.

tional stimulus, which has bedeviled the search for an effective gradient-creating mechanism. A speculative scheme is here proposed (Figures 3A, B, C). In the normal vertical position, under the pressure of the terminally situated statoliths, all the plasmodesmata in the transverse walls are closed, obstructing polar movement. There is some evidence that longitudinal fluxes use the plasmodesmatal pathway (4). All the plasmodesmata in the longitudinal walls are open, hence transverse movement is unrestricted. As the statoliths begin to move under a gravitational stimulus the plasmodesmata in the transverse walls will begin to open and the plasmodesmata in the longitudinal walls will begin to close in a definite sequence. The sequence in which they open and close creates a situation in which any symplastically moved compound can move from statocyte to statocyte, but preferentially in a stepwise and

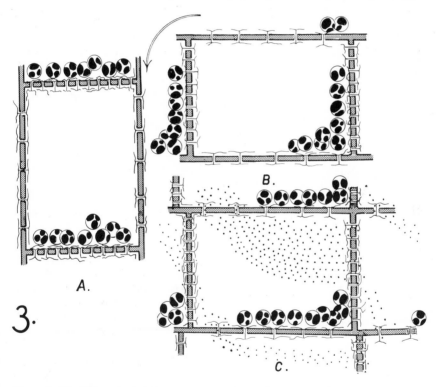

Figure 3   The proposed amyloplast/plasmodesmatal valve system in operation in the core cells of a cap.
A. Cell vertical, all transverse valves closed.
B. Immediately after displacement to a horizontal position, transverse valves begin to open, longitudinal valves begin to close.
C. Extended stimulation, most transverse valves now open. Hypothetical growth-controlling substance (dotted lines) follows shortest path via open transverse and longitudinal valves alternately, in a stepwise direction.

partially transverse direction. The existence of several files of cells within each perceptive zone and several stories of cells within each file is obviously crucial to this model and such an organisation is well documented (50, 53, 59, 91, 92). The model is consistent with the very short presentation times of some organs (6, 7, 40, 41, 55), with the requirements for a quorum of statocyte cells before perceptive mechanisms will work (11) or work satisfactorily (67, 141), and for the many observations that treatments which allow the statoliths to slide parallel to the longitudinal walls are those that give rise to the most vigorous curvatures (52, 53, 74, 75).

It is consistent also with the observations of Barlow and his co-workers (8, 9, 11) that the quiescent center of the root tip may, with limited efficiency, take over the functions of the root cap. His observations indicate that such recovery is dependent on some accumulation of starch in the plastids, and the patterns of plasmodesmatal distribution as the cells begin to elongate are similar to those of caps.

This model system would function with any of the proposed growth-controlling substances and does not preclude secondary physiological roles by the statoliths themselves or by any other displaced organelles within the statocytes, e.g. Golgi bodies or mitochondria.

The Nature of and Transmission of the Signal

If there is no clear consensus of opinion concerning the initial graviperception mechanism, there is now even less agreement on how this proposed physical event is transmitted and translated into a perceived response. Some phenomena can, however, be removed as possible candidates.

THE GEOELECTRIC EFFECT   After the statoliths have fallen to the bottom, or near the bottom of the cells, the transverse electrical potential of up to 80 mv may be set up. The phenomenon is most easily demonstrated in cylindrical plant organs, e.g. coleoptiles, but will also occur in pieces of undifferentiated plant parenchyma (6). This geoelectric effect (GEE) does not seem to be linked directly to the primary perception, and thus cannot be held responsible for the asymmetric IAA distribution (44). It is dependent on IAA concentration gradients, and a symmetrical source of artifically applied IAA can, for example, substitute for a normal coleoptile tip (139, 140). In summary, the GEE seems to be a secondary phenomenon, caused by the asymmetrical IAA distribution combined with other factors (135). The GEE should not be ignored; it is likely that potentials (26) could affect the function of membranes and thereby bring about changes in the differentiation of cells, but it does not seem that this effect has a direct function in graviperception.

THE CHOLODNY-WENT HYPOTHESIS   The role of IAA in signal transmission in the shoot is well established, and many experiments indicate that applied IAA can substitute (27, 135, 136). It has long been assumed also that IAA is synthesized in the root tip, exerts a "braking" control of cell elongation at supraoptimal concentrations and, under a stimulation, moves preferentially to the lowermost cells in the elongation zone. Chadwick & Burg (20) propose that the braking effect comes about by the secondary production of ethylene by low concentrations of IAA. It has also been demonstrated (50, 51, 68) that IAA applied to the bases of intact *Pisum* and *Vicia* roots enhances the geotropic growth curvature.

More support comes from the experiments of Keeble, Nelson & Snow (63), who showed that a coleoptile tip of *Zea* substituted for a removed root tip, retarded the growth of the root and, if placed asymmetrically on the root, caused a curvature towards the side on which the coleoptile tip was placed. This is exactly the effect predicted from the Cholodny-Went hypothesis. Konings (66) applied labeled IAA in small blocks of agar to the extreme tips of intact roots. Various parts of the tip were subsequently divided into upper and lower halves and tested for ^{14}C content. IAA moved into the root from the tip of the cap and on into the meristem and elongating zones, but only a small fraction could be detected beyond 4 mm from the root tip. The distribution was uniform in vertically grown roots, but much more moved to the lower side in horizontal roots reaching about two-thirds of the total in 30 min. This redistribution depended on the presence of an intact root cap. Furthermore, Konings concluded that neither natural nor induced levels of IAA oxidases, operating at different levels on the now upper and lower sides, could account for the differences in IAA concentration observed. These experiments must be borne in mind when considering the possible role of statolith-bound IAA oxidases (1, 50). Acropetally transported IAA may be similarly redistributed in a stimulated root (66–68, 98). Again, however, removal of the cap caused the ratios in the upper and lower halves of the stimulated roots to revert to approximately unity.

If there is incontrovertible evidence for the role and redistribution of exogenously applied IAA, comparable evidence for endogenous IAA in intact roots is thin (7, 65, 112). The earlier evidence is reviewed by Audus (7), and he concludes from this earlier work and more recent work in his own laboratory (73) that there is no evidence at the present for consistent differences in IAA concentrations in the upper and lower halves of, for example, geostimulated 7 mm root tips of *Vicia*. IAA is certainly present in 5–7 mm segments of *Zea* root tips (14, 25, 35, 80). However, it appears to be predominantly in the stele, and the evidence suggests that it gets there via acropetal movement (35, 39, 64, 116). Most workers have found that movement of IAA in roots is either exclusively or predominantly acropetal (13, 18, 23, 42, 45, 50, 64, 82, 113, 116, 137, 138).

There is some evidence to suggest that IAA is normally present in the cap (14, 25, 108). Rivier & Pilet (108) have shown that there is twice as much IAA in the cap as in the apex of the root. However, there is no evidence that this endogenous IAA moves out of the cap, and other workers have failed to find IAA in the cap at all even with the most sophisticated of detection methods (70, 136). Whether or not IAA is present in the cap, there is a measure of agreement between most workers currently studying this problem that IAA is not the principal growth-controlling substance produced by the cap.

THE EVIDENCE FOR A SPECIAL CAP-PRODUCED INHIBITOR SUBSTANCE
There is now a general measure of agreement on the thesis that some substance, probably water-soluble as indicated by Pilet's cap-replacement experiments (98),

is produced by the core cells of root caps, moves rapidly out of the cap, and is transported asymmetrically to the response zone. This latent period can be shortened by a rise in temperature (88). The evidence for its rapid movement is given by Schachar (110), who subjected *Zea* primary roots to their minimal presentation time and then immediately removed only the root caps according to the method proposed by Juniper et al (61). The substance had already passed the cap boundary and, after the normal latent period, the roots curved in the usual way. This limited experiment, which because of its importance and technical difficulty requires repetition on different material and under different sets of conditions, suggests that the signal travels at a rate of approximately a millimeter in 5 min. This is almost the same, for example, as the observed rate of movement of IAA in shoots, which has been measured at 11 mm per hour (82), but faster than that for the acropetal transport of IAA in *Phaseolus* roots of 7.2 mm per hour (51).

In the original decapping experiments on *Zea* roots (61) the authors claimed, in conflict with previous decapitating experiments on roots, that there was no change in the rate of elongation of roots. Subsequent experiments on the same lines have, on the whole, tended to confirm this observation (8, 67, 95, 96, 110), but other workers have claimed to find a small stimulation of elongation (97, 100, 133). Barlow, however, using *Zea* variety "Golden Bantam," compared the growth rates of decapped roots after *both* sets of roots, the control and experimental, had been handled to cancel out the trauma of manipulation and then placed in a horizontal position (8). Barlow found no statistically significant differences between the growth rates of the control and the decapped during the first 23 hr after decapping.

Indirect evidence on the role of the cap has come from the elegant half-cap experiments of Gibbons & Wilkins (32). They dissected lateral halves of caps from the roots of *Zea,* under a binocular microscope. Such half-capped roots in the vertical position curved with virtually identical response parameters to normal roots in the horizontal position. Half-capped roots in the horizontal position, with the half-caps uppermost, curved upwards against gravity, although a little less actively than the vertical roots. These experiments and the subsequent more elaborate ones by Pilet (101) and Shaw & Wilkins (115) seem to offer incontrovertible evidence for the cap as a source of a growth inhibitor. There is no evidence for an inhibitor in the tip, as opposed to the cap, up to at least 6 hr after decapping (136). However, it is possible to reconcile the two opposing camps by supposing that under normal conditions, i.e. with hypothesis *h* operating, the root cap does not produce any growth-controlling substance. A growth-controlling substance is only produced when the stimulus exceeds the presentation time. Barlow (8) states that in his experiments decapping took 1 min, i.e. substantially less than the presentation time for *Zea* roots. It is possible that the essential difference between the opposing camps is the length of the handling times. Vertical roots grow a little faster than horizontal roots, which is also consistent with this idea (18). A catenary process whereby the cap produced a neutral substance which was then modified into a growth inhibitor in the meristem now seems unlikely. Pilet (101) has shown that half-meristems as opposed to half-caps produce nonsignificant curvatures, whereas half-meristems with their half-caps produced results identical to those of Gibbons & Wilkins. Shaw

& Wilkins (115) produced similar results. A unilateral barrier (mica, polythene, or metal) just behind the cap in intact roots produced more than five times the curvature when inserted in the upper half of horizontal roots than when in vertical roots. However, when the barrier was put in the lower side in horizontal roots, the curvature was upwards. When barriers were placed 4–5 mm from the tip of intact roots (115), no interference with a normal geotropic response could be observed and no curvature was induced in normal vertical roots of *Zea* and *Pisum.* This observation suggests that a possible role for acropetally flowing IAA, put forward by several authors (18, 19, 68, 96), can no longer be maintained.

THE NATURE OF THE CAP INHIBITOR   The earlier work on the possible identification of a growth inhibitor other than supraoptimal IAA has been reviewed by Audus (7). The first positive identification of a different inhibitor, abscisic acid (ABA), in plants came in 1969 (2), and the first in roots in 1970 (12, 94, 128). More recent work by Milborrow and co-workers (78, 79) and Newton (83) have confirmed its general presence. Something is known about its general mode of action in plants (99), and its identification in root caps of *Zea* is now confirmed. Kundu & Audus (69, 70) found in the *Zea* cap not only ABA, but also a second, as yet unidentified inhibitor and, incidentally, no trace of IAA. Although the second inhibitor has not yet been identified, it resembles xanthoxin. Xanthoxin is produced by the oxidation of certain xanthophylls and has already been recognized as an endogenous inhibitor in shoots (28, 126). There is thus good evidence for the existence of an inhibitor in the cap, one which is not species-specific (97, 99), is transported basipetally to the extension zone (115), and can move laterally in the root cap (101, 102).

THE EXISTENCE OF A CAP-PRODUCED GROWTH-PROMOTING SUBSTANCE Although it is generally accepted that the principal response of a horizontal root to gravity is by the inhibition in the elongating zone of the lower side, there is also evidence for the presence and activity of growth promoters. El-Antably & Larsen (24) have recently confirmed that gibberellic acid (GA_3) is present in the primary roots of *Vicia faba,* that in vertically grown roots its distribution is virtually symmetrical, and in horizontal roots its distribution is preponderantly in the upper half. The direction of this gradient is opposite to that in the horizontal coleoptile of *Zea Mays* (107). Webster & Wilkins (130) have shown that ^{14}C-labeled GA_3 when applied asymmetrically to the root tips of *Zea* is laterally distributed, predominantly to the upper side of horizontal roots, but there is very little longitudinal movement. The evidence for the controlling activity of GA_3 in roots, cited and described in El-Antably & Larsen's paper (24), is mixed, depending upon the concentration, the length of exposure, and the species, but the action is predominantly stimulatory. Further evidence for the existence of a redistributed growth promoter in roots comes from the work of Iversen (50), in which the first response of geotropically stimulated *Lepidium* roots, after 10 min, is a downward curvature in the cap. This very rapid response in the cap takes place after stimulation in the 135° position, which is known to be the most effective angle for a geotropic response (52). Even in the normal 90° stimulatory position the effect develops more slowly but is still marked; it cannot be explained by the inhibition of the cap cells of the lower half, but comes about as a result of an asymmetrical stimulation of growth of the cap cells, reaching 10 μm in the upper epidermal cells of the cap and 6.3 μm in the lower epidermal cells in 20 min. Iversen (personal communication, 1975) has also now confirmed the effect in the roots of *Picea abies.*

Iversen proposes that these initial stages in the response are brought about by differences in water potentials. The preferential accumulation of a substance on the upper side of the cap very shortly after geotropic stimulation is consistent with the valve hypothesis (*h*) previously proposed.

THE COUNTER-CURRENT THEORY   There is, as we have seen, considerable evidence that IAA is present in the stele of roots and moves in the stele predominantly acropetally. A role is suggested for this acropetal IAA countercurrent to the proposed inhibitor moving basipetally from the cap (18). However, Greenwood & Yčas (36) have shown than neither removal of the stele, which contains over 90% of the IAA found in *Zea* primary roots and is its principal route of transport, nor its replacement by exogenous IAA solutions had any effect at normal concentrations on the elongation of root tips. They also point out that elongating cells in the cortex of the root do not appear to have the same requirements for IAA as those in the coleoptile. The acid growth effect which can stimulate growth in coleoptiles by lowering the pH does not appear to apply to roots (15, 31). Nor do the asymmetric insertions of barriers of mica or metal foil 4–5 mm from the tip of roots of *Zea* or *Pisum* upset in any way normal bending responses (115). Greenwood & Yčas (36) suggest that the IAA in the stele may play a part in the differentiation of the vascular tissue and in the maintenance of the meristematic tissue in the pericycle that will ultimately give rise to lateral roots.

The Role of Light in Geotropism

If and when the proposed inhibitor is produced in or moved from the cap, it may be influenced by light. It was observed in 1961 that the primary shoots and roots of a number of species of plants were dependent on light for the normal processes of geotropism (72, 81). Masuda in 1962 (76) isolated an inhibitor from *Triticum* roots. The acid fraction of the inhibitor was much more active from root tips grown in the light rather than the dark. The position was complicated by the discovery that *Vanilla* roots, which are diageotropic in the dark and in light wavelengths 550–740 mm, are only positively geotropic after exposure to blue light (48). Scott & Wilkins (114) showed that the primary roots of *Zea,* variety "Giant Horse Tooth," do not respond to gravity at all when grown in total darkness. In addition, the authors noted that net acropetal movement of IAA through root segments was enhanced by light. This effect might be related to the known antagonistic effect of ABA on IAA. It has also been shown recently that certain cell organelles, e.g. Golgi bodies, demonstrate very slightly different patterns of distribution in statocyte cells under the influence of light as opposed to total darkness (77). Tepfer & Bonnett (127) showed in *Convolvulus* roots not only that the light-dependent factor in geotropism in these roots was phytochrome, i.e. the effect was elicited by red and reversed by far-red light, but that statoliths were totally unaffected by the light regime. However, *Lepidium* roots (50) respond completely normally to a gravitational stimulus in the dark. To complicate the position further (103), in the response of *Zea* roots, the variety "Anjou" appears to react normally, like *Lepidium,* in both darkness and light, whereas variety "Kelvedon 33" is for the first few hours like "Giant Horse Tooth," geotropic only in light. As Pilet points out, the production or activity of the growth-inhibiting substance, when tested by using vertical half-decapitated root segments, is quite similar to that seen in the georeaction (103). This finding is good evidence that in "Kelvedon 33" the production of the inhibitory substance may depend on light. Experiments in which the caps of these two varieties were exchanged under different regimes showed that the georeaction was related only to the nature of the cap. These experiments confirm the findings of Wilkins & Wain (134), who found that decapping released the roots from the action of a light-produced inhibitor.

The Response to the Stimulus

Iversen (50) has observed that the first detectable response of a root to a gravitational stimulus is the bending of the root cap. In *Lathyrus* the bending of the elongation zone is perceived after about 30 min at 30°C (41). Apart from the observed inhibition of the lower side of a horizontal root, there is also a slight inhibition of growth on the upper side as well (87). The root georeaction appears to be due to an asymmetrical increase in length of the cortical cells of the elongating zone (97, 105, 106). However, when *Pisum* roots were subjected to a regime of continuous gravitational disturbance over a period of 24 hr, they did not differ significantly in fresh or dry weight from control roots (Gilchrist and Juniper, unpublished results). This is consistent with Glinka & Reinhold's observations (34) that ABA alters the permeability of plant cells to water. The minute wet weight changes would be very difficult to detect.

A General Synthesis

The evidence is now overwhelming that, at least in roots, the site of perception of a gravitational stimulus lies in the core of the root cap. The evidence is almost as convincing for the theory that gradients of growth-controlling substances within the root cap are brought about in some way by relatively small movements of the statoliths. There is as yet no convincing hypothesis to explain how the movements of these statoliths can be translated into chemical gradients; most of the current theories can easily be dismissed on the available evidence. Whatever the mechanism is, it must be relatively simple since completely different cells, e.g. those of the quiescent center of the root, can fairly quickly be adapted to function as statocytes and produce the growth controller (8). Additional evidence for its simplicity comes from the mechanism's ability to bring about lateral transport in the cap of ABA, IAA, and some growth-promoting substance, possibly GA_3. The few strands of evidence for a mechanism fulfilling these criteria point towards some relationship between the statoliths and the plasmodesmata which in the statocytes have precise patterns of distribution, acting jointly in some way as valve systems.

The evidence is now good that IAA plays no direct part in the transmission of the signal. On the other hand, ABA is found in the cap, can be shown to be redistributed in the cap, moves basipetally in the root proper, and acts as an inhibitor on the cells of the extension zone. Since the removal of the cap immediately removes the ability to perceive gravity, there can be no lateral movement of the inhibitor in the enlongating zone. This and the evidence that removal of the cap results in no change in the rate of elongation suggest that the inhibitor is laterally transported only in the cap and is only released by the cap on the receipt of a stimulus above the presentation time. The presentation times in many organs are so short that stimulated synthesis of inhibitor seems highly unlikely. Once the root is stimulated there must be sufficient inhibitor present at all times. Once stimulated the inhibitor moves rapidly across the cap boundary and the limited evidence suggests that this stage of the transmission is not dependent on plasmodesmatal contact.

The enigmas which remain are numerous. What is the role of IAA in the root now that it has been displaced from a central function? What is the function of the second inhibitor, possibly xanthoxin, detected by several workers? What is the function of the growth promoter observed by Iversen (50), and what is the overall role of light? If the pattern of investigation into geotropism has shifted considerably in the past 9 years, the obstacles to a clear understanding of the mechanism are still formidable.

ACKNOWLEDGMENTS

My thanks to Dr. A. J. Gilchrist and Dr. C. C. McCready for criticizing the text and to Mr. Jeremy Roberts for stimulating discussions.

Literature Cited

1. Aasheim, T., Iversen, T-H. 1972. Presented at Proc. Adv. Study Inst. Izmir 1971. *Hormonal Regulation in Plant Growth,* ed. H. Kaldewey, Y. Vardar.
2. Addicott, F. T., Lyon, J. L. 1969. *Ann. Rev. Plant Physiol.* 20:139–64
3. Anderson, H., Johnsson, A. 1972. *Physiol. Plant.* 26:44–51
4. Arisz, W. H. 1969. *Acta Bot. Neerl.* 18:14–38
5. Audus, L. J. 1962. *Symp. Soc. Exp. Biol.* 16:197–226
6. Audus, L. J. 1969. *Physiology of Plant Growth and Development,* ed. M. B. Wilkins, London: McGraw-HIll
7. Audus, L. J. 1975. In *The Development and Function of Roots,* ed. J. G. Torrey, D. T. Clarkson. London: Academic. 618 pp.
8. Barlow, P. W. 1974. *J. Exp. Bot.* 25:1137–46
9. Barlow, P. W. 1974. *New Phytol.* 73:937–74
10. Barlow, P. W. 1975. In *The Development and Function of Roots,* ed. J. G. Torrey, D. T. Clarkson. London: Academic. 618 pp.
11. Barlow, P. W., Grundwag, M. 1974. *Z. Pflanzenphysiol.* 73:56–64
12. Belhanafi, A., Collet, G. F. 1970. *Physiol. Plant.* 23:859–70
13. Bowen, M. R., Wilkins, M. B., Cane, A. R., McCorquodale, I. 1972. *Planta* 105:273–92
14. Bridges, I. G., Hillman, J. R., Wilkins, M. B. 1973. *Planta* 115:189–92
15. Bridges, I. G., Wilkins, M. B. 1973. *Planta* 114:331–39
16. Buder, J. 1961. *Ber. Dtsch. Bot. Ges.* 74(S):14–23
17. Bünning, E., Glatzle, D. 1948. *Planta* 36:199–202
18. Burström, H. G. 1969. *Am. J. Bot.* 56:679–84
19. Burström, H. G. 1971. *Physiol. Plant.* 25:283–93
20. Chadwick, A. V., Burg, S. P. 1967. *Plant Physiol.* 42:415–20
21. Cholodny, N. 1923. *Beih. Bot. Zentralbl.* 39:222–30
22. Cholodny, N. 1926. *Jahrb. Wiss. Bot.* 65:447–59
23. Davies, P. J., Mitchell, E. K. 1972. *Planta* 105:139–54
24. El-Antably, H. M., Larsen, P. 1974. *Nature* 250:76–77
25. Elliott, M. C., Greenwood, M. S. 1974. *Phytochemistry* 13:239–41

26. Etherton, B., Dedolph, R. R. 1972. *Plant Physiol.* 49:1019–20
27. Filner, B., Hertel, R., Steel, C., Fan, V. 1970. *Planta* 94:333–54
28. Firn, R. D., Burden, R. S., Taylor, H. F. 1972. *Planta* 102:115–26
29. Fitting, H. 1905. *Jahrb. Wiss. Bot.* 41:221–39
30. Fraser, T. W., Gunning, B. E. S. 1969. *Planta* 88:244–54
31. Ganot, D., Reinhold, L. 1970. *Planta* 95:62–71
32. Gibbons, G. S. B., Wilkins, M. B. 1970. *Nature* 226:558–59
33. Giesenhagen, K. 1901. *Ber. Dtsch. Bot. Ges.* 19:277–85
34. Glinka, Z., Reinhold, L. 1971. *Plant Physiol.* 48:103–5
35. Greenwood, M. S., Hillman, J. R., Shaw, S., Wilkins, M. B. 1973. *Planta* 109:369–74
36. Greenwood, M. S., Yčas, J. 1975. *Planta* 122:311–14
37. Griffiths, H. J., Audus, L. J. 1964. *New Phytol.* 63:319–33
38. Haberlandt, G. 1914. *Physiological Plant Anatomy.* London: MacMillan
39. Hartung, W., Phillips, I. D. J. 1974. *Planta* 118:311–22
40. Hawker, L. E. 1932. *Ann. Bot. London* 46:121–57
41. Ibid 1933. 47:503–15
42. Hejnowicz, Z. 1968 *Acta Soc. Bot. Pol.* 37:451–60
43. Hertel, R., de la Fuente, R. K., Leopold, A. C. 1969 *Planta* 88:204–14
44. Hertz, C. H. 1971. *Gravity and the Organism,* ed. S. A. Gordon, M. J. Cohen. Univ. Chicago Press
45. Hillman, S. K., Phillips, I. D. J. 1970. *J. Exp. Bot.* 21:959–67
46. Hinchman, R. R., Gordon, S. A. 1974. *Plant Physiol.* 53:398–401
47. Huber, W., de Fekete, M. A. R., Ziegler, H. 1973. *Planta* 112:343–56
48. Irvine, J. E., Freyre, R. H. 1961. *Science* 134:56–57
49. Iversen, T-H. 1969. *Physiol. Plant.* 22:1251–62
50. Iversen, T-H. 1974. *K. Nor. Vidensk. Selsk. Mus. Miscellanea* 15:1–216
51. Iversen, T-H., Aasheim, T., Pedersen, K. 1971. *Physiol. Plant.* 25:417–24
52. Iversen, T-H., Larsen, P. 1971. *Physiol. Plant.* 25:23–27
53. Ibid 1973. 28:172–81
54. Iversen, T-H., Pedersen, K., Larsen, P. 1968. *Physiol. Plant.* 21:811–19
55. Johnsson, A. 1971. *Physiol. Plant.* 25:35–42
56. Juniper, B. E. 1972. *The Dynamics of Meristem Cell Populations,* ed. M. W. Miller, C. C. Kuehnert. New York: Plenum
57. Juniper, B. E. 1976. *Textbook of Developmental Biology,* ed. C. F. Graham, P. F. Wareing, Chap. 3.3. Oxford: Blackwells. In press
58. Juniper, B. E., Barlow, P. W. 1969. *Planta* 89:352–60
59. Juniper, B. E., French, A. 1970. *Planta* 95:314–29
60. Ibid 1973. 109:211–24
61. Juniper, B. E. Groves, S., Landau-Schacher, B., Audus, L. J. 1966. *Nature* 209:93–94
62. Juniper, B. E., Roberts, R. M. 1966. *J. R. Microsc. Soc.* 85:63–72
63. Keeble, F., Nelson, M. G., Snow, R. 1931. *Proc. R. Soc. B* 108:537–45
64. Kirk, S. C., Jacobs, W. P. 1968. *Plant Physiol.* 43:675–82
65. Konings, H. 1965. *Acta Bot. Neerl.* 13:566–622
66. Ibid 1967. 16:161–76
67. Ibid 1968. 17:203–11
68. Ibid 1969. 18:528–37
69. Kundu, K. K., Audus, L. J. 1974. *Planta* 117:183–86
70. Kundu, K. K., Audus, L. J. 1974. *J. Exp. Bot.* 25:479–89
71. Kutschera-Mitter, L. 1972. *Land-und Forstwirtschaftliche Forschung in Österreich* 5:35–89
72. Lake, J. V., Slack, G. 1961. *Nature* 191:30–32
73. Lahiri, A. N. 1968. *Proc. Natl. Inst. Sci. India Part B (Biol. Sci.)* 34:21–26
74. Larsen, P. 1965. *Physiol. Plant.* 18:747–65
75. Larsen, P. 1973. *COSPAR. Life Sciences and Space Research XI.* Berlin: Akademie Verlag
76. Masuda, Y. 1962. *Physiol. Plant.* 15:780–90
77. McNitt, R. E., Glessner, L., Shen-Miller, J. 1974. *Plant Physiol.* 53(Suppl.):46
78. Milborrow, B. V. 1974. *Phytochemistry* 13:131–36
79. Milborrow, B. V., Robinson, D. R. 1973. *J. Exp. Bot.* 24:537–48
80. Mitchell, E. K., Davies, P. J. 1972. *Plant Cell Physiol.* 13:1135–38
81. Mohr, H., Pichler, J. 1961. *Planta* 55:57–66
82. Morris, D. A., Briant, R. E., Thomson, P. G. 1969. *Planta* 89:178–97
83. Newton, R. J. 1974. *Physiol. Plant.* 30:108–12

84. Northcote, D. H., Pickett-Heaps, J. D. 1966. *Biochem. J.* 98:159–67
85. Nougarède, A., Pilet, P. E. 1971. *C. R. Acad. Sci. Paris* 273:348–51
86. Perbal, G. 1971. *C. R. Acad. Sci. Paris* 273:789–92
87. Ibid 1973. 276:745–48
88. Ibid, 1289–92
89. Perbal, G. 1974. *Planta* 116:153–71
90. Perbal, G. 1974. *C. R. Acad. Sci. Paris* 278:2783–86
91. Phillips, H. L., Torrey, J. G. 1974. *Am. J. Bot.* 61:871–78
92. Ibid, 879–87
93. Pickard, B. G., Thimann, K. V. 1966. *J. Gen. Physiol.* 49:1065–86
94. Pilet, P. E. 1970. *J. Exp. Bot.* 21:446–51
95. Pilet, P. E. 1971. *Nature New Biol.* 233:115–16
96. Pilet, P. E. 1971. *Bull. Soc. Bot. Suisse* 81:51–65
97. Pilet, P. E. 1972. *Planta* 106:169–71
98. Pilet, P. E. 1972. *Physiol. Vég.* 10:347–67
99. Pilet, P. E. 1972. *Hormonal Regulation in Plant Growth and and Development,* ed. H. Kaldewey, Y. Vardar. Weinheim: Verlag Chemie
100. Pilet, P. E. 1973. *Plant Sci. Lett.* 1:137–40
101. Pilet, P. E. 1973. *Planta* 111:275–78
102. Ibid 1975. 122:299–302
103. Pilet, P. E. 1975. *Physiol. Plant.* 33:94–97
104. Pilet, P. E., Nougarède, A. 1971. *C. R. Acad. Sci. Paris* 272:418–21
105. Pilet, P. E., Nougarède, A. 1974. *Plant Sci. Lett.* 3:331–34
106. Pilet, P. E., Nougarède, A., Perbal, G. 1969. *C. R. Acad. Sci. Paris* 268:2056–59
107. Railton, I. D., Phillips, I. D. J. 1973. *Planta* 109:121–26
108. Rivier, L., Pilet, P. E. 1974. *Planta* 120:107–12
109. Robards, A. W. 1968. *Planta* 82:200–10
110. Schachar, B. L. 1967. *The Root Cap and its Significance in Geoperception.* PhD thesis. Univ. London, England
111. Schröter, K., Läuchli, A., Sievers, A. 1975. *Planta* 122:213–25
112. Scott, T. K. 1972. *Ann. Rev. Plant Physiol.* 23:235–58
113. Scott, T. K., Wilkins, M. B. 1968. *Planta* 83:323–34
114. Ibid 1969. 87:249–58
115. Shaw, S., Wilkins, M. B. 1973. *Planta* 109:11–26
116. Shaw, S., Wilkins, M. B. 1974. *J. Exp. Bot.* 25:199–207
117. Shen-Miller, J., Hinchman, R. R. 1974. *Bioscience* 24:643–51
118. Shen-Miller, J., Miller, C. 1972. *Plant Physiol.* 49:634–39
119. Ibid 50:51–54
120. Sievers, A. 1965. *Z. Pflanzenphysiol.* 53:193–213
121. Sievers, A. 1967. *Protoplasma* 64:225–53
122. Sievers, A. 1971. *Gravity and the Organism,* ed. S. A. Gordon, M. J. Cohen. Univ. Chicago Press
123. Sievers, A., Schmitz, U. 1973. *Planta* 114:373–78
124. Sievers, A., Schröter, K. 1971. *Planta* 96:339–53
125. Sievers, A., Volkmann, D. 1972. *Planta* 102:160–72
126. Taylor, H. F., Burden, R. S. 1970. *Nature* 227:302–4
127. Tepfer, D. A., Bonnett, H. T. 1972. *Planta* 106:311–24
128. Tietz, A. 1971. *Planta* 96:93–96
129. Volkmann, D. 1974. *Protoplasma* 79:159–83
130. Webster, J. H., Wilkins, M. B. 1974. *Planta* 121:303–8
131. Went, F. W. 1926. *Proc. K. Ned. Akad. Wet. Amsterdam* 30:10–19
132. Westing, A. H. 1971. *Gravity and the Organism,* ed. S. A. Gordon, M. J. Cohen. Univ. Chicago Press
133. Wilkins, H., Larqué-Saavedra, A., Wain, R. L. 1974. *Nature* 248:449–50
134. Wilkins, H., Wain, R. L. 1975. *Planta* 123:217–22
135. Wilkins, M. B. 1966. *Ann. Rev. Plant. Physiol.* 17:379–408
136. Wilkins, M. B. 1975. *Curr. Adv. Plant Sci.* 6:317–28
137. Wilkins, M. B., Cane, A. R., McCorquodale, I. 1972. *Planta* 105:93–113
138. Ibid. 106:291–310
139. Wilkins, M. B., Woodcock, A. E. R. 1965. *Nature* 208:990–92
140. Woodcock, A. E. R., Wilkins, M. B. 1970. *J. Exp. Bot.* 21:985–96
141. Zinke, H. 1968. *Planta* 82:50–72

Ann. Rev. Plant Physiol. 1976. 27:407–34

MODELING OF PLANT GROWTH

♦7616

Ralph O. Erickson[1]

Department of Biology, University of Pennsylvania, Philadelphia, Pennsylvania 19174

CONTENTS

The notion of modeling in science has many connotations. There are physical models, such as the atomic models of chemistry which consist of wooden or plastic balls proportional in size to atoms, together with connectors to represent chemical bonds, or realistic sculptures representing the overall form or the histology of an organ such as a leaf, etc. In enzyme kinetics, reaction diagrams are frequently used, in which symbols for reactants are connected by arrows to indicate theorized reactions. Similar diagrams are also used in less well understood areas of plant physiology such as the photoperiodic induction of flowering. In many cases a model is in the form of a differential equation, or a system of differential equations, or equations which result from the solution of differential equations, in which the variables and parameters are intended to correspond to measurable attributes and relationships in a system which is being investigated. Recently, logical systems have been proposed to model the development of organisms, the L-systems of Lindenmayer (50, 51), which can be studied by the methods which are used in automaton theory, related to computer applications. There are many other sorts of models, that is to say, more or less abstract representations of natural phenomena. This review will deal primarily with morphogenetic aspects of growth, that is, with dimensions and with the cellular aspects of form. Much of the mathematics will therefore be related to geometry. I will be concerned mainly with the use of differential equations

[1]The author's research which is referred to here has had the support of grants from the National Science Foundation. Discussions with Dr. Wendy Kuhn Silk, and her generous assistance, have played a crucial part in the conception and completion of this review.

to model plant growth, since the power of differential equations has been abundantly proven in the physical sciences, and the resources of classical mathematics are available for characterizing and solving them. Highly developed computer methods are also available for finding numerical solutions of differential equations, even when they may be mathematically intractable (57).

When devising a scientific model that is to have explanatory power, it is extremely important that the parameters of the model and the relationships which it expresses correspond with the biological system which is being investigated. In discussing models of growth, I will therefore be at pains to point out the correspondence between features of the model and of the growing structure. As a matter of fact, much of the discussion will center around appropriate expressions of growth rates. I will also discuss methods which can be used to study growth empirically and to analyze growth data in such a way as to make the results amenable to theoretical consideration.

I shall first discuss the growth of entire plants, plant organs, or excised portions of plants, making reference to theoretical growth equations which have been proposed for them. Methods of making growth measurements will be considered, and in particular I will discuss methods of analyzing empirical growth data so as to yield efficient and suitable estimates of growth rates and growth parameters.

For more detailed analysis, particularly of morphogenetic processes, it is important to consider how growth rates may differ from point to point within the growing system, as in a meristem. To have meaning in a differential equation, data must here be obtained with good spatial resolution as well as good resolution in time. The growth rates estimated from such data should be elemental, that is, they should be stated in terms of differentials of length, area, or volume (dx, dA, or dV) as well as the time differential dt. Following mathematical usage, these differentials of the spatial coordinates are referred to as *elements* of length, area, and volume, and they appear in *elemental rates* of change of length, area, or volume. It goes without saying that these rates should also be *instantaneous*.

Analyses of growth in length, as in a root, in the internode cell of *Nitella* and other examples will be discussed. In the case of *Nitella*, a model for the regulation of the growth rate of the cell, in the form of two differential equations, will be reviewed.

The elemental analysis of growth in two dimensions will be exemplified by a study of the growth of the lamina of a leaf, and a model for growth in surface of an idealized surface of revolution will be discussed.

The elemental analysis of growth in three spatial dimensions presents formidable difficulties which have not been resolved, as does the analysis in even one or two dimensions of a morphologically complex system such as the shoot apex with its leaf primordia. In such cases, a developmental index is useful in referring detailed measurements or analyses, made, for example, on samples of tissue, or histological preparations, to the time axis and hence to allow estimation of growth rates. Illustrations of developmental indices are log bud length in flower development of *Lilium* and the plastochron index for vegetative shoot development.

Much of the content of this essay is also discussed in another article (20).

GROWTH CURVES

In a sense, any equation which is purported to correspond to a living phenomenon can be termed a model of the phenomenon. In discussions of plant growth, many growth equations have been put forward in which an attempt is made to account for the increase in size (usually height or weight) of a plant or a plant organ on the basis of simple assumptions. Williams (69–71) and Leopold & Kriedemann (49) provide references to some of the literature. In the simplest case, the growth rate may merely be assumed constant, $dx/dt = a$, where x is a measure of the size (e.g. length) of a plant or plant organ. This obviously leads to a straight line, $x = x_0 + at$. The growth in length of a root or a shoot is often found to be approximately linear over a considerable period of time. Examples are the primary root of *Zea*, which grows in length linearly at nearly 2 mm·hr^{-1} for 3 days or more, and the shoot of the bamboo *Dendrocalamus* sp., studied by Kraus (48), which grew linearly at about 0.28 m·day^{-1} for nearly 2 months. (A native assistant climbed the culm daily with a tape, to a height of 14 m).

Another simple example is Blackman's (10) proposal of the compound interest law of plant growth. If one assumes that the rate of growth in size x is simply proportional to its size, the assumption can be stated as the differential equation $dx/dt = r \cdot x$, which has as its solution the simple exponential equation $x = x_0 e^{rt}$, x_0 being the size at time $t = 0$, e the base of natural logarithms, and r a constant which I will term the relative growth rate, since it is the rate of growth in size divided by the size $(1/x)(dx/dt)$. A simple test of the applicability of this equation is suggested by writing it in logarithmic form, $\ln x = \ln x_0 + rt$, which is the equation of a straight line. Plotting measurements of x vs t on semilogarithmic graph paper will yield an approximate straight line if the equation is applicable, and a straight line can be fitted by the least squares method. It is often found empirically to fit the early phases of growth in weight, dry weight, length, etc of many plants such as seedlings, sporelings, cuttings, etc. In some cases, exponential growth continues for a long period. For example, the flower buds of *Lilium longiflorum* grow in length exponentially from the time they can first be measured without injury until 3 or 4 days before anthesis, a period of about a month (15).

It is usually found, however, that if the growth of a plant or a plant organ is followed over a long period, it departs from the simple exponential relationship. For instance, in the growth of a herbaceous plant throughout the growing season, or the growth of a leaf from a primordium to maturity, the plot of size (e.g. length or weight) vs time forms a sigmoid curve. Several equations have been proposed to account for such inflected curves. One, which might be termed the autocatalytic equation, follows from the assumption that the rate of growth in size is proportional to the size attained and to the difference between the size attained and some assumed final size, that is, $dx/dt = kx(x_f - x)$. This is analogous to an assumption that the rate of a chemical reaction is proportional to the amount of product and to the amount of substrate remaining, the first proportionality implying autocatalysis. In the chemical case, x_f is the initial amount of substrate, and in the analogy to plant growth, it is the final size. On integration this is $x = x_f/(1 + ce^{-kt})$. It may be put into linear form by rearranging and making the logarithmic transformation $\ln[x/(x_f - x)] = kt$, and tested by plotting measurements in the form $x/(x_f - x)$ vs t on semi-log paper. The curve represented by this equation is symmetrical about the point of inflection, which corresponds to $\frac{1}{2}x_f$ and it is asymptotic to $x = 0$ and $x = x_f$. In a chemical reaction, x_f is known, but in applying this equation to growth, the final size is not definitely known, and estimation of x_f may be troublesome. One procedure is by trial and error, making semi-log plots with various values of x_f and selecting the one which is most nearly linear. An adaptation of this method for computer solution is to calculate the residual sum of squares about the calculated line, in either the sigmoid or linear form, iteratively, altering x_f at each iteration, so as to find the value which gives the least sum of squares. Actually, the chemical analogy implying that there is a "substrate" for growth is dubious. Robertson's (65) argument that growth is controlled by a "master reaction" whose kinetics are autocatalytic also seems dubious to me, at least for plant growth. Nonetheless, one may have legitimate reasons for using this equation if it fits growth data satisfactorily.

If it is assumed that the rate of growth in size of a plant organ x is simply proportional to the difference between some final size and the size attained, $dx/dt = k' (x_f - x)$, the equation $x = x_f(1 - e^{-kt})$ results. In linear form it is $\ln(x_f - x) = \ln x_f - kt$. It may be called the monomolecular equation, again by analogy with a chemical reaction equation. The procedure for testing and fitting it are similar to that for the autocatalytic equation. The growth in length or weight of excised plant parts can often be approximated by this equation.

The sigmoid growth curves of plants are frequently not symmetrical about an inflection point, as the autocatalytic growth equation predicts. For such cases the Gompertz equation is sometimes considered. It was proposed in actuarial science for fitting of human mortality data, and it has been used in studies of the growth of mammals, where it has been observed that the relative growth rate decreases with time. If it is assumed that the logarithm of the relative rate of growth in weight, say, decreases linearly with time, we may write $\ln(d \ln x/dt) = a - k't$. Two integrations are required to obtain the Gompertz equation $x = a(e^{-ce})^{-kt}$, where a, c, and k are arbitrary constants. Perhaps the best scheme for a preliminary test of its applicability is to plot estimates of the relative growth rate vs time on semi-log paper. For a careful fitting of the equation, the constants a, c, and k can be evaluated by successive approximation, for which a least-squares computer program would be useful, as suggested above.

Richards (63) has pointed out that an equation of Bertalanffy (9) is flexible enough to fit a wide variety of asymmetrically sigmoid growth data. It was derived on hypotheses about the proportionality of anabolism and catabolism in animal systems. If this and other restrictions are dropped, Richards (63) and Williams (71) argue that it has wide applicability to plant growth data. It can be written as $x = a(1 - be^{-kt})^{1/(1-m)}$ when $m < 1$, and as $x = a(1 + be^{-kt})^{1/(1-m)}$ when $m > 1$. If $m = 0$ is substituted into the first equation, it reduces to the monomolecular equation, and if $m = 2$, the second equation reduces to the autocatalytic equation.

If $m = 1$ the equations cannot be solved, but Richards (63) shows that as m approaches 1 from either side, the limiting form of the equation is the Gompertz equation. The flexibility of this function depends on its containing four arbitrary constants, which as above might be evaluated by successive approximation. Williams (71) provides an example of fitting of this function to data on the growth in length of leaves of flax, *Linum usitatissimum.*

Even though the hypotheses (differential equations) underlying these equations may not be pertinent to the growth of a plant system, and may therefore be of little theoretical value, they may legitimately be used as arbitrary functions to fit data for the purpose of estimation or prediction. If this is one's intent, it might be that other exponential, trigonometric, or hyperbolic functions could be useful. Functions known as rational, and in particular polynomial equations (59), are especially useful as arbitrary functions for these purposes since they can be evaluated by fairly simple numerical procedures, and the statistics of polynomials is well understood.

MEASUREMENT AND ANALYSIS OF PLANT GROWTH

In studying the growth of a plant or some part of the plant, such as the aerial shoot, the root system, a leaf, or an excised part such as a coleoptile segment, the experimental procedures are usually quite simple. For linear dimensions all that is usually needed is a rule, tape, or caliper, though for some purposes a more sensitive device may be needed, as in the study by Evans & Ray (26) of rapid responses of *Avena* coleoptiles to added auxin. Sometimes it is useful to make photographs and to obtain measurements from them. Linear measurements can usually be made without injury to the plant, and one can make repeated measurements of the same plant or organ. Plotting such measurements vs time yields growth curves which apply to individuals. Such data have been termed Type A by Kavanagh & Richards (46), and in studies of human growth are curiously known as "longitudinal."

For measurements such as fresh weight and dry weight, the procedures are also simple. Frequently interest centers on measurements such as the content of the plant or its part, of protein, chlorophyll, etc, for which a chemical analysis is required that may be simple or more complex. Or histological preparations may be made, perhaps for the study of cellular processes. From the present point of view, the essential characteristic of many such measurements is that they are destructive, and a measurement of a given plant or part cannot be repeated. In order to obtain a growth curve for such measurements, one must resort to the statistical procedure of sampling from a population of similar plants growing under similar conditions, taking precautions to assure that sampling is random. For instance, a randomized block design might be desirable for a growth study. It is interesting to note that the development of classical small sample statistics, largely by Fisher (27), had its impetus from related problems which arise in agricultural crop testing. Where this statistical sampling procedure must be used, the data are sometimes called "cross-sectional," and Kavanagh & Richards (46) spoke of them as Class C data. If type A data are to be obtained for a number of similar plants, sampling questions also arise, and Kavanagh & Richards distinguish this situation as Class E. As they observed, the problem of making efficient estimates of growth parameters from Class E data presents some statistical problems which have not been resolved.

However growth data are obtained, it is almost always desirable to analyze them in such a way as to estimate *growth rates.* These should be interpretable as derivatives, as defined in the differential calculus, rather than in any of the less desirable ways which have sometimes been used. The reason for this is that in any attempt at modeling it should be possible to relate the experimental data to the differential equations which represent the process being modeled. If x is a measured attribute of a plant or organ, its growth curve can be viewed as a function of time $x = f(t)$. Frequently the first derivative, dx/dt, is of interest, and I will refer to it as the *absolute growth rate.* In some cases, the absolute rate is found to be approximately constant over some period of time, but more often it is found to vary continuously. In either case, it is often instructive to plot out the absolute rate vs time, in addition to plotting the growth curve.

As Briggs, Kidd & West (11) proposed, the *relative growth rate* is frequently a very appropriate way to express plant growth data, for heuristic reasons given below. Considering the measured attribute x to be a function of time $x = f(t)$, the relative or specific growth rate is $(1/x)(dx/dt)$. It can also be expressed as d ln x/dt. One reason for the desirability of the relative rate is the same as stated above, that it often appears in useful differential equations. Another follows from the fact that, to an approximation at least, the rate of deposition of dry matter by a growing green plant is proportional to the bulk of its photosynthetic tissue, and this in turn is roughly proportional to its fresh or dry weight. This reasoning led Blackman (10) to propose the term "efficiency index" for the relative growth rate, and led to other formulations of growth rates such as the leaf specific rate, in which the absolute rate, dx/dt, usually for increase in dry weight, is divided by the total leaf area of a shoot (10, 49, 69). Furthermore, since the dimension of the relative rate is simply time $^{-1}$, direct comparisons may be made of the relative rates of change of any measured attributes of the growing system.

The estimation of growth rates from experimental data often presents some problems because, while growth is continuous, measurements are for practical reasons made only at intervals, and errors arising from the measurement, from imperfect control of growing conditions, or from the sampling procedure used, are always present. These errors are propagated into the estimated rates. To see this in a simple case, assume that measurements of length x_i have been made at equal intervals of time Δt, and that rates are estimated as increments of x_i divided by the time increment $\Delta x/\Delta t$, or $(x_{i+1} - x_i)/(t_{i+1} - t_i)$. We make the usual assumption in regression analysis, that t, and hence Δt, are free of error. If the measurement error of x_i is represented by σ_i, then the standard deviation of the increments of x_i is $\sigma_{\Delta x} = (\sigma_{i+1}^2 + \sigma_i^2 - 2\rho\sigma_i\sigma_{i+1})^{1/2}$, or assuming that errors of successive x_i are uncorrelated ($\rho = 0$), this equation is $\sigma_{\Delta x} = (2\sigma_i^2)^{1/2}$. That is, the standard deviation of increments of x_i is greater than that of x_i. This is in keeping with one's usual experience that plots of $\Delta x/\Delta t$ vs t are more or less erratic (Figure 1C). If the measurements have not been made at equal intervals of time, further problems of estimation arise.

If the estimation of growth rates by calculating increments is not satisfactory, the original data may be smoothed, and rates of change of the smooth curve may be estimated in some way. The smoothing may be done by drawing a curved line through a graph of the data by eye ("eyeballing it"), or a growth function may be fitted to the data by a method suggested above. The function may be quite arbitrary. A third method is to use the numerical smoothing and differentiation formulas described below.

If an eye-fitted curve has been drawn, slopes can be estimated by the construction method described in analytical geometry, drawing straight lines tangent to the curve at selected points. Each of these lines can be viewed as the hypotenuse of a right triangle with legs parallel to the axes. If the altitude of the triangle is a and its base b, the slope of the line is a/b. If measurements x_i were plotted vs t_i, the absolute rate $(dx/dt)_i$ at a point is proportional to the slope, the proportionality depending on the scaling of the x- and t-axes of the graph. The relative rate $(1/x)(dx/dt)$ can be gotten by dividing each estimate of dx/dt by corresponding x. Alternatively, $\ln x_i$ can be plotted vs t_i, and this same graphical procedure used to estimate the relative rate as $d \ln x/dt$. It is usually more convenient to use a protractor, adjusting its base line to be tangent to the curve at selected points, and reading the angle ϕ which the tangent line makes with the abscissa. The slope is $\tan \phi$. Richards & Kavanagh (64) describe a convenient double prism devise, a Tangentmeter, for this purpose. We have made a protractor which is graduated directly in units of $\tan \phi$ rather than degrees, which makes it unnecessary to look up or compute $\tan \phi$ (23). Highly developed data-recording equipment, adapted for computer applications, is also available for measuring angles, and can be had from several manufacturers. For careful work, however, these graphical methods lack objectivity and reproducibility.

If a growth equation is used to smooth data, the equation can be differentiated to give explicit equations for the absolute growth rate dx/dt and the relative growth rate $d \ln x/dt$. These equations, written with the parameters found by fitting the data, can then be solved at selected times. However, my experience has been that there is often some bias in these estimates if the equation has been fitted to data covering an extended period of time. This bias stems from systematic discrepancies between the growth equation and the empirical data.

Smoothing formulas (1, 59) and formulas for the first derivative may be based on the least squares fitting of polynomials to empirical data. For growth data we may consider the polynomial $x_i = a + b_1 t_i + b_2 t_i^2 + b_3 t_i^3 + \ldots$, fitted to measurements x_i at various t_i, and its first derivative $(dx/dt)_i = b_1 + 2b_2 t_i t + 3b_3 t_i^2 \ldots$, and digress to consider the properties of such polynomials. The symbol $\bar{x}_i$ represents a calculated or smoothed value, as distinct from a measurement x_i. The degree of the polynomial is arbitrary. Thus, if the first two terms are taken, the function is linear; if the first three terms are used, it is quadratic; and there are polynomials of third degree, fourth degree, etc. Methods for fitting polynomials have been highly systematized, in particular by the use of orthogonal polynomials (47). When values of the independent variable, t_i in our application, are equally spaced, the coefficients of a polynomial take the particularly simple form of a sum of products of the x_i by tabulated values of orthogonal polynomials, divided by a tabulated divisor (7). Tables of these polynomials are available for fitting polynomials up to the fifth degree, to any number of data points from 3 to 75 (28, 66). If one carries out the least squares fitting of a polynomial to a certain number n of equally spaced t_i and corresponding x_i, symbolically instead of numerically, and solves for $\bar{x}_i$, a series of n smoothing formulas results. These are similar in appearance to orthogonal polynomials, giving a series of multipliers and a divisor, which allow $\bar{x}_i$ to be calculated readily from given x_i. A number of these formulas are published (1, 59) and some are listed in abbreviated form in Table 1. As an example, the quadratic smoothing formula for the third of five points is $\bar{x}_i = (-3x_{i-2} + 12x_{i-1} + 17x_i + 12x_{i+1} - 3x_{i+2})/35$. Applying linear formulas of this sort is equivalent to the familiar process of calculating running averages, but the linear formulas have the drawback that they do not accommodate as well to curvature as do the quadratic and higher degree formulas. In practice, a formula is applied to a limited odd number of points, e.g. 3, 5, or 7. A "centered" formula should be used for all the x_i in a column except for the first and last $(n-1)/2$ points. For example, if the formula quoted above is applied to the 5 points centered on (t_i, x_i), $\bar{x}_i$ is calculated. Then advance one space and apply the formula again. For the beginning and end points the noncentered formulas are used, but they sometimes give erratic results. If one is working with an ordinary desk calculator, it is helpful to write the coefficients of a formula in a column at the edge of a card with the same spacing as the column of x_i on one's data sheet, and to move the card down one step for each x_i. This process is tedious since it requires entering each x_i value repeatedly. Programming it for a computer is a very simple matter, and it can also be carried out efficiently with a programmable desk or hand-held calculator with several storage registers. Some judgment is required in the use of these formulas, perhaps choosing those formulas which give the least amount of smoothing that will serve one's purpose.

Smoothing by this procedure is illustrated in Figure 1, using data of Williams (70) on increase of dry weight of field-grown wheat, Class C data. In Figure 1A is shown the smoothed curve calculated with the 5-point quadratic smoothing formula of Table 1. In Figure 1B, logarithms of the dry weights have been fitted with the same 5-point smoothing formulas. In both Figure 1A and B, the curves follow the points more closely than do the autocatalytic and polynomial equations which Williams (70) fitted. The effect has been merely to remove some of the variability from the data. If one desired, one could calculate the standard error of estimate for each x_i, using a standard formula from regression analysis, but this scarcely seems worth while in many applications.

Numerical differentiation formulas are found in the same way as the smoothing formulas, solving for $(d\bar{x}/dt)_i$ instead of $\bar{x}_i$. Since dx/dt has the dimension of time^{-1} as well as the dimension of x, the spacing along the time axis Δt must be considered. This appears in the denominators of the formulas as h. The published

Table 1 Smoothing and numerical differentiation formulas based on least squares fitting of polynomials to 3, 5, or 7 points (x_i, y_i), where x_i are equally spaced with interval h[a]

Smoothing formulas

Linear, 3 points: $\quad \tilde{y}_{i-1} = (5 +2 -1)/6 \qquad\qquad \tilde{y}_{i+1} = (-1 +2 +5)/6$

2nd degree, 3 points: $\quad \tilde{y}_{i-1} = (4 -1 +1)/3 \qquad\qquad \tilde{y}_{i+1} = (1 -1 +4)/3$

Linear, 5 points:

$\tilde{y}_{i-2} = (\ 3\ +2\ +1\quad\ -1)/5$

$\tilde{y}_{i-1} = (\ 4\ +3\ +2\ +1\quad\ )/10$

$\tilde{y}_i \ \ = (\ 1\ +1\ +1\ +1\ +1)/5$

$\tilde{y}_{i+1} = (\quad\ 1\ +2\ +3\ +4)/10$

$\tilde{y}_{i+2} = (-1\quad\ +1\ +2\ +3)/5$

2nd degree, 5 points:

$\tilde{y}_{i-2} = (\ 31\ +9\ -3\ -5\ +3)/35$

$\tilde{y}_{i-1} = (\ \ 9\ +13\ +12\ +6\ -5)/35$

$\tilde{y}_i \ \ = (\ -3\ +12\ +17\ +12\ -3)/35$

$\tilde{y}_{i+1} = (\ -5\ +6\ +12\ +13\ +9)/35$

$\tilde{y}_{i+2} = (\ \ 3\ -5\ -3\ +9\ +31)/35$

2nd degree, 7 points:

$\tilde{y}_{i-3} = (\ 32\ +15\ +3\ -4\ -6\ -3\ +5)/42$

$\tilde{y}_{i-2} = (\ \ 5\ +4\ +3\ +2\ +1\ -1\ -2)/14$

$\tilde{y}_{i-1} = (\ \ 1\ +3\ +4\ +4\ +3\ +1\ -2)/14$

$\tilde{y}_i \ \ = (\ -2\ +3\ +6\ +7\ +6\ +3\ -2)/21$

$\tilde{y}_{i+1},\ \tilde{y}_{i+2},\ \tilde{y}_{i+3},$ by symmetry

Numerical differentiation formulas

Linear, 3 points: $\quad y' = (-1 +0 +1)/2h$

2nd degree, 3 points: $\quad y'_{i-1} = (-3 +4 -1)/2h \qquad y'_{i+1} = (1 -4 +3)/2h$

Linear, 5 points: $\quad y'_i = (-2 -1 +0 +1 +2)/10h$

2nd degree, 5 points:

$y'_{i-2} = (-54 +13 +40 +27 -26)/70h$

$y'_{i-1} = (-34 +3 +20 +17 -6)/70h$

$y'_i \ \ = (-2 -1 \quad +1 +2)/10h$

$y'_{i+1} = (\ 6 -17 -20 -3 +34)/70h$

$y'_{i+2} = (26 -27 -40 -13 +54)/70h$

3rd degree, 5 points:

$y'_{i-2} = (-125 +136 +48 -88 +29)/84h$

$y'_{i-1} = (-19 -1 +12 +13 -5)/42h$

$y'_i \ \ = (\ 1 -8 \quad +8 -1)/12h$

$y'_{i+1} = (\ 5 -13 -12 +1 +19)/42h$

$y'_{i+2} = (-29 +88 -48 -136 +125)/84h$

2nd degree, 7 points:

$y'_{i-3} = (-13 -2 +5 +8 +7 +2 -7)/28h$

$y'_{i-2} = (-29 -6 +9 +16 +15 +6 -11)/84h$

$y'_{i-1} = (-19 -6 +3 +8 +9 +6 -1)/84h$

$y'_i \ \ = (\ -3 -2 -1 \quad +1 +2 +3)/28h$

$y'_{i+1},\ y'_{i+2},\ y'_{i+3},$ by symmetry

[a]Only the coefficients of y_i are given. Smoothed values are $\tilde{y}_i$; y'_i is $d\tilde{y}_i/dx$.

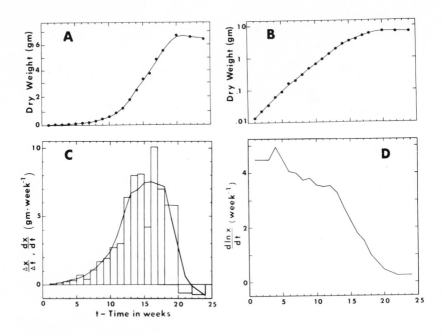

Figure 1 Dry weights of field-grown wheat (70). A. Curve fitted to points with 5-point quadratic smoothing formulas (Table 1). B. Curve fitted to log dry weight with the same 5-point smoothing formulas. C. Bar diagram ($\Delta x/\Delta t$) and absolute rate of increase in dry weight (dx/dt) estimated with 5-point quadratic formulas for the first derivative (Table 1). D. Relative rate of increase in dry weight (d ln x/dt) estimated with the same 5-point formulas for numerical differentiation.

differentiation formulas (1, 59) are derived from polynomials which pass precisely through the points to which they are fitted, leaving no degrees of freedom for error estimates, and hence having no smoothing effect. They could be applied to previously smoothed data, but it seems more efficient in dealing with empirical data to use formulas for estimating the derivative which also provide some smoothing. Some such formulas are given in Table 1, and I can provide others. They are used in the same way as the smoothing formulas, except that h must be specified. Their application to the data on wheat plants is illustrated in Figure 1C, where estimates of the absolute rate dx/dt are plotted vs t as a smooth curve, and in Figure 1D, showing estimates of the relative rate of increase in dry weight, d ln x/dt. Both curves were obtained with the 5-point quadratic differentiation formulas given in Table 1, applied in the first case to the original values of dry weight x_i, and for the second curve to the natural logarithms ln x_i. Alternatively, the relative rate might have been calculated by dividing each estimate, dx_i/dt, by x_i or $\tilde{x}_i$. The results would differ slightly from those plotted.

GROWTH OF THE PLANT AXIS

In the preceding section methods were suggested for the accurate estimation of growth rates of entire plants and plant organs from measurements of various kinds. Now I will describe a more detailed analysis in which both the spatial and temporal components of growth rate are analyzed, growth along a plant axis, which is essentially one-dimensional growth. It will be seen that, while more elaborate methods of measurement may be required, the methods of estimation of rates described above are directly applicable. A good example is growth of a root (21, 29, 30, 39). In our experiments (23), roots of *Zea mays* seedlings were marked with particles of carbon (lamp black) and photographed through a slit onto a moving strip of film to produce streak photographs such as Figure 2. Hejnowicz & Erickson (40) used fluorescent particles, and List (52) utilized reflections of light from epidermal cells of the root to produce similar streak photographs. Goodwin & Stepka (30) and Goodwin & Avers (29) measured positions of cross walls of epidermal cells microscopically to obtain similar records. If one takes the distance of a point on the root from the tip of the meristem (or the root cap) as x, streak photographs such as Figure 2 constitute automatic plots of distance x vs time t. Slopes of the streaks can be measured, using the tangent protractor, for example, and these slopes are proportional to rates of displacement of points from the tip $dx/dt = x'$. If these are plotted vs x (Figure 3), they can be interpreted as growth rates of apical segments of the root of length x. The velocity dx/dt can also be taken as proportional to an element of length of the root dx, so that if dx/dt were plotted vs t, the resulting graph could be interpreted as a growth curve of a length element dx. This curve has a markedly asymmetrical sigmoid shape with a prolonged period of slow increase, then a sharp acceleration, and a sudden cessation of growth (23).

It is more instructive to estimate the rate of growth of a length element dx. The appropriate expression is dx'/dx, and I have termed it the relative elemental rate of elongation. It can also be interpreted as the one-dimensional case of the divergence of the velocity vector div **v** of vector analysis. It can be estimated from the data of Figure 3, where x' is represented as a function of x, by means of numerical differentiation formulas (Table 1), taking x as the independent and x' as the dependent variable. Relative elemental rates of elongation, dx'/dx, estimated from a number of streak photographs like Figure 2, are plotted as a solid line in Figure 4. Under our experimental conditions, the divergence rises from 0 at the tip of the root, to a maximum of about 0.4 hr^{-1}, 4 mm from the tip, and declines to 0 at about 8 mm. This contrasts greatly with the conclusion drawn from marking experiments by Julius Sachs and many later authors that the maximum rate of elongation is much nearer to the tip. The flaw in these experiments is that the rates estimated are neither elemental nor instantaneous. The single curve (solid line) of Figure 4 suffices to describe the pattern of elongation of an element of the root, if one assumes that the growth pattern is time invariant. In general, we would assume that the velocity of displacement of a point is a function of both time and position, $x' = f(x, t)$. Then $dx' = (\partial x'/\partial x)dx + (\partial x'/\partial t)dt$. If we assume time invariance, then $\partial x'/\partial t = 0$,

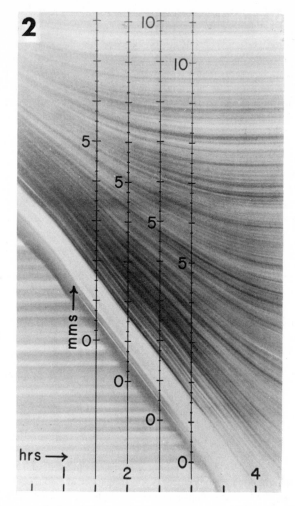

Figure 2   Root growth. Streak photograph recording the displacement of marks placed on a growing root of *Zea mays* (23).

and $dx'/dx = \partial x'/\partial x$, so that one curve suffices. This is approximately true for a considerable period of root growth, but is not so for the initial stages, for very long roots which are approaching the end of their period of growth, nor for some experimentally treated roots. List (52) has described an oscillatory aspect of root growth which also requires a modification of this assumption of time invariance.

Although this analysis is one-dimensional, the growth data from the streak photographs can be used indirectly to estimate the rates at which other processes are

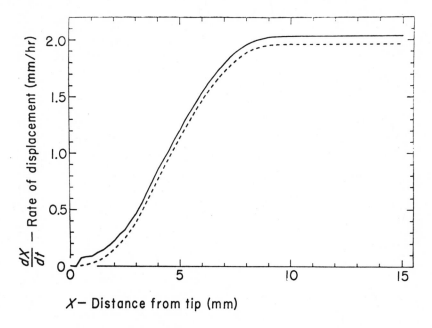

Figure 3   Root growth. Rates of displacement of points from the tip (dx/dt) estimated from streak photographs.

occurring. For instance, we have estimated the rate of increase in cell number from cell counts of macerated segments of roots (24). If c is the total number of cells in an apical portion of the root of length x, then the number of cells in a segment of length Δx is Δc and the data can be plotted as $\Delta c/\Delta x$ (Figure 5). A smooth curve fitted to this bar diagram such that the area under each segment of the curve equals the area of the corresponding bar can be construed as a graph of dc/dx vs x. This procedure is justified on the assumption that c and x can be taken as parametric functions of t, and therefore that c is a function of x alone, $c = f(x)$, just as x' was taken as a function of x alone. Multiplying these estimates of dc/dx by corresponding estimates of dx/dt gives dc/dt ($= c'$), the absolute rate at which cell number of an apical segment is increasing. For the entire meristem which consists of over 250,000 cells in a *Zea* root, new cells are being formed at the rate of about 18,000 cells·hr^{-1}. The relative elemental rate of cell formation dc'/dc can also be evaluated. If dc/dt is taken as a function of x, numerical differentiation will give values of dc'/dx, and these may be divided by dc/dx to yield estimates of dc'/dc. This rate peaks at about 0.16 hr^{-1}, 1.25 mm from the tip of the root, as shown by the dotted lines in Figure 4.

We have also made measurements of cell length of randomly chosen cells in longitudinal sections of root segments, and calculated the mean cell length L_c at various distances from the tip. Numerical differentiation gives dL_c/dx, and again

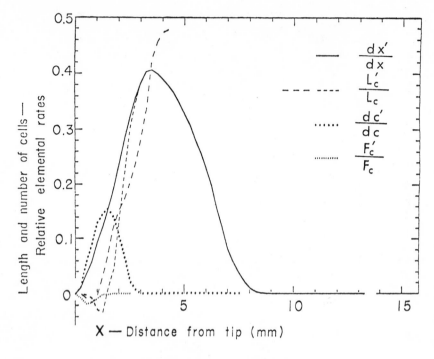

Figure 4 Root growth. Relative elemental rates of elongation (dx'/dx) and of cell formation (dc'/dc) and relative rates of change in average cell length (1/L_c) (dL_c/dt) and number of files of cells (1/F_c) (dF_c/dt).

multiplying these estimates by corresponding dx/dt and dividing by L_c yields values of the relative rate of cell elongation $(1/L_c)(dL_c/dt)$ (Figure 4, longer dashes). Note that this is not an elemental rate since it pertains to cells, the biological units of plant structure. Cells are microscopic, to be sure, but they are not infinitesimal. For the most part the cells are arranged in longitudinal files, cell divisions being predominantly at right angles to the root axis. The files, however, merge and converge on the initial region of the apical meristem of the root, since this is where all the cells of the root originate. The number of files of cells F_c is therefore a function of distance from the tip, and this was estimated by counting the numbers of cells which can be seen in transverse sections of roots. The relative rate of change in number of files, estimated as already described, is plotted as a fine dotted line below the abscissa in Figure 4.

The rates described above can be related to each other by considering a formula which has sometimes been used to estimate cell number in samples of plant tissue (6) in which cells are arranged in longitudinal files. If Δx is the length of a segment of tissue (root, internode, coleoptile, etc) being sampled, L_c is the mean cell length, and F_c is the number of files of cells in the segment, then the number of cells

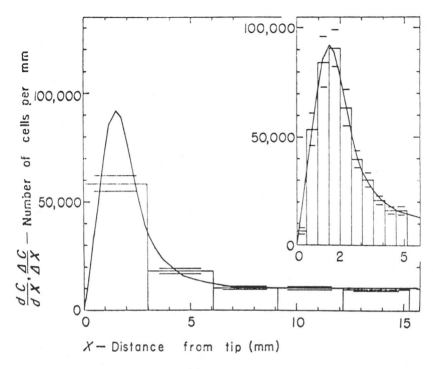

Figure 5 Root growth. Cell counts (Δc) of root segments of length (Δx) shown as bars (Δc/Δx). Curve representing dc/dx fitted to the bars.

Δc can be estimated from the formula $\Delta c = \Delta x \cdot F_c/L_c$, or in differential form, $dx/dt = (dc/dt) \cdot L_c/F_c$. Differentiating this equation and making some substitutions gives the following equation relating the relative rates and relative elemental rates discussed above: $dx'/dx = (1/L_c)(dL_c/dt) + dc'/dc - (1/F_c)(dF_c/dt)$. This differential equation can be considered as a model of root growth, in which the relative elemental rate of elongation is analyzed into constituent rates. The first term on the right describes the process of increase in average cell length. The second and third might be considered as longitudinal and radial components of the cell partitioning process. This equation conceivably has many solutions, but at the present state of our knowledge, we can do little more than cite the empirical results of experiments which describe root growth.

This method can be extended to the estimation of the relative elemental rate of net change of a biochemical constituent of the root during growth. If root segments are analyzed, say for protein nitrogen, P can be defined as the protein nitrogen content of an apical portion of the root of length x, and the analyses of the segments ΔP can be put in the form $\Delta P/\Delta x$, then dP/dx, dP/dt, and finally dP'/dP, just as was done for cell counts Δc. Furthermore, the average protein content per cell, $\Delta P/\Delta c$, can be smoothed to $dP/dc = P_c$, and this can be used with corresponding values of dx/dt from the streak photograph analysis to estimate $(1/P_c)(dP_c/dt)$, as was done for L_c, the average cell lengths. Erickson & Goddard (21) presented such rate estimates for fresh weight, dry weight, total nitrogen, protein nitrogen, cell wall constituents, and for crude analyses of the nucleic acids, with highly suggestive results. Unfortunately, this work has not been verified nor extended.

A more direct view of the role of cell divisions at the root meristem is given by Goodwin & Avers' (29) study of *Phleum pratense*. The seedling roots of this grass are so small that individual cells of the epidermis can be distinguished in photomicrographs. The positions of end walls of cells were measured and plotted as distance from the tip x vs t, giving graphs which are essentially similar to the streak photographs and can be analyzed in the same terms. Their method has the great advantage, however, of presenting direct information about cell division. The results of their analysis are consistent with those of *Zea*, allowing for the great difference in size of the roots. The relative elemental rate of elongation reaches a maximum of 0.6 hr^{-1} at 0.6 mm from the tip, and falls to 0 at 1.3 mm. The cell division rate can be estimated simply by tabulating the observed occurrences of new cell walls. The maximum rate, 0.11 hr^{-1}, also occurs nearer the tip than in *Zea*, 0.15 mm. Within the first 0.10 mm of the meristem all cells eventually divide at least once, that is, the probability that a cell will divide is 1.0. Beyond 0.10 mm there are cells which differentiate but do not divide further. That is to say that the probability of division declines beyond 0.10 mm and becomes 0 at about 0.28 mm. This probability might be incorporated into the differential equations for root growth (18).

These analyses provide a far more dynamic and accurate concept of root growth than do the classical histological descriptions. There have also been limited experimental applications of this method to a study of temperature responses of the root (16), to the inhibition of root growth by scopoletin (4) and auxin (40), and the response of roots to lowered oxygen concentration and added auxin (52), and to step changes of turgor pressure (38).

The relative elemental rate analysis is applicable to other cases than the root, for example, Castle's (12) data on the growth in length of the syncytial sporangiophore of *Phycomyces*. He photographed growing hyphae on which marks had been placed, to provide detailed records of their displacement. He analyzed his data in terms of the relative velocity of displacement of a mark, and a restudy of the data shows that the sporangiophore has pronounced tip growth. The maximum rate dx'/dx at the tip is about 1.7 hr^{-1}, though extrapolation problems make it difficult to estimate accurately.

Another example is the growth of the syncytial internode cell of the shoot of *Nitella*. Green (31) followed the displacement of marks during growth of these cylindrical cells from 0.5 mm to 12 mm in total length and found that the marks retained their relative positions; hence, the relative elemental rate of elongation dx'/dx is uniform, about 1.0 day^{-1}, throughout the length of the cell. A series of studies of the fine structure of the cell wall (32, 33) showed that there is a predominant circumferential orientation of cellulose microfibrils, and this is undoubtedly related to a pronounced anisotropy of growth, the longitudinal component being 5 to 10 times greater than the transverse. In addition to these growth and structural studies, a study of the role of turgor pressure on the growth of the cells has led to a model of the regulation of the relative elemental elongation rate of the cells (35, 36). On a slight reduction of the turgor of the cell, produced by replacing the external medium with an osmoticum, growth in length ceases. After some time, depending on the amount by which the turgor was reduced, the cell resumes growth, dx'/dx gradually increasing until it has reached approximately the normal value. The recovery is not the result of the cell increasing its turgor, as shown by a micromanometer inserted into the vacuole. If a cell has been kept in an osmoticum for some time, growing very little, and is then returned to the normal medium, its turgor immediately increases to the normal 5 or 6 atm, and it undergoes a "growth burst," elongating at an initial rate dx'/dx, which may be as much as 25 times the normal rate. It again regulates gradually to about the normal rate.

To account for the growth burst, it is hypothesized that the relative elemental rate, which will now be symbolized r, is proportional to the longitudinal stress on the wall measured by the turgor pressure p, minus a yield stress y, characteristic of the wall material $r = m(p - y)$. In differential form this is $dr/dt = -m(dy/dt)$. The factor m is thought of as the extensibility of the wall. Experiments varying the strength of the osmoticum, and the time during which cells were placed in it, indicate that the yield tension of the wall can be changed, increased by strain hardening brought about by elongation of the cell, and decreased by a presumed metabolic process. Assuming that the rate of change by strain hardening is proportional to the growth rate, and that the "softening" is independent of it, suggests the equation $dy/dt = hr - s$, where h and s are the strain hardening coefficient and the softening coefficient. These two equations should hold simultaneously so that they can be combined to give the first order differential equation with constant coefficients $(dr/dt)/(mh)+r = s/h$. This is a familiar form of equation, which can be taken to represent the operation of a feedback, control, or servo-mechanism (45), and it can be readily solved, $r = s/h + ce^{-mht}$, c being a constant of integration. A second integration gives an equation describing the growth burst. Since $r = d \ln x/dt$, the equation is $\ln x = \ln x_0 + st/h + (p_1 - p_0)(1 - e^{-mht})/h$, where t is measured from the instant that p_0 is increased to p_1 by changing the solution, and x_0 is the length at the time of change. This equation fits the experimental growth burst data well.

To account for the cessation of growth and subsequent recovery when a cell is transferred from the growth medium to an osmoticum, one may assume that when $y > p$, $r = 0$, but that wall softening proceeds linearly with time, $dy/dt = -s$, or $y = y_0 - st$. When the yield stress y has decreased so that $p > y$, the kinetics described above apply, and an equation can be derived which simulates the return to the normal growth rate quite well. Finally, this model predicts that the normal or equilibrium growth rate which is approached in time after a change in the turgor is $r_{eq} = s/h$. In other words, we have a model for the control of the rate of elongation of the *Nitella* internode cell by the interplay of strain hardening and metabolic softening of the cell wall.

GROWTH IN TWO DIMENSIONS

Two-dimensional growth is well exemplified by the growth of the lamina of a leaf. Richards & Kavanagh (64) have proposed that a useful measure of growth rate is the divergence of the velocity vector. For two dimensions this is div $\mathbf{v} = \partial\dot{x}/\partial x + \partial\dot{y}/\partial y$, where x and y are coordinates of a point on the surface (of the leaf), $\dot{x} = \partial x/\partial t$, and $\dot{y} = \partial y/\partial t$. In keeping with the discussion above, this might be termed the relative elemental rate of increase in area. Richards & Kavanagh (64) illustrated a method of carrying out this analysis, using data of Avery (5) on growth of a leaf of *Nicotiana*. I should like to illustrate it with data from our laboratory on the growth of *Xanthium* leaves (19, 20) and some other systems. A leaf is photographed on successive days, taking care that it is held as flat as possible. A photograph, taken at time t_i, is marked with an equally spaced net of points by pricking it with a needle. By inspection of the venation pattern, corresponding points were identified and marked on the photographs for t_{i-1} and t_{i+1}, as shown in Figure 6. The coordinates of these points were punched on cards, using semi-automatic scanning equipment, and a computer program was devised to estimate the divergence of velocity at each point at t_i (19). Estimates of $\dot{x}$ and $\dot{y}$ were made with the 3-point centered formula of Table 1. Displacement vectors $\mathbf{v} = \dot{x}\,\mathbf{i} + \dot{y}\,\mathbf{j}$ might of course be estimated from these, but they are not particularly instructive. Quadratic differentiation formulas such as those in Table 1 were applied to the estimates of $\dot{x}$ and $\dot{y}$ to evaluate $\partial\dot{x}/\partial x$, $\partial\dot{y}/\partial y$, and also $\partial\dot{x}/\partial y$ and $\partial\dot{y}/\partial x$. Values of div $\mathbf{v}$ or the area rate A, as I will refer to it below, were calculated as $\partial\dot{x}/\partial x + \partial\dot{y}/\partial y$, and displayed as a contour map printed by the line printer. Figure 7A is a tracing of this contour map of a leaf in which lines of equal area rate (day^{-1}) are drawn. To determine whether the expansion in area of the leaf is isotropic, or to what extent it is anisotropic, that

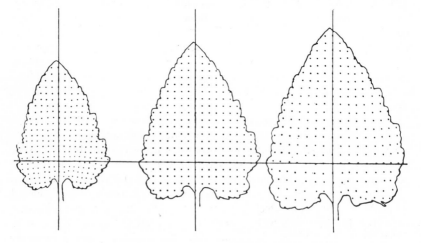

Figure 6   Leaf growth. Drawings of a leaf of *Xanthium* on three successive days, with corresponding points shown, identified by inspecting photographs (19).

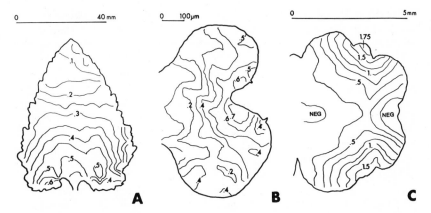

Figure 7   Relative elemental rates of increase in area $(\partial \dot{x}/\partial x + \partial \dot{y}/\partial y)$. A. Analysis of the *Xanthium* leaf shown in Figure 6 (19). B. Similar analysis of the prothallus of *Onoclea* (13). C. Analysis of the thallus of *Marchantia* (20).

is, unequal in different directions θ, relative elemental linear rates of expansion L_θ were evaluated with the equation given by Richards & Kavanagh (64).

$L_\theta = \cos^2\theta(\partial\dot{x}/\partial x) + \cos\theta\sin\theta(\partial\dot{x}/\partial y + \partial\dot{y}/\partial x) + \sin^2\theta(\partial\dot{y}/\partial y)$ and values of L_θ were displayed by the line printer as small plots of L vs θ for each point in which a circular outline indicates that the rate is equal in every direction, that is, isotropic, whereas plots which are elongate indicate anisotropic expansion (19).

In this leaf (Figure 7A) which is approaching maturity, there is a pronounced gradient of the area rate A from a high value of about 0.75 day^{-1} at the base to less than 0.05 day^{-1} at the tip. This is undoubtedly related to the gradient in degree of tissue differentiation from base to tip described by Maksymowych & Erickson (54). There is also a gradient of decreasing area rate from the midrib toward the margin of the leaf, which may be related to the activity of the marginal meristem. The growth of the leaf is nearly isotropic, the small degree of anisotropy being in the longitudinal direction. At earlier stages of development, the leaf grows more uniformly with a less pronounced gradient of the area rate from base to tip (20).

This analysis has also been applied by Chen (13) to the growth of the prothallus of the fern *Onoclea* and of the liverwort *Marchantia* (20). In *Onoclea* (Figure 7B) there is a single initial cell located in the notch of the heart-shaped prothallus, and it is interesting to note that the area rate A has a maximum of 0.6 or 0.7 day^{-1} on either side of the notch. The analysis of *Marchantia* is based on time-lapse motion pictures made in collaboration with Dr. M. Sampson. Growth of the *Marchantia* thallus is similar to that of *Onoclea*, but the initial region is somewhat more complex, and there is the additional feature that the thallus branches, by periodic appearance of a new apical cell near an existing one. In Figure 7C, in which two new notches have recently appeared, the maximal area rate of about 1.75 day^{-1} appears in the notch region.

These exploratory analyses of the relative elemental rate of increase in area are purely empirical and leave one with questions of what sorts of growth patterns one might expect a priori, that is, what distributions of area rate are possible and what are impossible. Such questions are certainly central to any theoretical consideration of plant morphogenesis, and we have made a small start in attacking them.

One aspect of surface growth—growth in two dimensions—which may be worth close attention is the anisotropy of expansion, which might be formulated simply as the ratio of linear expansion rates in two orthogonal directions. This notion seems particularly appropriate in developmental studies of plants, since there are no conspicuous changes in intercellular relationships nor cell migrations involved in plant morphogenesis. Growth is symplastic, in Priestley's terminology (25, 61), and changes in form seem intuitively to be a matter of plastic deformation.

A model of growth in two dimensions of the apical cell of *Nitella* has been proposed by Green & King (37) in terms of the anisotropy of surface expansion. As stated above, the cylindrical internode cell of *Nitella* grows greatly in length, and the longitudinal component of wall expansion is many times greater than the circumferential. One might formulate an anisotropy ratio k as the ratio of relative rate of linear expansion in the longitudinal direction to that in the circumferential. The ratio is much greater than 1. This marked anisotropy of growth is matched by a pronounced circumferential orientation of microfibrils of the wall. It was the intent of Green & King (37) to consider whether the origin of the anisotropy of growth could be traced to the apical initial cell, which gives rise both to internode cells and node cells which are forerunners of branches. They present equations relating the anisotropy ratio k to the relative rate of increase in area of an element of the apical cell wall, assuming that the cell can be approximated by a hemisphere. This model allows them to predict the rate of displacement of a point as it moves down from the apex, with various assumed growth rates and values of anisotropy. They conclude that the hemisphere can maintain its form during growth with a variety of combinations of growth rate and anisotropy. Green (34) had earlier placed marks on the apical cell and followed their displacement photographically. Analysis of these marking data, in the light of the equations of Green & King (37), indicates that growth is most rapid at the pole, falling off toward the base of the cell, and that k decreases from unity at the pole to a value less than 1 at the base. This implies that growth is isotropic at the apex and anisotropic at the base of the shoot apex, with the most rapid rate in the circumferential direction. Jahn (44) extended this analysis of growth of a hemispherical surface to other figures of revolution, specifically the cone and the ellipsoid, with the aim of explaining the transformation of the apical cell of a lateral shoot of *Nitella* from a rapidly growing hemispherical cell into a sharply pointed conical cell which stops growing.

It then became apparent to us that the relationships worked out for the hemisphere, cone, and ellipsoid might be generalized for an arbitrary surface of revolution. Consider such a surface, referred to a system of curvilinear coordinates s and c (Figure 8A). Both s and c may be taken as functions of time t, and the relative elemental rate of increase in area or the divergence of velocity can be formulated. As above, I will refer to it as the area rate A. It can be proven for curvilinear coordinates that $A = \text{div } \mathbf{v} = \partial\dot{s}/\partial s + \partial\dot{c}/\partial c$, where $s = \partial s/\partial t$, $c = \partial c/\partial t$. If the surface is rotationally symmetrical, we may define s as the meridional coordinate and c as the circumferential, analogous to latitude and longitude in geography. It will be convenient to take the origin of s at the pole rather than at the equator as in geography. In Figure 8A the coordinates s and c are shown, and in addition, the cylindrical coordinates r, z, and ϕ. In the growth movement of a point over the surface, each of its coordinates changes with time. Assume at first that growth occurs without a change in shape of the surface. This is equivalent to assuming a functional relationship between s and r, or between s and z. Because of the rotational symmetry, the circumference through any point is $2\pi r$, and changes in ∂c are proportional to changes in r. Therefore, $\partial\dot{c}/\partial c$ in the equation for div $\mathbf{v}$ given above can be replaced by $\partial r/r\partial t$ or $\dot{r}/r$. This substitution is made by Green & King (37) and also by Hejnowicz & Sievers (41) in their discussion of geotropic bending of *Chara* rhizoids. If this is done, the partial differentiation notation may be dropped and the area rate written

$$A = \text{div } \mathbf{v} = ds'/ds + r'/r \qquad\qquad 1.$$

where $s' = ds/dt$, $r' = dr/dt$. The anisotropy ratio, the ratio of meridional to circumferential rates of expansion, can be written

$$k = (ds'/ds)/(r'/r) \qquad\qquad 2.$$

In this form k may take values from 0 to ∞. By substituting the value of ds'/ds from Equation 2 into Equation 1 one has

$$dr/dt = A \cdot r/(1 + k) \qquad\qquad 3.$$

In the same way, one finds, $ds'/ds = A \cdot k/(1 + k)$, and therefore,

$$ds/dt = \int A \cdot k/(1 + k)ds \qquad\qquad 4.$$

Equations 3 and 4 hold simultaneously and are the conditions for growth of a surface of revolution without change of shape, given certain values of A and k at each point. If they are solved analytically, a single differential equation results

$$dA/A - dk/(1 + k) + d(ds/dr)/(ds/dr) + (1 - k)(dr/r) = 0 \qquad\qquad 5.$$

or, on integration

$$\ln[A(ds/dr)/(1+k)] = \int(k - 1)/r \, dr \qquad\qquad 6.$$

For a simple figure, the shape of the surface can be expressed as a simple equation relating s and r, thereby describing a meridian or profile of the surface. When this is done for the hemisphere, the equations given by Green & King (37) can be derived from Equation 6. Similarly, Jahn's (44) equations for the cone and the ellipsoid result from Equation 5 or 6, and solutions of Equation 6 for a paraboloid are also possible (20). For example, in the case of the hemisphere of fixed radius R, the meridian is described by the equation $r = R \sin(s/R)$, or $dr/ds = \cos(s/R)$. Substituting into Equation 6 and assuming k constant leads to this equation giving the area rate as a function of meridional position s, $A = C \sin^{(k-1)R}(s/R) \cos (s/R)$, where C is a constant of integration. When $k = 1$, the area rate is the cosine of meridional position, as Green & King (37) stressed. Other relationships can be worked out, for instance, to predict the position of a point as a function of time, i.e. its trajectory. Other integer values of k yield solutions. The assumption that k is constant over the surface or that it is an integer is arbitrary; for other assumptions Equation 6 may be solvable only by successive approximation. The case of the cone is particularly simple, since s and r are simply proportional, $ds/dr = a$. For a paraboloid of revolution, it is convenient to use a special parameter, the semi-latus rectum p, in terms of which the parabola can be represented as $r^2 = 2\,pz$. Since $ds^2 = dr^2 + dz^2$, we have $ds/dr = (r^2 + p^2/p)^{1/2}$, and again, if k is assumed constant, closed solutions of Equation 6 can be found.

Solutions of Equation 6 for the growth of an ellipsoidal surface without change of shape can also be found by making use of a table of the elliptic integral of the second kind $E(e, \theta)$, where e is the eccentricity of the ellipse and θ is the angle between the minor axis and the line from the center to a point. No doubt other specified figures could be solved.

Equations 3 and 4 have also been solved by numerical approximation methods with a digital computer, using quadratic predictor-corrector formulas (57). These are closely related to the numerical formulas discussed above. When this is done for a hemisphere, starting with a semicircular profile and specifying the relation $ds/dr = \cos(s/R)$, appropriate for a circle, the computer plots semicircular profiles monotonously through many iterations. The same is true of other simulations which we have made of growth without change of shape, of rotationally symmetrical surfaces, such as the cone or paraboloid. We have also made simulations in which the profile of the surface changes by specifying the initial profile of one surface and the kinetics of another. In Figure 8B, for instance, the kinetics of a hemisphere, $A = 0.5 \cos (s/R)$, $k = 1.0$, was used with an initially conical surface. After 20 iterations it is approaching the form of a hemisphere. In Figure 8C, starting with a hemisphere and the relation $A = 0.5 \cos (s/R)$, a linear gradient of k was specified from 1.25 at the pole to 0.75 at the equator. Again the shape is changing, but after 100 iterations it has not stabilized. Many other such simulations of growth of a surface with a change of shape might be tried. However, we cannot yet predict the outcome of such simulations with any degree of certainty. Further study is required.

DEVELOPMENTAL INDICES

One may wish to study an aspect of a developmental system which cannot be followed directly in time because the measurements or analyses required are destructive or complex, or there may be other reasons. As pointed out above, it is then customary to resort to a sampling procedure (46). One often finds that, for various reasons, plants of the same chronological age may have reached different stages of development, and the same is true of plant organs. One may then take the statistical

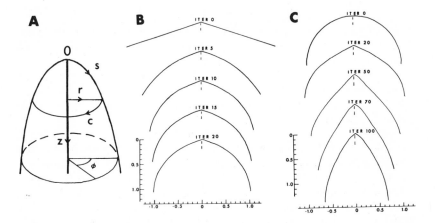

Figure 8   Growth of an idealized surface of revolution (20). A. Diagram to define coordinates. B. Computer simulation of the growth of an initially conical surface, with kinetics appropriate for growth of a hemisphere. C. Growth of an initially hemispherical surface with a decreasing gradient of anisotropy from the apex to the base.

precaution of taking samples of sufficient size at each time to reduce standard errors to acceptable size.

An alternative procedure is to use a developmental index. This is preferably based on a simple measurement which changes in a predictable way during development and which can be recorded for each plant, each specimen of an organ, or each sample which is to be studied or analyzed. The measurements or the results of analysis of each specimen can then be plotted vs the developmental index, and if the index is linearly related to time, the resulting plot can be interpreted as a plot vs time, i.e. a growth curve. If the index is not linear with time, it is still possible to make this interpretation, relying on a functional or empirical relationship of the developmental index to time. If it is desired, the error involved in this procedure can be specified using standard statistical techniques.

A simple example of a developmental index is the logarithm of length of the flower bud of *Lilium longiflorum* (15). A study of the growth of the flower buds in a greenhouse and in a growth chamber showed that they grow exponentially from a length of about 10 mm, when they can first be measured without injury, to about 155 mm, 3 or 4 days before anthesis. The relative rate of elongation, r in the equation given above, is about 0.07 day^{-1}, and its standard error indicates that the index, log bud length, can be used to specify the age of a bud within a few hours. The growth of several floral organs was also studied: anther length, fresh weight, and dry weight; filament length; and length of the ovary and style. For these studies flower buds were cut from the plant, their lengths were recorded, and they were dissected to obtain the floral organs. Measurements of the organs were then plotted vs log bud length, and the resulting graphs interpreted as growth curves of the organs. An interesting feature of these data can be illustrated with the data on anther length. The early portion of the anther growth curve appears to be exponential, as shown by the fact that the plot of log anther length vs log bud length is satisfactorily linear. It can also be said that this is the allometric relationship expounded by Huxley (43, 46) since it satisfies the equation $y = y_0 x^k$, where x is bud length, y the anther length, and k the allometric (relative growth, heterogonic, heteroauxetic) coefficient. In this case, however, the relationship of bud length to time has been made explicit by the preliminary growth study.

Cytological observations were also made of the microsporocytes, microspores, and developing pollen grains by removing these cells from anthers from buds of known length (15). It was found, as in many other species, that the meiotic divisions and the microspore mitosis are synchronized within the anthers of a bud. But, in addition, these cytological events are closely correlated with bud length. It is possible, for example, to predict for a specified bud length that a particular stage of meiosis, or that mitosis will be found, with high probability. Bennett & Stern (8) have shown that the meiotic divisions of the embryo sac mother cell (megasporocyte) can also be predicted from bud length. This ability to select material of a desired stage of development on the basis of a simple measurement is of great value for analytical and experimental studies.

The use of this developmental index in *Lilium* has played a part in a number of studies of physiological and biochemical aspects of meiosis and mitosis. The respiratory rate of anthers has been found to fluctuate during their development, reaching minima which coincide with metaphase I of meiosis and with microspore mitosis (14). Crude analyses for DNA and RNA of cells removed from anthers showed suggestive correlations with the cytological events (60). Stern (68 and other references) in particular has investigated a number of biochemical correlates of anther development. The sulfhydryl content of anthers, for instance, reaches two peaks, coinciding with pachytene of meiosis and with microspore mitosis. The deoxyriboside content of anthers reaches several transient peaks, which perhaps might not have been resolved without using the bud length index. In later work Stern and his collaborators have used this material for extensive studies of the mechanism of meiosis in biochemical terms which are beyond the scope of this article (42).

There is no doubt that similar indices could be devised for other species, as suggested by Al-Ani's (2) study of *Nicotiana* cv. Daylight.

A developmental index for shoot development, the plastochron index, has been proposed (17, 22). The term plastochron (or *Formungszeit*) was proposed by Askenasy (3) in a description of shoot growth of *Nitella* to indicate the time interval from the formation of one internode cell to the next. The term has been used in a qualitative way by many later students of shoot development for the time interval in initiation of successive leaf primordia at the shoot apex. It might well be generalized to apply to any repetitive process in plant morphogenesis, e.g. procambial strand initiation or initiation of the floral primordia of an inflorescence.

Our formulation of the *plastochron index* is based on a study of the vegetative shoot growth of *Xanthium* (22). The leaves of a primary shoot, above the cotyledons, are identified with successive integers $n = 1, 2, \ldots$, in order of their appearance, and the age of the plant is roughly designated by the number of leaves which have appeared, n. Since one leaf appears each plastochron, a plant with n leaves can also be said to be roughly n plastochrons old. That is, we visualize a scale of plastochrons, which is continuous, since it corresponds with time, and which coincides with the leaf number scale n at integer values. Daily measurements of the length of each leaf yields a family of growth curves for each plant. The early portions of these curves appear approximately exponential, suggesting a plot of log leaf length vs time. In this form, the early portions of the curves are nearly straight lines, implying a constant relative growth rate r; they are nearly parallel to each other, implying that the relative growth rates of successive leaves are nearly equal; and they are nearly equally spaced along the time axis, implying that leaf number n, and hence the plastochron age, are linearly related to time. If the early growth of a leaf is represented by the exponential equation $x_n = x_{no} \cdot e^{rt}$, that of the next can be formulated as $x_{n+1} = x_{(n+1)o} \cdot e^{rt}$, where x is leaf length and r is the relative growth rate. Eliminating e^{rt} between these two equations, we have $x_n / x_{n+1} = x_{no} / x_{(n+1)o}$, implying that the growth equations for two successive leaves differ only by this ratio. This may be termed the plastochron ratio (62) and symbolized a. Its logarithm, $\ln a$, was symbolized p by Erickson & Michelini (22). It is the ratio of lengths of successive leaves in their exponential phase of growth, and *pari passu*, it is the ratio by which a leaf increases in length during a plastochron. In terms of the plastochron ratio, the constant terms of the two growth equations above are related by $x_{no} = a \cdot x_{(n+1)o}$, and using this, a single equation can be written for the length of any leaf in terms of its serial number and time, $x_n = x_0 \cdot e^{rt - (\ln a)n}$, or in logarithmic form, $\ln x_n = \ln x_0 + rt - (\ln a)n$.

We can now put the rough relationship between leaf number and plastochrons in more definite form. Rearranging the last equation, $rt = n + (\ln x_n - \ln x_0) / \ln a$, we will consider each of its terms. In most morphological discussions, the plastochron is defined in terms of the instant leaf initiation. Leaf primordia cannot be measured at this stage without dissection, so that we may arbitrarily refer the plastochron scale to a conveniently measurable leaf length x_0. In *Xanthium* we take $x_0 = 10$ mm, since leaves of about this length can be measured without injury, and they are growing exponentially. The continuous scale of plastochrons is represented by rt, and we will refer to it as the *plastochron index* (*PI*) of a plant. Since $a = x_n / x_{n+1}$, $\ln a$ may be replaced with $\ln x_n - \ln x_{n+1}$, and the formula for the plastochron index written as $PI = n + (\ln x_n - \ln 10)/(\ln x_n - \ln x_{n+1})$. In applying it, one measures the length of two leaves on a shoot, that which is just longer than 10 mm (n), and that which is just shorter ($n + 1$), and calculates *PI*. Other methods of estimating *PI* are possible; this formula has the advantage of little smoothing effect.

A leaf plastochron index (*LPI*) is defined as the leaf number $\hat{n}$, of the leaf in question minus the plastochron index of the plant on which it is borne. The *LPI* of a leaf which is 10 mm long is 0, the *LPI* of a leaf shorter than 10 mm is negative, and that of a leaf longer than 10 mm is positive. *LPIs* can be estimated for leaf primordia which are inaccessible without dissection and for older leaves which are no longer growing exponentially, or have stopped growing.

This model of the plastochronic growth of a shoot predicts that the *PI* of a plant and the *LPI* of a leaf should advance linearly with time. This has been verified for a number of *Xanthium* plants grown under a variety of noninductive conditions (22 and unpublished). Michelini (58) has demonstrated the utility of the *LPI* in analyzing measurements of fresh weight, dry weight, chlorophyll content, and respiratory rate of leaves of greenhouse-grown *Xanthium* plants. When the data are plotted vs time, i.e. days from planting, an almost uninterpretable scatter of points results. Plotted vs *LPI*, each of these measurements was shown to increase exponentially until about *LPI* = 3, with little residual variance. Maksymowych (53) has surveyed his extensive studies of leaf development in *Xanthium,* and presented nearly all of his data on dimensional changes, cell numbers, histological and histochemical data, in terms of this model, giving a very graphic and detailed account of leaf development in this plant. Recent studies of the morphogenetic effects of gibberellin on *Xanthium,* including changes in leaf form and phyllotaxis, have been greatly aided by use of the plastochron index (55, 56).

The plastochron index should be applicable to a large number of species of vascular plants and many nonvascular plants, as instanced by the reference to *Nitella* above, since the pattern of initiation of successive leaves or lateral organs at the apex, and their subsequent growth, represented by a family of similar growth curves, is nearly universal. Williams (71) and many other authors have published such curves. Minor modifications of the index, such as choosing an appropriate reference length x_0, are to be expected, and will become obvious from a preliminary growth study. In a decussate-leaved plant, for instance, the plastochron might be defined as the interval between initiation of successive pairs of leaves. In some applications, estimation of the plastochron might be based on other measurements than leaf length, as in our use of an *LPI* based on radial distances of leaf primordia from the center of the shoot apex, measured in sections of *Xanthium* apical buds (55).

Other developmental indices are possible. The numbered stages of development of the staminate inflorescence of *Xanthium,* illustrated by Salisbury (67), might serve as a convenient developmental index for the inflorescence, since he shows that floral stage is linearly related to time under continuous induction. Salisbury used this floral stage index to judge the effect of various treatments on floral bud development. In the study of any developing system, it should be possible to devise a simple and useful developmental index by making a preliminary growth study and exercising some ingenuity. Using such an index should add greatly to the objectivity and dynamic interpretation of one's conclusions.

SUMMARY

I have in effect argued that in all studies of plant development one should give explicit and detailed attention to the growth of one's plants or plant tissues. I have suggested techniques and methods of analysis for the study of growth. Since a large part of plant physiology is concerned with the investigation of growing structures, even when the main focus of research may be on another topic rather than growth, the methods and concepts discussed here should have wide applicability.

Traditionally, plant growth has been discussed in terms of growth curves and growth equations. The equations sometimes have little theoretical value, but may be useful for prediction or estimation. An example of their utility is in the devising of developmental indices which can be used to select and specify the developmental age of specimens for study and to correlate one's results. Polynomials may be used to fit growth data, and they lend themselves to the derivation of orthogonal polynomials, smoothing formulas, and differentiation formulas, which have the great advantage of ease of calculation and statistical evaluation. Their use is illustrated.

Relative elemental rates of growth, pertaining to an element of length dx or an element of area, dA and an instant of time dt, have been applied to detailed studies of axial growth and growth in area. Theoretical consideration of these results has led to a model for the regulation of the rate of elongation of a cell, and a preliminary model of the growth in area of an idealized surface of revolution.

Literature Cited

1. Abramowitz, M., Stegun, I. A. 1965. *Handbook of Mathematical Functions.* New York: Dover
2. Al-Ani, B. 1964. *Contrib. 1964 Peking Symp. Gen.:* 275
3. Askenasy, E. 1880. *Verh. Natur.-medic. Ver. Heidelberg* 2:70–153
4. Avers, C. J., Goodwin, R. H. 1956. *Am. J. Bot.* 43:612–20
5. Avery, G. S. 1933. *Am. J. Bot.* 20: 565–92
6. Avery, G. S. Jr., Piper, M., Smith, P. 1945. *Am. J. Bot.* 32:575–79
7. Bennett, C. A., Franklin, N. L. 1954. *Statistical Analysis in Chemistry and the Chemical Industry.* New York: Wiley
8. Bennett, M. D., Stern, H. 1975. *Proc. R. Soc. London B* 188:459–75
9. Bertalanffy, L. V. 1957. *Q. Rev. Biol.* 32:217–31
10. Blackman, V. H. 1919. *Ann. Bot.* 33:353–60
11. Briggs, G. E., Kidd, F., West, C. 1920. *Ann. Appl. Biol.* 7:103–23; 202–23; 403–6
12. Castle, E. S. 1937. *J. Cell. Comp. Physiol.* 9:477–89
13. Chen, M. H. 1965. *Studies on the development of young gametophytes of Onoclea sensibilis.* MS thesis. Univ. Pennsylvania, Philadelphia
14. Erickson, R. O. 1947. *Nature* 159:275
15. Erickson, R. O. 1948. *Am. J. Bot.* 35: 729–39
16. Erickson, R. O. 1959. *Am. Nat.* 93: 225–35
17. Erickson, R. O. 1960. *Am. J. Bot.* 47: 350–51
18. Ibid 1961. 48:268–74
19. Erickson, R. O. 1966. *J. Exp. Bot.* 17: 390–403
20. Erickson, R. O. 1976. In *Automata, Languages and Development,* ed. A. Lindenmayer, G. Rozenberg. Amsterdam: North Holland
21. Erickson, R. O., Goddard, D. R. 1951. *Growth Symp.* 10:89–116
22. Erickson, R. O., Michelini, F. J. 1957. *Am. J. Bot.* 44:297–305
23. Erickson, R. O., Sax, K. B. 1956. *Proc. Am. Philos. Soc.* 100:487–98
24. Ibid, 499–514
25. Esau, K. 1965. *Plant Anatomy.* New York: Wiley
26. Evans, M. L., Ray, P. M. 1969. *J. Gen. Physiol.* 53:1–20
27. Fisher, R. A. 1950. *Statistical Methods for Research Workers.* New York: Hafner. 11th rev. ed.
28. Fisher, R. A., Yates, F. 1953. *Statistical Tables for use in Biological, Agricultural and Medical Research.* Edinburgh: Oliver & Boyd. 4th ed.
29. Goodwin, R. H., Avers, C. J. 1956. *Am. J. Bot.* 43:479–87
30. Goodwin, R. H., Stepka, W. 1945. *Am. J. Bot.* 32:36–46
31. Green, P. B. 1954. *Am. J. Bot.* 41:403–9
32. Green, P. B. 1958. *J. Biophys. Biochem. Cytol.* 4:505–16
33. Ibid 1960. 7:289–96
34. Green, P. B. 1965. *J. Cell Biol.* 27: 343–63
35. Green, P. B., Erickson, R. O., Buggy, J. 1971. *Plant Physiol.* 47:423–30
36. Green, P. B., Erickson, R. O., Richmond, P. A. 1970. *Ann. NY Acad. Sci.* 175:712–31

37. Green, P. B., King, A. 1966. *J. Biol. Sci.* 19:421–37
38. Grenetz, P. S., List, A. 1973. *J. Theor. Biol.* 39:29–45
39. Hejnowicz, Z. 1956. *Acta Soc. Bot. Pol.* 25:459–78; 615–28
40. Hejnowicz, Z., Erickson, R. O. 1968. *Physiol. Plant.* 21:302–13
41. Hejnowicz, Z., Sievers, A. 1971. *Z. Pflanzenphysiol.* 66:34–48
42. Hotta, Y., Stern, H. 1975. *Dev. Biol.* 26:87–99
43. Huxley, J. S. 1932. *Problems of Relative Growth.* London: Lincoln Mac Veagh
44. Jahn, E. 1968. *Growth and form in the lateral tip cell of Nitella: a mathematical discussion.* MS thesis. Univ. Pennsylvania, Philadelphia
45. Kaplan, W. 1952. *Advanced Calculus.* Reading, Mass: Addison-Wesley
46. Kavanagh, A. J., Richards, O. W. 1942. *Proc. Rochester Acad. Sci.* 8:150–74
47. Kendall, M. G. 1946. *The Advanced Theory of Statistics, I and II.* London: Griffin
48. Kraus, G. 1895. *Ann. Jard. Bot. Buitenzorg* 12:196
49. Leopold, A. C., Kriedemann, P. E. 1975. *Plant Growth and Development.* New York: McGraw-Hill. 2nd ed.
50. Lindenmayer, A. 1968. *J. Theor. Biol* 18:280–99; 300–15
51. Ibid 1971. 30:455–84
52. List, A. 1969. *Planta* 87:1–19
53. Maksymowych, R. 1973. *Analysis of Leaf Development.* Cambridge Univ. Press
54. Maksymowych, R., Erickson, R. O. 1960. *Am. J. Bot.* 47:451–59
55. Maksymowych, R., Erickson, R. O. 1976. *Phyllotactic change induced by*

gibberellic acid in Xanthium. In preparation
56. Maksymowych, R., Maksymowych, A. G. 1973. *Am. J. Bot.* 60:901–6
57. McCracken, D. D., Dorn, W. S. 1964. *Numerical Methods and Fortran Programming.* New York: Wiley
58. Michelini, F. J. 1958. *Am. J. Bot.* 45:525–33
59. Milne, W. E. 1949. *Numerical Calculus.* Princeton Univ. Press
60. Ogur, M., Erickson, R. O., Rosen, G. U., Sax, K., Holden, C. 1951. *Exp. Cell Res.* 2:73–89
61. Priestley, J. H. 1930. *New Phytol.* 29:96–140
62. Richards, F. J. 1951. *Philos. Trans. R. Soc. London Ser. B* 235:509–64
63. Richards, F. J. 1959. *J. Exp. Bot.* 10:290–300
64. Richards, O. W., Kavanagh, A. J. 1943. *Am. Nat.* 77:385–99
65. Robertson, T. B. 1923. *The Chemical Basis of Growth and Senescence.* Philadelphia: Lippincot
66. Rohlf, F. J., Sokal, R. R. 1969. *Statistical Tables.* San Francisco: Freeman
67. Salisbury, F. B. 1955. *Plant Physiol.* 30:327–34
68. Stern, H. 1960. In *Developing Systems and Their Control*, ed. D. Rudrick. New York: Ronald
69. Williams, R. F. 1946. *Ann. Bot.* 10:41–72
70. Williams, R. F. 1964. In *Grasses and Grasslands*, ed. C. Barnard, 89–101. London: Macmillan
71. Williams, R. F. 1975. *The Shoot Apex and Leaf Growth, A Study in Quantitative Biology.* Cambridge Univ. Press

Ann. Rev. Plant Physiol. 1976. 27:435–59

ROOT HORMONES
AND PLANT GROWTH

❖7617

John G. Torrey

Cabot Foundation, Harvard University, Petersham, Massachusetts 01366

CONTENTS

INTRODUCTION

In recent years the subject of root development has received more than usual attention. The increased interest in roots can be attributed to a number of reasons. For morphogenetic studies, roots can be excised and grown in simple sterile nutrient culture where they grow at near normal rates with normal morphogenesis. The organization of the apical meristem can be readily explored anatomically and experimentally; it is less complex than the shoot apex, having appendages formed some distance behind the apex itself. The root serves the important function of water uptake from substrates and the absorption of inorganic ions whose uptake and transport to the rest of the plant it controls. Furthermore, the root synthesizes hormones which also move to the above-ground parts of the plant, influencing the rates and nature of shoot development. Roots form not only lateral roots as part

435

of a plant's branching system, but also may function in vegetative propagation by formation of buds. In addition, roots may develop nodular structures in response to microorganisms such as *Rhizobium,* actinomycetes, and other bacteria or blue-green algae. These associations lead to symbioses of importance in the fixation of atmospheric nitrogen.

For all these reasons, a wide variety of studies has been initiated over the past decade by botanists in diverse fields including plant anatomy, physiology, ecology, biochemistry, horticultural, agronomy, and others. A number of books were published in the past few years in addition to reviews for specialists. Starting in 1953 with a review by Burström (33), the subject of roots and root growth was reviewed in these volumes at regular intervals: e.g. Torrey (215), Åberg (3), Street (198), and Scott (183). A general review on root development was published by Torrey (218). Reviews on nitrogen fixation (20, 53), mycorrhizae (133), and ion uptake and transport (6, 148) in these volumes also bear extensively on root function.

The following books devoted largely to roots and root function were published in the past decade: Whittington (235), Carson (39), Kolek (111), Hoffmann (94), Torrey & Clarkson (220). Each of these covers a wide range of topics, resulting from presentations and discussions at symposia or special meetings. Miller (136) published a bibliography on root anatomy. Ion uptake and transport have been extensively explored in books by Epstein (62), Anderson (7) and Clarkson (44). Mertz (132) discussed hormonal control of root growth. Nitrogen fixation and especially symbiotic nitrogen fixing systems have been dealt with at length in several recent books including those by Stewart (197), Macura & Vancura (126), Mishustin & Shil'nikova (137), Postgate (162), Lie & Mulder (120), Quispel (165), and Burns & Hardy (31). Books on mycorrhizae include publications by Hacskaylo (82), Marks & Kozlowski (129), and Hacskaylo & Tompkins (83).

METHODS USED IN THE STUDY OF ROOTS

Roots are usually subterranean organs, and special efforts must be made to sample root systems or to examine them and determine their role in the development of the plant as a whole. Progress in methods for studying roots and root systems has been made, and a brief review of recent technical innovations may prove useful to the experimentalist who considers roots too intractable to work with. Schuurman & Goedewaagen (181) brought together in book form the many methods used in the Institute of Soil Fertility at Haren-Groningen in the Netherlands for the study and sampling of root systems. Their bibliography cites the work of many other laboratories as well.

One method for studying root systems which is not new but has been increasingly exploited involves the examination and recording of activities of roots in situ. This is achieved by excavating a trench along which trees or other plants already exist or can be planted, constructing viewing chambers of soil profiles and building a laboratory around the underground facility to allow observations to be made underground and at the level of sophistication desired. Rogers (179) described the construction features of the root-observation laboratories of the East Malling Research

Station in England, and a number of papers on the growth of roots of woody perennial species especially of horticultural interest have been published (cf Rogers & Head 180). Similar structures, designated rhizotrons, have been described by Hilton et al (91), Bhar et al (21), Lyford & Wilson (125), and others.

Methods for sampling root systems in and from soils are numerous. Many of these are described by Schuurman & Goedewaagen (181). These techniques, such as the pinboard method, provide means of examining horizontal or vertical profiles of root systems, especially of herbaceous plants taken from a solid physical matrix. Techniques also have been devised for statistical samplings from borings and the analysis of plant roots in soil cores. All such methods necessarily deal with samples only and not with the whole root systems. For plant physiologists interested in whole root systems, water culture methods, with or without aeration, provide means of direct access to the root systems (e.g. Hewitt 90, Hoagland & Arnon 93). Development in such plants may differ from that in plants growing in soil. Some plants grow well with their root systems in nutrient mist. Methods for achieving such culture were described by Went (233), and a new modification of the method of aeroponics has been developed (Zobel et al 247). Root systems of herbaceous plants grown aeroponically have the advantage for analysis of being completely clean, well formed with extensive root hairs, and easily accessible for histological or biochemical analysis.

A useful compendium of methods for growing plants so as to allow application of substances to root systems or studying the root systems themselves, especially of herbaceous plants, was assembled by Mitchell & Livingston (138). A comprehensive review of methods and results of research with excised roots grown in sterile nutrient culture was made by Street & Henshaw (201) and extended by Street (199, 200). In recent years interest has increased in the effects of root temperature on root systems and on plant growth. Methods and results of study were reviewed by Cooper (46) and by Nielsen (147). A brief review of root-shoot relations was given by Aung (10).

The use of models in the analysis of root development is being explored, using extensive data from field collections for the design and then the testing of the model. Hackett & Rose (80, 81) developed a model based on *Hordeum vulgare;* Wilson (238) developed a model based on *Pinus* but applicable to both gymnosperm and angiosperm tree root systems. Such models should expand our view of the factors controlling root development.

PLANT HORMONES IN ROOTS

The present review summarizes research of the past decade which focuses on hormonal aspects of root growth and the role of root development in relation to the development of the plant as a whole. An area of particularly active research has been the organization of the root apex and the role of the quiescent center. This literature has been excluded from the present review except insofar as it relates to hormone synthesis and function in the root apex. No attempt has been made to produce an exhaustive review of the literature.

Auxins

The presence and role of auxins in roots has been debated since the early 1930's when indole-3-acetic acid was first identified and applied to roots (209). The presence of indole-3-acetic acid (IAA) has now been demonstrated conclusively in roots of *Zea mays* using rigorous methods acceptable for explicit chemical identification, i.e. gas chromatographic separation coupled with mass spectrometric analysis (GC-MS) (29, 61). Root apices, steles, and cortices were extracted separately and IAA was shown to occur in the highest amounts on a fresh weight basis in the stelar tissue (29). Using mass spectrometry, Hall & Medlow (85) identified IAA in the phloem sap and root exudate (xylem sap) of *Ricinus.* Rivier & Pilet (178), also using a GC-MS technique, reported IAA was present in root caps of *Zea mays* at a concentration twice that in the root meristem itself. Greenwood et al (78) analyzed the distribution of auxin in *Zea* roots using extraction, paper and thin-layer chromatography, and bioassay. Their data show high levels of auxin in the root stele. They did not analyze the root cap content separately. Dullaart (54, 55) made quantitative estimates of IAA in roots and nodules of *Lupinus.* Taken together, these papers give reassurance concerning the reality of IAA presence in roots and confirm the reliability and usefulness of the older methods of extracting, separating, and measuring auxins by bioassay.

The actual amounts of IAA present in roots can be estimated at least to an order of magnitude from these studies, since the different methods give estimates which allow fairly direct comparisons to be made. Auxin occurs in root tissues of *Zea mays* in the range of concentration from 356 μgm/kg fr wt in the root cap [based on GC-MS by Rivier & Pilet (178)] to 53 μgm/kg fr wt in root stelar tissues [based on GC-MS by Bridges et al (29)] or 142 μgm/kg fr wt for root stelar tissues [based on chromatography and bioassay by Greenwood et al (78)]. These estimates place the level of IAA in the corn root tip in the range of 0.1 ppm or about $5 \times 10^{-7} M$ (based on an average value of 150 μgm/kg fr wt).

With evidence that IAA does in fact occur in the root tip of corn and probably (by extrapolation based on extensive publications of work using extraction and bioassay) in a wide variety of other plants, a number of long-debated questions still stand, e.g. is auxin made in the tip or is it transported into the tip? Does auxin play a role in root elongation? Does it function in root geotropism? Some progress has been made over the last decade in attempts to answer these questions.

TRANSPORT OF AUXINS   The bulk of the evidence accumulated to date indicates that auxins are transported within roots from root base to root apex, that is, in an acropetal direction and that the transport is polarized. The subject has been reviewed in detail recently (15, 183). The evidence that auxin occurs at high concentration in the stelar tissues (29, 78) suggests that movement occurs predominately in vascular tissues or in the living cells of the central cylinder. Polar transport of auxin has been confirmed in roots of many plant species, using root segments, cultured roots, and roots of intact seedlings. Acropetal polar transport of auxin is dependent on metabolic energy, is enhanced by light, and is temperature-sensitive.

Polar transport exists along the length of the root axis but is strongest close to the root apex. Velocities of polar auxin transport determined from root segment tests are of the same order of magnitude as that for stem tissues, i.e. 7.5 mm/hr for sunflower stem (223), 4–6 mm/hr for corn roots (184), 9–10 mm/hr for Convolvulus roots (24). Thus one can visualize, at least for seedlings and young plants, a continuous flow of auxin from the shoot apex down the stem and continuing into the root to the extreme tips of the root.

The source of auxin which moves in the root and into the root tip has not been studied carefully or directly. Excised roots grown in continuous culture usually do not show a requirement for exogenous auxin (198). If auxin is involved in root elongation (see later discussion), the cultured roots must form their own auxin in culture. Mature tissues of roots are possible sources of auxins as was suggested many years ago by the studies of van Overbeek on subcultured roots of Pisum (224) and by Thurman & Street (211) for clonally propagated roots of tomato. In such cultured root systems, mature tissues presumably serve as source of auxin synthesis. Transport in cultured roots is toward the tip (24, 184) even though other components such as sugars, amino acids, or inorganic ions may be distributed symmetrically toward tip and root base from a point of application (via a root bud, for example) (25). A site for IAA synthesis in older root tissues is not obvious, especially since it is generally conceded that mature root tissues have relatively high capacities for IAA oxidation (161). Sheldrake (189) stated that the published evidence he reviewed suggested that root apices were not sites of auxin formation. Rather, he believed auxins were formed from differentiating vascular tissues proximal to the apex where cell autolysis gives rise to proteolytic products easily convertible to IAA (and also perhaps to cytokinins). No direct evidence for this view has been provided for roots.

That auxin applied to the shoot moves into the root has been known for a long time. Synthetic auxins such as 2,4-D move rapidly to the root tip when applied to cotyledons or leaves (47). Movement accompanied the transport of carbohydrates and presumably occurred in the phloem. Morris et al (141) showed that radioactivity associated with ^{14}C-labeled IAA applied to the shoot tip was transported into the root system in pea seedlings. McDavid et al (146), and Eliasson (60) both demonstrated the rapid movement of ^{14}C-labeled IAA into roots, the latter into rooted woody cuttings of Populus and the former into roots of seedlings of Pisum. The rapidity of the transport suggested that the applied IAA moved in the phloem. Bourbouloux & Bonnemaw (26) studied the fate in the root of radioactive IAA applied to the shoot apex of Vicia faba. It may well be that auxin formed in the shoot is continuously supplied to the root system in amounts related to its fluctuating levels in the shoot. Functions of polarly transported auxin in the root will be discussed later.

Gibberellins

Information about the presence of gibberellins in roots comes largely from indirect evidence based on collection by diffusion and extraction combined with bioassay of materials from roots or from activity measured by bioassay from root exudates.

Murakami (144) showed that cereal grass roots contained gibberellin-like substances at levels comparable to the shoots. Excised tomato roots grown in sterile nutrient culture through many subcultures contained gibberellins (35). Carr & Reid (37) extracted fresh carrot root tissues and demonstrated the presence of gibberellin-like activity. Carrot callus tissue after subculture was also found to contain gibberellins, although differing in pattern from those in the intact root. Frydman & Wareing (68) demonstrated gibberellins by bioassay of root extracts of *Hedera helix*. Radley (167) reported that rhizobial nodules of *Phaseolus* and *Pisum* contained high levels of gibberellins compared to the roots of the same plants. Dullaart & Duba (56) reported gibberellins in roots and root nodules of *Lupinus*.

More extensive evidence, but even more indirect for the formation of gibberellins by root systems, comes from studies of the gibberellins present in root exudate or xylem sap. Carr et al (38) and Phillips & Jones (159) reported gibberellin-like activity determined by bioassay from xylem exudate collected from decapitated plants of *Helianthus*. Since these early reports a number of studies have demonstrated gibberellins in root exudates and the important role of the root environment in determining the amount of gibberellin found in the bleeding sap. Phillips (158) showed the importance of root aeration on gibberellin content of the root exudate. Reid et al (172) demonstrated that flooding the root system of tomato plants reduced the amount of gibberellin exported in the xylem sap and the reduction could be correlated directly with reduced stem elongation. Skene (194) found gibberellin activity in xylem sap of grapes (*Vitis*) and Reid & Burrows (169) in the spring sap of trees (*Acer pseudoplatanus* and *Betula pubescens*). Sembdner et al (185) described the presence of the glucoside of GA_8 in the xylem sap of *Acer platanoides* and the glucoside of GA_3 in the xylem sap of *Ulmus glabra*. Some evidence that synthesis by the root system was involved came from experiments by Reid & Carr (170) and Reid and Crozier (171), showing that CCC, a growth retardant believed to block gibberellin biosynthesis, when applied to the roots reduced the export of gibberellins in the xylem sap of *Pisum arvense*.

Attempts to demonstrate gibberellin biosynthesis in roots have been almost as indirect. Jones & Phillips (102) extracted gibberellins from 4-mm-long root tips of the sunflower *Helianthus annuus* which they measured by bioassay. They concluded that gibberellins were formed in the tip and little or none in the proximal tissues. Excised sunflower root apices incubated in a dilute sucrose solution with buffer and mevalonic acid 2-^{14}C-lactone were shown by Sitton et al (193) to incorporate the label into (–) kauren-19-ol, a precursor of gibberellic acid.

The evidence on gibberellin biosynthesis in roots was reviewed carefully by Crozier & Reid (50, 51). They made the important point that sources and sites of use of hormones in plants must be considered in the context of the whole organism, rather than in isolated parts. In their studies of gibberellins in seedlings of *Phaseolus coccineus* they extracted gibberellins from all plant parts, not just the roots, and characterized the different gibberellins and their changing distribution within the plant. They found that the major gibberellin in the intact plant was GA_1. Removal of root tips led to the accumulation of GA_{19} in the plant and a coincident reduction in shoot growth. They concluded that in bean GA_{19} is synthesized in the shoot, primarily in the leaves, moves to the root tips where it is converted to GA_1, and is then reexported to the shoot. Thus the root tips serve not for primary gibberellin synthesis but for its conversion to another active form.

The directional flow of gibberellins in experimental studies on xylem exudation is that of export from the roots. In the intact plant, such gibberellin transport in the xylem sap is presumed to be via the transpiration stream. In decapitated plants, gibberellins are exuded by root pressure. Jacobs & Pruett (101) studied the movement of gibberellin in *Zea* root segments. They reported a polar movement from tip to base. This conclusion has been extended to root segments of *Phaseolus coccineus* by Hartung & Phillips (88).

Results from studies of excised roots grown in culture are useful in attempting to determine a hormonal role in root development. From Butcher's studies (35) one can conclude that excised roots of tomato synthesize gibberellins. From the studies on roots of dwarf corn (131), one is led to conclude that gibberellins may be essential for root development (see later discussion). Whether in the intact plant root tips serve as a major primary site of gibberellin synthesis remains to be established. That roots serve as the source of gibberellins which move in the xylem sap to the shoot and there elicit effects seems established beyond doubt.

Cytokinins

In 1939 Chibnall (42) proposed that the protein status of leaves was affected by a hormone-like factor from the roots. He later showed (43) that in detached leaves, the development of adventitious roots prevented leaf senescence, an idea pursued by Richmond & Lang (175) in their demonstration that the synthetic cytokinin kinetin prolonged the survival of detached leaves of *Xanthium* and maintained protein and chlorophyll levels in the leaf. Mothes & Engelbrecht (143) reported that protein levels in detached leaves actually increased when adventitious roots developed and the leaf resumed growth. In 1962 Kulaeva (115) found that xylem exudate from decapitated tobacco plants delayed senescence of leaves, and Kende (106, 107) showed that substances from xylem exudate from sunflowers, presumed to come from the roots, caused chlorophyll retention in detached leaves.

Since those early studies, a large literature has developed concerning the relationship between roots and shoot growth, centering on the view that cytokinins produced in the root move to the shoot and there influence or determine the nature of shoot development. In his recent review of this subject, Skene (196) cited nearly 150 references. Interested readers should turn to that review for a comprehensive analysis of the field through 1974. Here only the major facts will be summarized.

EXTRACTED CYTOKININS   Direct demonstration of the presence of cytokinins in roots, based on extraction and chemical identification, has been achieved by Babcock & Morris (11) for pea roots using column and gas-liquid chromatography. Four cytokinins were reported to occur, namely, zeatin [6-(4-hydroxy-3-methyl-2 transbutenylamino) purine], zeatin riboside, 2iP[6-(3-methyl-2-butenylamino) purine] and its riboside. These same cytokinins were reported to occur in tRNA extracted from pea shoots (Vreman et al 227), with the additional qualification that both the *cis* and *trans* form of the zeatin could be identified.

Gordon et al (77) fed ³H-zeatin to radish seedling roots. Within 1 hr they were able to isolate the zeatin riboside-5-monophosphate from the roots and after 9 hr, 40% of the radioactivity was isolated as the glucoside,7-glucosylzeatin (termed by them raphanatin). According to their view, the glucoside represented a storage form of cytokinin and the riboside a transport form.

Direct extraction, purification, and identification by paper or thin-layer chromatography, coupled with a specific cytokinin bioassay, have been reported for a number of roots. Weiss & Vaadia (231) extracted two cytokinins from root tips of sunflower plants which were shown to be identical to cytokinins from xylem exudate of decapitated sunflower plants (108) and were tentatively identified as zeatin and probably its riboside. Evidence for synthesis in the root was suggested by the fact that cytokinin levels in the xylem exudate did not decrease over a 4-day period of daily collection.

Isolation of zeatin riboside from roots of *Chicorium* was reported by Bui-Dang-Ha & Nitsch (30), and zeatin glucoside was extracted from roots of young rice seedlings (243).

Short & Torrey (190) found that the terminal 0–1 mm tip of the seedling root of *Pisum sativum* contained 44 times more free cytokinin than the subjacent 1–5 mm segment. Cytokinins extractable from tRNA of pea roots represented only 1/27 that of the free cytokinins in the same tips. In this study zeatin was found to be the major cytokinin, but evidence was presented for the presence of its riboside and ribotide. A fourth unidentified cytokinin was also reported. Radin & Loomis (166) reported zeatin and its riboside and ribotide to be the major cytokinins extractable from radish roots, and these were associated by them with the development of secondary thickening in the root. Another unidentified cytokinin occurred late in the development of the thickened root. They speculated that zeatin and its derivatives might move from shoot to root and the unidentified cytokinin move from root to shoot.

Feldman (65) extracted terminal 1 mm tips of *Zea mays* and characterized cytokinins from purified extracts separated by TLC and assayed in the soybean callus assay. Four cytokinins were reported: zeatin, zeatin riboside, zeatin ribotide, and a fourth unidentified cytokinin. Separate analyses of root caps and subjacent tissues of the 1 mm tip showed that root caps contained only 1/5 the amount of total cytokinin present in the subjacent tissues, site of the quiescent center and the proximal meristem of the root. Decapping root tips of *Zea* seedlings and allowing them to regenerate demonstrated dynamic changes in cytokinin concentrations in the root tip, which strongly suggested the synthesis of these cytokinins in the tip itself and not simply their transport from other parts of the plant.

Direct extraction, purification, and identification by co-chromatography of cytokinins from rhizobial root nodules of *Phaseolus vulgaris* has been reported by Puppo et al (164), and dramatic changes in cytokinin content in root nodules of *Pisum sativum* have been observed by Syōno & Torrey (203), suggesting a role in root nodule morphogenesis.

CYTOKININS IN XYLEM EXUDATE   Considerable evidence has accumulated demonstrating the presence of cytokinins in the xylem exudate of decapitated plants.

This evidence is reviewed in some detail by Skene (196). Phloem sap can also be shown to contain cytokinin activity (157), in fluid tapped by aphids feeding on the shoots, not roots.

Using xylem exudate or sap as the basis for measuring cytokinin "production" by the root system, new information has been gained that helps in our understanding of the effects of the environment which acts on the root system and thereby influences or affects the shoot system. Although the detailed mechanisms remain to be worked out, in many cases it seems that changes in the root environment modify the hormone production in the root, change the export of the hormone via the xylem sap to the shoot, and thereby elicit changes in the shoot. Thus, for example, root systems subject to water stress (drought) export lowered amounts of cytokinins via the xylem sap to the shoot system (100, 140), resulting in reduced cytokinin activity in the leaves. Roots subjected to salinity stress show similar changes in exported cytokinins in the xylem sap (98, 99). Flooding of the root system resulting in reduced root aeration is another stress on root systems which changes the hormone flow from roots to shoots (32, 173) and results in severe chlorosis in the leaves. Burrows & Carr (32) found that in sunflower plants flooded for 96 hr many root apices were dead and cytokinin exported in the xylem sap was at a minimum. These changes were accompanied by a decrease in amino acid content in the xylem sap as well. Reid & Railton (173) reported in tomato that benzyladenine application as a foliar spray counteracted many of the injurious effects on the shoot caused by flooding. They found that flooding caused a reduction in gibberellin levels in the leaves, an effect reversed by direct application of benzyladenine to the leaves. They suggested an interaction between these two hormones such that cytokinin acts to control gibberellin levels in the leaves.

Heat stress of the roots also appears to effect hormone levels in the root and their export to the shoot. Itai et al (98), and Itai & Ben-Zioni (97) showed that when roots of bean or corn seedlings were exposed for 2 min to 47.5°C temperatures by dipping, cytokinin levels in the xylem exudate decreased to one-sixth that of untreated plants after 6 hr and the abscisic acid content of the sap increased by fourfold. Thereafter one could observe a marked reduction in stem and leaf growth.

These authors point out the parallel nature of the responses plants show to heat and water stress and hypothesize that plants have a similar regulatory mechanism for responding to different kinds of climatic stress which involves in part rapid changes in hormonal balance within the plant.

The experimental imposition of stress on the root system leading to reduced hormone production, especially cytokinins and gibberellins, provides further strong evidence that the site of synthesis of these hormones resides in the roots themselves and most probably in the root tips.

Seasonal variations in cytokinin levels in xylem exudate have been reported, reflecting changes in the physiological status of the plant. In apple trees, cytokinin content in the xylem sap is highest in the spring and drops to zero in late autumn and winter (123). In *Perilla,* plants induced to flower by appropriate daylength exposure have five times more cytokinin in the xylem sap than plants still vegetative (16). In *Solanum,* root extracts of plants grown under long days showed higher cytokinin levels than plants grown under short days (240, 241).

SITE OF CYTOKININ SYNTHESIS   Direct demonstration of cytokinin synthesis in root apices has thus far not proved possible. In part this is because we do not know precisely the biosynthetic pathways for cytokinin formation and thus cannot manipulate its formation by metabolic blocks or by following precursor incorporation and changes. Skene (195) showed that treatment of grapevine roots with CCC (an inhibitor of gibberellin biosynthesis) resulted in an increase in cytokinins in the xylem sap. Carr & Reid (37) found a reduction in gibberellins in xylem sap of detopped plants of field pea (*Pisum arvense*) after CCC treatment of the roots, a somewhat more expected result. They did not examine changes in cytokinins in these experiments on peas.

Cytokinins occur in high levels in meristematic tissues. From tissue culture studies, one can show that tobacco pith tissues or soybean callus tissues have sufficiently low synthetic capacity for cytokinins that they do not grow in the absence of exogenous supplies - the basis for the callus tissue bioassays for cytokinins (121, 135). Yet normal callus tissues in culture have been shown to produce cytokinins sufficient for growth (191) and even callus tissues heterotrophic for cytokinins may develop the capacity to synthesize endogenous cytokinins adequate for excellent growth [cf (66) for tobacco tissues and (139) for soybean callus]. Recently Syōno & Furuya (202) showed that temperature manipulation of cultured tissues could be used to modify cytokinin synthesis in cultured tobacco tissues. One is faced with the interesting dilemma: cells require cytokinin in order to divide, but actively dividing populations of cells seem to be the source of cytokinins.

Wagner & Michael (228) suggest that protein synthesis in root tips may be necessary for cytokinin biosynthesis. Klemen & Klämbt (110) pursued the idea that cytokinins present in tRNA could serve as the source for free cytokinins following degradation of the nucleic acid (cf 84). They measured the half-life of tRNA of roots of *Zea mays* by feeding ^{14}C-orotic acid to excised cultured root tips and following the time course of the dilution of radioactivity in sRNA of the growing roots. According to their calculation, the daily possible free cytokinin production from transfer RNA metabolism in the root system of an 18-day-old corn plant would be about 2×10^{-10} mol. Until we have a better knowledge of the biosynthetic pathway for cytokinins in plants, we will be faced with continuing speculation.

Abscisic Acid

Inhibitors of cell division and cell elongation have long been associated with extracted materials from roots. Bennet-Clark & Kefford (18) and Kefford (105) characterized a complex of inhibitory substances removed by ether extraction of roots of *Vicia faba, Pisum sativum,* and *Zea mays* as the β-inhibitor complex. Since those early experiments, a large number of compounds have been interpreted as involved in the inhibitions caused by the β-inhibitor complex [cf review by Bentley (19) and Kefeli & Kadyrov (104)]. Naturally occurring phenolic compounds were identified as components of this complex, including as prominent members cinnamic acid, *m*- and *p*-coumaric acid. Other phenolic compounds are known which stimulate growth.

In 1965, the most potent component of the β-inhibitor complex was chemically identified and characterized as abscisic acid (151, 242). Since that time abscisic acid

(ABA) has taken its place among the major classes of hormones occurring in plants and interacting in hormonal regulation of plant development. The physiology and biochemistry of abscisic acid have been reviewed in detail (4, 134). In this review attention will be paid in particular to the physiology of abscisic acid in relation to root development and root function. It should be noted that all of the inhibitory action attributed to the β-inhibitor complex cannot be accounted for by abscisic acid alone, since other components probably play a physiological role within the plant. On the other hand, the possible involvement of abscisic acid as inhibitor or stimulator in a number of growth processes formerly attributed to the β-inhibitor complex has yet to be explored. As in all studies with inhibitors extractable from plant tissues, demonstration that the substance functions in vivo in the same manner as when exogenously applied is often difficult or impossible to achieve. There is always the possibility that the inhibitor is compartmentalized within the plant cell where it cannot act (as, e.g., in the vacuole) and only on extraction is it freed to act when reapplied to the test system.

Abscisic acid has been reported to occur in extracts of roots of *Lens culinaris* (67), *Pisum sativum* (212, 213), and *Zea mays* (116, 117, 236). Other related inhibitory substances have also been found in root tips, including xanthoxin, a possible precursor to ABA (116, 117). According to these authors, ABA was associated primarily with the root cap and another inhibitor, possibly xanthoxin, was associated with the "root meristem," i.e. 5 mm root tips minus the cap. ABA was extracted from seedling roots of *Vicia faba* by El-Antably & Larsen (58) and demonstrated by gas-liquid thin-layer chromatography of purified preparations.

The presence of abscisic acid in xylem exudate was reported for *Salix viminalis* by Lenton et al (118) and Bowen & Hoad (27), and for *Helianthus annuus* by Hoad (92). ABA was also detected in phloem exudate in *Salix* (27).

Radioactively labeled ABA applied to the shoot apex in light-grown pea seedlings moves down the stem but does not enter the root. When 2- ^{14}C ABA is applied to young expanded leaves, radioactivity moves into the aerial parts but also into the lateral roots (17). There seems to be no convincing evidence that ABA which increases rapidly in leaves subjected to water stress (130, 134) has its origin in the root. Rather, the evidence favors the view that ABA levels change quickly and quite locally within the leaf. According to Milborrow (134), the chloroplast is a major site of ABA biosynthesis.

If ABA in the root tip originates in the cells of the root cap (cf review by Wilkins 237), it might serve locally in root cell inhibitions such as would occur in the geotropic response of roots and might be used up or modified in the tissues of response. Hartung & Behl (86, 87) provided evidence for a radial movement of ABA in roots of *Phaseolus coccineus*. At present it is not clear how ABA gets into the xylem exudates of decapitated plants.

The effect of hormones on stomatal movement, which controls water loss from leaves, has been studied intensively since the evidence that ABA causes stomatal closure (cf Milborrow 134 for details). With the demonstration that cytokinins caused stomatal opening (cf Meidner & Willmer 130) and IAA as well as ABA caused closure, there has been considerable interest in the relationship between root-originating hormones and wilting of the above-ground parts of the plant. These interrelationships have been approached by Tal and associates in the mutant tomato *flacca* which synthesizes only about 10% of the ABA-like material found in the normal plant (204) but shows four times more auxin-like material in the shoot. Examination of the root exudates of the normal and mutant strain showed that *flacca* plants possessed higher cytokinin content in the root exudate than normal and this was correlated with higher cytokinin content in the leaves (206). Such plants also showed greater resistance to water absorption than normal plants, an effect attributed to the higher cytokinin content of the roots (205). Both normal and mutant plant showed higher root exudation rates after the treatment of the shoots with ABA. Although the hormonal interactions in this plant are complex, it seems clear that ABA effects on stomatal movement are largely localized in the leaf while cytokinin effects on stomatal activity may have their origin in the root followed by transport to the shoot.

That ABA has local effects in the root on water and ion uptake has been reported. Glinka & Reinhold (74, 75) found that ABA applied at 20 ppm to carrot root tissue disks increased the flux of water either into or out of the root cells. Cytokinins antagonized this effect. Glinka (73) pointed out that increased rates of root exudation caused by treatment of the roots with ABA could be attributed to the effects of ABA on increased permeability of the cells, that is, to the hydraulic conductivity of the root system. Whether ABA plays this role in the normal physiology of the plant remains to be demonstrated.

Cram & Pitman (48) and Shaner et al (186) reported that ABA inhibited ion accumulation in roots. These and related effects have been studied, more in relation to guard cell physiology (96, 128) than in roots, but it seems possible that effects of ABA on ion uptake might prove equally important in the physiology of such uptake by roots. The fact that cytokinins have been shown to inhibit uptake of cations by root disks of *Beta vulgaris* and *Brassica napobrassica* storage roots (226) suggests a possible similarity to ABA. In most systems, however, ABA and cytokinin seem to produce opposite effects.

Ethylene

Ethylene production by plant cells and its involvement in a wide variety of plant developmental responses are firmly established. The subject has been recently reviewed by Abeles (1, 2). Since ethylene is a gas it does not fit into the usual model applied to other known plant hormones. By the time the gas has been formed by a tissue and evolved so as to be measured, it presumably already has had its effect. Ethylene formation is markedly stimulated following treatment of tissues with auxins (at least at concentrations higher than 10^{-6} M) and perhaps other hormones. Sorting out ethylene effects per se and related hormone effects has proved difficult.

Ethylene is produced by roots of *Pisum sativum* at very low levels (40), but its formation is markedly increased by treating the roots with 10^{-4} M IAA, an effect which lasts for up to 16 hr and is accompanied by inhibition of root elongation. Ethylene production by roots is proportional to the concentration of externally applied auxin (41), from 10^{-6} M IAA. Externally applied ethylene causes 50% inhibition of root elongation at a concentration of about 0.2 ppm ($\sim 10^{-6}$ M). These authors concluded that auxin-induced inhibition of root elongation was due to ethylene production. Andreae et al (8) also found that 10^{-4} M IAA markedly stimulated ethylene production by 2-day-old seedling pea roots but that ethylene inhibition could be experimentally separated from IAA inhibition. Unlike inhibition caused by IAA, ethylene inhibition was irreversible, showed a time lag of a number of hours, and was dependent on tissue age and solution composition. Scott & Norris (182) also presented evidence suggesting that auxin and ethylene elicited separate responses in pea roots.

Recently, Rauser & Horton (168) measured short term changes in root elongation rates in pea. They found both IAA and ethylene inhibited root elongation within 20 min of application and that these short term effects were reversible. Auxin proved to be a more effective inhibitor at low concentrations (5×10^{-6} M) than ethylene at 1000 μl/liter, suggesting to these authors that the auxin inhibition is not primarily an ethylene effect. The possibility that ethylene is the normal effector in root geotropism (41) is made more unlikely by the recent developments involving ABA and perhaps gibberellins in root geotropic curvature (see below).

The best evidence for a role for ethylene in root development comes from the discovery of a tomato mutant, *diageotropica*, which was found to be deficient in its tissues in auxin-induced ethylene biosynthetic capacity (245, 246). The roots of intact plants fail to form lateral roots, a morphological abnormality which could be corrected by spraying seedling leaves with either 10^{-4} M IAA or ethrel. Seedling roots exposed to 5 nl/l ethylene have normal root branching. Roots of the mutant show plagiotropic or diageotropic growth similar to that of the shoot. Excised roots of the mutant grown in culture, which have no lateral root formation, still do not show lateral root initiation when exposed to ethylene even up to 1 μl/liter (1 ppm). Zobel (246) suggested that in the mutant ethylene treatment of the shoot leads to the formation of a substance which causes normal initiation of laterals in the root. The nature of the root initiating substance was not established but it is probably not auxin. Nevertheless, an interaction of auxin and ethylene perhaps in some sort of feedback relationship was suggested.

HORMONAL CONTROL OF ROOT ELONGATION

With evidence that seedling roots probably contain auxin, cytokinin, gibberellin, abscisic acid, and low levels of ethylene simultaneously or under certain circumstances, where do we stand with respect to our understanding of the physiology of root cell elongation? Roots are usually quite sensitive to applied hormones. Their response to applied auxin continues to be of interest to physiologists, and some believe that a good case can be made that auxin controls root cell elongation. Some authors (76) adhere to the model proposed by Burström (34), that auxin acts in a 2-phase system, one primarily stimulatory, the other inhibitory.

Batra et al (15) proposed the view that auxin transported acropetally in the root controls cell elongation in the zone proximal to the apical meristem. Their conclusion was based on evidence that auxin transported acropetally stimulates root cell elongation, that root cells showed an acid-induced growth inhibition related to reduced auxin transport, and that increased pH (7.0) favored both auxin transport in the root and root elongation. Acropetal auxin transport in the root occurs primarily in the vascular tissues of the central cylinder (28, 79, 88, 188). Lateral redistribution of auxin in roots was studied by Konings (112, 114). The possible importance of the radial distribution of auxin in relation to root elongation has been pointed out by Hejnowicz & Erickson (89) and makes more interesting the model proposed by Batra et al (15).

Others have presented the view that gibberellins control root elongation [see, for example, the proposals by van Overbeek (225)]. This imaginative view is supported by little evidence. Reports on the effects of exogenously supplied gibberellins on root elongation are surprisingly few. Whaley & Kephart (234) found a stimulation in growth of excised roots of *Zea mays* provided gibberellic acid. Peckett (153) reported in one variety of peas that second-transfer roots in culture showed stimulation of growth and increased root hair development in response to gibberellins. Mertz (131) found that in the mutant dwarf-1 of *Zea mays,* he could demonstrate a requirement for gibberellic acid (GA_3) for growth of excised roots in vitro. Amo 1618, an inhibitor of gibberellin biosynthesis, reduced the elongation of normal roots by 35%, suggesting that gibberellin was acting as a growth hormone in corn roots. Butcher & Street (36) showed that in excised tomato roots grown in culture, the effect of exogenous gibberellin depended upon the sucrose concentration in the medium; at sucrose concentrations below 1%, gibberellic acid stimulated root elongation, while at higher sucrose concentrations gibberellic acid inhibited root elongation. Interactions with other hormones, including auxins and cytokinins, were not excluded. Some of these interrelationships have been summarized by Mertz (131). El Hinnawy (59) reported that excised roots of tomato, cv. Moneydor, showed enhanced elongation when provided a mixture of different gibberellins. The roots showed stimulation of cell divisions and elongation and exhibited enhanced amylase and invertase activity. An interaction with abscisic acid was observed. A role for cytokinins in root cell elongation seems unlikely from the evidence (or lack thereof). Rather, cytokinin effects in the root seem to center on a role, probably in conjunction with other hormones, in cell division and the function of the apical meristem.

In general, ABA has been considered an inhibitor of physiological processes, especially of growth. Externally supplied ABA is remarkably effective as an inhibitor. El-Antably & Larsen (58) reported ABA to inhibit root elongation in seedlings of *Vicia faba* at all concentrations tested down to $3.8 \times 10^{-9}M$ (0.001 mg/1) over a 48-hr treatment. In seedling roots of *Lepidium sativum,* ABA at concentrations of 0.01 mg/1 was inhibitory to root elongation as early as 1 hr after treatment and persisted for up to 48 hr. These authors (58) cite root inhibitions by ABA reported by a number of other workers. Khan (109) found ABA inhibition of root elongation in barley seedlings could be slightly reversed by treatment with GA_3. The possible importance of ABA as root growth inhibitor in relation to root geotropism will be discussed below.

On the other hand, like the other major hormones, ABA has been reported to cause stimulations of physiological and developmental processes. In this respect ABA falls into the general description applicable to all plant growth hormones, that they elicit responses of stimulation or inhibition dependent upon the applied concentration, the endogenous levels already present, and their interaction with other hormones involved. ABA may become stimulatory in circumstances in which it antagonizes the action of other hormones which are inhibitory (229). Thus, in root development ABA has been reported to stimulate lateral root initiation in *Lycopersicon esculentum* (45) and to stimulate root elongation in excised root tips of *Pisum sativum* (70).

One is left with a less-than-satisfactory view of what hormones control root cell elongation. Auxins have been most carefully studied. Similar detailed analyses of the distribution, transport, and function are needed of the gibberellins and abscisic acid and perhaps ethylene. Progress in that direction has been accelerated by new discoveries with respect to root geotropism, which is a specialized expression of root cell elongation and worthy of special attention.

ROOT GEOTROPISM

Geotropism in roots has been studied seriously for almost a century and a voluminous literature has developed with new additions almost every year. Recent developments in the subject have been reviewed (9, 237) and a complete reexamination of theories and mechanisms is in progress (see also this volume pp. 385–406). The Cholodny-Went hypothesis centering on a redistribution of auxin in the root in response to gravity leading to inhibition of root cell elongation on the lower side no longer seems tenable [for an extended review of earlier work see Thimann (210)]. As pointed out by Audus (9), the problem has three major facets: (*a*) what is the nature of the gravity perception? (*b*) what is the nature of the chemical regulation which leads to differential cell growth during root curvature? (*c*) and how are these two processes coupled?

The recent renewal of interest was sparked by the clear demonstration from root decapitation studies by Juniper et al (103) that the root cap serves as the gravity sensor. This idea has a long history and many contributory opinions and experiments. In a recent careful study of the time course of root cap regeneration in *Zea mays*, Barlow (12, 13) and Barlow & Grundwag (14) showed that starch grains in the columella of the root cap served as the statoliths perceiving the stimulus of gravity.

Removal of the root cap has been reported to have no effect on the growth rate of the decapped root (103, 113) or to cause a transitory increase in growth rate (160) for about 4 hr in *Zea* roots which then returns to the rate of intact roots. Asymmetric removal of half of the root cap from *Zea* root tips (72) caused root curvatures in the direction toward the side with the cap, implying the action of an inhibitor of root cell elongation coming from the cap tissue. Shaw & Wilkins (187) studied further the lateral transport of growth inhibitors from the root cap in *Zea mays* and *Pisum sativum*. They concluded that positive geotropic responses in seedling radicles depended upon a growth inhibitor which arises in the root cap and which moves proximally through the apex into the extending zone of the root where it becomes asymmetrically distributed, inhibiting cell elongation on the lower half. Kundu &

Audus (116) extracted and identified abscisic acid from root caps of *Zea* and proposed that this or its precursor xanthoxin may be the root cap inhibitor involved in the geotropic response. Wilkins & Wain (236) have likewise postulated ABA as active in geotropism of roots and have studied the distribution of the inhibitor in response to gravity stimulation.

In a series of papers by Pilet and by Wilkins and his associates and Kundu & Audus (see review by Wilkins 237), the case for an inhibitor originating in the root cap and achieving asymmetrical distribution on the lower side in the region of root cell elongation seems well established. The identity of the inhibitor is not certain but ABA seems a good candidate. Rivier & Pilet (178) state that the root cap contains twice as much IAA as the apex proximal to it and reopened the possibility that local production of IAA by the cap provides the inhibition rather than the ABA-like compound.

The question remains concerning the positive stimulation of root cell elongation on the upper, growing side of a geotropically responsive root. Based on the arguments of Batra et al (15), one could argue that auxin moving acropetally stimulates root elongation but that asymmetrical distribution of the root cap inhibitor, perhaps ABA, causes inhibition and consequently curvature. A similar role for GA instead of IAA might be postulated. El-Antably (57) examined indirectly the redistribution of IAA, ABA, and GA in roots of *Ribes nigrum* after geostimulation by flooding the system with excesses of the hormones. Only IAA prevented the geotropic response. His conclusion that both GA and ABA are excluded from having a role in the geotropic response seems unwarranted from such indirect evidence. Further evidence concerning redistribution of the possible interacting hormones will be needed before a resolution can be made of the effective substance. Also needing explanation is the coupling between the starch grain redistribution in the cap and redistribution of active hormones several millimeters distant in the extending zone of the root.

LATERAL ROOT INITIATION

The literature concerned with the physiology of lateral root initiation was reviewed by Torrey (218). A more anatomical review of the development of lateral roots has been made by McCully (145). The distribution and frequency of lateral roots is of importance in the determination of the shape and size of the root system, and some attention has been given over the past decade to the analysis of lateral root distribution. In his analysis of the distribution of nonwoody lateral roots in trees, Lyford (124) estimated that a mature red oak tree may possess as many as 500 million living root tips (based on counts showing a frequency of about 70 live tips per cm for first-order nonwoody laterals and with root branching up to the fifth order). The importance of understanding the physiology of lateral root initiation is apparent from such an estimate. Its importance is also emphasized by the fact that, upon injury to an elongating "long root," new lateral roots are initiated, one of which becomes the main axis or replacement root, a common occurrence in tree root systems (95, 239). The problems in sampling root systems of trees and large herbaceous plants are considerable and foresters (174), pomologists (232), agronomists

(152), and ecologists (see volume edited by Hoffman 94) have all been concerned with assessing root systems in which lateral roots (to the fifth order or more) form the bulk of the structure.

In herbaceous plants, lateral root distribution has been shown to have more precision of sites for initiation than had been formerly recognized. The precision of lateral root origin in the pericycle opposite the protoxylem points or between xylem and phloem in diarch roots has long been known (cf Esau 63). We still do not understand the precision of such radial transverse origin. Along the longitudinal axis the sites of initiation are not randomly arranged (127, 176, 177) but show influences from preexisting laterals and a direct effect of the parent root apex itself. In the developing root, lateral primordia were consistently observed closer to the root apex than mature elements of the protoxylem.

Most recent experimental work on lateral root initiation has been with seedling roots or excised roots grown in culture. Street (200) reviewed some of this work, including the essentiality of auxin for initiation and the possible interaction with other hormones including cytokinins and gibberellins. Blakely et al (23) confirmed the requirement for auxin in an elegant test system using cultured roots of *Haplopappus ravenii.* They found that cytokinin inhibited lateral root initiation and gibberellic acid was without effect. Lateral branches elongated 3–5 cm, then stopped and soon died, a situation reminiscent of lateral root death reported for forest trees (124). The suggestion was made that older parts of the root form a substance that may accelerate the aging and death of the tip, an idea proposed earlier by Street in his studies of cultured tomato roots (200).

Older evidence for the production by the root apex of an inhibitor of lateral root initiation which would account in part for the usual acropetal sequence of lateral root initiation in most roots was reviewed by Torrey (218). The active substance has not yet been identified. If auxin, moving from root base to tip in its usual polar transport pathway, is involved in lateral root initiation, one could imagine a flow of inhibitor from root apex to base affecting inhibition near the tip but allowing initiation some distance proximal to the tip. Gibberellic acid, cytokinins, and ABA seem to be formed at the root apex. Gibberellic acid appears to play no role in lateral root initiation. A role for cytokinin of root apex origin in the inhibitory control of lateral root initiation seems still possible (217). This possibility has been increased by the studies of Webster & Radin (230) on lateral root formation in basally fed isolated roots of *Raphanus sativus.* With the recognition that ABA and/or xanthoxin are formed at the root tip, these inhibitors become of interest in this process. Inhibitors extracted from root apices by Libbert (119), Torrey (216), and others were a part of the β-inhibitor complex of which ABA is now known to be a part.

Reports concerning ABA as an inhibitor of lateral root initiation are sparse and contradictory. Street (200) reported that ABA inhibited the number of lateral roots formed on excised tomato roots in culture but more or less in proportion to its effect in inhibiting main root extension. Collet (45) found that ABA stimulated lateral root initiation in tomato. Phillips (156) reported that ABA at 10^{-6}M reduced the number of nodules per plant by 61% without affecting root growth (fresh weight or dry weight). The possibility that ABA could be the lateral root inhibitor produced by the root apex in seedling roots seems not to have been investigated. Red light inhibition of auxin-induced lateral root initiation (69) makes the ABA interaction all the more interesting in view of the complex auxin-ABA effects on red-far red light induced changes in electrical charges on surfaces of root cap cells reported by Tanada (208; cf also 134).

Ethylene as an indirectly acting control agent for lateral root initiation has been discussed above. Direct effects of ethylene on lateral root initiation are few. Zobel (246) commented in passing that normal tomato roots grown in culture and exposed to ethylene gas (up to 1 ppm) showed increased lateral root formation. Chadwick & Burg (40) showed that ethylene (1000 ppm) induced root hair formation on pea roots but made no report of the effect of ethylene on lateral root initiation. The observation of root hair initiation caused by ethylene and related gases goes back to the early 1930s (cf 49) as does also a report that ethylene induced lateral roots on roots. Further work on ethylene effects on lateral root initiation seems warranted. Thus, for example, the fact that elevated carbon dioxide levels in cultured roots of wheat increased lateral root formation (207) suggests the need to explore the possibility of ethylene: CO_2 interaction in the enclosed system. McCully (145) suggested that certain phenomena of root branching might be interpretable in terms of ethylene effects.

Special mention should be made of root nodule formation in relation to lateral root initiation. There exists a long-standing argument over the question of whether root nodules on legumes induced by rhizobial infections are modified lateral roots or distinctive structures in their own right (cf 5). Because of their initiation in the root cortex (rather than pericycle) and the involvement of polyploid cortical cells in nodule proliferation, the argument that rhizobial nodules are unique structures has been favored. However, under special circumstances such nodules do develop organized roots, usually from the nodule meristem. As Dart has reported (52), exposure of nodulated plants of *Trifolium* and *Medicago* to a temperature of 35°C for a week, causes the nodules to form roots at their meristematic apices, suggesting an upset in the hormone status of the nodules. Raised temperatures change cytokinin biosynthetic activities in plant tissues (see earlier discussion), and it is possible that nodule roots are the result of such a change.

In contrast, nodules induced on nonlegume roots by actinomycete infection appear to be composed of complexly branched lateral root systems. A study of nodule initiation in *Casuarina* reported by Torrey (219) clearly demonstrated that the nodule is initiated in association with a lateral root branch and that nodule development depends upon repeated lateral root initiations. The nodule roots which develop are peculiar and of considerable physiological interest since they tend to grow vertically upward, defying the usually positive geotropic response. Silver et al (192) have attributed such peculiar root geotropism to an upset in the hormone, probably auxin, relations produced by the infective agent. These structures offer interesting material for the analysis of root behavior.

SECONDARY THICKENING IN ROOTS

Since Torrey's review (218) of this subject in 1965, considerable progress has been made in developing an understanding of the hormonal control of vascular cambium activation in roots and of the factors influencing the formation of the secondary vascular tissues of the root. These processes are of considerable importance commercially in the production of root crops, carrots, radishes, turnips, and the like (*Daucus, Raphanus, Brassica,* etc) and in the important tropical root crops, sweet potato (*Ipomoea batatas*), the yam (*Dioscorea alata*), and cassava (*Manihot utilissima*). Roots of forest trees show remarkable secondary thickening, two tonnes of new tree root matter being added annually per hectare in a closed forest (238). Some understanding of the physiological control of this development is of considerable theoretical and practical interest.

A primarily descriptive study of radial growth in roots of 5–20 year old trees of *Pinus sylvestris* and *P. banksiana* was made by Fayle (64), who summarized much of the pertinent literature on tree root thickening. Wilson (238) developed a model of secondary thickening in roots of forest trees which takes into account the distribution of photosynthetic products from the shoot system and the possible hormonal feedback systems active in partitioning of dry matter between root and shoot. The model is used in conjunction with data taken primarily from root systems of *Pinus strobus.* Because of complications in planning experiments with tree root systems, most of the experimental work with secondary thickening in roots has been pursued with herbaceous annuals or perennials.

In some genera it has been shown that secondary thickening in roots is related to photoperiod. Garner & Allard (71) observed effects of day length on root thickening in *Phaseolus* and *Dioscorea.* The importance of daylength on root tuber formation in *Dahlia* was studied by Zimmerman & Hitchcock (244), substantiated in experiments by Tincker & Darbishire (214) and others (142). The literature relating photoperiodism and tuber formation, both in stems and roots, was reviewed by Nitsch (149, 150). The implication of these experiments is that shoots under appropriate day length produce stimuli which are transported to the root and there induce sustained vascular cambial activity. In many species, short days favor root thickening.

In the experiments to test this possibility, Loomis & Torrey (122) provided cultured excised roots of *Raphanus sativus* with mixtures of hormones and carbohydrates via the cut basal end. Vascular cambium, which never occurred in excised roots in culture without basal feeding, was formed in response to optimal concentrations of sucrose, auxin, cytokinin, and myoinositol. This system has since been used to study effective concentrations of hormones in radish and to study ontogeny (221, 222, 230). Radin & Loomis (166) extracted and characterized the effective cytokinins in mature radish roots as zeatin and its riboside and ribotide. These cytokinins were active in inducing cambial activity when applied to cultured radish roots. The authors propose that the shoot provides the cytokinin to the root to induce secondary thickening, which proceeds ontogenetically from root base to tip. Thickened radish roots produce another unidentified cytokinin which they suggest may be the form exported to the shoot. In this connection, it should be pointed out that auxin is always essential to cambial initiation and continued activity in these experiments. It is possible that auxin flow toward the root tip accounts for the acropetal progression of cambial initiation and that cytokinins originating in the root are active together with the auxin. Studies of hormone flow from shoot to root are needed, preferably on plants grown under different day lengths, in order to unravel the question of the nature and sources of hormones active in root cambial activation.

Peterson (154) applied the basal feeding technique to excised roots of turnip (*Brassica rapa*) and found that an auxin, a cytokinin, sucrose, and myoinositol were all necessary for maximum radial growth of the roots, thus behaving like radish. In experiments with dark-grown seedlings he found that excising the root tip had no effect on the formation of cambial derivatives while removal of the shoot or one or both cotyledons drastically reduced secondary xylem formation, suggesting that the root depended on the shoot system for stimuli which produced the cambial initiation.

There exists a large literature on tuberization in plants, that is, the formation of thickened structures which are technically modified stems, as for example in *Helianthus tuberosus* and tuberous *Begonia*. These stem structures have many features in common with the thickened root structures described above. They are stimulated by short-days, subject to hormonal influences, and act as storage structures. As pointed out in the review by Nitsch (150), their formation is under multiple hormonal control. No doubt much can be learned about secondary thickening in roots by exploring on a comparative basis the literature on tuber formation in stems. That our present view of secondary thickening in roots is too narrow is suggested by the study by Biran et al (22), who found that short days favor tuberization in growing plants and that ABA, ethylene, and GA applied as sprays to the leaves of plants grown under long days also influenced tuber formation, the first two as stimulators and the last as inhibitor. Whether these effects were direct or only through effects on general growth rates remains to be sorted out. Clearly, the physiology of the whole plant needs to be taken into account.

BUD FORMATION BY ROOTS

This subject was very interestingly and usefully reviewed in 1929 by Priestley & Swingle (163). An extensive updating of the subject has been made by Peterson (155), including a discussion of the hormones involved in the process and the environmental parameters which influence bud formation and development.

CONCLUDING REMARKS

The intention of this review was to focus on roots as sources of hormones and to study the effects of these hormones on root structure and function and how roots develop. There is ample evidence that roots contain the major known plant hormones, perhaps serve as centers for their synthesis, and frequently export these hormones via the xylem sap and probably also on occasion via the phloem to the other parts of the plant. In this review, less attention has been paid to the effects of root hormones on shoot development than on the development of the root system itself. However, it should be clear by implication from this discussion, and can be made manifest by a further review of the literature, that roots markedly influence the activities of the shoot. Skene (196) listed and documented in some detail the manifold effects of root cytokinins on shoot development. They include the control of protein and CO_2 metabolism in leaves, enzyme formation in leaves, leaf aging and senescence, elongation of the shoot, including bud burst and stem elongation, lateral shoot development, and the release of floral bud dormacy, inflorescence branching, and fruit set. A less extensive but similar list could be assembled of the effects of root gibberellins on shoot development. And these effects involve interactions of cytokinins and gibberellins with other hormones.

Thus a strong case can be made that roots and root systems play an important role in the overall hormonal physiology of the plant. Environmental influences which affect the root system, such as water stress, flooding, excessive heat or cold, act not only on water uptake, ion uptake, and transport of organic substrates, but also on the hormonal flow from root to shoot and vice versa.

In recognizing the importance of the root system to the rest of the plant, it becomes apparent that manipulation of the root system, of its size and shape and physiology, by genetic means together with selection and field testing, offers an almost unexplored avenue to the improvement of plant growth and productivity. In the past, one deterrent to our better understanding has been that roots are typically subterranean. With methods now available, this fact is no longer an excuse. Roots and root systems should be taken into account.

Literature Cited

1. Abeles, F. B. 1972. *Ann. Rev. Plant Physiol.* 23:259–292
2. Abeles, F. B. 1973. *Ethylene in Plant Biology.* New York: Academic. 302 pp.
3. Aberg, B. 1957. *Ann. Rev. Plant Physiol.* 8:153–80
4. Addicott, F. T., Lyon, J. L. 1969. *Ann. Rev. Plant Physiol.* 20:139–64
5. Allen, E. K., Allen, O. N. *Handb. Plflanzenphysiol.* 8:48–118
6. Anderson, W. P. 1972. *Ann. Rev. Plant Physiol.* 23:51–72
7. Anderson, W. P., Ed. 1973. *Ion Transport in Plants.* New York, London: Academic. 648 pp.
8. Andreae, W. A., Venis, M. A., Jursic, F., Dumas, T. 1968. *Plant Physiol.* 43:1375–79
9. Audus, L. J. 1975. See Ref. 220, 327–63
10. Aung, L. H. 1974. See Ref. 39, 29–61
11. Babcock, D. F., Morris, R. O. 1970. *Biochemistry* 9:3701–5
12. Barlow, P. 1974. *New Phytol.* 73:937–54
13. Barlow, P. 1974. *J. Exp. Bot.* 25(89):1137–46
14. Barlow, P. W., Grundwag, M. 1974. *Z. Pflanzenphysiol.* 73:56–64
15. Batra, M. W., Edwards, K. L., Scott, T. K. 1975. See Ref. 220, 299–325
16. Beever, J. E., Woolhouse, H. W. 1974. *R. Soc. N. Z. Bull.* 12:681–86
17. Bellandi, D. M., Dörffling, K. 1974. *Physiol. Plant.* 32:365–68
18. Bennet-Clark, T. A., Kefford, N. P. 1953. *Nature* 171:645–47
19. Bentley, J. A. 1958. *Ann. Rev. Plant Physiol.* 9:47–80
20. Bergersen, F. J. 1971. *Ann. Rev. Plant Physiol.* 22:121–40
21. Bhar, D. S., Mason, G. F., Hilton, R. J. 1969. *Can. J. Plant Sci.* 49:104–6
22. Biran, I., Gur, I., Halevy, A. H. 1972. *Physiol. Plant.* 27:226–30
23. Blakely, L. M., Rodaway, S. J., Hollen, L. B., Croker, S. G. 1972. *Plant Physiol.* 50:35–42
24. Bonnett, H. T. Jr. Torrey, J. G. 1965. *Plant Physiol.* 40:813–18
25. Ibid 1976. In press
26. Bourbouloux, A., Bonnemain, J. L. 1974. *Planta* 119:169–82
27. Bowen, M. R., Hoad, G. V. 1968. *Planta* 81:64–70
28. Bowen, M. R., Wilkins, M. B., Cane, A. R., McCorquodale, I. 1972. *Planta* 105:273–92
29. Bridges, I. G., Hillman, J. R., Wilkins, M. B. 1973. *Planta* 115:189–92
30. Bui-Dang-Ha, D., Nitsch, J. P. 1970. *Planta* 95:119–26
31. Burns, R. C., Hardy, R. W. F. 1975. *Nitrogen Fixation in Bacteria and*

456   TORREY

Higher Plants. Berlin: Springer-Verlag. 225 pp.
32. Burrows, W. J., Carr, D. J. 1969. *Physiol. Plant.* 22:1105–12
33. Burström, H. 1953. *Ann. Rev. Plant Physiol.* 4:237–52
34. Burström, H. 1957. *Soc. Exp. Biol. Symp.* 11:44–62
35. Butcher, D. N. 1963. *J. Exp. Biol.* 14:204–5
36. Butcher, D. N., Street, H. E. 1960. *J. Exp. Bot.* 11:206–16
37. Carr, D. J., Reid, D. M. 1968. In *Biochemistry and Physiology of Plant Growth Substances,* ed. F. Wightman, G. Setterfield, 1169–85. Ottawa, Canada: Runge
38. Carr, D. J., Reid, D. M., Skene, K. G. M. 1964. *Planta* 63:382–92
39. Carson, E. W., Ed. 1974. *The Plant Root and Its Environment.* Charlottesville: Univ. Press of Virginia. 689 pp.
40. Chadwick, A. V., Burg, S. P. 1967. *Plant Physiol.* 42:415–20
41. Ibid 1970. 45:192–200
42. Chibnall, A. C. 1939. *Protein Metabolism in the Plant.* New Haven: Yale Univ. Press
43. Chibnall, A. C. 1954. *New Phytol.* 53:31–37
44. Clarkson, D. T. 1974. *Ion Transport and Cell Structures in Plants.* New York: McGraw Hill
45. Collet, G. F. 1970. *C. R. Acad. Sci. Ser. D* 271:667–70
46. Cooper, A. J. 1973. *Root Temperature and Plant Growth* Res. Rev. No. 4, Comm. Bur. Hortic. Plantation Crops. 74 pp.
47. Crafts, A. S. 1956. *Hilgardia* 26:287–334
48. Cram, W. J., Pitman, M. G. 1972. *Aust. J. Biol. Sci.* 25:1125–32
49. Crocker, W. 1948. *Growth of Plants.* New York: Reinhold
50. Crozier, A., Reid, D. M. 1971. *Can. J. Bot.* 49(6):967–75
51. Crozier, A., Reid, D. M. 1972. In *Plant Growth Substances 1970,* 414–19 Berlin: Springer-Verlag
52. Dart, P. J. 1975. See Ref. 220, 467–506
53. Dilworth, M. J. 1974. *Ann. Rev. Plant Physiol.* 25:81–114
54. Dullaart, J. 1967. *Acta. Bot. Neerl.* 16:222–30
55. Ibid 1970. 19:573–618
56. Dullaart, J., Duba, L. I. 1970. *Acta. Bot. Neerl.* 19:877–83
57. El-Antably, H. M. M. 1975. *Z. Pflanzenphysiol.* 75:17–24
58. El-Antably, H. M. M., Larsen, P. 1974. *Physiol. Plant.* 32:322–29
59. El Hinnawy, E. 1973. *Z. Pflanzenphysiol.* 69:1–12
60. Eliasson, L. 1972. *Physiol. Plant.* 27:412–16
61. Elliott, M. C., Greenwood, M. S. 1974. *Phytochemistry* 13:239–41
62. Epstein, E. 1972. *Mineral Nutrition of Plants: Principles and Perspectives.* New York: Wiley. 412 pp.
63. Esau, K. 1965. *Plant Anatomy.* New York: Wiley. 2nd ed.
64. Fayle, D. C. F. 1968. *Radial Growth in Tree Roots.* Tech. Rep. No. 9, Faculty of Forestry, Univ. Toronto, Canada
65. Feldman, L. J. 1975. See Ref. 220, 55–72
66. Fox, J. E. 1963. *Physiol. Plant.* 16:793–803
67. Fries, D., Gaspar, T., Verbeek, R. 1971. *Ann. Physiol. Vég.* 16:27–37
68. Frydman, V. M., Wareing, P. F. 1973. *J. Exp. Bot.* 24:1139–48
69. Furuya, M., Torrey, J. G. 1964. *Plant Physiol.* 39(6):987–91
70. Gaither, D. H., Lutz, D. H., Forrence, L. E. 1975. *Plant Physiol.* 55:948–49
71. Garner, W. W., Allard, H. A. 1923, *J. Agric. Res.* 23:871–920
72. Gibbons, G. S. B., Wilkins, M. B. 1970. *Nature* 226:558–59
73. Glinka, Z. 1973. *Plant Physiol.* 51:217–19
74. Glinka, Z., Reinhold, L. 1971. *Plant Physiol.* 48:103–5
75. Ibid 1972. 49:602–6
76. Goodwin, R. H. 1972. *Bot. Gaz.* 133:224–29
77. Gordon, M. E., Wilson, M. M., Parker, C. W., Letham, D. S. 1974. *R. Soc. N. Z. Bull.* 12:773–80
78. Greenwood, M. S., Hillman, J. R., Shaw, S., Wilkins, M. B. 1973. *Planta* 109:369–74
79. Greenwood, M. S., Ycas, J. 1975. *Planta* 122:311–14
80. Hackett, C., Rose, D. A. 1972. *Aust. J. Biol. Sci.* 25:669–79
81. Ibid, 681–90
82. Hacskaylo, E., Ed. 1971. *Mycorrhizae* Washington DC: Supt. Documents, US GPO. 255 pp.
83. Hacskaylo, E., Tompkins, C. M. 1973. *Contrib. Reed Herb.* 22:1–142
84. Hall, R. H. 1973. *Ann. Rev. Plant Physiol.* 24:415–44
85. Hall, S. M., Medlow, G. C. 1974. *Planta* 119:257–61
86. Hartung, W., Behl, R. 1975. *Planta* 122:53–59

87. Ibid, 61–65
88. Hartung, W., Phillips, I. D. J. 1974. *Planta* 118:311–22
89. Hejnowicz, Z., Erickson, R. O. 1968. *Physiol. Plant.* 21:302–13
90. Hewitt, E. J. 1966. *Sand and Water Culture Methods used in the Study of Plant Nutrition.* Comm. Agric. Bur., Farnham Royal, U.K.
91. Hilton, R. J., Bhar, D. S., Mason, G. F. 1969. *Can. J. Plant Sci.* 49:101–4
92. Hoad, G. V. 1975. *Planta* 124:25–29
93. Hoagland, D. R., Arnon, D. I. 1950. *The Water-Culture Method for Growing Plants Without Soil.* Calif. Agric. Exp. Sta. Cir. 347. Univ. Calif., Berkeley. 32 pp.
94. Hoffmann, G., Ed. 1974. *Ecology and Physiology of Root Growth.* Int. Symp. Akademie-Verlag, Berlin
95. Horsley, S. B. 1971. *For. Sci.* 17:341–48
96. Horton, R. F., Moran, L. 1972. *Z. Pflanzenphysiol.* 66:193–96
97. Itai, C., Ben-Zioni, A. 1974. *R. Soc. N. Z. Bull.* 12:477–82
98. Itai, C., Ben-Zioni, A., Ordin, L. 1973. *Physiol. Plant.* 29:355–60
99. Itai, C., Richmond, A., Vaadia, Y. 1968. *Isr. J. Bot.* 17:187–93
100. Itai, C., Vaadia, Y. 1965. *Physiol. Plant.* 18:941–44
101. Jacobs, W. P., Pruett, P. E. 1973. *Am. J. Bot.* 60:896–900
102. Jones, R. L., Phillips, I. D. J. 1966. *Plant Physiol.* 41:1381–86
103. Juniper, B. E., Groves, S., Landau-Schacher, B., Audus, L. J. 1966. *Nature* 209:93–94
104. Kefeli, V. I., Kadyrov, C. S. 1971. *Ann. Rev. Plant Physiol.* 22:185–96
105. Kefford, N. P. 1955. *J. Exp. Bot.* 6:129–51
106. Kende, H. 1964. *Science* 145:1066–67
107. Kende, H. 1965. *Proc. Natl. Acad. Sci. USA* 54:1302–7
108. Kende, H., Sitton, D. 1967. *Ann. NY Acad. Sci.* 144:235–43
109. Khan, A. A. 1969. *Physiol. Plant.* 22:94–103
110. Klemen, F., Klämbt, D. 1974. *Physiol. Plant.* 31:186–88
111. Kolek, J., Ed. 1974. *Structure and Function of Primary Root Tissues.* Bratislava: Veda, Publ. House of Slovak Acad. Sci. 477 pp.
112. Konings, H. 1967. *Acta Bot. Neerl.* 16:161–76
113. Ibid 1968. 17:203–11
114. Ibid 1969. 18:528–37
115. Kulaeva, O. N. 1962. *Sov. Plant Physiol.* (Eng. Transl.) 9:182–89
116. Kundu, K. K., Audus, L. J. 1974. *Planta* 117:183–86
117. Kundu, K. K., Audus, L. J. 1974. *J. Exp. Bot.* 25:479–89
118. Lenton, J. R., Bowen, M. R., Saunders, P. F. 1968. *Nature* 220:86–87
119. Libbert, E. 1957. *Z. Bot.* 45:57–76
120. Lie, T. A., Mulder, E. G., Eds. 1971. *Biological Nitrogen Fixation in Natural and Agricultural Habitats.* Plant & Soil, Spec. Vol.
121. Linsmaier, E. M., Skoog, F. 1965. *Physiol. Plant.* 18:100–27
122. Loomis, R. S., Torrey, J. G. 1964. *Proc. Natl. Acad. Sci. USA* 52:3–11
123. Luckwill, L. C., Whyte, P. 1968. In *Plant Growth Regulators.* Soc. Chem. Ind. (London) Monogr. 31, 87–101
124. Lyford, W. H. 1975. See Ref. 220, 179–97
125. Lyford, W. H., Wilson, B. F. 1966. *Harv. For. Pap.* 16:1–12
126. Macura, J., Vancura, V., Eds. 1965. *Plant Microbe Relationships.* Prague: Czechoslovak Acad. Sci. 333 pp.
127. Mallory, T. E., Chiang, S. H., Cutter, E. G., Gifford, E. M. Jr. 1970. *Am. J. Bot.* 57:800–9
128. Mansfield, T. A., Jones, R. J. 1971. *Planta* 101:147–58
129. Marks, G. G., Kozlowski, T. T., Eds. 1973. *Ectomycorrhizae—Their Ecology and Physiology.* New York, London: Academic. 444 pp.
130. Meidner, H., Willmer, C. 1975. *Curr. Adv. Plant Sci.* 7:1–15
131. Mertz, D. 1966. *Plant Cell Physiol.* 7:125–35
132. Mertz, D. 1974. In *Humoral Control of Growth and Differentiation,* Vol. 2, ed. J. LoBue, A. S. Gordon. New York: Academic
133. Meyer, F. H. 1974. *Ann. Rev. Plant Physiol.* 25:567–86
134. Milborrow, B. V. 1974. *Ann. Rev. Plant Physiol.* 25:259–307
135. Miller, C. O. 1963. *Mod. Methods Plant Anal.* 6:194–202
136. Miller, F. H. 1974. *Root Anatomy and Morphology: A Guide to the Literature.* Hamden, Conn: Archon. 271 pp.
137. Mishustin, E. N., Shil'nikova, V. K. 1971. *Biological Fixation of Atmospheric Nitrogen.* London: Macmillan. 420 pp.
138. Mitchell, J. W., Livingston, G. A. 1968. *Methods of Studying Plant Hormones and Growth-Regulating Substances.* Washington DC: USDA Handb. No. 336 USDA, 140 pp.

139. Miura, G. A., Miller, C. O. 1969. *Plant Physiol.* 44:1035–39
140. Mizrahi, Y., Richmond, A. E. 1972. *Aust. J. Biol. Sci.* 25:437–42
141. Morris, D. A., Briant, R. E., Thomson, P. G. 1969. *Planta* 89:178–97
142. Moser, B. C., Hess, C. E. 1968. *Proc. Am. Soc. Hortic. Sci.* 93:595–603
143. Mothes, K., Engelbrecht, L. 1956. *Flora* 143:428–72
144. Murakami, Y. 1960. *Bot. Mag.* 73:186–90
145. McCully, M. E. 1975. See Ref. 220, 105–24
146. McDavid, C. R., Sagar, G. R., Marshall, C. 1972. *New Phytol.* 71:1027–32
147. Nielsen, K. F. 1974. See Ref. 39, 293–333
148. Nissen, P. 1974. *Ann. Rev. Plant Physiol.* 25:53–79
149. Nitsch, J. P. 1966. *Bull. Soc. Fr. Physiol. Vég.* 12:233–46
150. Nitsch, J. P. In *Plant Physiology, A Treatise,* 6A:403–501. New York: Academic
151. Ohkuma, K., Lyon, J. L., Addicott, F. T., Smith, O. E. 1965. *Science* 142:1592–93
152. Pearson, R. W. 1974. See Ref. 39, 247–70
153. Peckett, R. C. 1960. *Nature* 185:114–15
154. Peterson, R. L. 1973. *Can. J. Bot.* 51(2):475–80
155. Peterson, R. L. 1975. See Ref. 220, 125–61
156. Phillips, D. A. 1971. *Planta* 100:181–90
157. Phillips, D. A., Cleland, C. F. 1972. *Planta* 102:173–78
158. Phillips, I. D. J. 1964. *Ann. Bot.* 28:17–35
159. Phillips, I. D. J., Jones, R. L. 1964. *Planta* 63:269–78
160. Pilet, P. E. 1972. *Planta* 106:169–71
161. Pilet, P. E., Galston, A. W. *Physiol. Plant.* 8:888–98
162. Postgate, J. R., Ed. 1971. *The Chemistry and Biochemistry of Nitrogen Fixation.* London, New York: Plenum. 326 pp.
163. Priestley, J. H., Swingle, C. F. 1929. *Vegetative Propagation from the Standpoint of Plant Anatomy.* Washington DC: USDA Tech. Bull. 151
164. Puppo, A., Rigaud, J., Barthe, P. 1974. *C. R. Acad. Sci. Ser. C* 279(26):2029–32
165. Quispel, A., Ed. 1974. *The Biology of Nitrogen Fixation.* Amsterdam: North-Holland 769 pp.
166. Radin, J. W., Loomis, R. S. 1971. *Physiol. Plant.* 25:240–44
167. Radley, M. 1961. *Nature* 191:684–85
168. Rauser, W. E., Horton, R. F. 1975. *Plant Physiol.* 55:443–47
169. Reid, D. M., Burrows, W. J. 1968. *Experientia* 24:189–90
170. Reid, D. M., Carr, D. J. 1967. *Planta* 73:1–11
171. Reid, D. M., Crozier, A. 1972. See Ref. 51, 420–27
172. Reid, D. M., Crozier, A., Harvey, B. M. R. 1969. *Planta* 89:376–79
173. Reid, D. M., Railton, I. D. 1974. *R. Soc. N. Z. Bull.* 12:789–92
174. Reynold, E. R. C. 1975. See Ref. 220, 163–77
175. Richmond, A. E., Lang, A. 1957. *Science* 125:650–51
176. Riopel, J. L. 1966. *Am. J. Bot.* 53:403–7
177. Riopel, J. L. 1969. *Bot. Gaz.* 130:80–83
178. Rivier, L., Pilet, P. E. 1974. *Planta* 120:107–12
179. Rogers, W. S. 1969. See Ref. 235, 361–76
180. Rogers, W. S., Head, G. C. 1969. See Ref. 235, 280–95
181. Schuurman, J. J., Goedewaagen, M. A. J. 1971. *Methods for the Examination of Root Systems and Roots.* Wageningen, Netherlands: Centre for Agric. Publ. & Doc. 86 pp. Rev. 2nd ed.
182. Scott, P. C., Norris, L. A. 1970. *Nature* 227:1366–67
183. Scott, T. K. 1972. *Ann. Rev. Plant Physiol.* 23:235–58
184. Scott, T. K., Wilkins, M. B. 1968. *Planta* 83:323–34
185. Sembdner, G., Weiland, J., Aurich, O., Schreiber, K. 1968. In *Plant Growth Regulators.* London: S. C. I. Monogr. No. 31., 70–86
186. Shaner, D. L., Mertz, S. M. Jr., Arntzen, C. J. 1975. *Planta* 122:79–90
187. Shaw, S., Wilkins, M. B. 1973. *Planta* 109:11–26
188. Shaw, S., Wilkins, M. B. 1974. *J. Exp. Bot.* 25:199–207
189. Sheldrake, A. R. 1973. *Biol. Rev.* 48:509–59
190. Short, K. C., Torrey, J. G. 1972. *Plant Physiol.* 49:155–60
191. Short, K. C., Torrey, J. G. 1972. *J. Exp. Bot.* 23:1099–1105
192. Silver, W. S., Bendana, F. E., Powell, R. D. 1966. *Physiol. Plant.* 19:207–18
193. Sitton, D., Richmond, A. E., Vaadia, Y. 1967. *Phytochemistry.* 6:1101–5
194. Skene, K. G. M. 1967. *Planta* 74:250–62
195. Skene, K. G. M. 1968. *Science* 159:1477–78
196. Skene, K. G. M. 1975. See Ref. 220, 365–95

197. Stewart, W. D. P. 1966. *Nitrogen Fixation in Plants*. London: Athlone Press. 168 pp.
198. Street, H. E. 1966. *Ann. Rev. Plant Physiol.* 17:315–44
199. Street, H. E. 1969. In *Plant Physiology, A Treatise* 5B:3–224. New York: Academic
200. Street, H. E. 1969 see Ref. 235, 20–41
201. Street, H. E., Henshaw, G. G. 1966. In *Cells and Tissues in Culture. Methods, Biology and Physiology* 3: 459–689. London: Academic
202. Syōno, K., Furuya, T. 1971. *Plant Cell Physiol.* 12:61–71
203. Syōno, K., Torrey, J. G. 1976. *Plant Physiol.* 57. In press
204. Tal, M., Imber, D. 1970. *Plant Physiol.* 46:373–76
205. Ibid 1971. 47:849–50
206. Tal, M., Imber, D., Itai, C. 1970. *Plant Physiol.* 46:367–72
207. Talbot, B., Street, H. E. 1968. *Physiol. Plant.* 21:800–5
208. Tanada, T. 1968. *Proc. Natl. Acad. Sci. USA* 59:376–80
209. Thimann, K. V. 1936. *Am. J. Bot.* 23:561–69
210. Thimann, K. V. 1972. In *Plant Physiology, A Treatise,* 6B:3–365. New York: Academic
211. Thurman, D. A., Street, H. E. 1960. *J. Exp. Bot.* 11:188–97
212. Tietz, A. 1971. *Planta* 96:93–96
213. Tietz, A. 1974. *Biochem. Physiol. Pflanz.* 165:387–92
214. Tincker, M. A. H., Darbishire, F. V. 1933. *Ann. Bot.* 47:27–53
215. Torrey, J. G. 1956. *Ann. Rev. Plant Physiol.* 7:237–66
216. Torrey, J. G. 1959. *Physiol. Plant.* 12:873
217. Ibid 1962. 15:177–85
218. Torrey, J. G. 1965. *Handb. Pflanzenphysiol.* 15/1:1256–1327
219. Torrey, J. G. 1975. *Am. J. Bot.* In press
220. Torrey, J. G., Clarkson, D. T., Eds. 1975. *Development and Function of Roots*. London: Academic. 618 pp.
221. Torrey, J. G., Loomis, R. S. 1967. *Am. J. Bot.* 54:1098–1106
222. Torrey, J. G., Loomis, R. S. 1967. *Phytomorphology* 17:401–9
223. van der Weij, H. G. 1932. *Rec. Trav. Bot. Neerl.* 29:379–496
224. van Overbeek, J. 1939. *Bot. Gaz.* 101:450–56
225. van Overbeek, J. 1966. *Science* 152:721–31
226. Van Steveninck, R. F. M. 1972. *Physiol. Plant.* 27:43–47
227. Vreman, J. J., Skoog, F., Frihart, C. R., Leonard, N. J. 1972. *Plant Physiol.* 49:848–51
228. Wagner, H., Michael, G. 1971. *Biochem. Physiol. Pflanz.* 162:147–58
229. Wareing, P. F., Good, J., Manuel, J. 1968. See Ref. 37, 1561–79
230. Webster, B. D., Radin, J. W. 1972. *Am. J. Bot.* 59:744–51
231. Weiss, C., Vaadia, Y. 1965. *Life Sci.* 4:1323–26
232. Weller, F. 1971. *Exp. Agric.* 7:351–61
233. Went, F. W. 1957. *The Experimental Control of Plant Growth*. Waltham, Mass: Chronica Botanica
234. Whaley, W. G., Kephart, J. 1957. *Science* 125:234
235. Whittington, W. J., Ed. 1969. *Root Growth*. London: Butterworths. 450 pp.
236. Wilkins, H., Wain, R. L. 1974. *Planta* 121:1–8
237. Wilkins, M. B. 1975. *Curr. Adv. Plant Sci.* 6:317–28
238. Wilson, B. F. 1975. See Ref. 220, 197–219
239. Wilson, B. F., Horsley, S. B. 1970. *Am. J. Bot.* 57:161–64
240. Woolley, D. J., Wareing, P. F. 1972. *Planta* 105:33–42
241. Woolley, D. J., Wareing, P. F. 1972. *New Phytol.* 71:1015–25
242. Wright, S. T. C. 1969. *Planta* 86:10–20
243. Yoshida, R., Oritani, T. 1972. *Plant Cell Physiol.* 13:337–43
244. Zimmerman, P. W., Hitchcock, A. E. 1929. *Bot. Gaz.* 87:1–13
245. Zobel, R. W. 1973. *Plant Physiol.* 52:385–89
246. Zobel, R. W. 1974. *Can. J. Bot.* 52:735–41
247. Zobel, R. W., Del Tredici, P., Torrey, J. G. 1976. *Plant Physiol.* In press

Ann Rev. Plant Physiol. 1976. 27:461–83

PHYSIOLOGICAL RESPONSES OF PHYTOPLANKTON TO MAJOR ENVIRONMENTAL FACTORS[1]

❖7618

Olga v. H. Owens

Department of Biology, Johns Hopkins University, Baltimore, Maryland 21218

Wayne E. Esaias

Marine Sciences Research Center, State University of New York, Stony Brook, New York 11794

CONTENTS

[1]Contribution No. 845 from the McCollum Pratt Institute and Department of Biology, Johns Hopkins University, and No. 154 from the Marine Sciences Research Center, State University of New York, Stony Brook.

INTRODUCTION

In this paper we review four major factors of the aquatic environment—phosphorus, nitrogen, carbon, and light—which exert influence on the physiological responses of phytoplankton. We have not considered those factors which under some conditions may become important such as vitamins, trace metals, specific pollutants, etc. The four factors have been discussed in a general way in several textbooks and symposia covering primarily marine studies (33, 84, 147) and fresh water studies (59, 71, 120, 189). Several recent papers review aspects of productivity (12, 32, 89, 126, 151, 215). Our literature search ended in June 1975 and is confined primarily to readily available journals and books, avoiding technical reports, obscure journals, or special reports of local agencies. Trophic level interrelationships and mathematical modeling are outside the scope of this review, but an introduction to these concepts is available in some of the above-mentioned symposium volumes.

PHOSPHORUS

Sources of Phosphorus

It has become clear in recent years that in order to assess the effect of phosphorus on production of phytoplankton, it is necessary first to investigate the supply and fate of phosphate entering a body of water. Many studies have shown that the measured concentration of dissolved inorganic orthophosphate is a poor indication of nutrient state of the water or the availability of phosphate for growth (1, 2, 35, 88, 98, 152, 164, 210). For example, in a study of a small estuary stream converted into a series of ponds to which PO_4 was added (1, 2), it was shown that the loss of PO_4 from solution was dramatic; within 15 min 80–85% of the added PO_4 was lost to the sediments or the suspended matter. In an earlier study (88) a competition for added PO_4 between higher plants, bacteria, and mud was demonstrated with a column of lake water over a mud core. Of the three competitors, bacteria had the highest PO_4 affinity. It has also been shown that bacteria have a higher affinity than some algae (161).

Pomeroy et al (154) showed that the half-time of PO_4 exchange between a column of shallow estuarine water over a natural sediment core was about 10 hr and was unaffected by the presence of poison, indicating a purely physical mechanism. The exchange with sediment in suspension was much faster and involved at least two processes: one with a half-time of about 15 sec and another with a half-time of about 15 min. The slower process was inhibited by poison, indicating that it was of biological origin. At least a partial mass action effect was demonstrated by the addition of excess PO_4 which increased the exchange rate. Washing of the PO_4-laden sediments with estuarine water caused losses from the sediments, but washing with distilled water had little effect. They concluded that the sediments in the estuary under study were in equilibrium with water having 0.7–0.9 μM PO_4. This concentration, if maintained, would be satisfactory for phytoplankton growth. Thus sediments can be a nutrient buffer in which phosphate at least is maintained at a constant level in the water.

Bray et al (18) examined the phosphate in the interstitial water of sediments from the deeper parts of an estuary where anoxic conditions prevailed. They found no significant quantity of dissolved organic phosphate but the inorganic orthophosphate in the upper 20 cm of sediment averaged 1000 times that of the relatively uniform value of 0.2 μg-atom/liter in the overlying water. Any disturbance of the sediment would greatly increase the phosphate content of the water, but the presence of sufficient oxygen and iron would cause the liberated phosphate to be reprecipitated as iron phosphate or be adsorbed onto iron hydroxide.

The fact that phytoplankton cells can survive and grow at concentrations below the detectable limit of phosphorus (about 0.03 μg-at/liter) has stimulated studies relating the rate of supply of phosphorus under natural conditions to its rate of utilization. There are several sources of phosphorus available to the phytoplankton other than inorganic orthophosphate. Phosphorus is found in natural waters also in the form of organic and inorganic polyphosphates of low molecular weight and bound to colloidal particles in suspension and in sediments (191). Presumably if any orthophosphate is liberated from these forms, a fraction of it is immediately utilized by organisms or becomes bound again. Unfortunately, investigators use methods for separation of phosphorus compounds such as solubility in water, hot or cold acid or base, which while useful in separating fractions do not necessarily define functional forms. Strickland & Parsons (191) have discussed all the forms of phosphate found in natural waters and the reliability of the methods for their analysis.

We have already pointed out that the sediments can be a reservoir for phosphorus, but another source of phosphorus is the cells themselves. Kuenzler (113) found that dissolved organic phosphate was released by all of the marine species that he tested in culture, but largely during the declining phase of growth.

Another possible major source of phosphorus is excretion by zooplankton. Pomeroy et al (153) calculated the demand for phosphate from the rates of photosynthesis in several regions and compared it to the phosphate available from zooplankton. In the Gulf stream, 53% of the demand could be supplied by zooplankton; on the continental shelf, 20%; and in an estuary (including the bordering salt marsh), 6%. Thus zooplankton can be a significant factor in the phosphorus budget.

Lean (118) studied the various forms of phosphate and the rate constants of the exchanges between them in whole water samples from a small eutrophic lake. He found that a rapid (1 hr) steady state was achieved when ^{32}P was added to a sample of the lake water with a total phosphorus concentration of 1.42 μg-at/liter. The percent of the total ^{32}P found in a filtrate of the lake water declined with two slopes, suggesting more than two compartments. The first slope had a half-time of about 1 min and the second had a half-time of about 15 min. At several times during the decline of ^{32}P in the filtrate, samples were taken for separation of fractions both particulate and in solution. Reaction rates between the fractions were measured and a four-compartment model was proposed consisting, at equilibrium, of particulate phosphate, 98.5%; inorganic phosphorus, 0.21%; a low molecular weight organic phosphorus excreted by the cells, 0.13%; and colloidal phosphorus, 1.16%. He found, in agreement with Kuenzler (113), that maximum excretion of the low molecular weight organic phosphorus occurred after the period of maximum growth. This fraction complexed with macromolecules or particles to form the colloidal phosphorus.

In a similar study of sea water by Watt & Hayes (210), it was shown that there were three forms of phosphorus: particulate, dissolved organic, and dissolved inorganic in a steady-state dynamic one-way system. They found no significant dissolved organic phosphorus appearing until after the death of organisms. The phosphorus of the organic form entered the particulate form but there was no direct conversion to inorganic phosphorus. At least six fractions of dissolved organic phosphorus could be separated by chromatography. The above studies have indicated that phosphorus is present in several forms and can be exchanged from one to the other depending on the environmental conditions.

Phosphorus and Eutrophication

The total phosphorus for a body of water is usually a reasonably constant value fixed by geochemical factors (30). If "cultural eutrophication" is occurring, then sewage, industrial waste, or runoff from agricultural lands usually is associated with an increase in the total standing crop of algae. This increase in algae as a result of phosphorus addition has been a controversial issue and has stimulated many field studies designed to show whether phosphorus is the main limiting factor regulating either immediate growth or the long-term standing crop. This issue has been covered excellently by a series of papers and discussions in a symposium volume (120). A clear statement of the "phosphorus controversy" has been made by Shapiro (175). In a continuing series of studies of a closely monitored eutrophic lake, Edmondson (40) stated that the summer algal crop was related to the surface phosphorus concentrations present during the previous winter. When the lake was receiving high phosphorus sewage effluent, there was phosphorus "left over" after the organisms had exhausted the nitrogen supply. Following the diversion of sewage, there was nitrogen "left over" after phosphorus exhaustion.

Papers by Schindler and colleagues (169–173) show conclusively that in a group of small lakes of various types used specifically for nutrient studies, phosphorus was the nutrient which could most often be called the "limiting nutrient" for the growth of phytoplankton and thus for eutrophication.

There is no evidence that algae can assimilate any form of phosphorus other than inorganic orthophosphate. As we will point out later, there is good evidence that algal cells have phosphatases in or near the outer membrane which allow them to hydrolyze organic phosphates. Therefore, studies of phosphate-limited growth, some of which we will review here, which make exclusive use of inorganic orthophosphate as the only phosphate source may not be strictly applicable to the conditions in which most phytoplankton exist.

Phosphorus Uptake and Effects on Growth

BATCH CULTURES   In a study using a culture of the marine diatom *Phaeodactylum*, Kuenzler & Ketchum (114) related the initial inorganic phosphate concentration to phosphorus uptake by phosphorus-depleted cells. The maximum phosphorus content achieved over a period of time in the cells was greater when the initial phosphate concentration was high. The time course of uptake was complex, neither linear nor exponential, because during growth the phosphorus concentration in the medium as well as that in the cell was changing. The rate of uptake was the same regardless of the initial phosphate concentration in the medium as long as the concentration was above the detectable limit. The phosphorus content per cell reached a maximum at a time which was dependent on the initial concentration: about 2 hr at 8 μM and about 12 hr at 32 μM, during which time phosphorus per cell increased from 4 to 66 X 10^{-9} μg-at.

The growth of the oceanic tropical diatom *Chaetocerus gracillis,* made phosphorus deficient in culture, was studied by Thomas & Dodson (202). They showed that growth of these cells whose internal phosphorus content was 2 X 10^{-9} μg-at was limited at a phosphate concentration in the medium of 0.22 μM. In its natural habitat, the tropical ocean, the phosphorus concentration is 0.3 to 0.76 μg-at/liter, so it was concluded that this diatom was not phosphorus limited in nature. Below the limiting concentration the growth relation to concentration was linear, not hyperbolic. At higher initial concentrations, ranging from 1.1 to 3.1 μM, growth rate was the same in all cultures, but the final yield of cells was dependent on initial concentration up to 2 μM.

Blum (14) showed that phosphate uptake by phosphorus-starved *Euglena* was an active process (see also 179) which could be inhibited by dinitrophenol or competitively inhibited by arsenate. The cells achieved an internal concentration of orthophosphate which was seven times the external orthophosphate. For *Euglena* there was no effect of external phosphate concentration on phosphate uptake down to 0.1 μM initial concentration. The kinetics of uptake appeared to obey the Michaelis-Menton expression with K_m equal to 0.016 μM.

CHEMOSTAT CULTURES   Batch studies described above are only partially applicable to the natural system. In some lakes, which for part of the year have a negligible water flux, a population of phytoplankton might be considered as a batch culture, albeit a complex one including exchange of nutrients with herbivores and sediments.

A river, an estuary, or the sea is far removed from a batch culture but may be somewhat related to a chemostat culture. Chemostats, which enable the investigator to maintain the nutrient conditions at a constant level, have been used with several well-known phytoplankton species.

Turbidostat studies by Fuhs and associates (61–63) on steady-state growth rates of two marine diatoms, *Cyclotella* and *Thalassiosira,* showed that growth rate was related directly to phosphorus per cell rather than to phosphate in the medium and was independent of population density. Growth vs cell concentration followed a saturation curve which did not fit Monod's equation. There was no growth at a certain minimum cell phosphate concentration. In all of the experiments, the phosphate concentration in the stirred medium in which the cells were growing (as opposed to the feeding solution) was too low for detection, therefore the phosphorus supplied in the feeding solution divided by the number of cells equalled the phosphorus per cell. High phosphorus per cell allowed maximum growth for a given light intensity and temperature. The minimum phosphorus per cell for maintenance of these diatoms was 0.9×10^{-9} μg-at for the smaller *Cyclotella* and 12.5×10^{-9} μg-at for the much larger *Thalassiosira.*

The cells were treated by various methods to separate out phosphorus-containing fractions and to determine which of them were significant in controlling growth rate. Although at three light and temperature regimes the curves for *total* cell phosphorus versus growth were identical, the individual fractions versus growth had curves giving different slopes. At minimal cell phosphorus, where no growth occurred, the cell phosphorus consisted of "structural" components such as DNA and lipid phosphorus. When growth was nearly linear with cell phosphorus in addition to the structural components, the cells contained "functional" phosphorus such as RNA and nucleotides. On the saturating part of the curve the cells contained the structural, functional, and "storage" fractions such as polyphosphates which appeared when phosphorus was abundant.

The growth-determining internal phosphorus was dependent on the uptake rate which in turn was dependent on the external phosphorus concentration. The uptake rate would have its own set of controlling factors. It was noted that the absence of external phosphorus was not an indication of phosphorus limitation for phytoplankton because of their ability to store phosphate which will occur whenever some other factor limits growth.

Fuhs et al (63) reported that the minimum amount of phosphorus per cell was constant for each species. The amount of cell phosphorus relative to this minimum amount determined the relative growth rate. For the two diatoms studied, there was no phosphorus limitation at six times the minimum phosphorus, the uptake of phosphorus was an active process enhanced by light, but the energy required for uptake could be derived from respiratory processes as well. Even though the larger of the two species had a more unfavorable surface-to-volume ratio, it had a greater affinity for phosphate so their phosphate requirements were identical.

The often quoted C:N:P ratio of 100:15:1 for phytoplankton was examined. Since cell size and cell carbon increased during phosphorus limitation, the C:P ratio rose to 480:1 and the N:P ratio rose to 35:1. The 100:15:1 ratio was reached when the cells were phosphorus limited at one-half to three-fourths maximum growth. The chlorophyll *a* per cell was little affected by phosphorus limitation but changed per unit of cell volume. The ratio of N:Chl *a* remained constant.

In an extensive chemostat study of *Scenedesmus,* Rhee (162, 163) attempted to produce an overall equation which would describe the relation of external phosphorus to both uptake and growth. In agreement with other investigators, no residual organic or inorganic phosphorus was detectable in the medium at any steady-state growth rate. If washed cells were resuspended in fresh medium, the initial phosphate uptake was very high. In the chemostat at steady state, the uptake rate was determined by the phosphate concentration in the feeding solution. The K_m was 0.6 μM. The maximum uptake rate varied inversely with growth rate and also inversely with cell phosphorus. Thus at steady-state growth the amount of nutrient taken up was equal to the amount used in making new cells. An intracellular soluble polyphosphate, "surplus phosphate," was included in an expression for phosphate uptake rate in a phosphorus limited culture. It behaved as a noncompetitive inhibitor to phosphate uptake.

N:P in nitrogen limited cells was relatively constant (4 to 10) but extremely variable (30 to 250) under phosphorus limitation. It was established that under the conditions used for these experiments and for the alga *Scenedesmus,* when the cellular N:P ratio was more than 30 the culture shifted from a nitrogen limited to a phosphorus limited condition.

In a study of the blue-green alga *Anacystis nidulans,* Batterton & van Baalen (9) noted that this blue-green apparently does not store polyphosphates, but its ATP synthesis after addition of phosphate to deficient cells was rapid and overshot the normal level. Aitchison & Butt (3) found that intracellular polyphosphates were formed when *Chlorella* cells which were nitrogen deficient were exposed to high phosphate.

Alkaline Phosphatase

It is apparent that although inorganic orthophosphate may be in short supply for phytoplankton, dissolved and colloidal organic phosphates and often inorganic polyphosphates are present. Phosphatases are part of the normal enzyme complement of all algal cells, and some phytoplankton make use of phosphatase to hydrolyze organic phosphates in the water.

Galloway & Krauss (64) showed that *Chlorella* could utilize the phosphorus of polyphosphates by means of an induced phosphatase. Kuenzler and Perras (115) studied the phosphatases of two marine algae, *Phaeodactylum* and *Coccolithus.* A phosphatase was found to be at the cell surface and was produced when the algae were in phosphorus-limited medium. Enzyme production began when there was cell phosphorus sufficient for one more division, then continued at a nearly linear rate for 5 days. Addition of phosphate repressed enzyme formation. Phosphorus-deficient cells showed an almost linear increase in phosphorus content when they were given glucose-6-phosphate, AMP, or α-glycerophosphate. Only the phosphate of these compounds was taken up; the organic part remained in solution. Fitzgerald & Nelson (58) found that in algae from lakes and cultures of fresh water greens, blue-greens, and diatoms, alkaline phosphatase activity was 5 to 25 times greater when the cells were phosphate limited. These results were confirmed by Berman (11) for samples from a eutrophic lake. He also looked for alkaline phosphatase activity in the filtered water and found an average of 16% of the total activity in the filtrate. The relative amount in the filtrate followed the seasonal changes in total activity. He concluded that the limiting step in a lake phosphorus cycle was the rate of release of inorganic orthophosphate rather than its uptake. The rates of phosphorus required by the phytoplankton were calculated from the rates of carbon fixation and compared to the total phosphate available including that available from hydrolysis. This "potential" phosphorus exceeded the requirement.

In a chemostat study of the blue-green *Anabaena flosaquae,* Bone (16) found low phosphatase activity when phosphate was in excess and high activity when nitrate was in excess (see also 90).

Reichardt, Overbeck & Steubing (159) investigated the free phosphatases of lake water. The enzyme activity had two pH maxima, 5.6 and 8.7 to 9.1, indicating both acid and alkaline phosphatase although the lake water itself was slightly alkaline. The activity was heat labile and its K_m was estimated to be 1 μM, a value 50 to 500 times lower than that of the phosphatase within the blue-green algae of the lake. In contrast to the intracellular activity, it was not inhibited by orthophosphate up to the maximum concentration found in the lake, 3.4 μM, but sulfide was completely inhibitory. The concentration of the enzyme in the lake water was correlated with the algal and bacterial populations. Destruction of algae at lower depths during summer stratification was associated with very high enzyme activity in the water.

Perry (149) examined alkaline phosphatase activity in subtropical sea waters using an extremely sensitive fluorometric method. In this oceanic region orthophosphate was less than 0.1 μM. When the orthophosphate was so low as to be undetectable, then alkaline phosphatase activity in the whole water, i.e. including plankton, was maximal. Phosphatase activity declined when orthophosphate became detectable at depth. When these samples were incubated in situ without added phosphate alkaline phosphatase activity increased, but decreased again when phosphate was added. There was no phosphatase activity in the filtrate of fresh samples but it appeared during incubation. Yentsch et al (214) obtained essentially the same results in a tropical region where organic phosphorus occurred at a concentration five to ten times the inorganic phosphorus and where a marine blue-green was found.

The appearance of organic phosphorus from phytoplankton during a declining phase of at least some segment of the population is coupled with the appearance of phosphatase either free or at the cell surface. It is not clear whether the phytoplankton excrete phosphatase in response to low orthophosphate, to the appearance of organic phosphorus, or whether phosphatase leaks out of dead cells. It is also not clear whether the amount of phosphorus ordinarily unavailable to the cells, but which becomes available by the action of phosphatase, might be a significant amount. At the present time each body of water examined appears to have its own set of factors which regulate the phosphate budget.

NITROGEN

Nitrogen appears to be the primary major nutrient limiting primary production in the world's oceans (167, 177, 178) as well as in certain freshwater systems (40, 120).

As with other major nutrients, the absolute requirement for nitrogen has been studied on several levels in order to explain (*a*) temporal and spatial variations in rates of production observed in nature, and (*b*) the relative distribution of phytoplanktonic species. Active research is concerned with species variations in the concentration dependency of membrane transport (or uptake) for the various combined nitrogen forms, rates of incorporation of the nitrogen into cellular components (or assimilation), and the relationships between uptake, assimilation, and growth in terms of cell number, cell nitrogen, and total biomass. All of these relationships and processes are strongly coupled to other factors which vary within the physical system, such as light intensity and quality, temperature, concentrations of other nutrients and growth factors, and the effects of higher trophic levels.

Most phytoplankton species are capable of utilizing many commonly occurring combined nitrogen compounds to satisfy their requirements, including nitrate, nitrite, and ammonium, as well as organic compounds such as urea, free amino acids, small peptides, etc. The ranges of concentrations for these compounds are 0.01–50 μM for NO_3, 0.01–5 μM for NO_2, 0.1–10 μM for NH_4^+, and less than 10μM for most of the organic forms (147).

Transport and Assimilation Processes

A large volume of literature on nitrogen metabolism in algae, based primarily on the systems of green and blue-green algae, has been reviewed recently (137). The major object of this section is to provide a framework for further work on natural populations.

TRANSPORT PROCESSES   Phytoplankton can take up combined nitrogen species at extremely low ($<$0.1μM) concentrations and against the negative gradient of the ion, indicating that active transport processes occur. Falkowski (51) reported the presence of a nitrate and chloride dependent ATPase in the cell membranes of several phytoplankton which may be responsible for active nitrate transport. He found a half saturation constant of less than 10^{-6}M for purified preparations from six marine planktonic algae. This finding is significant in that the half saturation constants for nitrate uptake (K_s) of whole cells is of the same order, which is about two orders smaller than the Michaelis constant for nitrate reductase. This raises the possibility that the enzyme may play a role in the ammonium regulation of nitrate uptake and assimilation (see below). Other uptake mechanisms such as facilitated diffusion must exist, as the dinoflagellate *Amphidinium carterii* showed no nitrate chloride ATPase activity (51), yet it grows very well at low nitrate concentrations. Active transport of amino acids has been demonstrated (213).

Recent theoretical analyses have indicated the possibility that nutrient uptake is diffusion limited, due to microzones of nutrient depletion surrounding individual cells. On this basis Hulbert (96) concluded that nutrient uptake by cells should be independent of nutrient concentration up to a cell density where the microzones begin to overlap. He estimated this concentration to be about 3×10^8/ml. Other workers have arrived at similar conclusions with regard to carbon (66) and other nutrients (148). Turbulence and motility would tend to decrease this effect.

ASSIMILATION OF INTERNAL NITROGEN   Ammonium appears to be the primary inorganic nitrogen form which enters into synthetic reactions; both nitrate and nitrite must first be reduced to ammonium prior to assimilation. Three possible pathways for ammonium assimilation are apparent. The predominate pathway is the reductive amination, via glutamic dehydrogenase, of α-keto-glutarate to form glutamate (8). The analogous formation of other amino acids has been postulated but they probably are of secondary importance to the glutamic dehydrogenase route, followed by transamination (8, 137).

Other possible pathways which have been reported include the further amination of amino acids to their amide forms (34, 137) as well as the synthesis of carbamoyl phosphate (91, 92, 121), a precurser of citrulline, although direct evidence of these pathways in phytoplankton is lacking (8, 137).

The reduction of nitrate to nitrite and thence to ammonium is catalyzed by the enzymes nitrate reductase and nitrite reductase, respectively. Nitrate reductase requires various electron donors (NADH, NADPH, $FMNH_2$, $FADH_2$) and metallic cofactors (molybdenum, magnesium) depending on the algal species. The enzymes from various marine planktonic species require magnesium ion and can use NADH as the primary electron donor (42, 43, 46), as compared to the more usual NADPH (8). Hattori & Meyers (86) reported that ferridoxin could serve as the primary electron donor in *Anabaena cylindrica* nitrate reduction. Nitrite, resulting from the activity of nitrate reductase or direct membrane transport, is reduced to ammonium in a single step (85, 217). Reduced ferridoxin has been shown to be the primary electron donor (85, 217). The direct role of ATP in nitrite reduction was discounted by Kessler (106).

It is widely recognized that cells growing solely on nitrate have high levels of nitrate reductase. When ammonium is the sole nitrogen source the enzyme levels are very low. Thus the activity of nitrate reductase in natural populations has been used by a number of workers to indicate the relative importance of nitrate nitrogen under various environmental conditions (43, 44, 145).

The mechanism for the regulation of nitrate assimilation by ammonium is not yet clear. Synthesis of nitrate reductase is induced by nitrate when added to N-limited populations (125, 143, 180). Similarly, nitrite appears to be an inducer of nitrite reductase (143). Assimilation and uptake of both nitrate and nitrite is inhibited rapidly by ammonium at relatively low (0.5 μM) concentrations. Ammonium has no similar inhibitory effects on the nitrate reductase system in vitro (180), and is thought to control the process by repressing enzyme synthesis. However, the rate of disappearance of the enzymes in the reductive sequence is too slow to explain the rapid decrease in nitrate uptake when ammonium is added (138, 198). This rapid inhibition by ammonium is unexplained at present, but it may be due to inhibition of active transport enzymes of the type discovered by Falkowski (51).

Uptake By Populations

Ammonium is the most energetically favorable source of inorganic nitrogen because of its reduced state, and both laboratory and field studies demonstrate that ammonium is taken up in preference to nitrate and nitrite when all forms are present (43, 47, 134, 190). The rate of uptake of all combined nitrogen forms is concentration dependent at limiting concentrations and can be described by the hyperbolic Michaelis-Menton expression. Half saturation concentrations for uptake have been determined for a number of species (23–25, 47, 128; see 119 for listing) and are generally in the range of 10^{-6} to 10^{-7} M for pelagic phytoplankton. Species (47, 128) and even clones (27) which are commonly found in eutrophic regions show consistently higher half saturation constants than species or clones isolated from oligotrophic waters. Blue-green algae appear to have some of the highest half saturation values. Under nitrogen limiting conditions, species with low uptake (half saturation) constants hold a competitive advantage over species having higher uptake constants, which can be used to explain species distribution in relation to nitrogen availability (47, 128).

The importance of urea as a nitrogen source has recently been substantiated. McCarthy (133) noted that urea-N accounted for 28% of the total N assimilation off a southern California coastal region. Eppley (45) and co-workers found that urea-N was assimilated in greater amounts than ammonium and nitrate in the central North Pacific Ocean. These and similar findings (177) stress the importance of nitrogenous compounds (predominately ammonium and urea), excreted by animals, for maintaining productivity especially under stratified conditions where the supply of nitrate in deeper waters in unavailable (70). High nitrogen turnover rates measured in planktonic communities substantiate this idea (45, 133, 177).

Free amino acids can be a significant although generally minor source of nitrogen under most natural conditions (142, 166, 168, 187, 213). North (142), using a very sensitive fluoresamine technique, measured the uptake of natural concentrations of primary amino compounds by *Platymonas.* It occurred at rates which could support growth. Greater information on the occurrence, generation rates, and uptake rates of amino-nitrogen must be accumulated before the overall importance of these sources can be determined. Bacterial uptake of the organic nitrogen compounds severely complicates field studies of organic nitrogen (65, 204). Gardner & Lee (65) reported that bacterial utilization in a eutrophic lake controlled the concentration of dissolved free amino acids and generally kept concentrations below 0.01 μM. Increases of dissolved amino acids accompanied degradation of *Aphanizomenon* blooms.

Many studies have shown that nitrogen uptake is related to light intensity in a hyperbolic fashion, saturating at high light intensities (42, 46, 68, 128, 145). Diel periodicities in nitrate uptake in natural populations show maxima in the first 6 hr of daylight and minima near midnight (128, 130). Since neither membrane transport nor reduction of oxidized nitrogen compounds require light per se (137), the dependency must be an indirect one. Production of reducing cofactors via photosynthesis for nitrate and nitrite reduction steps and ATP derived from either cyclic or noncyclic phosphorylation for uptake processes (8, 51) could account for the observations. Secondarily, the supply of carbon skeletons (α-keto-glutarate) for amination steps might be partially limiting under low light conditions (77, 78, 197).

Growth

Under optimal conditions, there is a prescribed amount of nitrogen required for cell growth and division, depending on species.

Assuming overall nitrogen limitation, rates of uptake and growth in cell number should be equivalent, as has been found in field studies (37, 199–201). When nitrate is present in larger amounts, "luxury consumption" or uptake in excess of the requirements for growth (i.e. uptake rates > assimilation rates) can occur, resulting in internal pools of unreduced nitrate (23–25, 48). These effects are reflected in the recent chemostat-batch culture studies of ammonium and nitrate uptake by Bienfang (13).

Dunaliella tertiolecta was grown using various combinations of the two compounds. The uptake rate of ammonium was sufficient to maintain concentrations below the threshold for suppression of nitrate assimilation ($<$ 0.6 μM) resulting in simultaneous uptake of both compounds. The total nitrogen per cell was higher when cells were presented with both compounds than when grown on ammonium alone. Upon removal from steady state to batch culture conditions, the subsequent growth was directly related to the nitrogen per cell (or yield coefficient). These findings reinforce the concept that ammonium resulting from reduction of nitrite and direct uptake enters a common small and active assimilation pool, and that rates of nitrogen assimilation, not uptake, determine maximum growth rates in terms of nitrogen (134). Nitrogen yield coefficients for several algae have been compiled by Lehman et al (119). Minimum yield coefficients are on the order of 0.05 pg-at N per cell, which represents a minimum cell nitrogen level. Bienfang (13) observed steady state yield coefficients on the order of 0.24 pg-at N per cell when cells were grown on both nitrate and ammonium, which was sufficient for one or two subsequent divisions.

Nitrogen Fixation

Fixation of molecular nitrogen by the blue-green alga *Oscillatoria* has been demonstrated in the tropical Atlantic (22, 26, 38, 39, 69), Red Sea (38), and in the Pacific (129). Recently the work of Carpenter & McCarthy (28) has permitted an evaluation of the importance of N_2 fixation by *Oscillatoria thiebautii* in the western Sargasso Sea. Using ^{15}N-labeled substrates of high specific activity, they were able to demonstrate that *O. thiebautti* derived the bulk of its nitrogen requirement from N_2 fixation, and report that the alga is unable to effectively utilize ammonium, nitrate, and urea nitrogen at concentrations normally found in those waters. With respect to nitrogen, doubling times based on measured N_2 fixation rates were nearly an order of magnitude greater than those based on measured ammonium uptake, and 20 times greater than for rates based on measured nitrate and urea uptake. Previous reports (69) that N_2 fixation was relatively unimportant compared to ammonium and nitrate utilization in *Oscillatoria* were based on rates measured with artificially high substrate concentrations from added ^{15}N-labeled material.

Oscillatoria is among the few N_2-fixing blue-greens which lack heterocysts (60, 188). In typical blue-greens these structures are thought to maintain a reducing environment necessary for the activity of nitrogenase, apart from sites of active photosynthesis. The mechanics of maintaining reducing areas in colonies of *Oscillatoria* and the site of N_2 fixation remains an open question (see 195).

With regard to the total nitrogen budget of the Sargasso Sea, N_2 fixation by *Oscillatoria* accounts for less than 10^{-3} of the nitrogen utilized in primary production. Deep water mixing and in situ remineralization and recycling were apparently the major sources of combined nitrogen (28). Similar conclusions were reached for the Pacific (129). N_2 fixation may be relatively more important to the total nitrogen budget in Caribbean waters, and there is substantial documentation of its greater role in brackish (101) and freshwater habitats at times (see 60). For example, Vanderhoef et al (204) found that N_2 fixation by *Aphanizomenon* in a bay bordering . a large lake accounted for a major fraction of the newly combined nitrogen used in primary production at certain times. *Aphanizomenon* increased in abundance after growth by other species had depleted the combined nitrogenous nutrient levels.

CARBON

The Carbonate System

The possibility that natural populations are limited in their photosynthesis and growth by carbon has a sound theoretical basis. It has been shown that the carbon compound that binds to ribulose diphosphate carboxylase is CO_2 and not bicarbonate (31) and that the minimum K_m value is 11–18 μM (4). The concentration of molecular CO_2 in solution in water, regulated by its solubility and atmospheric partial pressure, is about 12 μM (variable with temperature and ionic strength). Thus, if CO_2 alone were the only usable carbon form, then its concentration in water at equilibrium with air is insufficient for maximum photosynthesis. In most waters, bicarbonate is present also, and in concentrations considerably greater than CO_2. In the surface water of the sea, where the bicarbonate system has been studied extensively (21, 79, 127, 155), the concentrations of the three major forms of carbon are set by the partial pressure of CO_2 in the atmosphere and the supersaturated solution of $CaCO_3$ (160). When the whole system is at equilibrium, at pH approximately 8.2, the equilibrium constants allow the determination of bicarbonate and carbonate (93, 146, 182). When any other pH value is found, which happens quite often, then the system is not at equilibrium with the atmosphere. This situation can occur because of two slow steps: the dehydration of bicarbonate (67, 105) and the diffusion of CO_2 across the diffusion barrier at the water surface (15, 50). This barrier, whose thickness is determined by the degree of turbulence (102), can prevent rapid equilibration of CO_2 with air. Thus CO_2 in molecular solution may be partially and temporarily out of equilibrium with the rest of the carbonate system. Its concentration can be considerably higher or lower than that predicted by the equilibrium constants (103, 104, 193). A large and rapid addition of CO_2 resulting from respiration will temporarily increase the CO_2 partial pressure and lower the pH, but the bicarbonate and carbonate concentrations might be changed only partially and unpredictably before equilibrium is reestablished. Similarly, removal of CO_2 by photosynthesis will have the opposite effect.

In brackish water where the total carbon is lowered by dilution with fresh water, the molecular CO_2 concentration will be approximately same as in the sea. The system is not stabilized by a large reservoir of $CaCO_3$, but the same nonequilibrium condition can exist. In fresh ("soft") water, where the total carbon is low, wide fluctuations in CO_2 concentration and pH can occur in unstirred waters. As pointed out by Park (146), the best indication of the state of the bicarbonate system is given by a measure of the pH, the CO_2 partial pressure, and the carbonate alkalinity.

The CO_2 partial pressure has been used to estimate productivity in some coastal regions (196). CO_2 partial pressures have been measured in many ocean regions and compared to theoretical values (193). The values indicated that CO_2 was taken up by photosynthetic activity which lowered its partial pressure in the water. The supply of CO_2 from bicarbonate, from the atmosphere, and from respiration did not keep pace with utilization. Alternatively, bicarbonate was taken up by photosynthetic activity and was replaced by hydroxyl ions which raised the pH and displaced the carbonate system toward bicarbonate more rapidly than CO_2 could enter from the atmosphere.

To explain the relation of phytoplankton distribution to carbon availability in a particular body of water, the following questions need answers: (*a*) Do phytoplankton use only CO_2 or can they use both CO_2 and bicarbonate? (*b*) If they use only CO_2, can the concentration of CO_2 be maintained at a sufficient level to support the observed photosynthesis? (*c*) If a species can adapt to bicarbonate, does the rate of adaptation play a role in distribution and succession?

CO_2 Uptake vs Bicarbonate Uptake

Several attempts have been made to determine whether a species under specified conditions is taking up CO_2 or bicarbonate. It has been noted that at the present time there is no unequivocal way of distinguishing between the two reactions (74, 158). An indirect method used by Hood & Park (94) consisted of measuring bicarbonate uptake in a medium in which CO_2 was purged with N_2. The method was criticized by Watt & Paasche (211), who claimed that during the purging, the formation of CO_2 from bicarbonate was too rapid to allow a distinction between uptake of the two compounds. Those algae which can live in acid media, such as some species of *Chlorella,* can be shown to take up CO_2 directly (157, 185). In these cases the relation of the concentration of CO_2 to the rate of CO_2 uptake can be precisely defined, but natural waters are rarely acid except in special cases such as bogs (29). Raven (157), using *Hydrodictyon,* measured CO_2 uptake rate versus CO_2 concentration at pH 5.7 and 7.3. In both cases the rate was the same at low CO_2 concentrations, indicating that pH within this range per se did not influence the rate. With the same organism, bicarbonate uptake was measured at pH 9.8. Both the limiting concentration rate and the maximum rate were considerably less than the uptake rate of CO_2. Even so, Raven noted that at this pH, with the extremely low CO_2 concentration, if the plant *were* taking up CO_2, then the uptake would have to be 100 times more efficient in order for the observed rate of carbon fixation to be obtained. The data suggested that the plant used CO_2 at low pH and bicarbonate at high pH, but at a lower rate. Steemann Nielsen & Jensen (185) showed that for *Chlorella* CO_2 uptake vs CO_2 concentration gave the same results whether the CO_2 concentration was determined by infrared analysis or by calculation from pH, indicating that moderate pH changes had no direct effect on photosynthesis rate, which is in agreement with Raven (157).

King (109), assuming that algae of highly eutrophic waters could not utilize bicarbonate, stated that in the high light of midday when the pH was high (9.5), algal photosynthesis was limited by the transfer rate of CO_2 from the atmosphere. The high chemical demand for CO_2 took precedence over algal demand. Oxygen production at midday was low, indicating a poor photosynthetic rate, even though the total carbon available remained high enough. He suggested that algal species succession was determined by the ability of species to tolerate low CO_2 levels. Blue-green algae would be characteristic of this type and would become predominant in sewage lagoons. In the specific case of a blue-green dominated lagoon, a high wind (presumably increasing the CO_2 transfer at the surface) lowered the pH, increased the alkalinity, and allowed the green alga *Chlamydomonas,* to replace the blue-greens. Shapiro (176) suggested that blue-greens become predominant in fertilized lakes because of their superior ability to scavenge CO_2 when it is at low concentration.

Lange (116, 117) found that the growth rate of blue-green algae, with bacteria present and in a CO_2-limited situation, could be increased by addition of organic compounds, mostly sugars. These compounds enhanced bacterial respiration, raising the CO_2 concentration in the medium. The bacteria were in intimate association with the algal cells. Axenic cultures were not stimulated by organic additions, and the effect of enhanced bacterial respiration could be duplicated by a direct supply of CO_2. Schulze (174) reported that when all organic matter was removed from waste water, the effluent would not support blue-greens. He concluded, in agreement with Lange, that CO_2 had become limiting because of the low rate of bacterial respiration. Koentzel (110) has found that in stagnant lakes there is an intimate mixture of algae and bacteria which supports massive algal growth. Bacilli were found in the gelatinous coats of blue-greens.

Although the above studies tend to show that CO_2 can be the limiting factor in some situations, Goldman and colleagues (72, 73) have maintained that growth of phytoplankton can be limited by total carbon but not by CO_2 alone (see also 100). His chemostat study of *Scenedesmus* and *Selenastrum* demonstrated that growth rate vs total carbon in a buffered feeding solution could be fitted to a Monod equation. The scatter in the data made determination of K_s values uncertain, but they were certainly much lower than the concentrations of total carbon usually present in natural waters. The dehydration of bicarbonate was not the limiting step in this study.

King's (109) study of CO_2-limited growth in eutrophic waters was partially disputed by Schindler et al (171), who studied the rate of invasion of CO_2 into a lake by measuring the evasion of ^{222}Rn. The lake was shielded from the wind, had no inlets or outlets during the summer, had very low total carbon content, and had been fertilized with phosphate and nitrate. They concluded that CO_2 from the atmosphere was sufficient for an algal bloom of 50–100 μg chl *a* per liter. The partial pressure of CO_2 during the summer bloom was 10^4 times lower than air equilibrium. The authors concluded that the CO_2 which entered the water from the atmosphere was available to the algae; chemical demand did not take precedence even though the pH was 9.5 to 10.2.

Carbonic Anhydrase

As mentioned previously, one of the steps which might limit the utilization of available carbon by phytoplankton is the relatively slow dehydration of bicarbonate. Carbonic anhydrase (CA) which greatly increases the rate of this reaction is widespread in planktonic algae but is apparently not always present or not always active enough for the plankton to make use of bicarbonate. Ward & Robb (209; see also 41, 95, 124, 156) have described the action of CA on CO_2 transport across an artificially prepared membrane. The diffusion of CO_2 could be increased sixfold by addition of CA.

There is no direct evidence for CA excretion by algae into natural waters, but Berger & Libby (10) measured the rate of CO_2 equilibration with the atmosphere by samples of sea water and found it to be variable with the origin of the sample. The addition of CA enhanced the rate of equilibration of surface waters twentyfold, but deep water samples had this elevated rate without CA addition, implying the presence of CA or some other catalyst.

Those algae which live in environments which are buffered by bicarbonate such as the sea or "hard" water lakes would be expected to have CA activity located at or near the outer cell membrane and would thus be able to utilize bicarbonate. CA activity has been found in marine macroalgae and microalgae (17, 122).

Early studies (19) showed that time and light were required for algae to adapt to low CO_2 or high bicarbonate. The adaptation time varied with the organism, e.g. 90 min for *Chlamydomonas,* 180 min for *Coelastrum* (75, 76). *Chlorella* adaptation time depended on the species (186), and some *Chlorellas* did not adapt at all (53–56). It is not clear in some of these studies what the bicarbonate concentration was in the experimental medium at high pH. When bicarbonate is high, adaptation to low CO_2 is correlated with an increase in CA activity, but when both bicarbonate and CO_2 are low, then adaptation means an increased ability to scavenge CO_2.

Moss (139) classified a large number of freshwater oligotrophic and eutrophic species on the basis of the range of pH in which they would grow in culture. The response to pH was interpreted as a response to availability of bicarbonate and CO_2. Most oligotrophic species would not grow above 8.85, indicating that these species either could not use bicarbonate or that they had a limited ability to take up CO_2 when its concentration was low.

If CA is to be used for facilitation of CO_2 transport, then it must be located at or in the outer cell membrane. Everson & Slack (49) showed that in higher plants with the C_3 pathway for carbon fixation, CA is located in the chloroplasts. If algae, which apparently all have the C_3 pathway, have CA in their chloroplasts, then these organelles must be located close to the cell outer membrane, a fact established for most algae (36).

Those cells which are fully adapted to high bicarbonate have CA levels 10 to 20 times that of the unadapted cells (57, 141). Findenegg (57) found that Cl^- uptake and bicarbonate uptake had similar characteristics, suggesting that the same mechanism was used for both ions. Raven (157), who had determined the Cl^- pumping rate in *Hydrodictyon,* calculated that it was 10^4 times too slow to account for the known rate of bicarbonate utilization in photosynthesis.

In future investigations, it should be made clear what is meant by "low CO_2". If a medium is buffered with bicarbonate, then low CO_2 means high pH, high bicarbonate, and high total carbon, but if little or no bicarbonate is present, then low CO_2 means moderately low pH and low total carbon. This distinction has not always been made in many of the investigations of the effect of CO_2 and bicarbonate. With this clarification in mind, it would be instructive to examine further several key species of bloom formers, especially blue-greens, for their ability to increase their CA activity and to see if the rate of increase in CA corresponds to the rate of change in availability of CO_2 and bicarbonate.

LIGHT

Of all the parameters which govern production in aquatic environments, light intensity and quality exhibit the greatest range of temporal and spatial variation. Seasonal, latitudinal, and especially diel variations in overall intensity are very pronounced. Light is attenuated exponentially with depth, limiting photosynthesis to the upper 200 meters in the most pristine waters. The magnitude and spectral dependence of the attenuation process is determined by the concentration and nature of all components of the hydrosol.

Since phytoplankton are an integral part of the system, the spectral attenuation is strongly influenced by their abundance, pigments, and distribution, and indirectly by the processes controlling their population. There are several recent reviews of the role of light in primary production (132, 183, 215; see also 71, 145). The physical and limiting biological aspects of light in the marine environment are discussed extensively in a recent symposium volume (99).

Phytoplankton can be considered as isotropic absorbers of light, with characteristic absorption spectra, and function as nonlinear integrators over time. In order to specify the light dependency on a cellular level, the cell's rate of photon absorption as well as the cell's response must be determined. In ideal systems this is derived from a knowledge of the incident spectral irradiance, the concentration and specific absorption coefficients of the absorber, and the optical path length. As discussed by Westlake (212), the use of specific absorption coefficients in field studies is limited because of the diffuse nature of the light field and lack of knowledge of the path length. In the majority of phytoplankton work, the light regime is specified in terms of percent surface irradiance and diffuse attenuation coefficients, covering broad spectral regions, which are written as a function of depth or geometrical distance. Only recently have sufficient measurements of spectral irradiance been performed to allow for rigorous treatment of the effected light quality on photosynthesis under natural conditions (136, 181, 203).

Mathematical Treatments

The interactions of phytoplankton and the light environment with respect to intensity are very apparent in recent mathematical descriptions of the intensity and depth dependencies of primary production (5, 6, 52, 150, 194, 205). The one developed by Bannister (5) is particularly attractive, since it is based on the maximum quantum yield of photosynthesis at low light intensities, whereas previous approaches began with maximum relative rates at saturating light levels and were of a more empirical nature. The model (6) incorporates diel variations in intensity, and emphasizes the interrelationship between the depth of mixing and the fractional absorbance of the phytoplankton (that fraction of light absorbance which is due to active photosynthetic pigments). The model predicts a direct relation between maximum production on an areal basis and the fractional absorbance. The use of a single extinction (attenuation) coefficient for chlorophyll was questioned by Riley (165; see 7 for reply) on the basis that light attenuation by nonphytoplankton material also appears to be related to the chlorophyll concentration. Part of this discrepancy may be due to the use of attenuation coefficients to describe light absorption processes.

The potential number of photons absorbed per unit time depends on (a) the sum of products of the concentration and specific absorption coefficient for each of the components of the system multiplied by (b) the optical path length. Attenuation coefficients cannot be partitioned in the manner of an absorption coefficient without regard for the effects of scattering implicit in them. Since phytoplankton can account for a large portion of the scattering material in marine systems, the optical path length will increase as their concentration increases. This serves to increase the absorption of light both by chlorophyll as well as by other material, including water, as a function of cell concentration.

Long-Term Adaptive Processes

Bannister's presentation of production equations represents a significant advance over previous ones because of its strong theoretical basis. Its general nature however, precludes an adequate consideration of spectral effects and time-dependent adaptive processes. In situations where strong density gradients lead to stratification, or where deep eutrophic zones exist, populations at various depths have sufficient time to adapt to given light regimes. This leads to the development of sun populations, in which photosynthesis saturates at high light intensities, and shade populations which saturate at lower intensities (183, 184, 215, 216). As discussed by Kowallik (111), changes in the spectral quality of incident light can have a profound effect on the related metabolic processes. The major process operating here is the exit point of fixed carbon from the Calvin-Bassham cycle, leading to a relative increase in the production of proteins under blue light and carbohydrates in red light. Wallen & Geen (206–208) studied the composition of *Cyclotella nana* and *Dunaliella terti-olecta* (207) and natural populations of phytoplankton (208) in relation to light intensity and spectral quality. The rate of photosynthesis, total and relative pigment concentrations and protein/carbohydrate ratios were dependent on the quality of light in the laboratory study. The relative composition of recently assimilated carbon in natural populations varied as a function of the depth and therefore spectral quality of illumination. In addition it was noted that release of cellular carbohydrate (usually glycollate) was much reduced at depth, where the preponderance of shorter wavelength light favored protein synthesis. Halldal (80, 81) has recently reviewed certain aspects of adaptive processes relating to pigment systems in the algae. Time scales for these changes are thought to be relatively long (i.e. one or two doubling times) since synthesis of new components are required.

Short-Term Effects

As the result of vertical mixing in shallow mixed layers or total depth, phytoplankton can experience changes in light intensity ranging over several orders of magnitude in fairly short times (minutes to a few hours). Harris & Lott (83) have investigated rates of photosynthesis (O_2 evolution) in several cultures of lake plankton in response to increasing and decreasing intensity regimes. Two time scales were used to mimic (a) wind induced mixing-related intensity changes (2 hr cycles), and (b) diel changes (8 hr cycles). A hysteresis effect was observed in most instances, with the rate of photosynthesis higher on the rising portion of the cycle. A major fault with this study was the use of a rheostat-controlled incandescent lamp to produce the intensity regimes. This undoubtedly resulted in a systematic spectral change as well. Harris (82) demonstrated a seasonality in the hysteresis effect for natural populations. He found it to be maximal during the summer or on bright days. These authors attribute their findings to an increase in the rates of photorespiration and note that the classic light-dark bottle incubations at fixed depths (intensities) may not reflect production in the system under conditions favoring rapid vertical mixing.

Evidence that light-mediated changes in chloroplast structure (135, 140, 144) and arrangement (20, 87, 192) alter the apparent absorption coefficient of chlorophyll a in vivo has been reported in studies of light effects on in vivo chlorophyll fluorescence of natural populations (107, 108, 123). Chloroplasts of several algae contract under high light intensity and expand under low light over short time periods (minutes). Self-shading of chlorophyll within chloroplasts is maximal in the contracted positions, resulting in less absorption per unit pigment per incident intensity at high light intensity. The implication of these responses in primary productivity studies is unclear, but they may contribute to variations in extinction values for chlorophyll and carbon assimilation/chlorophyll ratios.

CONCLUSIONS

It has become evident that phytoplankton are subjected to a continuously changing environment and must therefore be able to adapt to short-term, e.g. diel, changes as well as changes that are seasonal or longer. Since species composition is usually not constant, some algae are not able to adapt. The dynamic aspect, especially the lack of equilibrium, in the relation of the algae to their environment was brought out in the classic paper by Hutchinson (97). Since then, others (12, 13) have discussed this aspect of phytoplankton. To make further progress in the field, methods must be developed for simple, precise, short-term determinations of both the algal response and the environmental factor without perturbing the dynamics of the system. Rate rather than concentration determinations should be made over periods of time and space. Some progress has been made in this direction, but further progress awaits the development of more simple, precise, and continuous methods.

Literature Cited

1. Abbott, W. 1967. *J. Water Pollut. Control Fed.* 39:113–22
2. Abbott, W. 1969. *Proc. 4th Int. Conf. Int. Assoc. Water Pollut. Res.* 729–38
3. Aitchison, P. A., Butt, V. S. 1973. *J. Exp. Bot.* 24:497–510
4. Bahr, J. T., Jensen, R. G. 1974. *Plant Physiol.* 53:39–44
5. Bannister, T. T. 1974. *Limnol. Oceanogr.* 19:1–12
6. Ibid, 13–20
7. Ibid 1975. 20:152–53
8. Bassham, J. A., Kirk, M. 1964. *Biochim. Biophys. Acta* 90:553–62
9. Batterton, J. C., van Baalen, C. 1968. *Can. J. Microbiol.* 14:341–48
10. Berger, R., Libby, W. F. 1969. *Science* 164:1395–97
11. Bérman, T. 1970. *Limnol. Oceanogr.* 15:663–74
12. Berman, T., Eppley, R. W. 1974. *Sci. Progr. Oxford* 61:219–39
13. Bienfang, P. K. 1975. *Limnol. Oceanogr.* 20:402–11
14. Blum, J. J. 1966. *J. Gen. Physiol.* 49:1125–37
15. Bolin, B. 1960. *Tellus* 12:274–81
16. Bone, D. H. 1971. *Arch. Microbiol.* 80:147–53
17. Bowes, G. W. 1969. *Plant Physiol.* 44:726–32
18. Bray, J. T., Bricker, O. P., Troup, B. N. 1973. *Science* 180:1362–64
19. Briggs, G. E., Whittingham, C. P. 1952. *New Phytol.* 51:236–49
20. Brown, T. E., Richardson, F. L. 1968. *J. Phycol.* 4:38–54
21. Buch, K. 1951. *Havforkn. Inst. Skr. Helsinf.* No. 151
22. Bunt, J. S., Cooksey, K. E., Heeb, M. A., Lee, C. C., Taylor, B. F. 1970. *Nature* 227:1163–64
23. Caperon, J. 1968. *Ecology* 49:866–72
24. Caperon, J., Meyer, J. 1972. *Deep-Sea Res.* 19:601–18
25. Ibid, 619–32
26. Carpenter, E. J. *Deep-Sea Res.* 20:285–88
27. Carpenter, E. J., Guillard, R. R. L. 1971. *Ecology* 52:183–89
28. Carpenter, E. J., McCarthy, J. J. 1975. *Limnol. Oceanogr.* 20:389–401
29. Cassin, P. E. 1974. *J. Phycol.* 10:439–47
30. Chiou, Charng-Jyi, Boyd, C. E. 1974. *Hydrobiologia* 45:345–55
31. Cooper, T. G., Filmer, D., Wishnick, M., Lane, M. D. 1969. *J. Biol. Chem.* 244:1081–83

32. Corner, E. D. S., Davies, A. G. 1971. *Adv. Mar. Biol.* 9:101–204
33. Costlow, J. D. 1971. *Fertility of the Sea.* New York: Gordon & Breach. 622 pp.
34. Dharmawardene, M. W. N., Haystead, A., Stewart, W. D. P. 1973. *Arch. Mikrobiol.* 90:281–95
35. Dillon, F. J. 1975. *Limnol. Oceanogr.* 20:28–39
36. Dodge, J. D. F. 1973. *The Fine Structure of Algal Cells.* New York: Academic. 261 pp.
37. Dugdale, R. C., Goering, J. J. 1967. *Limnol. Oceanogr.* 12:196–206
38. Dugdale, R. C., Goering, J. J., Ryther, J. H. 1964. *Limnol. Oceanogr.* 9:507–10
39. Dugdale, R. C., Menzel, D. W., Ryther, J. H. 1961. *Deep-Sea Res.* 7:298–300
40. Edmondson, W. T. 1970. *Science* 169:690–91
41. Enns, T. 1967. *Science* 155:44–47
42. Eppley, R. W., Coatsworth, J. L. 1968. *J. Phycol.* 4:151–56
43. Eppley, R. W., Coatsworth, J. L., Solórzano, L. 1969. *Limnol. Oceanogr.* 14:194–205
44. Eppley, R. W., Packard, T. T., MacIsaac, J. J. 1970. *Mar. Biol.* 6:195–99
45. Eppley, R. W., Renger, E. H., Venrick, E. L., Mullin, M. M. 1973. *Limnol. Oceanogr.* 18:534–51
46. Eppley, R. W., Rogers, J. N. 1970. *J. Phycol.* 6:344–51
47. Eppley, R. W., Rogers, J. N., McCarthy, J. J. 1969. *Limnol. Oceanogr.* 14:912–20
48. Eppley, R. W., Strickland, J. D. H. 1968. In *Advances in Microbiology of the Sea*, ed. M. R. Droop, E. J. F. Wood, 23–62. London: Academic. 246 pp.
49. Everson, R. G., Slack, C. R. 1968. *Phytochemistry* 7:581–84
50. Ewing, G., McAllister, E. D. 1960. *Science* 131:1374–76
51. Falkowski, P. G. 1975. *Limnol. Oceanogr.* 20:412–17
52. Fee, E. J. 1969. *Limnol. Oceanogr.* 14:906–11
53. Felfoldy, L. J. M. 1960. *Acta Biol. Acad. Sci. Hung.* 11:67–75
54. Ibid, 175–85
55. Ibid 1962. 113:207–14
56. Ibid 1965. 15:351–59
57. Findenegg, G. R. 1974. *Planta* 116:123–31
58. Fitzgerald, G. P., Nelson, T. C. 1966. *J. Phycol.* 2:32–37
59. Fogg, G. E. 1965. *Algal Cultures and*

Phytoplankton Ecology. Madison: Univ. Wisconsin. 126 pp.
60. Fogg, G. E . 1974. See Ref. 189, 560–82
61. Fuhs, G. W. 1969. *J. Phycol.* 5:312–21
62. Fuhs, G. W., Canelli, E. 1970. *Limnol. Oceanogr.* 15:962–67
63. Fuhs, G. W., Demmerle, S. D., Canelli, E., Chen, M. 1972. See Ref. 120, 113–32
64. Galloway, R. A., Krauss, R. W. 1963. In *Studies in Microalgae and Photosynthetic Bacteria,* ed. Jap. Soc. Plant Physiol., 569–75. Univ. Tokyo Press
65. Gardner, W. S., Lee, G. F. 1975. *Limnol. Oceanogr.* 20:379–88
66. Gavis, J., Ferguson, J. F. 1975. *Limnol. Oceanogr.* 20:211–21
67. Gibbons, B. H., Edsall, J. T. 1963. *J. Biol. Chem.* 238:3502–7
68. Goering, J. J., Dugdale, R. C., Menzel, D. W. 1964. *Limnol. Oceanogr.* 9: 448–51
69. Ibid 1966. 11:614–20
70. Goering, J. J., Wallen, D. D., Nauman, R. M. 1970. *Limnol. Oceanogr.* 15: 789–96
71. Goldman, C. R., Ed. 1969. *Primary Productivity in Aquatic Environments.* Mem. Inst. Ital. Idrobiol. 18 Suppl. Berkeley: Univ. California Press. 464 pp.
72. Goldman, J. C. 1973. *Science* 182: 306–7
73. Goldman, J. C., Oswald, W. J., Jenkins, D. 1974. *J. Water Pollut. Control Fed.* 46:554–73
74. Goldman, J. C., Porcella, D. B., Middlebrooks, E. J., Toerien, D. F. 1972. *Water Res.* 6:637–79
75. Graham, D., Atkins, C. A., Reed, M. L., Patterson, B. D., Smillie, R. M. 1971. In *Photosynthesis* and *Photorespiration,* ed. M. D. Hatch, C. B. Osmund, R. O. Slatyer, 267–74. New York: Wiley-Interscience
76. Graham, D., Reed, M. L. 1971. *Nature New Biol.* 231:81–83
77. Grant, B. R. 1967. *J. Gen. Microbiol.* 48:379–89
78. Grant, B. R., Turner, I. M. 1969. *Comp. Biochem. Physiol.* 29:995–1004
79. Hannson, I. 1973. *Acta Chem. Scand.* 27:931–44
80. Halldal, P. 1970. *Photobiology of Microorganisms.* New York: Wiley-Interscience. 479 pp.
81. Halldal, P. 1974. See Ref. 99, 345–60
82. Harris, G. P. 1973. *J. Fish. Res. Bd. Can.* 30:1779–87
83. Harris, G. P., Lott, J. N. A. 1973. *J. Fish. Res. Bd. Can.* 30:1771–78
84. Harvey, H. W. 1969. *The Chemistry*

and Fertility of Sea Water. London: Cambridge Univ. Press. 240 pp.
85. Hattori, A., Myers, J. 1966. *Plant Physiol.* 41:1031–36
86. Hattori, A., Myers, J. 1967. *Plant Cell Physiol. Tokyo* 8:327–37
87. Haupt, W., Schönbohm, E. 1970. See Ref. 80, 283–307
88. Hayes, F. R., Phillips, J. E. 1858. *Limnol. Oceanogr.* 3:459–75
89. Healey, F. P. 1973. *CRC Crit. Rev. Microbiol.* 3:69–113
90. Healey, F. P. 1973. *J. Phycol.* 9:383–94
91. Holden, J., Morris, I. 1960. *Ark. Mikrobiol.* 74:58–68
92. Holm-Hansen, O., Brown, G. W. 1963. *Plant Cell Physiol.* 4:299–306
93. Hood, D. W. 1963. *Oceanogr. Mar. Biol. Ann. Rev.* 1:129–36
94. Hood, D. W., Park, K. 1963. *Physiol. Plant* 15:273–82
95. Hoover, T. E., Berkshire, D. C. 1969. *J. Geophys. Res.* 74:456–64
96. Hulbert, E. M. 1970. *Ecology.* 51: 475–84
97. Hutchinson, G. E. 1961. *Am. Nat.* 95:137–45
98. Jaworski, N. A., Lear, D. W. Jr., Villa, O. Jr. 1972. See Ref. 120, 246–73
99. Jerlov, N. G., Steemann Nielsen, E., Eds. 1974. *Optical Aspects of Oceanography.* New York: Academic. 494 pp.
100. Jolliffe, E. A., Tregunna, E. B. 1970. *Phycologia* 9:293–303
101. Jones, K., Stewart, W. D. P. 1969. *J. Mar. Biol. Assoc. U.K.* 49:701–16
102. Kanwisher, J. 1963. *Deep-Sea Res.* 10:195–217
103. Kelley, J. J., Hood, D. W. 1971. *J. Geophys. Res.* 76:745–52
104. Kelley, J. J., Longerich, L. L., Hood, D. W. 1971. *J. Geophys. Res.* 76:8687–93
105. Kern, A. M. 1960. *J. Chem. Educ.* 37:14–23
106. Kessler, E., Hofmann, A., Zumft, W. G. 1970. *Arch. Mikrobiol.* 72:23–26
107. Kiefer, D. 1973. *Mar. Biol.* 22:263–69
108. Ibid. 23:39–46
109. King, D. L. 1970. *J. Water Pollut. Control Fed.* 42:2035–51
110. Koentzel, L. E. 1969. *J. Water Pollut. Control Fed.* 41:1737–47
111. Kowallik, W. 1970. See Ref. 80, 333–79
112. Kretovich, W. L., Evstigneeva, Z. G., Tomova, N. G. 1970. *Can. J. Bot.* 48:1179–83
113. Kuenzler, E. J. 1970. *J. Phycol.* 6:7–13
114. Kuenzler, E. J., Ketchum, B. H. 1962. *Biol. Bull.* 123:134–45
115. Kuenzler, E. J., Perras, J. P. 1965. *Biol. Bull.* 128:271–84

116. Lange, W. 1967. *Nature* 215:2177–78
117. Lange, W. 1971. *Can. J. Microbiol.* 17:303–14
118. Lean, D. R. S. 1973. *Science* 179:678–80
119. Lehman, J. T., Botkin, D. B., Likens, G. E. 1975. *Limnol. Oceanogr.* 20:343–64
120. Likens, G. E., Ed. 1972. *Nutrients and Eutrophication: The Limiting Nutrient Controversy.* Am. Soc. Limnol. Oceanogr. Spec. Symp. I. Lawrence, Kans.: Allen Press. 328 pp.
121. Linko, P., Holm-Hansen, O., Bassham, J. A., Calvin, M. 1957. *J. Exp. Bot.* 8:147–56
122. Lichtfield, C. D., Hood, D. W. 1964. *Verh. int. Ver. Theor. Angew. Limnol.* 15:817–28
123. Loftus, M. E., Seliger, H. H. 1975. *Chesapeake Sci.* 16:79–92
124. Longmuir, I. S., Forster, R. E., Woo, C. Y. 1966. *Nature* 209:393–94
125. Losada, M. et al 1970. *Biochem. Biophys. Res. Commun.* 38:1009–15
126. Lund, J. W. G. 1965. *Biol. Rev.* 40:231–93
127. Lyman, J. 1961. *Limnol. Oceanogr.* 6:80–83
128. MacIssac, J. J., Dugdale, R. C. 1972. *Deep-Sea Res.* 19:209–32
129. Mague, T. H., Weare, N. M., Holm-Hansen, O. 1974. *Mar. Biol.* 24:109–19
130. Malone, T. C., Garside, C., Haines, K. C., Roels, O. A. 1975. *Limnol. Oceanogr.* 20:9–19
131. Mann, K. H. 1969. In *Advances in Ecological Research,* ed. J. B. Cragg, 1–81. New York: Academic
132. McAllister, C. D., Shah, N., Strickland, J. D. H. 1964. *J. Fish. Res. Bd. Can.* 21:159–81
133. McCarthy, J. J. 1972. *Limnol. Oceanogr.* 17:738–48
134. McCarthy, J. J., Eppley, R. W. 1972. *Limnol. Oceanogr.* 17:371–382
135. Mohanty, P., Govindjee 1973. *Biochim. Biophys. Acta.* 305:95–104
136. Morel, A., Smith, R. C. 1974. *Limnol. Oceanogr.* 19:591–600
137. Morris, I. 1974. See Ref. 189, 583–609
138. Morris, I., Syrett, P. J. 1965. *J. Gen. Microbiol.* 38:21–28
139. Moss, B. 1973. *J. Ecol.* 61:157–79
140. Murakami, S., Packer, L. 1970. *Plant Physiol.* 45:289–99
141. Nelson, E. B., Cenedella, A., Tolbert, N. E. 1969. *Phytochemistry* 8:2305–6
142. North, B. B. 1975. *Limnol. Oceanogr.* 20:20–27
143. Ohmori, K., Hattori, A. 1970. *Plant Cell Physiol.* 11:873–78
144. Packer, L., Nobel, P. S. 1965. *Plant Physiol.* 40:1080–85
145. Packard, T. T., Blasco, D. 1974. *Tethys* 6:269–80
146. Park, P. K. 1969. *Limnol. Oceanogr.* 14:179–86
147. Parsons, T. R., Takahashi, M. 1973. *Biological Oceanographic Processes.* New York: Pergamon. 186 pp.
148. Pasciak, W. J., Gavis, J. 1974. *Limnol. Oceanogr.* 19:881–88
149. Perry, M. J. 1972. *Mar. Biol.* 15:113–19
150. Platt, T. 1968. *Limnol. Oceanogr.* 14:653–59
151. Platt, T., Subba Rao, D. V. 1973. *Fish Res. Bd. Can.* Tech. Rep. 370. 89 pp.
152. Pomeroy, L. R. 1960. *Science* 131:1731–32
153. Pomeroy, L. R., Mathews, H. M., Min, H. S. 1963. *Limnol. Oceanogr.* 8:50–55
154. Pomeroy, L. R., Smith, E. E., Grant, C. M. 1965. *Limnol. Oceanogr.* 10:167–72
155. Pytkowicz, R. M. 1963. *Deep-Sea Res.* 10:633–38
156. Quinn, J. A., Otto, N. C. 1971. *J. Geophys. Res.* 76:1539–49
157. Raven, J. A. 1968. *J. Exp. Bot.* 19:193–206
158. Raven, J. A. 1970. *Biol. Rev.* 45:167–221
159. Reichardt, W., Overbeck, J., Steubing, L. 1967. *Nature* 216:1345–47
160. Revelle, R., Fairbridge, R. 1957. In *Treatise on Marine Ecology and Paleoecology,* ed. J. W. Hedgepeth, 239–95. Geol. Soc. Am. Mem. 67
161. Rhee, G. Y. 1972. *Limnol. Oceanogr.* 17:505–14
162. Rhee, G. Y. 1973. *J. Phycol.* 9:495–506
163. Ibid 1974. 19:470–75
164. Rigler, F. H. 1964. *Limnol. Oceanogr.* 9:511–18
165. Riley, G. P. 1975. *Limnol. Oceanogr.* 20:150–52
166. Riley, J. P., Segar, D. A. 1970. *J. Mar. Biol. Assoc. U.K.* 50:713–20
167. Ryther, J. H., Dunstan, W. 1971. *Science* 171:1008–13
168. Schell, D. M. 1974. *Limnol. Oceanogr.* 19:260–70
169. Schindler, D. W. 1971. *J. Phycol.* 7:321–29
170. Schindler, D. W., Armstrong, F. A. J., Holmgren, S. K., Brunskill, G. J. 1971. *J. Fish. Res. Bd. Can.* 28:1763–82
171. Schindler, D. W. et al 1972. *Science* 177:1192–94

172. Schindler, D. W., Holmgren, S. K. 1971. *J. Fish. Res. Bd. Can.* 28:189–201
173. Schindler, D. W., Nighswander, J. E. 1970. *J. Fish. Res. Bd. Can.* 27:2009–36
174. Schulze, K. L. 1966. *J. Water Pollut. Control Fed.* 38:1944–58
175. Shapiro, J. 1970. *J. Water Pollut. Control Fed.* 42:772–75
176. Shapiro, J. 1973. *Science* 179:382–84
177. Smayda, T. J. 1973. *Norw. J. Bot.* 20:219–47
178. Smayda, T. J. 1974. *Limnol. Oceanogr.* 19:889–901
179. Smith, F. A. 1966. *Biochim. Biophys. Acta* 126:94–99
180. Smith, F. W., Thompson, J. F. 1971. *Plant Physiol.* 48:299–313
181. Smith, R. C. 1968. *Limnol. Oceanogr.* 13:423–29
182. Spencer, C. P. 1965. *Oceanogr. Mar. Biol. Ann. Rev.* 3:31–57
183. Steemann Nielsen, E. 1974. See Ref. 99, 361–88
184. Steemann Nielsen, E., Hansen, V. K. 1959. *Physiol. Plant.* 12:353–70
185. Steemann Nielsen, E., Jensen, P. K. 1958. *Physiol. Plant.* 11:170–80
186. Steemann Nielsen, E., Willemoes, M. 1966. *Physiol. Plant.* 19:279–93
187. Stephens, G. C., North, B. B. 1971. *Limnol. Oceanogr.* 16:752–57
188. Stewart, W. D. P. 1973. In *The Biology of Blue-green Algae,* ed. N. Carr, B. A. Whitten, 260–78. Oxford: Blackwell. 686 pp.
189. Stewart, W. D. P., Ed. 1974. *Algal Physiology and Biochemistry.* Berkeley: Univ. California Press. 989 pp.
190. Strickland, J. D. H., Holm-Hansen, O., Eppley, R. W., Linn, R. J. 1969. *Limnol. Oceanogr.* 14:23–34
191. Strickland, J. D. H., Parsons, T. R. 1972. *Bull. Fish. Res. Bd. Can.* 167. 310 pp.
192. Swift, E., Taylor, W. R. 1967. *J. Phycol.* 3:77–81
193. Takahashi, T. 1961. *J. Geophys. Res.* 66:477–94
194. Talling, J. F. 1971. *Mitt. Int. Ver. Theor. Angew. Limnol.* 19:214–43
195. Taylor, B. F., Lee, C. C., Bunt, J. S. 1973. *Arch. Mikrobiol.* 88:205–12
196. Teal, J. M., Kanwisher, J. 1966. *J. Mar. Res.* 24:4–14
197. Thacker, A., Syrett, P. J. 1972. *New Phytol.* 71:423–34
198. Ibid, 435–41
199. Thomas, W. H. 1970. *Limnol. Oceanogr.* 15:380–85
200. Ibid, 386–94
201. Thomas, W. H., Owen, R. W. Jr. 1971. *Fish. Bull.* 69:87–92
202. Thomas, W. H., Dodson, A. N. 1968. *Biol. Bull.* 134:199–208
203. Tyler, J. E., Smith, R. C. 1970. *Measurements of Spectral Irradiance Underwater.* New York: Gordon & Breach. 103 pp.
204. Vanderhoef, L. N., Huang, C., Musil, R., Williams, J. 1975. *Limnol. Oceanogr.* 20:119–25
205. Vollenweider, R. A. 1965. See Ref. 71, 425–57
206. Wallen, D. G., Geen, G. H. 1971. *Mar. Biol.* 10:34–43
207. Ibid, 44–51
208. Ibid, 157–68
209. Ward, W. J., Robb, W. L. 1967. *Science* 156:1481–84
210. Watt, W. D., Hayes, F. R. 1963. *Limnol. Oceanogr.* 8:276–85
211. Watt, W. D., Paasche, E. 1963. *Physiol. Plant.* 16:674–81
212. Westlake, D. F. 1965. *Photochem. Photobiol.* 4:849–68
213. Wheeler, P. A., North, B. B., Stephens, G. C. 1974. *Limnol. Oceanogr.* 19: 249–59
214. Yentsch, C. M., Yentsch, C. S., Perras, J. 1972. *Limnol. Oceanogr.* 17:772–74
215. Yentsch, C. S. 1974. *Oceanogr. Mar. Biol. Ann. Rev.* 12:41–75
216. Yentsch, C. S., Lee, R. W. 1966. *J. Mar. Res.* 24:319–37
217. Zumft, W. G., Paneque, A., Aparicio, P. J., Losado, M. 1969. *Biochem. Biophys. Res. Commun.* 36:980–86

Ann. Rev. Plant Physiol. 1976. 27:485–505

OSMOREGULATION

❖7619

Johan A. Hellebust

Department of Botany, University of Toronto, Ontario M5S, 1A1 Canada

CONTENTS

INTRODUCTION

Osmoregulation in plants has not been reviewed earlier in this series, although several aspects of osmoregulation have been dealt with in numerous reviews on water relations and ion transport. Recent reviews on such related topics in this series are by Lüttge (135) on plant glands, Hsiao (90) on water stress, Anderson (6) on ion transport, Läuchli (128) on long-distance ion transport, and Raschke (173) on stomatal action. An excellent recent review and discussion of transport systems and osmoregulation in both higher and lower plants has been written by Cram (37).

The term osmoregulation, although commonly used by animal physiologists and microbiologists, is very seldom used by scientists concerned with water relations in higher plants. The most likely reason for this is the difficulty in conceiving of a plant either as an autonomous osmoregulating unit, in the sense of an animal, or as consisting of independently osmoregulating cells, in the sense of bacteria, yeasts, or unicellular algae. The plant is obviously osmoregulating due to the complex interactions of regulatory mechanisms at all levels of organization; organs, tissues, and cells, but since these interactions are so poorly understood the problem is nevertheless a real one.

This review will deal most extensively with osmoregulation in fungi and algae, since mechanisms at the cell level are best understood from work on the lower plants, and since much of this work has not been reviewed recently (37, 73, 76, 182). The much more complex problem of osmoregulation in higher plants will be discussed more briefly, both due to lack of detailed information and because many related aspects have been reviewed recently elsewhere. By osmoregulation is understood the processes and mechanisms by which plants regulate the osmotic pressure in their cells. In walled cells this also includes regulation of turgor pressure, while in naked cells volume control is involved. Osmoregulation must satisfy both the growth requirement for sufficient turgor pressure in most plant cells, as well as the physiological demands that the solutes used for osmoregulation do not interfere with the efficient operations of metabolic reactions. The nature of osmotic solutes and also their compartmentation in the cell are therefore important. Osmoregulation in cell organelles, such as chloroplasts and mitochondria, will not be dealt with here.

FUNGI

Many fungi tolerate media of very high external osmotic pressures, particularly species belonging to the genera *Aspergillus* and *Penicillium,* many of which can grow on agar media containing up to 30% sodium chloride, or in soil or other substrates at comparable relative humidities (26). In general, fungi respond to increased osmotic pressures of the external medium in a way similar to equivalent reductions in water activities in terms of relative humidities (175), except at very low water potentials where they appear to be less tolerant to matric as compared with osmotic water potential stress (1). This is possibly due to problems of solute transport in matric-controlled systems.

Osmophilic (sugar-tolerant) fungi appear to require low water potentials in their environment rather than high concentrations of solutes, and therefore differ fundamentally from halophilic bacteria which require high concentrations of specific salts to stabilize their membranes as well as for metabolic reasons (24, 125, 127). The ability to accumulate polyols in response to a decrease in water potential of the external medium (upshock[1]) is a key feature in the osmoregulation of sugar-tolerant yeasts (5, 23). While all of the sugar-tolerant strains tested by Anand & Brown (5, 22) contained one or more polyols as major intracellular components, polyols were not detected in nontolerant yeasts. Brown (22) points out that while the synthesis of polyols by yeasts and molds is well known (131, 156, 206), the high concentrations achieved and the significance of intracellular polyol accumulation in water relations of these microorganisms have not been recognized. It is noteworthy that even in osmophilic yeast cells grown in dilute basal media, the level of arabitol accounts for over 10% of the dry weight (22). Much more polyol is lost in washing cells grown at high solute concentrations than from those grown in basal media. The high total polyol concentrations produced per cell at high external solute concentrations reflect the extremely high internal polyol content under these conditions, the bulk of which

---

[1]For convenience, two terms commonly used by microbiologists referring to a sudden increase (upshock) or a sudden decrease (downshock) of osmotic pressures of the external medium will also be used here when discussing osmoregulation of fungi and algae.

is released in response to downshock. Fungal mycelia have also been reported to contain very high levels of different polyols (131), which are probably important in maintaining low internal water potentials under conditions of low external relative humidities. Polyols apparently can be accumulated as a compatible solute within the cells to maintain water potentials sufficiently low to create the positive turgor pressures needed for growth without causing large reductions in enzyme activities, as would be the case with similar concentrations of salts (23).

Several obligate osmophilic mutants of the yeast *Saccharomyces rouxii* have recently been isolated by Koh (120). None of the many osmophilic yeasts which have been previously isolated have shown an obligate requirement for high sugar or salt concentrations for growth, except for a few strains when grown at high temperatures (156). The obligate osmophilic mutants were unable to grow in media of low solute concentrations, which indicates either lesions in their ability to osmoregulate and/or requirements for low water activities or high solute concentrations inside the cells. A more detailed study of one of these mutants which failed to grow at osmotic pressures corresponding to 20% sucrose or less showed that it had a weak cell envelope due to altered chemical composition (119). It appears that the most important cause of obligate osmophilism of this mutant may be its inability to synthesize a wall capable of protecting the plasmamembrane in environments of low osmotic pressures where wild-type osmophilic yeast cells maintain very high turgor pressures (22). The mutant is lysed by extensive downshocks (119), while other osmophilic yeast strains only exhibit temporary losses of cellular solutes (22).

Many species belonging to the Phycomycetes, Ascomycetes, and Fungi Imperfecti are found in marine environments (97). While vegetative growth of these fungi can occur equally well in fresh water (98), their reproductive stages require sea water (97). Considerable evidence exists showing that a large proportion of terrestrial as well as marine fungi can tolerate concentrations of sodium chloride up to 2 M or higher (94, 222). Jennings (94) has recently discussed the mechanisms for salt tolerance by these fungi. Unless the sodium concentration is excessively high, and in the presence of potassium, the latter cation is rapidly taken up while sodium, and to a lesser extent chloride, is excluded (25, 146, 196). Much of the potassium taken up is exchanged for H^+ (192, 196) produced by the cell, and organic acids (28, 192) and phosphate groups (196) provide the main negative charges within the mycelia. Another significant aspect of the osmoregulation of these fungi is their ability to synthesize polyols such as arabitol or mannitol in response to increased salinities, and these polyols may contribute large fractions of their intracellular osmotic pressure (4, 94).

It has been shown for several marine fungi that their salinity tolerance is temperature-dependent, and that this phenomenon is primarily an osmotic one (176, 177). The requirement for increased osmotic pressure of the medium becomes most notable at the high end of the temperature tolerance range. It is, therefore, possible that high external osmotic pressures allow the fungi to maintain relatively high internal concentrations of ions accumulated from the medium, or of organic molecules produced metabolically, which may be required for the stability and efficient function of enzyme systems at supraoptimal temperatures (27).

The nonosmophilic yeast *Saccharomyces cerevicae* has a very active transport system for K^+ which it accumulates to create very high internal osmotic pressures in exchange for H^+ derived from metabolism, with K^+ being balanced by organic anions such as succinate, citrate, and acetate (161, 180, 182). The electrolyte level in the cells varies considerably depending on the supply of metabolizable substrate, pH, and concentrations of electrolytes in the medium (181, 182). The activity and specificity of the electrolyte transport systems vary considerably with the physiological state of the yeast cell (99, 182). In resting cells the sodium and potassium levels are about equal. Upon resumption of growth sodium decreases and potassium increases rapidly. Stationary-phase yeast cells resemble *Eschericia coli* in their loss of cation selectivity (180), but differ from the bacterial cells in that active transport systems and positive turgor is maintained (99). The importance of turgor pressure to fungal growth has been described by several workers (2, 160, 178, 179).

ALGAE

Algae are found in habitats of widely different water potentials (73), and have accordingly evolved osmoregulatory mechanisms to deal with environments which are either very saline (95, 123, 141, 223), very dry (134, 198), subject to rapidly fluctuating salinities (46, 47, 60), or of very low salt content (59, 73). Algal cells, furthermore, differ in their abilities to develop and sustain turgor pressure (73, 76), which may at least in part be related to different mechanical properties of their cell walls (72, 75, 76). One particularly interesting group of algal flagellates appears to lack cell walls entirely, such as *Dunaliella tertiolecta* (96) or *Ochromonas malhamensis* (21), or instead of a proper cell wall are covered by organic scales which are loosely held together by an organic matrix such as in *Platymonas* spp. (140) or *Pyramimonas parkeae* (153). These cells appear unable to withstand significant turgor pressures and behave as osmometers when subjected to media of varying osmotic pressures.

Naked Cells

The naked algal cells studied so far have all evolved mechanisms for osmoregulation involving the synthesis or degradation of osmotically active polyols or polyol derivatives. Craigie & McLachlan (32) first demonstrated the ability of an algal cell to adjust its polyol content in response to changes in external salinity. They showed that the euryhaline green flagellate *Dunaliella tertiolecta* diverts an increasing amount of its photoassimilated carbon into glycerol as the NaCl of the medium is raised. Stimulation of glycerol production by increasing NaCl concentration had earlier been reported by Onishi (157) for the halophilic yeast *Pichia miso*. The genus *Dunaliella* includes species found in waters ranging in salt content from nearly fresh water to brine lakes (130), and several of the species, including *D. tertiolecta* (143) and *D. parva* (95), are strongly euryhaline. The osmoregulatory mechanisms of the latter two species have recently been studied by several workers (10–14, 20, 96, 227). It has been clearly shown that all of these euryhaline flagellates adjust their glycerol content as a direct function of the external osmotic pressure, whether the latter is made up by salts or by nonpenetrating organic molecules (10–14, 20, 227). Ben-Amotz has further demonstrated that *D. parva*, being a wall-less cell, behaves as a perfect osmometer, shrinking when the external osmotic pressure is increased and swelling when it is decreased, due to rapid water fluxes. Metabolic adjustments of the level of glycerol, requiring about 90 min for completion, then cause the cell to return to its original volume. However, when *D. parva* (12, 14) or *D. tertiolecta* (96) are subjected to extensive downshocks, reversible, and in extreme cases irreversible, damage to the membrane takes place due to extensive stretching, and glycerol is lost to the media within 10 min. The cell is in this way normally protected against lysis by rapid loss of its high glycerol content, followed by resealing of the plasmalemma and adjustment to the new external osmotic pressure.

Earlier investigators studying *D. salina*, which is a halophile similar to *D. viridis*, concluded that the reversible cell volume changes of this flagellate were mediated by NaCl fluxes through a very permeable cell membrane, and that the cells contained high concentrations of NaCl (62, 141, 223). However, in light of the work by Ben-Amotz (12) on *D. parva*, and the finding that enzymes from *D. viridis* (20, 95) are strongly inactivated by NaCl concentrations approaching those of the external environment, these assumptions are probably incorrect. Recent work by Borowitzka & Brown (20) on *D. tertiolecta* and *D. viridis* indicates that these algae virtually exclude NaCl, while K^+ is taken up to produce low intracellular levels (0.2–0.4 M). The enzymes of these flagellates, which grow over very different salinity ranges, are inhibited in a similar manner by high salt concentrations. In contrast, high concentrations of glycerol do not inhibit the enzymes and may even somewhat reverse salt inhibitions (20). Since the tolerance of enzymes to salt is quite similar for all the *Dunaliella* species tested, the degree of tolerance to high salinities appears to be directly related to the maximum intracellular glycerol level that can be maintained by the species. Studies of enzymes involved in glycerol metabolism in *Dunaliella* species (10, 20) have not as yet revealed the mechanism by which the intracellular glycerol level is adjusted in response to changes in external osmotic pressures.

Kauss and co-workers (103–110, 172, 186) have shown that osmoregulation in the naked golden brown flagellate *Ochromonas malhamensis* is based mainly on changes in the intracellular concentration of isofloridoside (O-α-D-galactopyrano-syl-(1$\longrightarrow$1)-glycerol). Like *Dunaliella parva*, *O. malhamensis* behaves as a perfect osmometer, since a plot of $1/\pi$ against V (π=external osmotic pressure, and V = cell volume) yields a straight line (108). *O. malhamensis* is essentially a freshwater alga, and tolerates a rather low range of external osmotic pressures, in contrast to the *Dunaliella* species. It also contains a contractile vacuole system, in common with most freshwater unicellular algae which lack a rigid cell wall (45). The contractile vacuoles serve to secrete water at external osmotic pressures below 75 mosM (103, 108) in this alga. At higher external osmotic pressures the contractile vacuoles are not visible, and the concentration of isofloridoside in the cells increases linearly with increasing osmotic pressures regardless of the nature of the nonpenetrating solute used (103, 108, 186). Changes in cell volume in response to changes in external osmotic pressure are complete in 2–3 min, while the time necessary to reach a new isofloridoside concentration with restoration of the original cell volume varies from 1 to 2 hr depending on the extent of the osmotic change (108). Changes in isofloridoside concentration were found to account for 70–90% of the necessary internal solute increase to balance increases in external osmotic pressures.

Biochemical investigations of the regulation of isofloridoside levels in *O. malhamensis* indicates that it probably involves activation of enzymatic steps both in its formation as well as its degradation (107–110, 172, 186). Isofloridoside is synthesized either from photoassimilated carbon in the light, or from reserve β-1-3-glucans in the dark upon upshock, and is converted back to β-1-3-glucans in response to downshock (107).

Another chrysophyte flagellate, *Monochrysis lutheri*, which is found in tidepools where it naturally encounters rapid and extensive changes in external osmotic potential, regulates its internal osmotic pressure with the cyclitol 1,4/2,5-cyclohexanetetrol, according to work by Craigie (30). Accumulation of the cyclitol takes place in direct proportion to increases in osmotic pressure of the medium. Dilution of the medium causes rapid expulsion from the cells. The ability of *M. lutheri* to tolerate high external salinities appears to be directly related to its ability to compensate for increased external osmotic pressure by increased net synthesis of cyclohexanetetrol. Nothing is known about the pathways of cyclohexanetetrol synthesis or degradation. However, according to Craigie (30), the cyclitol is not synthesized in the dark. Although this may mean that the flagellate is unable to osmoregulate in the dark, it may not have any serious consequences since it is an obligate photoautotroph (48). *Escherichia coli,* for instance, does not osmoregulate during nongrowth conditions; its turgor pressure is virtually eliminated and its ion gradients dissipated (118, 188–190). However, the cell regains its normal turgor and ion gradients when transferred to conditions supporting growth.

The wall-less but scale-covered green flagellates *Platymonas subcordiformis* (115, 116) and *P. suecica* (82, 83), which are tolerant to wide changes in salinities, regulate their internal osmotic pressures in response to changes in external osmotic pressure with mannitol. Mannitol is either synthesized by photoassimilation in response to upshock in the light or from starch in the dark (116). However, the increase in mannitol synthesis in the dark takes place much more slowly than in the light when cells are exposed to upshock conditions. Also, the steady state level of mannitol reached in *P. subcordiformis* in the dark following a given increase in external osmotic pressure is considerably less than in the light. Rapid and extensive downshock conditions lead to rapid losses of mannitol and other metabolites from *P. suecica* cells (83), and cause a temporary but almost complete loss of photosynthetic ability. During a 2-hr period following downshock, the photosynthetic capacity is largely regained, presumably following resealing of the plasmamembrane and osmoregulatory and metabolic adjustments to the new external osmotic conditions. Another member of this group of scale-bearing green flagellates, the Prasinophyceae (33), a *Pyramimonas* sp., also uses mannitol for osmoregulation (Hellebust, unpublished data).

Walled Cells

Algae possessing proper cell walls vary greatly as to their mechanisms for osmoregulation, including the use of contractile vacuoles, regulation of organic solutes or inorganic ion levels, or a combination of these.

Contractile vacuoles in walled algae appear mainly to be confined to green flagellates belonging to the Volvocales (45). Guillard (72) showed that the only irreplaceable function of the contractile vacuole system of *Chlamydomonas moewusii* is the elimination of water. A mutant of this species lacking functional contractile vacuoles survived and grew only in media with osmotic pressures exceeding 1.5 bars. Similar mutants of *C. eugametos* have been isolated by Gowans (63). Wild-type *C. moewusii* cells have active contractile vacuoles only at external osmotic pressures below 1.5 bars (72). Contractile vacuoles may be important in these cells as a mechanism to prevent rapid dilution of the cell contents by water entering the cells along negative potential gradients chiefly because they do not possess strong cell walls allowing high turgor pressures to develop. Another interesting vacuolar system which appears to be involved in osmoregulation by secreting salt solutions occurs in the heterotrophic halophilic flagellate *Choanogaster plattneri* (168).

The osmoregulation of a highly salt-tolerant *Chlamydomonas* sp. has been extensively investigated by Okamoto and co-workers (155, 231–233). Their observation that K^+ and Na^+ levels in the cells are considerably less than those of the external medium (233) suggests that organic solutes may play an important part in maintaining high internal osmotic pressures, while salts are partly excluded. Craigie et al (33), who found high levels of glycerol in three other *Chlamydomonas* strains, suggest that this polyol may be important in osmoregulation in marine *Chlamydomonas* species in general.

A number of taxonomically very different algae possessing cell walls have recently been reported to employ organic solutes for osmoregulation. The marine lichen *Lichina pygmaea*, which contains a blue-green algal symbiont, regulates its level of the polyol derivative mannosido-mannitol in approximately linear dependence on the salt content of the incubation medium (53). This intertidal lichen is often exposed to seawater and rain water in rapid succession without suffering any obvious damage. The aerophilic green alga *Trentepohlia aurea* synthesizes erythritol, ribitol, and mannitol which may be involved in osmoregulation, although this has not been demonstrated as yet (54). Phycobionts belonging to the genus *Trentepohlia* are found in several lichens (3) in which their polyol metabolism may contribute to osmoregulation.

Wetherell (228), in a very interesting study on osmoregulation of the green alga *Scenedesmus obliquus*, showed that upshock conditions, brought about by high salt or polyethylene glycol solutions, caused plasmolysis which was only reversed during conditions allowing photosynthesis. Increased synthesis of sucrose appears to be responsible for the adjustment to the increased external osmotic pressures, since the ionic concentration of the cells after replasmolysis could account for only about one-third of the new internal osmotic pressure. The accumulation of sucrose and also of insoluble carbohydrates began at salinities below the level causing visible plasmolysis and may have resulted from inhibition of competing biosynthetic pathways without concomitant inhibition of photosynthesis (228). Increase in sucrose synthesis induced by low water potentials has also been reported for *Chlorella pyrenoidosa* (87). In a euryhaline marine *Chlorella* sp. proline accumulates with increasing salinities (Bell & Hellebust, unpublished data), and the same strain has been shown to channel a large fraction of its photoassimilated carbon into amino acids when incubated in seawater (81). The use of amino acids in osmoregulation is well known in protozoans (102) and invertebrates (169).

When the small euryhaline diatoms *Cyclotella meneghiniana* (185) and *C. cryptica* (132, 133) are exposed to upshock conditions there is a rapid increase in proline, which rapidly decreases again in response to downshock conditions. The accumulation of proline from glutamate or arginine appears at least in part to be due to a decrease in end-product control of proline biosynthesis during upshock conditions, and probably also partly due to a general inhibition of protein synthesis allowing accumulation of free amino acids (133). However, since the proline level decreases in cells after adaptation to a higher level of increased osmotic pressure (133), its accumulation must be considered a phenomenon associated primarily with water stress as in some higher plants (8, 194), rather than as playing a major role in osmoregulation. Since the increase in total amino acids and cellular potassium and its associated anions is not sufficient to compensate for the increase in external salinity following adaptation to the new level by *C. cryptica* (133), other organic solutes are probably involved in osmoregulation. Increased levels in proline and total amino acids associated with increased salinities have also been reported for the marine diatom *Phaeodactylum tricornutum* (17).

Kauss (105) has shown that the synthesis of the α-galactosyl-glycerols floridoside and isofloridoside in the red seaweed *Porphyra perforata* and floridoside in *Iridophycus flaccidum* is stimulated in an almost linear fashion by increasing salt concentrations. In view of the fact that isofloridoside serves in osmoregulation in *Ochromonas malhamensis* (103), it seems likely that floridoside and isofloridoside serve a similar function in the above intertidal seaweeds. Eppley & Cyrus (52) have shown that the intracellular K^+ of *Porphyra perforata* increases in a linear manner with increased salinity, while Na^+ and Cl^- are largely excluded (51). In spite of this increase in cellular potassium, it is not sufficient to account for the increased external salinity according to their data (Figure 2 in 52), and the difference is probably accounted for by increased floridoside and isofloridoside levels.

Mannitol is abundant in brown seaweeds and may play a role in osmoregulation in intertidal species (31, 121). The finding by Munda (151) that mannitol levels vary proportionally with salinities in *Ascophyllum nodosum* and *Fucus* spp. in transplant experiments supports such an assumption.

A considerable number of algae from freshwater as well as marine and brackish water environments appear to osmoregulate chiefly by adjustment of intracellular levels of inorganic ions. These algae generally consist of large cells containing vacuoles occupying large fractions of the cell volume. Potassium is usually highly concentrated and sodium excluded by the cells while chloride is the main intracellular anion (76, 139). Most of the published data refer only to the composition of the vacuolar sap. It appears that the cytoplasm discriminates more strongly than the vacuole in favor of potassium over sodium, and also that the concentration of chloride is much lower than in the vacuole (see, however, 183). The problem of isolating cytoplasm for analysis from cells containing vacuoles occupying over 90% of the total cell volume without contamination from vacuolar ions is an extremely difficult one (117, 211, 212). In the following discussion of work on osmoregulation based chiefly on inorganic ions, the conclusions about changes in cellular levels apply strictly only to changes in vacuolar composition. Significant changes in osmotic pressure based on regulation of organic solute levels could occur in the cytoplasm without contributing appreciably to the overall changes in osmotically active particles in the cell, because of the very small fraction of the cell volume occupied by the cytoplasm.

Many marine and brackish water algae have been shown to adjust their cellular osmotic pressure in parallel with changes in external salinity so as to maintain almost constant turgor pressures (19, 44, 111–114). A mechanism for maintaining constant turgor has been demonstrated by the elegant experiments of Gutknecht (75) on *Valonia ventricosa* and by Hastings & Gutknecht on *V. macrophysa* (78). By measuring K^+ fluxes as a function of artificially varied turgor pressures in these giant marine cells it was found that a decrease of turgor pressure increases the K^+ influx, while the K^+ efflux is not significantly affected. At the normal turgor pressure for *V. ventricosa*, about 1 bar, there was no net uptake of K^+ (75). It appears that turgor pressure, which may be interpreted as a pressure gradient across the plasmalemma and the cell wall (78), directly affects the mechanism responsible for active K^+ uptake in *Valonia*, and that the cells therefore possess a feedback mechanism for controlling their turgor pressure (75). The control of K^+ influx by turgor pressure has recently been confirmed for *V. ventricosa* (35) and *V. utricularis* (202, 235).

The turgor pressure-controlled K^+ ion pump system may be viewed as a pressure-sensitive transducer located in the plasmalemma or plasmalemma-cell wall complex (78). This system functions in a negative feedback loop in which an increase in turgor pressure is sensed and causes a reduction in K^+ transport. Zimmermann & Steudle (201, 202, 235, 236) have shown that membrane properties in *Valonia utricularis*, such as hydraulic conductivity and electrical resistance, are dependent on hydrostatic pressure, indicating that structural changes take place in the cell membrane due to extension or contraction caused by variations in turgor pressure. Recent work by Solomon and co-workers (49, 170, 171) demonstrates that osmotic volume perturbations in red blood cells lead to specific changes in cation fluxes. When the cells are shrunken due to upshock conditions, influxes of Na^+ and K^+ increase, and effluxes of both cations decrease. Thus all four fluxes react to increased external osmotic pressure in a cooperative sense to cause a net accumulation of cations so that water enters the cell to maintain osmotic equilibrium, and the cell returns to its original volume. Poznansky & Solomon (171) suggest that conformational changes in membrane proteins are responsible for the observed flux changes and thus volume regulation. It is possible that turgor or volume-induced conformational changes in membrane-associated proteins or protein complexes, such as enzymes or ion pumps, may be involved both in turgor pressure regulation in walled algae and volume regulation in naked algal cells.

The interesting finding by Guillard & Myklestad (74) that the addition of sucrose to the external medium will allow growth of the open-ocean diatom *Cyclotella nana* at low salinities may be understood in the light of a turgor-regulating mechanism of salt uptake. If the turgor pressure is maintained constant during lowering of the external salinity, the levels of cellular ions may become limiting for metabolic requirements, resulting in inhibition of growth. The addition of sucrose to the external medium lowers the turgor pressure, thus stimulating K^+ influx, if the same turgor mechanism applies as in *Valonia* (75), and sufficiently high intracellular ionic concentrations can be maintained for efficient metabolism and growth. Paasche and co-workers (159) have recently shown that variations in external concentrations of organic solutes or NaCl result in similar changes in morphology of the centric diatom *Skeletonema subsalsum*. This phenomenon may also be due to turgor-dependent regulations of intracellular ion levels.

The green euryhaline alga *Chaetomorpha linum,* which maintains almost constant turgor over a large range of salinities (113), differs from *Valonia* spp. in that its internal osmotic pressure does not vary strictly as a function of the external pressure, but also depends on the external potassium concentration (200, 234). However, during conditions commonly encountered by this alga in nature, where the salinity of the seawater is either increased due to evaporation or diluted due to rain or freshwater runoff, there is essentially no change in the relative ionic composition, and the net effect of external salinity changes is that turgor pressure is maintained approximately constant.

The small unicellular green alga *Chlorella pyrenoidosa,* which normally lives in freshwater environments, maintains a homeostatic control of its intracellular K^+ concentration (163–172 mM) over a range of external K^+ concentrations from 1 to 100 mM (193). Na^+ is virtually excluded except at external concentrations of K^+ considerably below 1 mM, when Na^+ gradually takes over as the predominant intracellular cation. It is possible that turgor pressure may be kept constant in this alga by regulation of the level of an internal organic solute such as sucrose (87, 228).

Osmoregulation in the giant internodal cells of the freshwater Characean alga *Nitella flexilis* has been extensively studied by Kamiya & Kuroda (101) and Tazawa and co-workers (117, 208–215). In their natural environment the cells maintain an internal osmotic pressure of about 300 mosM, which is essentially balanced by an equivalent turgor pressure since the osmotic pressure of the external medium is negligible. The internal osmotic pressure is almost entirely accounted for by ions (117, 209), chiefly K^+, Na^+, and Cl^-, and osmoregulation in these cells involves therefore mainly ion regulation. Furthermore, the fluxes of K^+, associated with comparable fluxes of Cl^-, are chiefly responsible for adjustments of internal osmotic pressure and thereby turgor under natural conditions (209, 214, 215). However, in contrast to osmoregulation in *Valonia* spp. (75, 78, 202, 235), the influx of K^+ in *Nitella flexilis* appears not to be appreciably affected when turgor pressure is varied by additions of sucrose to the external medium (209). The level of internal osmotic pressure, and therefore turgor, increases considerably by increasing the external potassium concentration (209), which is also the case with *Chaetomorpha linum* (234).

Further information about osmoregulation in *N. flexilis* has been obtained by the following techniques: (*a*) transcellular osmosis (101), which results in functional cell fragments with vacuoles containing different concentrations, but unchanged relative composition of ions; and (*b*) vacuolar perfusion (210), in which artificial cell saps containing different ionic compositions and osmotic pressures (e.g. adjusted with mannitol) can be introduced. The results clearly show that K^+ is of key importance in osmoregulation, and that both influxes and effluxes of K^+, in cells modified to contain lower or higher internal osmotic pressures than normal, are approximately linearly dependent on the amount of deviation from the normal osmotic value (215). Cells with artificially modified internal osmotic concentrations of natural composition always adjust their internal osmotic pressure back to that typical for the incubation medium (209, 215). Results from vacuolar perfusion studies show that *N. flexilis* exhibits a pronounced tendency to regulate its osmotic pressure rather than the K^+ level in the vacuole (215). However, in the case of artificial cell saps with very high K^+ concentrations, the cell regulates its K^+ level towards a more normal value. Tazawa and co-workers (215) believe that both mechanisms, one to regulate the osmotic value and the other the K^+ level, are important in maintaining the cytoplasmic K^+ concentration at a fairly constant level.

Light is very important in determining the internal osmotic level, and therefore turgor, in *N. flexilis* (209, 214). The internal osmotic pressure increases considerably with increasing light intensities with a maximum being reached at about 500 lux (209). Tazawa (209) demonstrated a daily periodicity of internal osmotic pressure with alternating light and dark periods. When both K^+ and Na^+ are present, K^+ is always taken up to a greater extent than Na^+ even in the dark, but light increases the selectivity for K^+ (209, 210). Increased osmotic pressures due to light have also been demonstrated for green seaweeds (218) and blue-green algae (61).

MOSSES

Although several reports have recently appeared regarding water stress effects and salt resistance of mosses (9, 18, 77), little appears to be known about their osmoregulatory mechanisms. The ability of seashore mosses to withstand high salinities without appreciable increases in intracellular salt content (9) may reflect the production and accumulation of organic solutes by the cells to maintain turgor, but this has not been demonstrated.

HIGHER PLANTS

The structural and functional complexities of higher plants make it difficult to decide which biochemical, biophysical, or physiological processes are relevant to osmoregulation and which are not. In contrast to fungi and algae, where osmoregulatory mechanisms obviously pertain to single cells, osmoregulation in higher plants involves the interaction of regulatory mechanisms at the cell level with those of tissues and organs. The complexities of the regulation of solute uptake, content, and composition in higher plants have been admirably demonstrated and discussed in a series of papers by Steward and co-workers (40, 147–150). They showed that plant cells have distinctly different osmoregulatory properties, depending on stage of growth and development, and described osmoregulatory responses of such cells in tissue cultures to complex changes in the cellular environment. Mott & Steward (147, 150) criticized the systems often employed in studies of solute uptake and regulation where most of the complications of growth and active metabolism have been drastically reduced or eliminated. Although a considerable amount of research has been reported on different aspects of osmoregulation of whole plants or plant tissues at different stages of growth and development, such as on water stress (90), ion uptake (6), long-distance translocation of ions (128), or on the function of specialized organs such as salt glands (135) or stomata (173), it is often difficult to relate these studies to osmoregulation at the cell level.

Interesting discussions of aspects of the problems of integration of osmoregulatory functions by organs, tissues, and cells have recently been published by Pitman & Cram (165) and by Lüttge (136). Cram (36, 37) has recently discussed evidence for the operation of control systems for transport and osmoregulation at the plant cell level. In view of these recent discussions and reviews of several aspects of osmoregulation in higher plants, only a rather brief review of selected aspects of this topic will be attempted here.

Major Osmotic Components

A good overview of the large body of early work on the nature of osmotic solutes in higher plants from different habitats is available by Steiner & Eschrich (199). Cram (37), in his recent review on transport control systems and osmoregulation, includes some more recent data. The major osmotic components of glycophytes (plants intolerant to high salt concentrations) are potassium salts of organic acids and sugars. Sodium and chloride are always present, but represent major components only in species with distinct halophilic tendencies, such as members of the Chenopodiaceae (142). The important contribution of sugars to the osmotic pressure in many glycophytes may be related to a low supply of mineral ions in some natural habitats (147, 165). Other organic solutes, in many cases unidentified, may account for large fractions of the observed internal osmotic pressures in some plants (42, 199, 203, 204, 226). In halophytes, sodium and chloride usually account for the major portion of the total osmotic solutes, which sulfate and divalent cations are important in some cases (199, 225). The relative proportions of osmotic components of plant cells vary considerably with stage of development (40, 88, 147–150, 199) as well as tissue type (15, 199).

Halophytes

Halophytes represent an interesting group of plants because of their successful adaptation to environments of very low water potentials and high salt concentrations. Since there is little evidence that halophytes possess enzyme systems, organelles, or membranes specially adapted to high salt concentrations (see later), in contrast to halophilic bacteria (125), these plants are faced with the problem of having to accumulate sufficient solutes—usually NaCl—to maintain turgor during growth, and at the same time to prevent inhibition of cell metabolism by excessive salt concentrations in their cytoplasm.

Halophytes have been classified into different types in terms of their mechanisms of dealing with the salt problem (see 199). The accumulation types accumulate salt throughout the growth season so that their internal osmotic pressure is continuously increasing until death of the plant, while the regulation types, to which most halophytes belong, possess regulatory mechanisms which allow their internal osmotic pressure to remain relatively constant. The regulatory mechanisms include salt glands, which actively secrete concentrated salt solutions, and continuous enlargement of cells in succulent tissues, or salt-accumulating epidermal bladder cells (135, 199, 225). In those mangroves which do not possess salt glands, salts are partially excluded by the roots (187), and in *Salicornia europea* some salt is apparently retransported via the phloem to the roots where it is lost to the medium (29, 224).

Evidence for a salt-inducible chloride transport system has been obtained by Hill and co-workers (85, 86, 191) for the salt glands of *Limonium vulgare,* an exceptionally euryhaline salt-marsh plant which can grow in fresh water as well as media twice the concentration of seawater. Tissues from plants grown at low salinities show no secretory activity. Upon transfer to NaCl solutions there is a rapid increase in a Cl^- activated ATPase after a 1 hr induction period (86). Hill (85) has further demonstrated that the level of chloride transport capacity induced depends on the salt load. The gland cells, which are symplastically connected to the mesophyll cells, are thus able to maintain relatively low and constant salt concentrations in the leaf tissue in response to widely fluctuating salt concentrations.

Another interesting adaptation to environments of rapidly changing salinities is the salt-stimulated increase in the specific activity of phosphoenolpyruvate carboxylase in halophytes from coastal foredunes (221). It has been demonstrated for other halophytes that the C-4 pathway of photosynthesis is very tolerant to high NaCl concentrations, while the C-3 pathway is easily inhibited (219, 230), and evidence has been obtained for tobacco (217) and *Kalanchoe marmorata* (220) that high sodium concentrations stimulate stomatal opening in the dark and closing in the light. These physiological effects of sodium should all contribute to efficient fixation of CO_2 at night and minimal water loss because of closure of the stomata during the day. Recent work demonstrating that enzymes and protein-synthesizing systems in halophytes are as sensitive to high salt concentrations as those with glycophytes (55–57, 69, 70, 100, 158) implies that the high salt content of halophytes must be chiefly in vacuoles, and that equivalent osmotic pressures in the cytoplasm must to a large extent be due to compatible organic solutes. Jefferies' (93) estimated level for cytoplasmic cations in the halophyte *Triglochin maritima* agree well with the relatively low levels required for optimal activation of some enzymes extracted from other halophytes (56, 69). It is also close to the concentration of potassium salts found in rapidly dividing nonvacuolated cells of carrot, a glycophyte (147).

The NaCl required for turgor maintenance in the highly vacuolated cells of halophytes is presumably actively pumped through the tonoplast into the vacuoles to maintain low cytoplasmic levels (124, 162, 205). In support of the assumption that sodium levels in the cytoplasm must be kept low, Kylin & Hanson (cited in 124) found ($Na^+ + K^+$)-stimulated ATPases with different properties in high-salt and low-salt strains of sugar beets. Nabors et al (152) have recently isolated several salt-tolerant mutant strains of tobacco cells from tissue cultures. It would be interesting to compare the properties of ion pumps in such mutant cells with those of the salt-sensitive parent strain.

Greenway & Sims (70) suggest that salt-induced increases in levels of metabolic intermediates may contribute significantly to osmotic potentials, which in turn would lower the required levels of salts for adequate osmotic adjustment of the cytoplasm. Flowers (55) showed that while enzymes and mitochondrial transport systems from *Suaeda maritima* are sensitive to moderate salt concentrations, similar concentrations of sucrose cause much less inhibition. The presence of sodium has been shown to stimulate increased sucrose content in sugar beet (50). The effect of sodium may be at the level of starch synthetase which is influenced by the relative concentrations of K^+ and Na^+ present (80).

Some very interesting demonstrations of organic compounds which may act as compatible solutes for intracellular osmotic adjustments in halophytes have been reported recently. Stewart & Lee (203) found high concentrations of proline in a majority of halopytes investigated, and also found that the concentration of proline increases with increasing salinity. Storey & Wyn Jones (204) found good correlation between the level of betaine in several plants with their salt resistance. An almost linear relationship was found between shoot betaine concentration and external salt level in *Chloris gayana*, a moderately salt-tolerant grass. In the halophyte *Suaeda monoica*, betaine is present at about 0.4% of the fresh weight, which means a concentration of about 0.5 M if one assumes that all of the betaine occurs in the cytoplasm and that the latter occupies 10% of the cell volume. Another halophyte, *Limonium vulgare*, accumulates the organic amine putricine in response to treatment with seawater (126). Thus a number of organic compounds may be important in different species as compatible osmoregulatory solutes which make efficient operation of biochemical processes possible.

Glycophytes

Plants with no specialized mechanisms for dealing with high external ion concentrations can regulate their ion content to only a moderate extent by limiting ion transfer to the shoot (16), by possible re-export of ions to the medium via the roots (91), or by redistribution of ions in different organs (144) and presumably also in different cell compartments. It has been shown by Greenway and co-workers (65, 67) that rapidly growing tissues of barley have ion compositions similar to plants grown in low sodium chloride, while older organs contain high sodium and chloride, and low potassium concentrations. Regulation of ion content and composition in plant tissues reflects the complex interactions of growth and ion concentrations (71). The plant as a whole appears to regulate its supply of ions from the roots to balance its growth rate and thus maintain relatively constant ion levels (7, 164).

Our understanding of mechanisms by which single plant cells regulate their solute concentrations and turgor pressure is still very unsatisfactory. The main reasons for this are experimental and conceptual difficulties related to their location and integration in complex plant tissues where they depend on rates of transfer of water and solutes from other plant parts as well as on hormonal signals. The problem has been discussed recently by Cram (37) and will be considered only briefly here.

The influx of inorganic ions into many plant cells and tissues is reduced when the internal concentration of these ions is high, i.e. by the apparent operation of a negative feedback mechanism (34, 165). In carrot and barley root cells the influx of chloride during salt accumulation appears to be regulated in a complex manner by negative feedback effects of the combined cell content of chloride and nitrate (35). This negative feedback relationship is probably involved in maintaining a relatively constant internal chloride concentration [homeostatic control (34, 38)], with changing external chloride concentrations (34, 163). Cram (36) points out that since chloride is usually only a minor osmotic component in glycophytes, its regulation cannot be of major importance to the total internal osmotic pressure. Changes in turgor pressure, in agreement with this view, have little effect on chloride influx in carrot and corn root cells (34, 35). More unexpectedly, turgor pressure also does not regulate the influx of potassium, frequently a major osmotic component in these cells, in contrast to the clear demonstration of a homeostatic turgor control of potassium influx in *Valonia* spp. (35, 75). However, there is evidence for stimulation of net K^+ influx in red beet tissue in response to decreased turgor pressure (207).

Several reports demonstrate increase in osmotic pressure of plant tissues in response to increases in external osmotic pressures, i.e., so-called "osmotic adjustment" (16, 195, 199, 225). However, the mechanisms for such adjustments, which seldom are sufficient to prevent considerable variations in turgor pressure, are not known (36, 37). In cells of barley leaves, the influx of potassium and chloride increase with increasing external KCl concentration with no evidence of a negative feedback mechanism operating to maintain the internal concentration at about 200 mM, the concentration usually found in the intact shoots (167). Pitman et al (167) suggest that the apparent regulation of potassium content in shoots of barley seedlings is due to regulation of export of ions from the root. Cram & Pitman (39) showed that abscisic acid inhibits net potassium transport into the exudate of excised corn and barley roots, in agreement with such an assumption. Similar but more complex hormone effects on ion uptake and transport have been observed in more recent work (166). Moderate water stress strongly inhibits ion transport from the roots, apparently by the action of abscisic acid, which is synthesized in response to low water potentials in the leaves (122, 173) and translocated to the roots via the phloem (89, 145). It influences ion secretion into the xylem (166), while it has little short-term effect on rates of ion uptake by root cells (66, 68, 167).

Increases in cellular levels of sucrose occur in sugarcane stems in response to lowering of turgor pressure, and it has been suggested by Gaylor & Glasziou (58) that this may reflect the operation of a negative feedback system for maintaining constant turgor pressure. Other reports demonstrating increases in internal osmotic pressure in response to decreases in external water potentials with nonpenetrating solutes (129, 216) indicate the production of osmotically active organic solutes, which probably include sugars. The uptake of sucrose by rapidly expanding cells and its conversion to reducing sugars by the extremely active invertase associated with these cells (79, 84) appears to be important in maintaining turgor during expansion growth (40, 84, 229).

Loss of turgor, apart from stopping growth (64, 174), also appears to seriously interfere with several biochemical processes (90). Dhindsa & Cleland (43) suggest that the decrease in protein synthesis observed upon reduction of turgor pressure may be due to effects on the protein-synthesizing machinery on membranes by turgor-related volume changes.

Organic acids are also important as organic osmoregulatory solutes in cells of some glycophytes (199), either as free acids (138), or more frequently as organic anions balancing K^+ present in excess of strong inorganic anions (35, 92). The synthesis of malate, which is the organic anion most frequently involved in balancing excess cation uptake, is probably regulated by pH and HCO_3^- availability in the cytoplasm, which are in turn dependent on K^+/H^+ exchange during K^+ uptake (197). The large concentrations of organic acids found in many plant cells are largely confined within vacuoles (138, 154). Lütge & Ball (137) present evidence that net (passive) efflux of malic acid from the vacuoles of leaf cells of *Bryophyllum daigremontianum* depends on turgor of the cells, and they hypothesize that this osmoregulatory mechanism is important in regulating crassulacean metabolism in vivo. Malic acid is presumably pumped actively into the vacuole during the CO_2 dark-fixation phase. The demonstration by Dainty & Ginzburg (41) of increased permeability of *Nitella translucens* tonoplasts to urea in response to increased turgor supports such an hypothesis. There is also excellent evidence that active and passive transport processes are important in volume and turgor regulation in specialized cells such as guard cells (173) and the motor cells controlling leaflet movements in *Albizzia julibrissin* (184). Turgor changes in stomatal movements are related to influx and efflux of K^+ and H^+, balanced by fluxes of chloride as well as metabolic regulation of organic anion levels (173). Raschke (173) suggests that the direction of these processes are controlled by the pH of the cytoplasm, and that stomatal closure in response to abscisic acid may be due to inhibition of H^+ expulsion. The massive literature on stomatal action (173) indicates the complexity of osmoregulation in guard cells with its dependence on ion concentrations and fluxes, metabolic energy, pH, CO_2, compartmentation of ions and metabolites, hormones, and interactions of these factors. Osmoregulation in other plant cells may prove to be almost equally complex.

CONCLUDING REMARKS

Some of the most interesting recent developments in this field have been the clear demonstrations of the role of polyols and their derivatives in osmoregulatory processes of fungi and unicellular algae. However, only in the case of *Ochromonas malhamensis* is definite evidence available about how the level of such an organic osmoregulatory solute is controlled enzymatically (108, 110). One would expect that organic substances also must play important roles as osmotic solutes in the cytoplasm of highly vacuolated plant cells to partly balance high concentrations of ions in the vacuoles and thus prevent inactivation of metabolic processes by high cytoplasmic salt concentrations. Some indirect evidence that this may be the case is available from recent work on halophytes (203, 204). Information regarding mechanisms of regulation of the concentrations and intracellular compartmentations of osmotically important organic as well as inorganic solutes is urgently needed.

Recent work demonstrating turgor-regulated influx of potassium in some giant algal cells (35, 75, 78, 202, 235), together with work demonstrating turgor-dependent membrane properties in these cells (201, 202, 235, 236), are exciting new developments in view of their importance in indicating control mechanisms and sites for osmoregulation. The extensive work by Tazawa et al (117, 208–215) on *Nitella translucens* continues to contribute valuable insight into mechanisms for osmoregulation in cells with large vacuoles where ions play the predominant role as osmotic solutes. Some important recent progress has also been made in demonstrating control mechanisms for ion accumulation in higher plant cells (35, 36).

The complex interactions of osmoregulatory mechanisms at different organizational levels in higher plants are still poorly understood. Some interesting progress has been made in recent work demonstrating effects of hormones on transport of ions from roots to shoots (39, 166). Hormones obviously play important roles in osmoregulation of the entire plant by controlling water transpiration through stomata (122) and presumably ion transport both at the cell level and, as has been demonstrated, at the level of long-distance transport.

The comprehensive papers by Steward and co-workers (40, 147–150), demonstrating the control of solute accumulation by cultured cells as influenced by environmental conditions and stage of growth and development, are valuable contributions to our understanding of the complexity of osmoregulation in higher plants.

ACKNOWLEDGMENTS

I am grateful to J. S. Craigie, R. L. Jefferies, H. Kauss, G. O. Kirst, U. Lüttge, J. McLachlan, E. Paasche, and U. Zimmermann for helpful discussions and for making available reprints and manuscripts of their work, and also to A. Ben-Amotz and W. J. Cram for access to manuscripts prior to publication. I am greatly indebted to J. Dainty for reading the manuscript and for helpful criticism and suggestions.

Literature Cited

1. Adebayo, A. A., Harris, R. F. 1971. *Soil Sci.* 36:465–69
2. Adebayo, A. A., Harris, R. F., Gardner, W. R. 1971. *Trans. Br. Mycol. Soc.* 57:145–51
3. Ahmadjian, V. 1958. *Bot. Not.* 111:632–44
4. Allaway, A. E., Jennings, D. H. 1970. *New Phytol.* 69:581–93
5. Anand, J. C., Brown, A. D. 1968. *J. Gen. Microbiol.* 52:205–12
6. Anderson, W. P. 1972. *Ann. Rev. Plant Physiol.* 23:51–72
7. Asher, C. J., Ozanne, P. G. 1967. *Soil Sci.* 103:155–62
8. Barnett, N. W., Naylor, A. W. 1966. *Plant Physiol.* 41:1222–30
9. Bates, J. W., Brown, D. H. 1974. *New Phytol.* 73:483–95
10. Ben-Amotz, A. 1973. *FEBS Lett.* 29:153–55
11. Ben-Amotz, A. 1974. *Membrane Transport in Plants*, ed. U. Zimmermann, J. Dainty, 95–100. Berlin: Springer. 437 pp.
12. Ben-Amotz, A. 1975. *J. Phycol.* 11:50–54
13. Ben-Amotz, A., Avron, M. 1972. *Plant Physiol.* 49:240–43
14. Ibid 1973. 51:875–78

15. Bernstein, L. 1963. *Am. J. Bot.* 50:
    360–70
16. Bernstein, L., Hayward, H. E. 1958.
    Ann. Rev. Plant Physiol. 9:25–43
17. Besnier, V., Bazin, M., Marcheli-
    don, J., Genevet, M. 1969. *Bull. Soc.
    Chim. Biol.* 51:1255–62
18. Bewley, J. D. 1972. *Can. J. Bot.*
    51:203–3
19. Biebl, R. 1956. *Ber. Dtsch. Bot. Ges.*
    69:75–86
20. Borowitzka, L. J., Brown, A. D. 1974.
    Arch. Microbiol. 96:37–52
21. Bouck, G. B., Brown, D. L. 1973. *J.
    Cell Biol.* 56:340–59
22. Brown, A. D. 1974. *J. Bacteriol.*
    118:769–77
23. Brown, A. D., Simpson, J. R. 1972. *J.
    Gen. Microbiol.* 72:589–91
24. Brown, A. D., Turner, H. P. 1963. *Na-
    ture* 199:301–2
25. Budd, K. 1969. *J. Gen. Microbiol.*
    59:229–38
26. Chen, A. W. C. 1964. *Trans. Kans.
    Acad. Sci.* 67:36–40
27. Christian, J. H. B., Waltho, J. A. 1962.
    J. Appl. Bacteriol. 25:369–77
28. Conway, E. J., Brady, T. G. 1950. *Bio-
    chem. J.* 47:360–69
29. Cooil, B. J., de la Fuente, R. K., de la
    Pena, R. S. 1965. *Plant Physiol.* 40:
    625–33
30. Craigie, J. S. 1969. *J. Fish. Res. Board
    Can.* 26:2959–67
31. Craigie, J. S. 1974. *Algal Physiology and
    Biochemistry,* ed. W. D. P. Stewart,
    206–35. Oxford: Blackwells. 989 pp.
32. Craigie, J. S., McLachlan, J. 1964. *Can.
    J. Bot.* 42:777–78
33. Craigie, J. S., McLachlan, J., Ackman,
    R. G., Rocher, C. S. 1967. *Can. J. Bot.*
    45:1327–34
34. Cram, W. J. 1973. *Aust. J. Biol. Sci.*
    26:757–79
35. Cram, W. J. 1973. *J. Exp. Bot.*
    24:328–41
36. Cram, W. J. 1974. *Mechanisms of Regu-
    lation of Plant Growth,* ed. R.L. Bieleski,
    A. R. Ferguson, M. M. Cresswell. Bull.
    12:183–89. Wellington: R. Soc. N.Z.
    934 pp.
37. Cram, W. J. 1975. *Encyclopedia of
    Plant Physiology, New Series,* ed. A. Pir-
    son, M. Zimmermann, Vol. 2. Berlin:
    Springer. In press
38. Cram, W. J., Laties, G. G. 1971. *Aust.
    J. Biol. Sci.* 24:633–46
39. Cram, W. J., Pitman, M. G. 1972. *Aust.
    J. Biol. Sci.* 25:1125–32
40. Craven, G. H., Mott, R. L., Steward,
    F. C. 1972. *Ann. Bot.* 36:897–914

41. Dainty, J., Ginzburg, B. Z. 1964. *Bio-
    chim. Biophys. Acta* 79:112–21
42. de la Cruz, A. A., Poe, W. E. 1974.
    Estuarine Coastal Mar. Sci. 3:243–46
43. Dhindsa, R. S., Cleland, R. E. 1975.
    Plant Physiol. 55:782–85
44. Dreus, P. 1896. *Arch. Ver. Freunde
    Naturgesch. Mecklenburg* 49:91–135
45. Dodge, J. D. 1973. *The Fine Structure
    of Algal Cells,* 182–86. New York: Aca-
    demic. 261 pp.
46. Droop, M. R. 1953. *Acta Bot. Fenn.*
    51:1–52
47. Droop, M. R. 1958. *Verh. Int. Ver.
    Limnol.* 13:722–30
48. Droop, M. R. 1974. See Ref. 31, 530–59
49. Elford, B. C., Solomon, A. K. 1974.
    Biochim. Biophys. Acta 373:253–64
50. El-Sheikh, A. M., Ulrich, A. 1970.
    Plant Physiol. 46:645–49
51. Eppley, R. W. 1958. *J. Gen. Physiol.*
    41:901–11
52. Eppley, R. W., Cyrus, C. C. 1960. *Biol.
    Bull.* 118:55–64
53. Feige, G. B. 1972. *Z. Pflanzenphysiol.*
    68:121–26
54. Ibid 1974. 71:459–62
55. Flowers, T. J. 1972. *J. Exp. Bot.*
    23:310–21
56. Flowers, T. J. 1972. *Phytochemistry*
    11:1881–87
57. Flowers, T. J. 1973. *Ion Transport in
    Plants,* ed. W. P. Anderson, 357–68.
    New York: Academic. 630 pp.
58. Gayler, K. R., Glasziou, K. T. 1972.
    Physiol. Plant. 27:25–31
59. Gessner, F. 1959. *Hydrobotanik.*
    2:401–67. Berlin: V.E.B. Deutscher
    Verlag der Wissenschaften. 701 pp.
60. Gessner, F., Schramm, W. 1971. *Ma-
    rine Ecology,* ed. O. Kinne, 1(pt. 2):
    705–820. London: Wiley-Interscience.
    1244 pp.
61. Ginzberg, D., Padan, E. 1972. *Arch.
    Mikrobiol.* 87:181–83
62. Ginzburg, M. 1969. *Biochim. Biophys.
    Acta* 173:370–76
63. Gowans, C. S. 1960. *Z. Vererbungsl.*
    91:63–73
64. Green, P. B., Erickson, R. O., Buggy, J.
    1971. *Plant Physiol.* 47:423–30
65. Greenway, H. 1962. *Aust. J. Biol. Sci.*
    15:39–57
66. Greenway, H. 1967. *Physiol. Plant.*
    20:903–10
67. Greenway, H., Gunn, A., Thomas,
    D. A. 1965. *Aust. J. Biol. Sci.* 18:525–40
68. Greenway, H., Hughes, P. G., Klepper,
    B. 1969. *Physiol. Plant.* 22:208–19
69. Greenway, H., Osmond, C. B. 1972.
    Plant. Physiol. 49:256–59

70. Greenway, H., Sims, A. P. 1974. *Aust. J. Plant Physiol.* 1:15–29
71. Greenway, H., Thomas, D. A. 1964. *Aust. J. Biol. Sci.* 18:505–24
72. Guillard, R. R. L. 1960. *J. Protozool.* 7:262–68
73. Guillard, R. R. L. 1962. *Physiology and Biochemistry of Algae,* ed. R. A. Lewin, 529–40. New York: Acadamic. 929 pp.
74. Guillard, R. R. L., Myklestad, S. 1970. *Helgol. Wiss. Meeresunters.* 20:104–10
75. Gutknecht, J. 1968. *Science* 160:68–70
76. Gutknecht, J., Dainty, J. 1968. *Oceanogr. Mar. Biol.* 6:163–200
77. Gwózdz, E. A., Bewley, J. D. 1975. *Plant Physiol.* 55:340–45
78. Hastings, D. F., Gutknecht, J. 1974. See Ref. 11, 79–83
79. Hatch, M. D., Glasziou, K. T. 1963. *Plant Physiol.* 38:344–48
80. Hawker, J. S., Marschner, H., Downton, W. J. S. 1974. *Aust. J. Plant Physiol.* 1:491–501
81. Hellebust, J. A. 1965. *Limnol. Oceanogr.* 10:192–206
82. Hellebust, J. A. 1973. *Plant Physiol.* 51 Suppl: (Abstr.)
83. Hellebust, J. A. 1976. *Can. J. Bot.* In press
84. Hellebust, J. A., Forward, D. F. 1962. *Can. J. Bot.* 40:113–26
85. Hill, A. E. 1970. *Biochim. Biophys. Acta* 196:73–79
86. Hill, B. S., Hill, A. E. 1973. See Ref. 57, 379–84
87. Hiller, R. G., Greenway, H. 1968. *Planta* 78:49–59
88. Hoagland, D. R. Broyer, T. C. 1936. *Plant Physiol.* 11:471–507
89. Hockling, T. J., Hillman, J. R., Wilkins, M. B. 1972. *Nature New Biol.* 235:124–25
90. Hsiao, T. C. 1973. *Ann. Rev. Plant Physiol.* 24:519–70
91. Hylmö, B. 1953. *Physiol. Plant.* 6:333–405
92. Jacoby, B., Laties, G. G. 1971 *Plant Physiol.* 47:525–31
93. Jefferies, R. L. 1973. See Ref. 57, 297–321
94. Jennings, D. H. 1973. See Ref. 57, 323–35
95. Johnson, M. K., Johnson, E. J., MacElroy, R. D., Speer, H., Bruff, B. S. 1968. *J. Bacteriol.* 95:1461–68
96. Jokela, A. C-C. Tang 1969. *Outer Membrane of Dunaliella tertiolecta: Isolation and Properties.* PhD thesis. Univ. California, San Diego. 109 pp.
97. Jones, E. B. G., Bryne, P., Alderman, D. J. 1971. *Vie Mileu* Suppl. 22:265–80
98. Jones, E. B. G., Jennings, D. H. 1964. *Trans. Br. Mycol. Soc.* 47:86–100
99. Jones, W. B. G., Rothstein, A., Sherman, F., Stannard, J. N. 1965. *Biochim. Biophys. Acta* 104:310–12
100. Kalir, A., Poljakoff-Mayber, A. 1975. *Plant Physiol.* 55:155–62
101. Kamiya, N., Kuroda, K. 1956. *Protoplasma* 46:423–36
102. Kaneshiro, E. S., Holz., G. G., Dunham, P. B. 1969. *Biol. Bull.* 137:161–69
103. Kauss, H. 1967. *Z. Pflanzenphysiol.* 56:453–65
104. Kauss, H. 1967. *Nature* 214:1129–30
105. Kauss, H. 1968. *Z. Pflanzenphysiol.* 58:428–33
106. Kauss, H. 1969. *Ber. Dtsch. Bot. Ges.* 82:115–25
107. Kauss, H. 1973. *Plant Physiol.* 52: 613–15
108. Kauss, H. 1974. See Ref. 11, 90–94
109. Kauss, H., Lüttge, U., Krichbaum, R. M. 1975. *Z. Pflanzenphysiol.* In press
110. Kauss, H., Schobert, B. 1971. *FEBS Lett.* 19:131–35
111. Kesseler, H. 1958. *Kiel. Meeresforsch.* 14:23–41
112. Ibid 1959. 15:51–73
113. Kesseler, H. 1964. *Helgol Wiss. Meeresunters.* 10:73–90
114. Kesseler, H. 1965. *Bot. Gothob.* 3: 103–11
115. Kirst, G. O. 1975. *Oekologia* 20:237
116. Kirst, G. O. 1975. *Z. Pflanzenphysiol.* 76:316–25
117. Kishimoto, U., Tazawa, M. 1965. *Plant Cell. Physiol.* 6:507–18
118. Knaysi, G. 1951. *Elements of Bacterial Cytology,* p.155. Ithaca:Comstock. 375 pp. 2nd ed.
119. Koh, T. Y. 1975. *J. Gen. Microbiol.* 88:101–14
120. Ibid, 184–88
121. Kremer, B. P. 1973. *Mar. Biol.* 22: 31–35
122. Kriedemann, P. E., Loveys, B. R. 1974. See Ref. 36, 461–65
123. Krishna Pillai, V. 1955. *Proc. Natl. Inst. Sci. India* 1:130–44
124. Kylin, A. 1973. See Ref. 57, 369–77
125. Lanyi, J. K. 1974. *Bacteriol. Rev.* 38:272–90
126. Larher, F. 1974. *C. R. Acad. Sci. D* 279:157–60
127. Larsen, H. 1967. *Adv. Microb. Physiol.* 1:97–132
128. Läuchli, A. 1972. *Ann. Rev. Plant Physiol.* 23:197–218
129. Lawlor, D. W. 1969. *J. Exp. Bot.* 20:895–911

130. Lerche, W. 1937. *Arch. Protistenkd.* 88:236–68
131. Lewis, D. H., Smith, D. C. 1967. *New Phytol.* 66:143–84
132. Liu, M. S., Hellebust, J. A. 1976. *Can. J. Bot.* In press
133. Ibid.
134. Lund, J. W. G. 1967. *Soil Biology,* ed. A. Burges, F. Raw, 129–47. New York: Academic. 532 pp.
135. Lüttge, U. 1971. *Ann. Rev. Plant Physiol.* 22:23–40
136. Lüttge, U. 1974. See Ref. 11, 353–62
137. Lüttge, U., Ball, E. 1974. *Z. Pflanzephysiol.* 75:326–38
138. MacLennan, D. H., Beevers, H., Harley, J. L. 1963. *Biochem. J.* 89:316–27
139. MacRobbie, E. A. C. 1974. See Ref. 31, 676–713
140. Manton, I., Parke, M. 1965. *J. Mar. Biol. Assoc. UK* 45:743–54
141. Marrè, E., Servattaz, O. 1959. *Atti Accad. Naz. Lincei Cl. Sci. Fis. Mat. Nat. Rend.* 26:272–78
142. Marschner, H., Possingham, J. V. 1975. *Z. Pflanzenphysiol.* 75:6–16
143. McLachlan, J. 1960. *Can. J. Microbiol.* 6:367–79
144. Meyer, R. F., Boyer, J. S. 1972. *Planta* 108:77–87
145. Milborrow, B. V., Robinson, D. R. 1973. *J. Exp. Bot.* 24:537–48
146. Miller, A. G., Budd, K. 1971. *J. Gen. Microbiol.* 66:243–45
147. Mott, R. L., Steward, F. C. 1972. *Ann. Bot.* 36:621–39
148. Ibid, 641–53
149. Ibid, 655–70
150. Ibid, 915–37
151. Munda, I. 1967. *Nova Hedwigia* 13:471–508
152. Nabors, M. V., Daniels, A., Nadolny, L., Brown, C. 1975. *Plant Sci. Lett.* 4:155–59
153. Norris, R. E., Pearson, B. R. 1975. *Arch. Protistenkd.* 117:192–213
154. Oaks, A., Bidwell, R. G. S. 1970. *Ann. Rev. Plant Physiol.* 21:43–66
155. Okamoto, H. 1962. *Z. Allg. Mikrobiol.* 2:32–44
156. Onishi, H. 1963. *Adv. Food Res.* 12:53–94
157. Onishi, H. 1963. *Agric. Biol. Chem.* 27:543–47
158. Osmond, C. B., Greenway, H. 1972. *Plant Physiol.* 49:260–63
159. Paasche, E., Johanssen, S., Evensen, D. L. 1975. *Phycologia.* 14:205
160. Park, D., Robinson, P. 1966. *Ann. Bot.* 30:425–39
161. Peña, A. 1975. *Arch. Biochem. Biophys.* 167:397–409
162. Pierce, W. S., Higinbotham, N. 1970. *Plant Physiol.* 46:666–73
163. Pitman, M. G. 1969. *Plant Physiol.* 44:1417–27
164. Pitman, M. G. 1972. *Aust. J. Biol. Sci.* 25:905–19
165. Pitman, M. G., Cram, W. J. 1973. See Ref. 57, 465–81
166. Pitman, M. G., Lüttge, U., Läuchli, A., Ball, E. 1974. *J. Exp. Bot.* 25:147–55
167. Pitman, M. G., Lüttge, U., Läuchli, A., Ball, E. 1974. *Z. Pflanzenophysiol.* 72:75–88
168. Pochmann, A. 1959. *Ber. Dtsch. Bot. Ges.* 72:99–108
169. Potts, W. T. W., Parry, G. 1964. *Osmotic and Ionic Regulation in Animals.* New York: Pergamon. 423 pp.
170. Poznansky, M., Solomon, A. K. 1972. *Biochim. Biophys. Acta* 274:111–18
171. Poznansky, M., Solomon, A. K. 1972. *J. Membr. Biol.* 10:259–66
172. Quader, H., Kauss, H. 1975. *Planta* 124:61–66
173. Raschke, K. 1975. *Ann. Rev. Plant Physiol.* 26:309–40
174. Ray, P. M. 1969. *Planta* 77:182–91
175. Rishbeth, J. 1951. *Ann. Bot.* 15:1–21
176. Ritchie, D. 1957. *Am. J. Bot.* 44:870–74
177. Ritchie, D., Jacobsohn, M. K. 1963. *Symp. Marine Microbiology,* ed. C. H. Oppenheimer, 286–99. Springfield: Thomas, 769 pp.
178. Robertson, N. F. 1965. *Trans. Br. Mycol. Soc.* 48:1–8
179. Robertson, N. F., Rizvi, S. R. H. 1968. *Ann. Bot.* 32:279–91
180. Rothstein, A. 1955. *Electrolytes in Biological Systems,* ed. A. M. Shanes, 65–100. Washington DC: Am. Physiol. Soc. 243 pp.
181. Rothstein, A. 1963. *The Cellular Functions of Membrane Transport,* ed. J. F. Hoffman, 23–39. Englewood Cliffs: Prentice-Hall. 291 pp.
182. Rothstein, A. 1968. *Microbial Protoplasts, Spheroplasts and L-Forms,* ed. L. B. Guze, 174–85. Baltimore: Williams & Wilkins. 523 pp.
183. Saddler, H. D. W. 1970. *J. Exp. Bot.* 21:345–59
184. Satter, R. L., Applewhite, P. B., Dreis, D. J., Galston, A. W. 1973. *Plant Physiol.* 52:202–7
185. Schobert, B. 1974. *Z. Pflanzenphysiol.* 74:106–20
186. Schobert, B., Untner, E., Kauss, H. 1972. *Z. Pflanzenphysiol.* 67:385–98

187. Scholander, P. F., Hammel, H. T., Hemmingsen, E., Garey, W. 1962. *Plant Physiol.* 37:722–29

188. Schultz, S. G., Epstein, W., Solomon, A. K. 1963. *J. Gen. Physiol.* 47:329–46

189. Schultz, S. G., Solomon, A. K. 1961. *J. Gen. Physiol.* 45:355–69

190. Schultz, S. G., Wilson, N. L., Epstein, W. 1962. *J. Gen. Physiol.* 46:159–66

191. Shachar-Hill, B., Hill, A. E. 1970. *Biochim. Biophys. Acta* 211:313–17

192. Shere, S. M., Jacobson, L. 1970. *Physiol. Plant.* 23:51–62

193. Shieh, Y. J., Barber, J. 1971. *Biochim. Biophys. Acta* 233:594–603

194. Singh, T. N., Aspinall, D., Paleg, L. G. 1972. *Nature* 236:188–90

195. Slatyer, R. O. 1963. *Environmental Control of Plant Growth,* ed. L. T. Evans, 33–54. New York: Academic. 449 pp.

196. Slayman, C. W., Slayman, C. L. 1968. *J. Gen. Physiol.* 52:424–43

197. Smith, F. A., Raven, J. A. 1974. See Ref. 11, 380–85

198. Smith, D. W., Brock, T. D. 1973. *J. Gen. Microbiol.* 79:219–31

199. Steiner, M., Eschrich, W. 1958. *Encyclopedia of Plant Physiology,* ed. W. Ruhland, 4:334–54. Berlin: Springer. 1210 pp.

200. Steudle, E., Zimmermann, U. 1971. *Z. Naturforsch.* 26b:1276–82

201. Steudle, E., Zimmermann, U. 1974. *Biochim. Biophys. Acta* 332:399–412

202. Steudle, E., Zimmermann, U. 1974. See Ref. 11, 72–78

203. Stewart, G. R., Lee, J. A. 1974. *Planta* 120:279–89

204. Storey, R., Wyn Jones, R. G. 1975. *Plant Sci. Lett.* 4:161–68

205. Spanswick, R. M., Stolarek, J., Williams, E. J. 1967. *J. Exp. Bot.* 18:1–16

206. Spencer, J. F. T. 1968. *Progr. Ind. Microbiol.* 7:1–42

207. Sutcliffe, J. F. 1954. *J. Exp. Bot.* 5:215–31

208. Tazawa, M. 1957. *Protoplasma* 48:342–59

209. Ibid 1961. 53:227–58

210. Tazawa, M. 1964. *Plant Cell Physiol.* 5:33–43

211. Tazawa, M. 1972. *Protoplasma* 75:427–60

212. Tazawa, M., Kishimoto, U., Kikuyama, M. 1974. *Plant Cell Physiol.* 15:103–10

213. Tazawa, M., Nagai, R. 1960. *Plant Cell Physiol.* 1:255–68

214. Tazawa, M., Nagai, R. 1966. *Z. Pflanzenphysiol.* 54:333–44

215. Tazawa, S., Kataoka, H., Tazawa, M. 1974. *Plant Cell Physiol.* 15:457–68

216. Thimann, K. V., Loos, G. M., Samuel, E. W. 1960. *Plant Physiol.* 35:848–53

217. Thomas, D. A. 1970. *Aust. J. Biol. Sci.* 23:961–79

218. Tramér, P. O. 1957. *Ber. Schweiz. Bot. Ges.* 67:411–19

219. Treichel, S. P. 1975. *Plant Sci. Lett.* 4:141–44

220. Treichel, S. P., Bauer, P. 1974. *Oecologia* 17:87–95

221. Treichel, S. P., Kirst, G. O., von Willert, D. J. 1974. *Z. Pflanzenphysiol.* 71:437–49

222. Tresner, H. D., Hayes, J. A. 1971. *Appl. Microbiol.* 22:210–13

223. Trezzi, F., Galli, M. G., Bellini, E. 1965. *G. Bot. Ital.* 72:127–63

224. von Willert, D. J. 1969. *Ber. Dtsch. Bot. Ges.* 81:442–49

225. Waisel, Y. 1972. *Biology of Halophytes.* New York: Academic. 395 pp.

226. Wallace, A., Kleinkopf, G. E. 1974. *Plant Sci. Lett.* 3:251–57

227. Wegmann, K. 1971. *Biochim. Biophys. Acta* 234:317–23

228. Wetherell, D. F. 1963. *Physiol. Plant.* 16:82–91

229. Winkenbach, F. 1971. *Ber. Schweiz. Bot. Ges.* 80:374–90

230. Winter, K. 1973. *Ber. Dtsch. Bot. Ges.* 86:467–76

231. Yamada, H., Okamoto, H. 1961. *Z. Allg. Mikrobiol.* 1:245–50

232. Yamanoto, M. 1967. *Z. Allg. Mikrobiol.* 7:267–77

233. Yamanoto, M., Okamoto, H. 1967. *Z. Allg. Mikrobiol.* 7:143–50

234. Zimmermann, U., Steudle, E. 1971. *Mar. Biol.* 11:132–37

235. Zimmermann, U., Steudle, E. 1974. *J. Membr. Biol.* 16:331–52

236. Zimmermann, U., Steudle, E. 1974. See Ref. 11, 64–71

Ann. Rev. Plant Physiol. 1976. 27:507–28

FREEZING AND INJURY IN PLANTS

❖7620

M. J. Burke
Department of Horticulture, Colorado State University, Fort Collins, Colorado 80523

L. V. Gusta
Crop Development Centre, Crop Science Department, University of Saskatchewan, Saskatoon, Saskatchewan, Canada SFN OWO

H. A. Quamme
Agriculture Canada, Research Station, Harrow, Ontario, Canada NOR 1HO

C. J. Weiser
Department of Horticulture, Oregon State University, Corvallis, Oregon 97331

P. H. Li
Laboratory of Plant Hardiness, Department of Horticulture Science, University of Minnesota, St. Paul, Minnesota 55101

CONTENTS

     507

INTRODUCTION

Freezing injury is a major cause of crop loss, and low temperature is reputedly the single most limiting factor to natural plant distribution (92). The stresses of late spring and early fall frosts, low midwinter minima, and rapid temperature changes cause various types of injury directly and indirectly associated with the freezing of water in plant tissues. These include crown kill in winter cereals, biennials, and herbaceous perennials; sunscald on thin-barked tree species; winter burn to evergreen foliage; blackheart and frost cracking in xylem of trees and shrubs; blossom kill; death of vegetative shoots in late maturing perennial species; death of buds and bark in plants which lose hardiness rapidly during transient warm spells in winter; and outright death of tender annuals.

While some species are always killed at the moment they freeze, others will tolerate extremely low temperatures ($-196°C$) in midwinter (104). The low temperature responses of most plants fall between these extremes, and freezing resistance may change markedly with season and stage of development. For example, hardy trees and shrubs which survive $-196°C$ during winter dormancy may be killed at $-3°C$ during active spring growth.

Acclimation is the term which describes the seasonal transition from the tender to the hardy condition in hardy species. The effects of shorter days, decreasing temperatures, and other factors which trigger or influence acclimation have been extensively studied (38, 94, 106, 118), as have the biochemical (32, 68, 69), physiological (23, 38, 39), and biophysical (8) changes which occur in plant cells and tissues during acclimation. Acclimation and the reverse process, deacclimation, will not be reviewed here. In short, some species acclimate extensively in response to environmental and endogenous factors; others acclimate only a few degrees; and some do not acclimate at all. In plants which acclimate, water content (degree of hydration) almost invariably decreases with increasing hardiness, and increases as plants deacclimate. Mature seeds and spores which contain little water are notably resistant to freezing stress.

The status of water in living tissues, its behavior during freezing, and its role in freezing injury are the subjects of this review. Our limited understanding of these topics restricts progress in attenuating or avoiding freezing damage via crop culture and management, physiological manipulation, or genetic improvement. We have attempted to write a review which will be useful to interested biologists and agriculturists who are not hardiness experts.

Plant freezing has been reviewed from several perspectives. In 1967 Olien (86) reviewed the thermodynamic aspects of freezing in herbaceous semihardy plants. Mazur (79) discussed the general physical aspects of freezing from a cryobiological viewpoint in 1969. Mayland & Cary (77) examined the biochemical and biophysical aspects of freezing injury in 1970. Parker's 1963 review (92) emphasized ecological aspects of freezing injury in hardy forest species, as did the review by Alden & Hermann (3) in 1971. Weiser (126) discussed freezing in hardy woody plants in 1970. Russian workers, notably Tumanov & Krasavtsev (124), have also written extensively on freezing in woody species. In their classic book on low temperature effects in biology in 1940, Luyet & Gehenio (73) discussed some aspects of plant freezing. Levitt (64, 66) has thoroughly surveyed the world literature on freezing injury in plants in his books on environmental stresses in 1956 and 1972. Of particular interest is the extensive research on woody species by Siminovitch & Scarth (113) and Sakai (105), on winter cereal by Johansson (43), and on herbaceous tissues by Asahina (4).

In this review similarities and differences in freezing and freezing injury in different plant types are discussed. We have emphasized relatively new methods which can be used to characterize freezing processes in plants, and recent findings which cast doubt on some generally accepted views.

KINDS OF FREEZING AND FREEZING RESPONSES

Plants have evolved a variety of mechanisms for resisting cold temperatures. Some survive by avoiding rather than tolerating freezing, such as the annual plants with little or no frost resistance which survive by means of dehydrated seeds that are very hardy. Roots, crowns, and even tops of some herbaceous biennials and perennials survive because snow and soil moderate extremes of air temperature.

When plant cells freeze, ice forms either inside (intracellular) or outside (extracellular) of cell walls. Intracellular freezing is a cataclysmic event in the living protoplasm which disrupts the integrity of the cell causing death. It occurs in tender plants that lack the capacity to acclimate and in hardy plants before they acclimate. Some "deep supercooled" tissues in hardy plants also freeze intracellularly (24).

Plants which are tolerant to freezing generally undergo extracellular freezing. Extracellular ice formation occurs in the vicinity of the cell walls (66). Apparently ice can often accumulate in this site with few ill effects. Some agriculturally important herbaceous plants such as winter cereals can survive extracellular freezing to −25°C, and numerous hardy woody species can survive extracellular freezing at the temperature of liquid nitrogen (−196°C) when fully acclimated. In the next section we summarize what we think takes place during freezing in several groups of plants which differ in hardiness. The evidence and rationale for these interpretations is discussed in the ensuing sections.

There are various modes of survival for plants exposed to subfreezing temperatures in nature. Plants with high solute concentrations can avoid a few degrees of freezing because of their depressed freezing point. However, few species of agricultural importance have freezing point depressions of more than 4°C, and most fall in the range of 1 to 2°C. A few halophilic plants have freezing point depressions as low as −14°C.

Freezing point depression is the temperature at which melting occurs, but not necessarily the temperature at which plants will freeze because almost all plants supercool several degrees regardless of their hardiness. Supercooling probably occurs because of a lack of nucleating substances necessary for ice initiation and ice growth barriers in some tissues. During controlled freezing, woody plant stems frequently supercool to −15°C. Under field conditions whole plants seldom supercool to this extent for reasons which will be discussed later. In mild climates the few degrees of protection afforded by supercooling and/or freezing point depressions could be a significant avoidance mechanism; survival of olive leaves has been attributed to their ability to supercool several degrees (60).

In the absence of nucleating substances pure water can supercool to −38°C. This temperature is called the homogenous nucleation point for pure water, i.e. the temperature at which spontaneous ice nucleation occurs in the absence of nucleating substances (22, 101). It has recently been found that some plant tissues (flower buds and living cells in the wood of most temperate zone trees) "deep supercool" to temperatures around −40°C even though adjacent cells in the same plant freeze at only a few degrees below 0°C. The lowest supercooling observed in xylem parenchyma cells has been −47°C (25). These very low supercooling points are thought to represent the homogeneous ice nucleation temperatures of the cellular solutions of the tissues involved. When nucleation does occur in cells which are "deep supercooled" freezing is probably intracellular and lethal.

Tender Plants with Little or No Freezing Tolerance

The first "killing frost" of autumn (−1° to −3°C) kills many tender annual plants such as corn, cucurbits, and beans, which have little if any capacity to acclimate. On the morning after such a frost, the injured foliage appears flaccid and water-soaked, cell membranes have lost their semipermeability, and intracellular compartmentalization is destroyed. During active periods of growth the leaves and new shoots of unacclimated hardy trees and shrubs are also injured by a −1° to −3°C frost. Supercooling and freezing point depression may afford slight protection in these cases, but when nucleation occurs in the plant, rapid intracellular freezing takes place causing irreparable damage; notably the destruction of membrane continuity.

Chilling injury in species of tropical origin occurs at temperatures well above freezing, usually between 0° and 14°C (74). This extreme example of low temperature injury in plants apparently results from temperature induced lipid structure transitions (99) which disrupt membrane proteins. Chilling injury is not a form of freezing injury, but lipid "phase" changes or other membrane structural changes below 0°C could be involved in freezing.

Plants with Limited Hardiness

Most plants which survive freezing temperatures do so by tolerating some ice formation in their tissues. Herbaceous plants such as spring wheat, peas, and potatoes, for example, withstand a few degrees of frost, and some (winter wheat, cabbage, and turf grasses) have the capacity to acclimate and may survive winter temperatures to about −25°C. Many of these species survive in regions where the minimum air temperature falls below the tissue-killing temperature because regenerative growing points are located at or below the soil surface and thus they are protected by residual soil heat and the insulating properties of snow.

Soil and air environments are markedly different; the temperature in soil frozen to a depth of several feet under a few inches of snow may be $-2°$ or $-3°C$ when the air temperature is $-25°C$. Plants with growing points below the soil surface are particularly subject to indirect forms of winter injury such as flooding and soil frost heaving which can lift the crowns (110). Soil moisture can also influence hardiness and survival because it affects tissue hydration (88) and soil temperature. The temperature of moist soil fluctuates less than dry soil because of the buffering influence provided by the heat of fusion of soil water.

Herbaceous plants seldom supercool more than $-1°$ or $-2°C$ unless tissue moisture content is very low (88). In desiccated tissues ice crystals do not spread uniformly, and some groups of cells may supercool several degrees and then freeze suddenly (probably intracellularly) with injurious effects. In herbaceous plants that tolerate ice formation within their tissues, ice appears to propagate primarily through the extracellular spaces, and, as noted, lethal intracellular freezing is rare. It may occasionally occur in highly hydrated tissues when freezing is too rapid to permit migration of cellular water to extracellular ice crystallization sites.

Although plants with limited hardiness may avoid intracellular freezing, a temperature is reached at which dehydration stresses resulting from extracellular freezing cause death. Generally, hardier plants can survive with more of their water frozen than less hardy plants. The "deep supercooling" that has been found in some woody plant tissues has not been observed in herbaceous species.

Woody Plants which Deep Supercool

Most deciduous forest species and fruit tree cultivars avoid freezing in some, but usually not all, of their tissues by "deep supercooling" to temperatures as low as $-40°C$ in midwinter (9, 25, 97). Apple is typical of such plants. During active summer growth apple tissues are very susceptible to freezing, and injury can occur at $-2°$ to $-3°C$ as a result of intracellular freezing. In the autumn and winter the tissues of apple trees acclimate and freezing becomes extracellular in some tissues while others supercool extensively. Acclimated bark and bud tissues freeze extracellularly after a few degrees of supercooling. Much of the water in the cambium, cortical, and phloem tissues of the living bark migrates to sites in the outer cortex where ice forms in large masses between cells (127). Considerable amounts of ice are accommodated in this region with little apparent damage. Ice masses also form between scales of dormant buds. Stem tissues of hardy apple cultivars which freeze in this manner survive slow freezing to $-60°C$ in midwinter or immersion in liquid nitrogen if frozen slowly to $-30°C$ first (105).

Xylem ray parenchyma cells supercool in such stems, however, and are killed at $-40°C$ or above. The extent of "deep supercooling" in hardy plant tissues varies with the season and the hardiness of the plant, reaching a maximum in midwinter. It appears that "deep supercooling" is a survival mechanism for some plant tissues and suggests that the cold acclimation process involves reduction or elimination of ice nucleating centers in cells of such tissues, development of effective barriers to nucleation by ice in or around adjacent cells, or both.

Death in xylem rays seems to be associated with a discrete and measurable freezing event in such plants, i.e. differential thermal analysis (DTA) measurements (Figure 1), revealing that heat is released at the temperature at which the xylem parenchyma cells are injured (Figure 1 and 2d). The DTA method will be discussed in a later section. In short, it is thought that the sudden release of heat observed at low temperature results from the intracellular freezing of supercooled water in living xylem cells and that it represents the killing point of these tissues (9).

This type of freezing pattern is typical of tree species native to the Eastern Deciduous Forest of North America, species with northern range limits extending only to latitudes where the minimum winter temperature reaches –40°C. Xylem rays

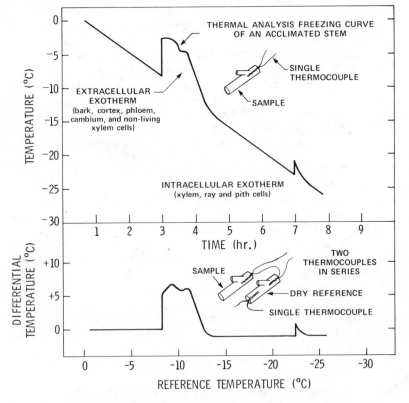

Figure 1 Comparison of thermal analysis and differential thermal analysis (DTA). In both experiments the sample is cooled over a period of time and the sample temperature or the differential temperature between the sample and a dry reference is monitored. The peaks or exotherms indicate freezing points.

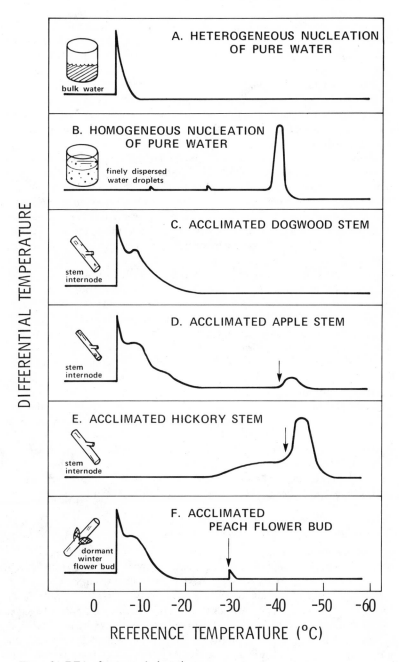

Figure 2   DTA of water and plant tissues.

are characteristically the least hardy stem tissue in midwinter, but they are often hardier (as much as 20°C) than the cambium, phloem, and cortical tissues of the bark in early autumn and late spring (97). Generally only part of the stem water supercools. One exception is shagbark hickory in which all the water in stem internodes supercools to about –40°C in midwinter (Figure 2e) (9).

Functional wood of trees and shrubs which transports water and nutrients consists largely of dead cells. Xylem ray parenchyma are apparently involved in lateral transport between young xylem sapwood and the cambium and living tissues of the bark, but their role is seldom considered to be vitally important to the survival of the plant. This gives rise to the question: Is death of xylem ray cells really important to the ultimate survival of a plant? The close relationship between the northern limits of the natural ranges of Eastern Deciduous Forest species and the probability of occurrence of minimum temperatures which will cause xylem injury (25) circumstantially suggests that the answer is yes. More extensive studies of blackheart injury in cultivated fruits such as apples and pears also support this conclusion. These fruit trees all exhibit deep supercooling in xylem, and blackheart injury is common in severe winters in northern production areas. In this type of winter injury the living xylem cells are killed, the wood becomes dark and discolored as a result of oxidation, and vessels become filled with gummy occlusions (20). Blackheart doesn't kill trees outright, but wood rotting organisms often invade injured trees and this combination of factors seriously limits productivity and tree longevity (11).

Deep supercooling also occurs in the dormant overwintering flower buds of some plants such as deciduous azalea, blueberries, apricots, peaches, cherries, and plums (Figure 2f). These plants also have "deep supercooling" xylem exotherms. Apple flower buds do not deep supercool although apple xylem does. In peach, for example, the flower primordia in dormant winter buds supercool to as low as –25°C. As in the case of xylem ray injury, the killing temperature of buds coincides with a sudden exotherm or release of heat (Figure 2f). These exotherms appear as buds begin to acclimate in the autumn, and shift to progressively lower temperatures as acclimation proceeds. They persist until flower buds expand in the spring. When flower buds begin expanding they supercool little and rapidly lose hardiness (98). Fully open flowers normally tolerate only –1° to –3°C of frost (5). Dormant winter buds of some hardy deciduous azaleas supercool in winter to temperatures as low as –41°C (26).

Woody Plants which Do Not Deep Supercool

Very hardy woody plants, such as those native to the Boreal Forest of North America, do not deep supercool. The extracellular freezing process is similar to that found in less hardy herbaceous plants, but ultimate hardiness is considerably greater. Ice formation begins somewhere in the plant after a few degrees of supercooling, and ice propagation proceeds through the extracellular spaces. This creates an extracellular vapor pressure deficit, and cell water is drawn from the protoplasm to the extracellular spaces where it freezes. In midwinter, many hardy woody plants survive the extreme dehydration that results when all of their freezable water crystallizes extracellularly. Generally, the hardier the plant the greater the capacity of cells to tolerate dehydration. Paper birch, red-osier dogwood, willow, trembling aspen, and many other plants with this type of freezing pattern have natural ranges that extend to the arctic zones and survive experimental freezing to –196°C when they are fully acclimated (25). At such low temperatures, all the freezable water is frozen extracellularly (108). The unfreezable (bound) water fraction in winter stems of such species may amount to about 30% of the total water in the tissue (9). There is no apparent relationship between the amount of bound water and hardiness (9, 31).

METHODS FOR STUDYING FREEZING IN PLANTS

Some early determinations of ice formation in plants were indirect and assumed that plant tissue solutions froze as "ideal solutions" (2, 44, 63). Ideal freezing curves have been described (31) and can be calculated if cell solute concentrations, hydrostatic pressures, and the amounts of unfreezable or "bound" water are known. Initially freezing curves were predicted from estimates of cell solute concentration arrived at by measuring the freezing point depression of expressed plant sap or by plasmolytic measurements on intact cells (2, 63). Calorimetric measurements of the liquid water contents of tissues at two subfreezing temperatures provided a further refinement in freezing curve predictions (44). Some of the direct methods which have been used to study freezing are nuclear magnetic resonance (NMR), calorimetry, differential scanning calorimetry (DSC), DTA, phase contrast light microscopy, electrical resistance measurements, electrophoretic mobility and diffusion of dyes, dielectric constant measurement, and dilotometry.

Electrical resistance, electrophoretic dye mobility, and dye diffusion techniques have been developed primarily by Olien and co-workers in studies on model systems (89, 90), cereals (84), and some woody plants (18). These methods were designed to measure the fraction of unfrozen water in the extracellular spaces. They are based on the hypothesis that the hydrated extracellular spaces form a continuous liquid network throughout a plant; i.e. the mobility of dyes and ions is reduced in proportion to the reduction in extracellular liquid water during freezing.

Phase contrast light microscopy has been used to study freezing in cortical parenchyma cells of elder, birch, and apple bark (54). The refractive index of dehydrated cells was determined during freezing. These measurements were used to compute cell solute concentrations which is proportional to the degree of cellular dehydration. Calculations estimating the unfrozen water fraction from refractive index measurements agree well with calorimetric values.

Freezing has also been studied by measuring the expansion of ice in tissue via changes in its displacement (dilotometry) and specific gravity. Levitt (66) has reviewed these methods.

Nuclear Magnetic Resonance

In recent years NMR has been used to study water and water interactions in a wide variety of materials ranging from trees (8, 9), biopolymers and cells (6, 14, 59, 125), to silica and clay (16, 91, 93, 102, 103), and has been used to study liquid water in frozen protein solutions (56–58), and to quantitatively measure the liquid water in frozen wheat-flour dough (121, 122), fish muscle (120), and plants (8). NMR is a type of spectroscopy which employs radio frequency light, and its utility for studying freezing in plant tissues depends on the large spectral differences between ice and liquid water. The spectrum for pure liquid water (a plot of radio frequency vs absorption intensity) is a single absorption line (Figure 3a). The width of this line is dependent on the state of the water. For example, ice and solids have such wide lines (30,000 to 100,000 Hertz) that they are not observed on conventional NMR spectrometers. Since line widths for liquid water in tissues are much narrower (usually one to several hundred Hertz) they show up clearly. The amount of liquid water is proportional to the area under the NMR line (Figure 3).

A stem section (0.5 cm long) placed in a refrigerated NMR sample chamber typically yields a single NMR line approximately 50 to 10,000 Hertz in width, depending on the temperature (Figure 3a). The line is narrowest above the freezing point and becomes progressively broader as freezing progresses. As the line broadens, the liquid water content—represented by the area under the line—becomes increasingly difficult to determine because of the low amplitude of the peak.

Pulse NMR is a particularly useful variation of NMR for studying plant samples (Figure 3b). It provides the same information as the NMR line method, i.e. continuous wave NMR, and the experimental configuration and sample requirements are similar. Detailed information on pulse NMR can be found in Farrar & Becker (21).

In pulse NMR studies, short radio frequency pulses (usually 90° or 180° pulses) are used to induce a transient magnetization in the sample. The signal following a 90° radio frequency pulse is called the free induction decay. It is recorded on an oscilloscope and the decay rate is related to the NMR line width (Figure 3b). The initial amplitude of the free induction decay is proportional to the area under the NMR line. Therefore, the initial amplitude is related to the liquid water content. The free induction decay for ice is so rapid that ice spectra are not observed in experiments designed to measure liquids (9). Pulse NMR methods have been used to characterize the freezing of winter cereal leaves (31), potato leaves (10), and woody stem tissues (8).

NMR methods provide one of the few ways to directly measure the liquid water content of partially frozen tissues. The curves obtained for winter cereal crowns (31) during freezing are similar to those predicted for ideal solutions. The shape of these curves suggests that there are two types of water in these tissues: a "free" or freezable water fraction which crystallizes progressively as the temperature is reduced, and a "bound" fraction of water that does not freeze at any temperature tested. The freezable water fraction behaves like a salt or sugar solution when it freezes, and the unfreezable fraction behaves like the bound water in frozen protein solutions (56–58).

It is widely thought that hardy plants contain more bound water than tender plants. Several attempts to correlate the quantity of unfreezable water in plant samples with their cold hardiness revealed no such relationship (8, 31). Dogwood stems and winter cereal all had 0.2 to 0.4 g of bound water/g dry tissue, and there was no correlation with hardiness (8, 31). This was true even though the hardiness

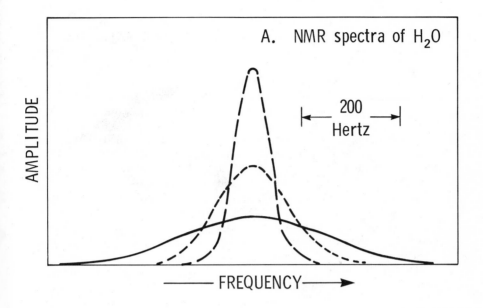

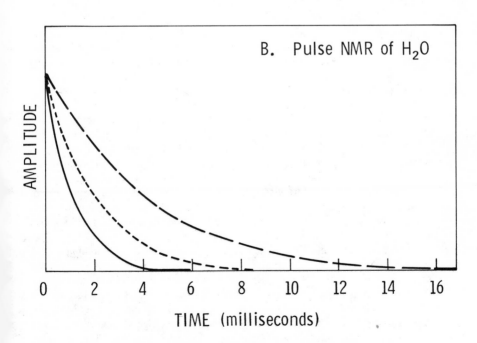

Figure 3 Nuclear magnetic resonance (NMR) spectra and pulse NMR of water.

of the tissues studied ranged from −3° to −196°C. Nonliving hydrated systems such as filter paper and proteins often contain more "bound" water than these plant samples (58, 89).

Calorimetry

Calorimetry basically involves the measurement of exothermic (heat releasing) and endothermic (heat consuming) events by recording relative temperature changes in a plant sample and a nonliving reference. Since the freezing of water is an exothermic reaction, temperature measurements of heat release in plant samples can be used to characterize freezing processes in plants. Similarly, water endotherms can be studied during thawing. The freezing and thawing of water are the predominant exothermic and endothermic events, respectively, in plant tissues.

There are basically three types of thermal analysis techniques which rely on these principles: (*a*) thermal analysis, (*b*) DTA, and (*c*) DSC. These methods are used primarily to determine the freezing and thawing points of tissue water, and, particularly DSC, to estimate the amount of water that freezes.

Thermal analysis is the simplest technique. It is particularly useful for determining the temperature at which exotherms occur during freezing by recording the temperature of a plant sample during freezing—e.g. inserting a thermocouple in a stem or bud and recording the temperature while the sample is frozen (Figure 1a).

DTA is a minor refinement to conventional thermal analysis as shown in Figure 1b. This is usually performed with two thermocouples in series, one in the reference and one in the sample. Data from the DTA are generally plotted as the temperature difference between sample and reference on the ordinate vs sample temperature, reference temperature, or time on the abscissa (Figure 1b). Several systems for DTA have been described for studying freezing in plants (26, 96).

DSC has been applied to freezing of plant tissues, and has employed two types of calorimeters: the Calvet calorimeter (43, 44, 51–53, 89) and the more conventional scanning calorimeter. These instruments provide the same information as thermal analysis or DTA, but they also quantify the amount of water that freezes or thaws between two experimental temperatures. Unlike other thermal analysis methods, which measure temperature or temperature difference, the differential scanning calorimeter measures differences in heat evolution or absorption between the sample and reference during cooling or warming. The amount of water which is frozen is determined by measuring the heat evolved during cooling, or absorbed during warming, and by making calculations based on the heat of fusion of water and the heat capacities of ice and liquid water.

A major weakness in using calorimetric measurements for determining liquid water content is in choosing the correct heat of fusion and, to a lesser extent, heat capacity for tissue water. When most of the water in a sample is still liquid it has a heat of fusion near that of pure water (79 cal/g). However, the heat of fusion may be considerably less at low subfreezing temperatures, where a larger fraction of the water is frozen (8, 89). Such unfrozen water will have a high solute concentration and will be at or near interfaces with macromolecules. In fact, NMR evidence suggests that a fraction of tissue water is bound in some way to macromolecular structures. To freeze "bound" water, it is necessary to unbind water molecules before they freeze; the correct heat of fusion is, therefore, 79 cal/g minus the heat of binding. In many cellulose and protein systems, heats of binding may be as high as the heat of fusion so the heat of fusion for "bound" water may be zero or at least significantly lower than that of pure water (116). For example, water freezing in cellulose at $-1°C$ has a heat of fusion of 12 cal/g. At $-10°C$ the heat of fusion is 0 cal/g (89). Many calorimetric studies have not taken this into account.

Calorimetric methods are extremely sensitive to the freezing of minute quantities of water, and the thermal and DTA methods require only simple equipment. The disadvantage of these techniques is that it is difficult to quantify the amount of freezing that takes place.

An important recent application of thermal analysis and DTA has been detection of "deep supercooling" in some plant tissues previously described (Figure 2). This finding will be useful in testing the efficacy of chemical and cultural means of increasing hardiness and in providing plant breeders with selection criteria because deep supercooling of certain key tissues limits plant survival and crop productivity.

Hardy North American species such as *Populus tremuloides,* which range into the arctic and subarctic regions where the temperature frequently falls below $-40°C$, do not have low temperature exotherms (Figure 4). Species such as *Quercus rubra,* which have low temperature exotherms, are native to parts of the United States and southern Canada (Figure 4). The northern limits of their ranges coincide closely

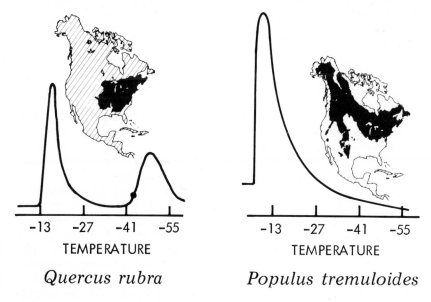

TEMPERATURE

TEMPERATURE

Quercus rubra   *Populus tremuloides*

Figure 4   DTAs and geographic ranges of two species.

with the –40°C average annual minimum temperature isotherm for North America (Figure 4). This is also true for 28 other North American species tested (25).

It seems likely that the capacity to supercool is an adaptive mechanism in the xylem of certain deciduous species for avoiding the effects of freezing, but species which do not deep supercool survive lower temperatures. Specified wood or bud tissues which supercool often do not survive temperatures as low as tissues in the same plant which do not supercool. The adaptive advantage of deep supercooling, if any, is unclear. Interestingly, supercooling is found in deciduous trees with hard woods. It has been hypothesized that wood stiffness does not allow extracellular freezing, and collapse of the ray parenchyma is not possible. Therefore the only mechanism of survival in the ray parenchyma cells is deep supercooling (9).

FACTORS AFFECTING THE FREEZING PROCESS

Freezing Point Depression

As previously pointed out, freezing point depression itself does not appear to be an important means of freezing avoidance in plants. It lowers the freezing point of cell water and changes the freezing curve. In plants with limited hardiness, however, it could be significant. It has been suggested that cold acclimation of winter wheats is partially due to an increase in solute concentrations during hardening (43, 44). In plants with some tolerance of freeze-induced dehydration, a scheme has been outlined suggesting a relationship between freezing point depression and hardiness (66). There appeared to be reasonably good correlations in some tissues like wheat and rye leaves (43) but not in others like *C. stolonifera* stem, wheat crowns, and potato leaves (8, 10, 31).

Supercooling and Ice Nucleation

Water can remain in a supercooled state in plants if there is no external ice nucleation, and/or if the temperature does not fall below the homogeneous nucleation temperature. External ice such as hoar frost or soil ice can readily nucleate plants via entry sites such as stomates, lenticles, and wounds. Once initiated, ice grows rapidly through the plant from one or more nucleation sites. Ice grows most rapidly through the vascular tissues. The extent of initial supercooling influences the number and distribution of nucleation sites. Several nucleation sites may arise simultaneously if there is considerable supercooling or if there are a large number of favorable sites for nucleation by external ice. Since spontaneous nucleation is a chance event, large plants or plant samples are less likely to supercool extensively than small ones. Mulberry leaves, for example, supercool less when they are attached to the stem than when they are detached (49). Short spruce needles supercooled to lower temperatures than long ones because longer needles have more external nucleation sites and more water subject to chance spontaneous nucleation (47, 111). The location and distribution of external nucleation sites in boxwood (*Buxus*) leaves varied with age and maturity; older leaves were less likely to supercool (45). In many plants the likelihood of nucleation (from external ice) appears to be dependent on morphological features of the plant rather than the presence of nucleating compounds suspended in water (46), e.g. a thick cuticle, if continuous, may be quite an effective barrier to seeding by external ice (114).

Nucleation and the extent of supercooling are important considerations in conducting tests on detached plant parts. Small excised plant samples tend to supercool more than whole plants for the reasons mentioned and may lead to erroneous conclusions when results from controlled freezing tests are extrapolated to the field. Freezing in a sample which is substantially supercooled is rapid, and may be more injurious than slower (equilibrium) freezing in a sample which has supercooled little. Excised samples are usually artificially seeded with ice crystals in various ways to circumvent this problem.

Deep supercooling observed in some woody plant tissues likely involves supercooling of an aqueous fraction which is effectively isolated from seeding by surrounding ice, and which is divided into small compartments. This may be analagous to the extensive supercooling observed in finely dispersed particles of pure water where homogeneous or heterogeneous ice nucleation in one particle (compartment) is isolated and confined to a small fraction of the total water (101). The majority of compartmentalized pure water then freezes at $-38°C$ where pure water spontaneously nucleates. The presence of solutes and solvents in water can further depress the spontaneous nucleation point. The deep supercooling exotherm of shagbark hickory stems has been lowered experimentally by adding solutes (9).

The nucleation point appears constant in acclimated plants which deep supercool. At a given sampling date it consistently occurs at a certain temperature and is little affected by freezing rate (9). Equilibration of this supercooled water does not take place even under the considerable vapor pressure deficit at $-35°C$. In such deep supercooled systems the very slow freezing rate observed is due to ice nucleations and is of the order of magnitude of weeks or years at $-35°C$ (9). In effect this supercooled fraction of tissue water is stable and present throughout the winter at temperatures below freezing, but above the homogeneous nucleation temperature of the supercooled fraction.

In xylem parenchyma and flower bud tissues, it is postulated that water is isolated in the tissues by barriers which prevent ice penetration from adjacent frozen tissues (9, 95), like the zone of relatively undifferentiated cells between the unfrozen flower primordia in the bud and the frozen stem tissues.

At the homogeneous nucleation temperature, however, freezing is rapid and almost certainly intracellular in deep supercooled tissues, causing death. It has been proposed (26) that barriers to ice propagation may involve fine microcapillaries of the cell wall; microcapillaries so small that they prevent ice seeding through the cell wall. An alternate hypothesis (26) is that antinucleating chemicals are present in protoplasm which prevent cellular nucleation. In any event, the deep supercooling phenomenon hinges on some structural feature because finely ground powders of tissues and tissue sectioned at 0.5 mm thickness do not deep supercool (9, 98). The structural feature does not directly involve the plasmalemma or protoplasm because supercooling can be demonstrated even in tissues killed by steam or chloroform treatments or oven drying and rehydration (98).

Ice Propagation and Growth

Once freezing is initiated, water molecules migrate and freeze at the surface. During much of the slow extracellular freezing, water becomes frozen in large ice masses at specific sites which accomodate ice with little damage to the plant. This type of localized freezing is apparent in the cortical tissues of the bark of hardy woody plants (127), in mesophyll of boxwood leaves (35), and in basal regions of flower and leaf bud scales (19, 127). The different patterns of water migration and ice formation observed in plants and plant tissues is probably related to their freezing resistance.

Electrophoretic methods indicate that water in cherry stems migrates to nucleating centers where ice grows unopposed. In azalea stems, which are less hardy than cherry, ice distribution is more diffuse and disruptive (18). In azalea flower buds, injury occurred at the base of the bud where large ice masses formed. The amount of injury appeared to be related to the amount of ice, which in turn was related to water content (71, 72).

Freezing rate influences patterns of ice growth and crystal size; fast freezing generally results in many small crystals, while fewer large crystals form when freezing is slow. Rapid freezing does not permit water migration to favored sites for ice crystal growth, and mechanical freezing damage can result. Furthermore, if freezing is very rapid, lethal intracellular freezing may occur (86). Single cells or small clusters of cells can survive $-196°C$ if they are cooled and warmed so rapidly (by plunging into liquid nitrogen followed by rapid warming) that the small ice crystals formed are not disruptive (107).

Freezing and Thawing Rates

Rapid experimental freezing or freezing that follows deep supercooling of some tissues in nature generally results in intracellular ice formation. The importance of slow freezing rates on survival has been demonstrated (86). Most of the freezable water in a plant crystallizes between $0°$ and $-10°C$, and at slow cooling rates ice grows extracellularly at preferred sites which can accommodate growing ice crystals (19, 35, 127). When freezing was initiated at $-2.6°C$ in winter cereals, the length of time for freezing to reach equilibrium at this temperature varied from 60 min in tender types to 30 min in hardier cultivars (Gusta, unpublished). Several investigators have shown that injury increases with the length of exposure to cold as the lethal temperature is approached (1, 29, 30, 40, 100). Hardy winter wheat was relatively unaffected by a cold treatment of $-16°C$ for 1 hr, whereas all the plants were killed after 120 hr at $-10°C$. Repeated freezing and thawing also has an amplifying effect on injury (86). Plants may be slightly injured when subjected to a low nonlethal temperature but killed by subsequent cold treatments, e.g. fully acclimated hardy winter wheat withstood slow freeze to $-19°C$ but was killed at $-12°C$ after two thawing and refreezing cycles (Gusta, unpublished). The reasons for this are not known, but it may be related to "pools" of bulk water created when large ice masses are thawed. This may be resolved by varying the time (for water re-equilibration within the plant) between thawing and freezing cycles.

Tissue Hydration

A slight difference in moisture content of hardy tissues such as winter cereal crowns has been shown to have a significant influence on the freezing process and on cold hardiness (13, 41, 77, 81, 84). The optimum moisture content for overwintering cereal crowns has been reported to be about 65% (81). At higher moisture contents, most of the water freezes rapidly at a single freezing point, and the resulting ice crystals cause disruption of the tissue. Roots of most plants contain more water than crown or stem, and are killed at warmer temperatures (84). Partial dehydration of woody stems can increase their hardiness by as much as 7°C (67), while water in dehydrated cereal crowns may supercool and freeze intracellularly in isolated pockets.

Cell Walls and Membranes as Freezing Barriers

Cell wall polymers interfere with the freezing process by interacting with ice (85, 87) and modifying the shape of ice that forms. The interference does not inhibit freezing, but modifies the structure of the ice crystal formed and determines where ice will form. Small and imperfect ice crystals are formed which are considered noninjurious to the cell. Cell walls and membranes may also restrict the movement of water molecules to the growing ice front (40, 41, 65, 83, 113) or act as barriers which impede the advance of an ice front.

The plasmalemma is a major barrier to ice crystal growth into the cell (65, 78, 88, 109). It is also the major barrier controlling water permeability. During cold acclimation of some tissues, membrane lipids become less saturated (17, 55, 75) and more permeable to water (55, 66). This could alter freezing patterns and reduce the chances of intracellular freezing (41, 65, 86). In potato, however, no differences in water permeability were found between hardy and tender selections and species (119).

MECHANISMS OF CELLULAR INJURY

Injury Resulting from Intracellular Freezing

Unfortunately, the mechanisms of freezing damage to plants are poorly understood. Intracellular freezing occurs suddenly as cells flash freeze, cell by cell, with thousands of tiny ice crystals forming throughout the protoplast and vacuole (4). Cells in which ice crystals are visible through a light microscope are almost always killed (4). Injury probably results from the cataclysmic mechanical stresses and dehydration imposed on macromolecular cellular structures by ice. Membrane destruction is one of the most readily apparent manifestations of intracellular freezing but may be only one of a myriad of cellular sites of injury. Enzymes loosed by the breakdown of cellular compartmentalization rapidly wreak havoc in the injured tissue.

In hardy cells frozen at less than 1°C per hour, intracellular freezing is not thought to occur, but tissues which deep supercool are probably an exception since the freezing in such tissues is very rapid even if cooling rates were slow. The death of supercooled tissues at the moment of freezing is, almost surely, the result of intracellular freezing. Light microscopic studies indicate that ice is present in ray parenchyma cells of shagbark hickory after they have frozen (9).

Injury Resulting from Extracellular Freezing

Hardiness in most plants appears to be related to tolerance of extracellular freezing (66). In effect this is a form of drought tolerance because removal of water from cells to extracellular ice imposes a considerable desiccation stress on the protoplasm. In many cases it is apparent, however, that desiccation alone is not the cause of freezing injury. Equivalent desiccation stress (from partial drying of samples) is also considerably less damaging when ice is formed in the plant than when it is not (119). Hence, damage caused by freezing cannot be attributed solely to desiccation but, in part, to the presence of ice in the tissue or other direct effects of low temperature such as the lipid phase separations in chilling injury or, as is more likely, by interaction of such factors.

Most of the current hypotheses proposed to explain freezing injury in one way or another suggest that dehydration of plant cells during freezing plays a primary role in the events which lead to death. These hypotheses include the sulfhydryl-disulfide hypothesis (65), the protein water shell hypothesis (36), the salting-out hypothesis (80), and the vital water hypothesis (126). A common denominator to all of these theories is the role that proteins play in cell structure and function. It has been shown that the membrane of most frost-injured cells are damaged (66) and that membrane-bound proteins may be involved (36, 66). There is direct evidence of loss in protein solubility (34, 61, 70, 123), and protein dissociation into subunits (28, 33, 48, 50) has been reported to occur following freezing. Loss in enzyme activity due to dehydration is also shown in cases of water stress (15, 117). Cyclic freezing and thawing of hydrated proteins increases denaturation in vitro (62). Glycerol, sucrose, dimethyl sulfoxide, polyvinylpyrrolidone, ethylene glycol, and other cryoprotective agents have been shown to inhibit protein denaturation during freezing (12, 66, 115).

Protein denaturation during freezing and thawing has been attributed to changed pH (12, 34, 61), increased salt concentration (115), oxidation of sulfhydryl groups (48), protein concentration (12), and loss of water which maintains essential conformation (70, 76). There is evidence that the membrane is the primary site of desiccation injury (30, 37, 41, 112, 128). Uncoupling of phosphorylation in thylakoid membranes during freezing is accentuated by increased concentrations of solutes which reach toxic level during freezing (36, 37). One or more of these desiccation effects could result in cellular injury and death. Much needs to be resolved before the picture is complete.

On a macro scale large ice masses cause shearing of tissues as in the vascular tissues of wheat crowns (88) and azalea flower buds (27) and frost cracks produced by ice in developing pear fruitlets (82). Little is known about ice effects at the cellular level, but tearing and disruption likely result as ice crystals grow and the desiccating protoplasts shrink. Protoplasts of hardy cells are more elastic (66).

Molecular level temperature effects are also likely. Olien (86) discusses low temperature-induced changes that could take place in membranes. In addition to lipid phase separations previously mentioned (99), lipoprotein membranes at low temperature are subject to fracture along hydrophobic regions due to weakening of intramolecular hydrophobic bonds at low temperature (42). Protein stability per se is also affected by low temperature alone (7).

SUMMARY

Freezing avoidance and tolerance mechanisms have been described in different plant types and tissues. Some plants and tissues are killed at the moment of freezing while others survive crystallization of all their freezable water; some supercool only a few degrees while in others "deep supercooling" (–20° to –45°C) is apparently a common freezing avoidance mechanism; living bark and cambium cells in a hardy twig may be 20°C hardier than adjacent xylem ray parenchyma cells on a given day in winter; massive membrane destruction apparently causes immediate death in crowns of winter cereals or bark tissues of trees when they are in the tender state, but destruction and other manifestations of death become apparent only after several days when they are acclimated.

The array of freezing processes and plant responses to freezing seems complex and confusing. Some similarities, even among diverse plant species and tissues, provide the basis, however, for some unifying concepts. Intracellular freezing in nature is probably invariably lethal. "Deep supercooling" is a common and effective freezing avoidance mechanism in tissues such as xylem ray parenchyma cells and dormant flower buds of many species native to climatic zones where minimum temperatures seldom fall below –40°C.

In woody and herbaceous plants which do not deep supercool (e.g. winter cereals, potato, and very hardy trees and shrubs), NMR patterns of water freezing and thawing are very similar. Thawing is essentially the reverse of the freezing pattern except that deep supercooled water thaws near 0°C, not at the temperature it froze. In effect, water in plants freezes and thaws essentially as an ideal salt solution. Unfortunately, increasing hardiness is not simply a matter of increasing cell solute concentration as has been suggested, and the amount of unfreezable (bound) water in plants does not appear to bear any relationship to hardiness. The difference between hardy and tender plants which survive freezing to some extent can be stated simply: hardy plants survive when more of their water is frozen than tender plants.

Relatively recent applications of calorimetric, NMR, and DTA techniques have elucidated several aspects of plant freezing processes. While no simple answers have been found, the prospects for further resolution of freezing injury and tolerance are encouraging.

ACKNOWLEDGMENT

The authors wish to acknowledge support from the Louis W. and Maud Hill Family Foundation.

Literature Cited

1. Ahring, R. M., Irving, R. M. 1969. *Crop Sci.* 9:615–18
2. Åkerman, Å. 1927. *Studien über den Kältetod und die Kälteresistens der Pflanzen.* Veröffentlichungen der Kunt und Alice Wallenberg-Stiftung X, Lund. 225 pp.
3. Alden, J., Hermann, R. K. 1971. *Bot. Rev.* 37:37–142
4. Asahina, E. 1956. *Low Temp. Sci.* 10:83–126
5. Ballard, J. K., Proebsting, E. L., Tukey, R. B. 1971. *Wash. State Univ. Ext. Serv. Circ.* 369
6. Berendson, H. 1974. *Water—A Comprehensive Treatise,* ed. F. Franks, 4:327–42. New York: Plenum. 5 vols. 889 pp.
7. Brandts, J. F., Fu, J., Nordin, J. H. 1970. *The Frozen Cell,* 189–208. Ciba Found. Symp. London: Churchill. 487 pp.
8. Burke, M. J., Bryant, R. G., Weiser, C. J. 1974. *Plant Physiol.* 54:392–98
9. Burke, M. J., George, M. F., Bryant, R. G. 1975. *Water Relations of Foods,* ed. R. B. Duckworth, 111–35. London: Academic. 715 pp.
10. Chen, P. 1975. *The study of freezing processes, biochemical changes and cold acclimation in Cornus and Solanum species in relation to the frost hardiness of water stress in controlled environments.* PhD thesis. Univ. Minnesota, St. Paul. 156 pp.
11. Childers, W. F. 1973. *Modern Fruit Science.* New Jersey: Sommerset. 185 pp.
12. Chilson, O. P., Costello, L. A., Kaplan, N. O. 1965. *Fed. Proc.* 24S:55–56 (Abstr.)
13. Clausen, E. 1964. *Bryologist* 67:411–17
14. Cooke, R., Kuntz, I. D. 1974. *Ann. Rev. Biophys. Bioeng.* 3:95–125
15. Darbyshire, B., Steer, B. T. 1973. *Aust. J. Biol. Sci.* 26:591–604
16. Davidson, D. W. 1973. See Ref. 6, 2:115–56
17. de la Roche, I. A., Andrews, C. J., Pomeroy, M. K., Weinberger, P., Kates, M. 1972. *Can. J. Bot.* 50:2401–9
18. Dennis, F. G. Jr., Lumis, G. P., Olien, C. R. 1972. *Plant Physiol.* 50:527–30
19. Dorsey, M. J. 1934. *Proc. Am. Soc. Hortic. Sci.* 11:130–37
20. Dorsey, M. J., Strasbaugh, P. D. 1923. *Bot. Gaz.* 74:113–42
21. Farrar, T. C., Becker, E. D. 1971. *Pulse and Fourier Transform NMR.* New York: Academic
22. Fletcher, N. H. 1970. *Chemical Physics of Ice.* Cambridge Univ. Press. 271 pp.
23. Fuchigami, L. H., Weiser, C. J., Evert, D. R., 1971. *Plant Physiol.* 47:98–103
24. George, M. F., Burke, M. J. 1976. *Curr. Adv. Plant Sci.* 8. In press
25. George, M. F., Burke, M. J., Pellett, H. M., Johnson, A. G. 1974. *HortScience* 9:519–22
26. George, M. F., Burke, M. J., Weiser, C. J. 1974. *Plant Physiol.* 54:29–35
27. Graham, P., Mullin, R. 1976. *J. Am. Soc. Hortic. Sci.* 101:4–7
28. Graves, D. J., Sealock, R. W., Wang, J. H. 1965. *Biochemistry* 2:290–95
29. Greenham, C. G. 1966. *Can. J. Bot.* 44:1471–83
30. Greenham, C. G., Daday, H. 1960. *Aust. J. Agric. Res.* 11:1–15
31. Gusta, L. V., Burke, M. J., Kapoor, A. C. 1975. *Plant Physiol.* 56:707–9
32. Gusta, L. V., Weiser, C. J. 1972. *Plant Physiol.* 49:91–96
33. Hanafusa, N. 1969. *Freezing and Drying of Microorganisms,* 117–29. Univ. Tokyo Press
34. Hashizume, K., Kakiachi, K., Koyana, E., Watanabe, T. 1971. *Agric. Biol. Chem.* 35:449–59
35. Hatakeyama, I., Kato, J. 1965. *Planta* 65:259–68
36. Heber, U. W., Santarius, K. A. 1964. *Plant Physiol.* 39:712–19
37. Heber, U. W., Tyankova, L., Santarius, K. A. 1971. *Biochim. Biophys. Acta* 241:578–92
38. Howell, G. S., Weiser, C. J. 1970. *Plant Physiol.* 45:390–94
39. Howell, G. S., Weiser, C. J. 1970. *J. Am. Soc. Hortic. Sci.* 95:190–92
40. Hudson, M. A., Brustkern, P. 1965. *Planta* 66:135–55
41. Hudson, M. A., Idle, D. B. 1962. *Planta* 57:718–30
42. James, R., Branton, D. 1971. *Biochim. Biophys. Acta* 233:504–12
43. Johansson, N. O. 1970. *Natl. Swed. Inst. Plant Prot.* 14:364–82
44. Johansson, N. O., Krull, E. 1970. *Natl. Swed. Inst. Plant Prot.* 14:343–62
45. Kaku, S. 1971. *Plant Cell Physiol.* 12:147–55
46. Ibid 1973. 14:1035–38
47. Kaku, S., Salt, R. W. 1968. *Can. J. Bot.* 46:1211–13
48. Khan, A. W., Davidkova, E., van den Berg, L. 1968. *Cryobiology* 4:184–88

49. Kitaura, K. 1967. *Int. Conf. Low Temp. Sci. II. Conf. Cryobiol.* 2:21–35
50. Kono, N., Ujeda, K. 1971. *Biochem. Biophys. Res. Commun.* 42:1095–1100
51. Krasavtsev, O. A. 1968. *Sov. Plant Physiol.* 15:191–97
52. Ibid 1969. 16:846–51
53. Ibid. 17:417–22
54. Ibid. 1973. 20:194–200
55. Kuiper, P. J. C. 1970. *Plant Physiol.* 45:684–86
56. Kuntz, I. D. 1971. *J. Am. Chem. Soc.* 93:514–18
57. Kuntz, I. D., Brassfield, T. S. 1971. *Arch. Biochem. Biophys.* 142:660–64
58. Kuntz, I. D., Brassfield, T. S., Law, G. D., Purcell, G. V. 1969. *Science* 163:1329–30
59. Kuntz, I. D., Kauzmann, W. 1974. *Adv. Protein Chem.* 28:239–83
60. Larcher, W. 1959. *Ber. Dtsch. Bot. Ges.* 72:18–40
61. Lea, C. H., Hawke, J. C. 1952. *Biochem. J.* 52:105–14
62. Leibo, S. P., Jones, R. F. 1964. *Arch. Biochem. Biophys.* 106:78–88
63. Levitt, J. 1939. *Plant Physiol.* 14:93–112
64. Levitt, J. 1956. *The Hardiness of Plants.* New York: Academic. 278 pp.
65. Levitt, J. 1962. *J. Theor. Biol.* 3:355–91
66. Levitt, J. 1972. *Responses of Plants to Environmental Stress.* New York: Academic. 697 pp.
67. Li, P. H., Weiser, C. J. 1971. *Cryobiology* 8:108–11
68. Li, P. H., Weiser, C. J., van Huystee, R. 1965. *J. Am. Soc. Hortic. Sci.* 86:723–30
69. Li, P. H., Weiser, C. J., van Huystee, R. 1966. *Plant Cell Physiol.* 7:475–84
70. Lovelock, J. E. 1957. *Proc. R. Soc. London Ser. B* 147:423–33
71. Lumis, G. P., Mecklenburg, R. A. 1974. *J. Am. Soc. Hortic. Sci.* 99:564–67
72. Lumis, G. P., Mecklenburg, R. A., Sink, K. C. 1972. *J. Am. Soc. Hortic. Sci.* 97:124–27
73. Luyet, B. J., Gehenio, P. M. 1940. *Biodynamica* 4:9–292
74. Lyons, J. M. 1973. *Ann. Rev. Plant Physiol.* 24:445–66
75. Lyons, J. M., Asmundson, C. M. 1965. *J. Am. Oil Chem. Soc.* 42:1056–58
76. Market, C. L. 1953. *Science* 140:1329–30
77. Mayland, H. F., Cary, J. W. 1970. *Adv. Agron.* 22:203–34
78. Mazur, P. 1966. *Cryobiology,* ed. H. T. Meryman, 213–315. New York: Academic, 985 pp.
79. Mazur, P. 1969. *Ann. Rev. Plant Physiol.* 20:419–48
80. Meryman, H. T. 1956. *Science* 124:515–21
81. Metcalf, E. L., Cress, C. E., Olien, C. R., Everson, E. H. 1970. *Crop Sci.* 10:362–65
82. Modlibowski, I. 1968. *Cryobiology* 5:175–87
83. Molz, F. J., Ikenberry, E. 1974. *Soil Sci.* 38:699–704
84. Olien, C. R. 1961. *Crop Sci.* 1:26–28
85. Olien, C. R. 1965. *Cryobiology* 2:47–54
86. Olien, C. R. 1967. *Ann. Rev. Plant Physiol.* 18:387–408
87. Olien, C. R. 1967. *Crop Sci.* 7:156–57
88. Olien, C. R. 1969. *Barley Genet.* 2:356–63
89. Olien, C. R. 1974. *Plant Physiol.* 53:764–67
90. Olien, C. R., Chao, S-E. 1973. *Crop Sci.* 13:674–76
91. Parker, K. J. 1967. *Progr. Nucl. Magn. Reson. Spectrosc.* 3:87–128
92. Parker, J. 1963. *Bot. Rev.* 29:124–201
93. Pfeifer, H. 1973. *Nucl. Magn. Reson.* 7:53–153
94. Proebsting, E. L. 1963. *J. Am. Soc. Hortic. Sci.* 83:259–69
95. Quamme, H. A. 1974. *J. Am. Soc. Hortic. Sci.* 99:315–18
96. Quamme, H. A., Evert, D. R., Stushnoff, C., Weiser, C. J. 1972. *HortScience* 7:24–25
97. Quamme, H. A., Stushnoff, C., Weiser, C. J. 1972. *J. Am. Soc. Hortic. Sci.* 97:608–13
98. Quamme, H. A., Weiser, C. J., Stushnoff, C. 1972. *Plant Physiol.* 51:273–77
99. Raison, J. K. 1973. *Bioenergetics* 4:285–309
100. Rammelt, R. 1972. *Proceedings of a Colloqium on the Winter Hardiness of Cereals,* ed. S. Rajki, 185–95. Agric. Res. Inst. Hung. Acad. Sci., Martonvasar.
101. Rasmussen, D. H., MacKenzie, A. P. 1972. *Water Structure at the Water-Polymer Interface,* ed. H. H. G. Jellinek, 126–45. New York: Plenum
102. Reeves, L. W. 1969. *Progr. Nucl. Magn. Reson. Spectrosc.* 4:193–233
103. Resing, H. A. 1967–68. *Adv. Mol. Relaxation Processes* 1:109–54
104. Sakai, A. 1960. *Nature* 185:393–94
105. Sakai, A. 1965. *Plant Physiol.* 40:882–87
106. Ibid 1966. 41:353–59
107. Sakai, A., Suka, O. 1967. *Plant Physiol.* 42:1680–94

108. Sakai, A., Yoshida, S. 1967. *Plant Physiol.* 42:1695–1701
109. Salcheva, G., Samygin, G. 1963. *Fiziol. Rast.* 17:800–7
110. Salmon, S. C. 1933. *Kans. Agric. Exp. Sta. Tech. Bull.* 35:1–66
111. Salt, R. W., Kaku, S. 1967. *Can. J. Bot.* 45:1335–46
112. Siminovitch, D., Gfeller, F., Rheaume, B. 1967. *Int. Conf. Low Temp. Sci. II, Conf. Cryobiol.* 2:93–117
113. Siminovitch, D., Scarth, G. W. 1938. *Can. J. Res.* 16:467–81
114. Single, W. V., Marcellos, H. 1974. *Aust. J. Agric. Res.* 25:679–86
115. Soliman, F. S., van den Berg, L. 1971. *Cryobiology* 8:73–78
116. Stamm, A. J. 1964. *Wood and Cellulose Science,* New York: Ronald. 549 pp.
117. Steer, B. T. 1973. *Aust. J. Biol. Sci.* 26:1435–42
118. Steponkus, P. L. 1971. *Plant Physiol.* 47:175–80

119. Sukumaran, N. P., Weiser, C. J. 1972. *Plant Physiol.* 50:564–67
120. Sussman, M. V., Chin, V. L. 1966. *Science* 161:324–25
121. Sussman, M. V., Chin, V. L., Karakum, O. 1967. *Chemical Engineering in Medicine and Biology,* ed. D. Hershy. New York: Plenum. 658 pp.
122. Toledo, R., Steinberg, M. P., Nelson, I. A. 1968. *J. Food Sci.* 33:315–17
123. Tsinger, N. V., Petrovskaya, L., Baranova, T. P. 1971. *Field Crop Abstr.* 24:418–19
124. Tumanov, I. I., Krasavtsev, O. A. 1962. *Sov. Plant Physiol.* 9:474–82
125. Walter, J. A., Hope, A. B. 1971. *Progr. Biophys. Mol. Biol.* 23:3–20
126. Weiser, C. J. 1970. *Science* 169:1269–78
127. Wiegand, K. M. 1906. *Bot. Gaz.* 41:373–424
128. Williams, R. J., Hope, H. J. 1974. *Plant Physiol.* 79:2241 (Abstr.)

AUTHOR INDEX

SUBJECT INDEX

carbonic anhydrase, 475-
77
CO₂ vs bicarbonate uptake,
474-75
limiting factor, 475
Carbon dioxide, 16
antagonist of ethylene, 326
compensation
oscillations, 167-68
concentration
algal species succession,
475
bicarbonate system equilibrium, 473
water, 473
fixation
Calvin cycle enzymes,
184
C₄ metabolism, 189-92
induction phenomenon, 188
inhibition by 3-phospho-
glycerate, 199
mechanism, 182-83
primary acceptor, 191-93
ribulose diphosphate car-
boxylase, 187, 193
flowering induction, 326
glycolate metabolism, 193-
96
hormone inhibition, 287
lateral root initiation, 452
output rhythmicity, 168-70
photorespiration, 197
phytoplankton growth, 474
bicarbonate effect, 476
limiting factor, 475
vs bicarbonate uptake, 474-
75
uptake, 13
Carbonic anhydrase, 188
chloride uptake, 476
phytoplankton growth, 475-
77
localization, 476
Carboxypeptidase, 107-8
barley, 110
corn, 110
Carrot (Daucus)
chloride influx regulation,
499
glycosyltransferase, 28
Casein, 113, 350
endopeptidase substrate,
103-6
Castor bean (Ricinus)
properties of lectins, 297-
300
Cathepsin D, 106
Cauliflower (Brassica)
RNA polymerase
homopolymer synthesis,
128
purification, 120
separation, 121
structure, 126
Cellulase
ethylene effect, 34

fruit softening, 223
Cellulose, 21, 243-44
biosynthesis
extracellular synthesis,
29-30
plasma membrane involve-
ment, 28-30
site, 26
Nitella growth, 422
slime mold growth, 255,
259
accumulation control, 261
Centroplast, 86
Cephalin, 277
Chaetomorpha linum
osmoregulation, 494
Chaetocerus gracillis
phosphorus and growth,
465
Chara
statolith system, 390-91
Cheiranthus cheiri
vegetative growth reversion,
324
Chemisomotic theory, 133
Chenopodium
polyspermum
bud development, 335
rubrum
CO₂ output rhythmicity,
168
enzyme systems oscilla-
tions, 169-70
estrogen-like substances,
334
mitotic rhythms, 167
photosynthesis rhythms,
167-68
Chenopodium spp.
floral stimulus movement,
328
flowering
abscisic acid, 337
DCMU effect, 326
IAA effects, 340
inhibitors, 334-35, 340
mitotic activity, 338
RNA synthesis, 339
photoperiodic timing, 172-
73
phytochrome role, 325
rhythmic timing
membrane changes, 165
Chinese cabbage (Brassica),
285
RNA-dependent RNA poly-
merase, 128
Chlamydomonas
eugametos, 491
moewusii
contractile vacuoles, 491
Chlamydomonas spp., 475-
76
osmoregulation, 491
tubulin, 359
assembly, 87
Chlorella pyrenoidosa

osmoregulation, 494
sucrose synthesis, 492
Chlorella spp.
adaptation to carbon type,
476
CO₂ uptake, 474
glycerate metabolism, 196
glycolate synthesis, 195
phosphatase, 467
polyphosphate formation,
467
proline accumulation, 492
ribulose-1,5-diphosphate
carboxylase
oxygenase activity, 194
6-phosphogluconate inhibition, 185
structure, 184
starch synthesis, 199
Chloride
influx regulation, 499
stomatal movement, 500
uptake
bicarbonate uptake, 476
Chloris gayana
betaine and salt, 498
m-Chlorobenzhydroxamic
acid
flavoprotein role, 137
2-Chloroethylphosphonic acid
see Ethephon
p-Chlorophenoxyisobutyric
acid, 280
Chlorophyll
separate functions, 376
special pair, 376-78
Chlorophyll a
absorption coefficient
light effect, 479
Chloroplast
abscisic acid synthesis,
445
glycolysis, 198
RNA polymerases, 121
structure, 126
structure changes
light effect, 479
Choanogaster plattneri
osmoregulation, 491
Cholodny-Went hypothesis,
398-99, 449
Chromatin
condensation, 53
types, 53-54
DNA length ration, 52
forms
RNA synthesis rates, 353
isolation, 120-21
organization, 46-49
decondensation, 49
histones, 47
RNA polymerase
activity modification, 127
forms, 123
metal ion stimulation, 124
problems in use, 129
solubilization, 121

CUMULATIVE INDEXES

CONTRIBUTING AUTHORS VOLUMES 23-29

Stafford, H. A., 25:459-86
Strobel, G. A., 25:541-66
Sussman, A. S., 24:311-52
Sussman, M., 27:229-65

T

Thornber, J. P., 26:127-58
Torrey, J. G., 27:435-59
Trebst, A., 25:423-58
Trewavas, A., 27:349-74
Turner, D. H., 26:159-86
Turner, J. F., 26:159-86

U

Urbach, W., 24:89-114

V

van Overbeek, J., 27:1-17
Van Steveninck, R. F. M., 26:237-58
Vickery, H. B., 23:1-28
Voskresenskaya, N. P., 23:219-34

W

Walsby, A. E., 26:427-39
Warden, J. T., 27:375-83
Wardlaw, I. F., 25:515-39
Weiser, C. J., 27:507-28

Went, F. W., 25:1-26
Wightman, F., 25:487-513
Wilson, C. M., 26:187-208

Y

Yoshida, S., 23:437-64

Z

Zalik, S., 24:47-68
Zeevaart, J. A. D., 27:321-48
Zucker, M., 23:133-56

CHAPTER TITLES VOLUMES 23-27